S0-AHP-902

The Traditional Tunes of the Child Ballads

THE TRADITIONAL TUNES OF THE CHILD BALLADS

With Their Texts, according to the Extant Records of Great Britain and America

BY

BERTRAND HARRIS BRONSON

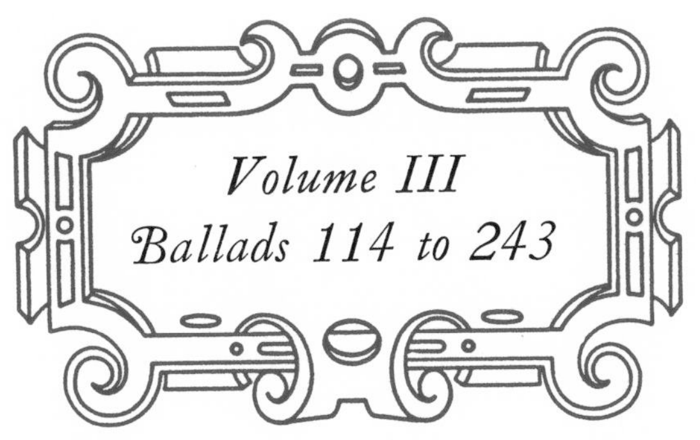

PRINCETON, NEW JERSEY
PRINCETON UNIVERSITY PRESS
1966

L. C. Card: 57-5468

✧

Bertrand Harris Bronson is a professor of English at the University of California in Berkeley. Noted for his significant contributions to the comparative study of folk-melodies, he has worked through the major collections of ballads and songs throughout the English-speaking world. This is the third of four volumes in a projected series that will, for the first time, combine both the texts and variant tunes for the Child Ballads.

✧

Publication of this third volume has been generously aided by the Bollingen Foundation.

✧

Printed in the United States of America
by Princeton University Press, Princeton, New Jersey

CONTENTS

ACKNOWLEDGMENTS

The budding generation of folk-singers that today seems opening into full bloom is already displaying a spirit of creative enterprise that appears less and less content to be confined within the passive rôle of traditional communicant. As the rewards of commercial success climb to impressive heights, the claims of individual achievement inevitably assert themselves along lines of distinctive and independent merit. Folk-singing as a profession begins to reassume the status of a calling, or way of life, that it occupied—so far as the comparison will extend—in the days of medieval minstrelsy, when the gifted singer, variously endowed with vocal and instrumental talent, or powers of memory and invention, could find hospitable lodging in the halls of the great, or earn a subsistence in camp or market place, as popular historian and entertainer. Doubtless, this development is mainly beneficial in so far as it serves to differentiate more sharply distinctions that of late have tended to grow clouded and confused. Creative genius ought to be recognized and acknowledged with commensurate rewards by a receptive and enlightened public. As competition intensifies, a higher value will naturally be set upon relative excellence. The more irresistible the individual attraction, the juster the claim.

The songs with which we are here concerned have no such title to prominence. But they have another, equally valid in its own kind. Without any adventitious aids to promote or enhance their appeal, they have perpetuated themselves by their own inherent vitality through successive generations of affectionate, self-effacing hosts, over mountains and seas, and even across the barriers of language. Where evidence of singers' self-interest or editors' interference has touched them visibly, the effect has been adverse to their native character and quality. By definition, they belong to every one and to no one. Unless the marks of individual influence have been abraded in their passage from singer to singer, unless they have been depersonalized by common possession, they lack that almost unmistakable anonymity of tradition wherein lies their widest appeal and much of their historical interest.

To emphasize the ideal community of our—national is too limiting a word—racial inheritance of traditional balladry is not to minimize our quite incalculable debt to those who at whatever personal cost of time, toil, and money have salvaged these treasures for posterity. Our obligation can only increase while the factors of exploitation, limitless spatial range in reception, mass diffusion, or identical performance obliterate the chances of following the course of traditional transmission as it has operated, hitherto, to form and re-form this genre in a continuum of human expression. It is therefore a welcome and agreeable duty to pay thanks to the many collectors, singers, editors, publishers, institutions, and organizations that have liberally and courteously contributed the use of their stores to the present venture, and encouraged its continuance by their friendly accord with its purpose.

As in earlier volumes, the editor's debt to the dedicated work of Cecil Sharp and Gavin Greig is deep and abiding. Although in this portion of Child's corpus the Sharp contribution, owing to the chances of traditional survival, is not so numerous as before, its huge and priceless total mass looms, like Everest, ever loftier on the horizon as our distance from it increases. Historically considered, its importance can never be surpassed. As Executor, Dr. Maud Karpeles has extended her former favors by permitting the free use of all of it that is relevant to the present purpose. She has added as before the unedited originals of her Newfoundland collection, and enhanced these donations with such a variety of friendly kindnesses as cannot be reckoned. Without her assistance, the editor's endeavors would ere now doubtless have ground to a halt.

To the collection of Greig a like acknowledgment is due. And as the present work passes the mid-point, the bulk of Greig's contribution, combined with that of his collaborator, the Rev. J. B. Duncan, grows larger.* For the use of these Aberdeenshire treasures I am indebted to Dr. W. Douglas Simpson, Librarian of the University's holdings, and to the hospitality of King's College, Aberdeen, where I first studied them in 1938.

Aberdeen and its vicinity, in fact, like the Appalachians in the time of Sharp's sojourn in this country, now appears to be the richest bed of traditional song in Britain. Christie's remarkable collection was a forerunner; and evidence that Aberdeenshire continues to be an unexhausted mine is still forthcoming. The School of Scottish Studies, especially through the wholehearted devotion of Hamish Henderson, has opened new veins in that region. In some of these later explorations Francis Collinson has done pioneering work; and thanks especially to these two collectors, whose good will and generosity have supplied painstaking transcriptions, the value of the present volume is notably enriched by many variants drawn from the growing stores of the young School. I am greatly indebted to Basil Megaw, its Director, for leave to include these materials from its Archive and from its journal, *Scottish Studies.*

The national Archive of American Folk Song continues to grow in bulk and importance, and thanks to its present Head, Mrs. Rae Korson, its former Head, Duncan B. M. Emrich, and the many collectors who have swelled its regional representation and given kind consent, I am able to include in this third volume virtually all the relevant Child materials that in the last decades have been coming in. The transcriptions, for which I must shoulder responsibility, have comparative study as their objective, and while they may not satisfy the most rigorous standards of those who insist upon a mirror image, stanza by stanza, of a unique rendition of every variant copy, they will, I trust, stand comparison for accuracy with similar attempts to represent the melodic character and chief deviations of each song as it was recorded. It is to be remembered that a laboratory analysis of any or all of these later versions is within actual reach of everyone for whose minute investigations such a thing may be required; but that for the vast majority of tunes in the present and foregoing volumes not the most distant approximation of the scientific ideal is possible. Where the choice was open, I have taken the *via media* of Sharp's transcriptions as a norm for the present purpose. For the materials, personal acknowledgments are due to the following contributors to the Archive: Horace P. Beck, Ray Browne, Mrs. Sidney Robertson Cowell, Sam Eskin, George Foss, Anne Grimes,

* The Duncan MSS have now once again been made available for study. They were, however, inaccessible to the present editor until after the page proof of this third volume was passed by the printer. The work, therefore, is still dependent on Greig and Keith, *Last Leaves of Traditional Ballads and Ballad Airs*, Aberdeen, 1925, and on the Walker transcript of ballad-tunes in King's College Library, Aberdeen University, for Duncan's copies.

Herbert Halpert, Frank A. Hoffmann, Max Hunter, MacEdward Leach, Alan Lomax, Alton C. Morris, Mary Celestia Parler, Vance Randolph, Ellen Stekert, Paul Clayton Worthington; and to Marvin A. Miller, Director of University Libraries, for permission to use material gathered under the auspices of the University of Arkansas and duplicated for the Archive.

To numerous friends and correspondents I am indebted for like permissions and courtesies: Dr. Otto Andersson, for a tune printed in *Budkavlen*; Mrs. Phillips Barry, for a tune from Phillips Barry, *The Maine Woods Songster*, 1939; Louis W. Chappell, for two tunes from *Folk-Songs of Roanoke and the Albemarle*, 1939; Francis Collinson, for a tune printed in *JEFDSS* and for material from *Songs of the Countryside* and other generous favors; Edward Cray, for the use of his MS of tunes transcribed from the singing of Fred Williams (collected by D. J. Kirkhuff and Phyllis Klein) and from members of the Harmon family (collected by Hilda Kasting and Mrs. Carl Wiseman); Dr. Helen Creighton, for tunes from *Songs and Ballads from Nova Scotia* [1933] and *Traditional Songs from Nova Scotia*, 1950, and other kindness; Professor A. K. Davis, Jr.,* for his cordial furtherance of the present work with cooperative good will; and Miss Mary O. Eddy, for material from *Ballads and Songs from Ohio*, 1939. Mrs. Helen Hartness Flanders, for tunes from *Ballads Migrant in New England*, 1953; *Country Songs of Vermont*, 1937; *A Garland of Green Mountain Song*, 1934; *The New Green Mountain Songster*, 1939; and *Vermont Folk-Songs and Ballads*, 1931. Hamish Henderson, for a tune printed in *Scottish Studies*, 1957, and much personal trouble on my behalf; Professor A. P. Hudson, for a tune published in *Folk Tunes from Mississippi*, 1937, and two tunes published in *North Carolina Folklore* (collected by Herbert Shellans and Walter McCraw); Peter Kennedy, for *The Child Ballads*, Caedmon recording No. TC 1146, ed. Peter Kennedy and Alan Lomax, and for personal assistance cordially extended; Dr. Edward C. Kirkland, for tunes printed in *SFQ*, 1938; George Korson, for tunes from *Pennsylvania Songs and Legends*, 1949; Alan Lomax, for two tunes from *Ballads and Breakdowns from the Southern Mountains*, Prestige International recording No. INT 25003; Ben Gray Lumpkin, for two tunes collected by him and published in *Colorado Folksong Bulletin*, 1964; Ewan MacColl, for ballads sung by him on Riverside recordings, Nos. RLP 12-621 to RLP 12-628 (*The English and Scottish Popular Ballads*, ed. Kenneth S. Goldstein), and on Riverside recording No. 12-637, ed. Kenneth S. Goldstein. Professor David Seneff McIntosh, for two tunes from "Some Representative Illinois Folk-Songs" (unpublished M.A. thesis in Music, Iowa State University, 1935); Mabel Major, for a tune published in *Publications of the Texas Folklore Society*, 1932; Professor Alton C. Morris, for tunes in *Folksongs of Florida*, 1950; Ruth Ann Musick, for tunes printed in *JAF*, 1957; Dr. John S. McLaren Ord, for tunes from his father's book: John Ord, *The Bothy Songs and Ballads*, 1930; Dr. William A. Owens, for songs from *Texas Folk Songs*, 1950; Sandy Paton, for permission to use a tune recorded by him from Frank Proffitt on Folk-Legacy recording No. FSA-1, and other favors; Vance Randolph, for tunes from *Ozark Folksongs*, I, 1946; Mrs. Jean Ritchie

* As in the second volume of the present work, the relevant items in Professor Davis's *More Traditional Ballads of Virginia*, Chapel Hill, 1960, have been cued alphabetically into the Lists of Variants in volume III also. The same procedure has been followed for the *Brown Collection of North Carolina Folklore*, IV, Durham, 1957.

Pickow, for material recorded on Folkways recording No. FA 2301, and for generous and long-continued helpfulness; Miss Jean Thomas, "The Traipsin' Woman," for tunes from *Devil's Ditties*, 1931, and *The Singin' Gatherin'*, 1939; the late Ralph Vaughan Williams, O.M., for unpublished tunes of his collecting and that of H.E.D. Hammond; Dr. Evelyn K. Wells, for a tune recorded from Frank Proffitt, and numerous courtesies over the years; and the late Charles A. Williams and Mrs. Mabel Williams Kemmerer, for permission to use a tune they had noted down from the singing of their mother, Mrs. John Williams.

To Society journals and their editors I acknowledge similar obligations: the American Folklore Society and its editor, John Greenway, for tunes from the *Journal of American Folklore*; the California Folklore Society and its editor, Professor Wayland Hand, for material published in *Western Folklore*; the English Folk Dance and Song Society, through its Librarian, Mrs. Ruth Noyes, for permission to use material published in *JFSS* and *JEFDSS*, and for facilitating the use of the Ralph Vaughan Williams and H.E.D. Hammond MSS; the Folk-Song Society of the Northeast, through Mrs. Phillips Barry, for items from its *Bulletin*; Archer Taylor, for the Missouri Folk-Lore Society, for permission to reprint items from *Ballads and Songs*, edited for that Society by H. M. Belden in 1940; and the Southeastern Folklore Society and its editor, Alton C. Morris, for materials from the *Southern Folklore Quarterly*.

For materials in manuscript or on disc or tape is owing special acknowledgment to the following institutions, their librarians and curators: the Trustees of the Boston Public Library, and John Alden, Keeper of Rare Books, for permission to use a tune from the Henry Hudson MS; Miss Marie Slocombe, Librarian, Sound Archives of the British Broadcasting Corporation, London, for material from the Archive; H. R. Creswick, Esq., Librarian, Cambridge University Library, for permission to use tunes from Cambridge University MSS Dd.v.78 and Dd.ix.33; Duke University Library and the Library of Congress, through the courtesy of Dr. Duncan B. M. Emrich, for the use of photostats of tunes in the Frank C. Brown Folklore Collection; Edinburgh University Library, E.R.S. Fifoot, Librarian, for tunes from the Guthrie MS and MS Dc.1.69; the Folger Shakespeare Library, Louis B. Wright, Director, for a tune from the Giles Lodge lute-book, MS 448.16; Harvard College Library, W. H. Bond, Acting Librarian, for tunes from the Barry Dictaphone Cylinders, the Phillips Barry MSS, the Child MSS, an Engraved Sheet (HCL 2710.900.860), the Harris MS, the Macmath MS, the William Macmath transcript of the C. K. Sharpe MS, and the Tolman MS; C. W. Black, City Librarian, Mitchell Library, Glasgow, for a tune of Frank Kidson in JFSS; the National Library of Scotland, Dr. William Beattie, Keeper of MSS, for tunes from the Blaikie MS, Lady John Scott's MSS, and Lady John Scott's Sharpe MSS; the New York Public Library, Philip L. Miller, Chief of Music Division, for tunes from the Drexel and Grainger MSS; the Librarian of the Plymouth Public Libraries, for leave to quote from the MSS of Sabine Baring-Gould; the Society of Antiquaries of Newcastle-upon-Tyne, and its Honorary Librarian, W. Tynemouth, F.L.A., for permission to use material from the James Telfer MS and from John Collingwood Bruce and John Stokoe, *Northumbrian Minstrelsy*, 1882; the

Society of Antiquaries of Scotland, for tunes from David Young, MacFarlan MS (NL Scotland MS 2084-5), and the Glenriddell MSS (in the National Museum of Antiquaries of Scotland); Dr. H. W. Parke, Librarian, Trinity College Library, University of Dublin, for two tunes from the William Ballet lute-book; the Rector and Visitors of the University of Virginia, the Alderman Library, and its Curator of Manuscripts, Mr. Robert E. Stocking, for material from the Winston Wilkinson Folklore Collections of 1935-37, and to Mr. Wilkinson for his courteous approbation.

Thanks are due to the following publishers, who have kindly permitted me to print ballads from the collections named below: Oxford University Press: Cecil J. Sharp, *English Folk Songs from the Southern Appalachians*, ed. Maud Karpeles, 1932 and 1952. Harvard University Press: J. H. Cox, *Folk-Songs of the South* (copyright 1925 by the Harvard University Press); A. K. Davis, Jr., *Traditional Ballads of Virginia* (copyright 1929 by the President and Fellows of Harvard College; copyright 1957 by Arthur Kyle Davis, Jr.); Elisabeth B. Greenleaf and Grace Y. Mansfield, *Ballads and Sea Songs of Newfoundland* (copyright 1933 by the President and Fellows of Harvard College and 1961 by Elisabeth Bristol Greenleaf and Grace Yarrow Mansfield); Roy W. Mackenzie, *Ballads and Sea Songs from Nova Scotia* (copyright 1928 by the President and Fellows of Harvard College and 1956 by William Roy Mackenzie); Reed Smith, *South Carolina Ballads* (copyright 1929 by the President and Fellows of Harvard College). J. J. Augustin, Inc.: Mellinger Edward Henry, *Folk-Songs from the Southern Highlands* [1938]. Messrs. Bayley & Ferguson, Ltd.: George Eyre-Todd, *Ancient Scots Ballads* [1894]; Alfred Moffat and Frank Kidson, *The Minstrelsy of England*, 1901. Messrs. Boosey & Hawkes, Inc.: Honoria Galwey, *Old Irish Croonauns*, 1910; Josephine McGill, *Folk-Songs of the Kentucky Mountains*, 1917; George Petrie, *The Complete Collection of Irish Music*, ed. Charles Villiers Stanford, 1902-05. The Columbia University Press: Dorothy Scarborough, *A Song Catcher in Southern Mountains*, 1937. Messrs. J. B. Cramer & Co., Ltd.: M. H. Mason, *Nursery Rhymes and Country Songs*, [1878]. Messrs. J. Curwen & Sons, Ltd.: Sabine Baring-Gould, H. Fleetwood Sheppard and F. W. Bussell, *Songs of the West*, 1905. Duke University Press: *The Frank C. Brown Collection of North Carolina Folklore*, II (*Folk Ballads from North Carolina*, ed. Henry M. Belden and Arthur Palmer Hudson), 1952, and IV (*The Music of the Ballads*, ed. Jan P. Schinhan), 1957. The Educational Company of Ireland, Ltd.: Patrick Weston Joyce, *Old Irish Folk Music and Songs*, 1909. Folkways Records and Service Corp.: Jean Ritchie, Folkways recording No. FA 2301(A1,5); Pete Steele, Folkways recording No. FS 3828(B8). The Friendship Press of the Joint Commission on Missionary Education: James W. Raine, *The Land of Saddle-bags*, 1924. Harcourt Brace and World, Inc.: Carl Sandburg, *The American Songbag* (copyright 1927 by Harcourt Brace and World, Inc.; copyright 1955 by Carl Sandburg). Harper & Row, Inc.: William Wells Newell, *Games and Songs of American Children*, 1883. Indiana University Press: Paul G. Brewster, *Ballads and Songs of Indiana*, 1940. *New York Herald Tribune*: H. E. Krehbiel, *New York Tribune*, August 17, 1902. Novello & Co., Ltd.: Cecil J. Sharp, *Folk Songs of English Origin Collected in the Appalachian Mountains*, 1921; and Cecil J. Sharp, *English Folk Songs*, Selected Edition,

[1920]. Messrs. Paterson Sons & Co., Ltd., through their American agents, Carl Fischer, Inc.: J. Michael Diack, *The New Scottish Orpheus*, 1923-24. Random House, Inc.: James Joyce, *Ulysses*, 1934. Routledge & Kegan Paul, Ltd.: Charlotte S. Burne, *Shropshire Folk-Lore* [1886]. G. Schirmer, Inc.: Maurice Matteson and Mellinger Edward Henry, *Beech Mountain Folk-Songs and Ballads*, 1936; and Susannah Wetmore and Marshall Bartholomew, *Mountain Songs of North Carolina*, 1926. Schott & Co., Ltd.: David Lumsden, *An Anthology of English Lute Music* [1953]; and John Playford, *The English Dancing Master*, 1651, ed. Margaret Dean-Smith, 1957. Messrs. Taphouse & Son: Frank Kidson, *Traditional Tunes*, 1891. University of Alabama Press: Byron Arnold, *Folksongs of Alabama*, 1950. University of Florida Press: Alton C. Morris, *Folksongs of Florida*, 1950. University of Michigan Press: Emelyn Elizabeth Gardner and Geraldine Jencks Chickering, *Ballads and Songs of Southern Michigan*, 1939. University of Missouri Studies: H. M. Belden, *Ballads and Songs*, 1940. University of North Carolina Press: Arthur Kyle Davis, Jr., *More Traditional Ballads of Virginia*, 1960. University of Utah Press: Lester A. Hubbard, *Ballads and Songs from Utah*, 1961. Radio Corporation of America, RCA Victor Record Division: RCA Victor recording No. V-40193(B). Yale University Press: Phillips Barry, Fannie H. Eckstorm, and Mary W. Smyth, *British Ballads from Maine*, 1929.

My primordial obligation to the John Simon Guggenheim Memorial Foundation and Dr. Henry Allen Moe still stands as an undischarged debt that I gladly acknowledge. Nor would I omit to express hearty thanks for more recent benefactions to the Bollingen Foundation, who have generously supported the publication of this and the previous volume. I owe likewise sincere appreciation for increasingly substantial assistance over the years to the Regents of the University of California and the Faculty Committees of Research on the Berkeley Campus.

To colleagues and friends to whom I have given extra trouble because they were close at hand, I wish to pay warm personal acknowledgment: to Professor Vincent Duckles, Librarian of the Music Department, for his never-failing helpfulness; to Professor Daniel Heartz, for disentangling me from the snares of flageolet tablatures and for firm treading among lute manuscripts; to Professor Claude M. Simpson, of Stanford University, who with superior knowledge rescued me from ill-informed assertions about Elizabethan and Jacobean tunes and their whereabouts.

For invaluable, responsible, and vigilant assistance in the preparation of this volume, demonstrably reflected on every page and at every stage of its progress, I owe probably more than even I myself realize to the knowledge, skill, and unfailingly cheerful toil of Mrs. Marjorie R. Menhenett, Miss Ruth Misheloff, Mrs. JoAn Johnstone Chace, and Mrs. Kate Shattuck Green.

As formerly, this book is of course the beneficiary of accomplished hands at the great Press that has assumed responsibility for it. I pay special tribute to Mr. Gordon Mapes, who has drawn all the music, and to Mrs. James Holly Hanford, who has borne the cares of tending this volume on its tortuous typographical journey toward publication.

ACKNOWLEDGMENTS

To my dear wife, who in despite of blasted holidays and the fell clutch of immitigable circumstance has, throughout a quarter of a century, not winced nor cried aloud, I give grateful homage for her sweet forgetting about the frozen time.

B.H.B.

Berkeley, California
May 1966

The Traditional Tunes of the Child Ballads

VOLUME III

Johnie Cock

CHILD NO. 114

Although Percy received a copy (Child A) of this very fine ballad in 1780, he did not introduce it into the fourth edition of the *Reliques*, and it was left for Scott to publish it for the first time. Scott published a conflated text and it is significant that his version has no refrain line. Scott was not interested in it as song. Nothing could be more distinct than the consistent refrain-pattern in the musical tradition. Only two copies lack a repetition of the fourth line of each quatrain as refrain, and both of these seem to have been inexactly set down. Of Child's texts, A to M, eight have the repetition.

This consistency of five-phrase tunes would suggest a single melodic tradition for the ballad. But modally, at any rate, the tunes subdivide into two classes, one in the Ionian galaxy, the other in the Dorian and Æolian. The first sort has relatives, in one or two of its forms, among the tunes found with Child No. 110, No. 236, and perhaps No. 78; the second is doubtless allied to the "Lazarus" tribe, and perhaps is made use of by "Trooper and Maid" (No. 299). In both its branches it is a sturdy and invigorating thing. The ballad's tradition appears not to have taken root south of the Border, in spite of melodic affiliates; but it was found in Ireland in the middle of the last century. Mrs. Harris's copy, in the first group, is perhaps of earliest record (learned c. 1790). The ballad has survived in Aberdeenshire down to our own day and living traditional singers continue to provide us with fresh variants. In Aberdeenshire, early in the present century, Greig collected seven records, all of which are of the second modal group.

The Palmer, or auld carl, in this ballad reminds one of Carl Hood in "Earl Brand" (No. 7).

LIST OF VARIANTS

GROUP Aa

1. "Johnie of Breadislee." William Motherwell, *Minstrelsy: Ancient and Modern*, 1827, App'x., No. 22 and p. xxi. Also in Blaikie MS., National Library of Scotland MS. 1578, No. 127, p. 39; and Robert Chambers, *Twelve Romantic Scottish Ballads*, 1844, p. 13.
2. "Johnie o' Braidislee." Lady John Scott's Sharpe MS., National Library of Scotland MS. 843, fol. 22.

3a. "What news, what news my gay old man?" Hudson MS., No. 704, c. 1840, Boston Public Library.

3b. "Johnny Cox," or "Johnny of Cockalie." George Petrie, *The Complete Collection of Irish Music*, ed. Charles Villiers Stanford, 1902-05, No. 743.

4. "Johnnie Brod." Harris MS., No. 18, and fol. 25, Harvard College Library. Also in Francis James Child, *The English and Scottish Popular Ballads*, 1882-98, V, p. 419, and III, p. 8(G).
5. "Johnnie o' Braidslie." Lady John Scott's MS., National Library of Scotland MS. 840.

GROUP Ab

6. "Jock o' Braidiesleys." Greig MSS., I, p. 155, King's College Library, Aberdeen. Also in Gavin Greig and Alexander Keith, *Last Leaves of Traditional Ballads and Ballad Airs*, 1925, p. 95(d). (Walker)
7. "Johnnie o' Braidisleys." Greig MSS., I, p. 155. Also in Greig and Keith, 1925, p. 95(c). (Spence)
8. "Johnnie o' Braidiesleys." Greig-Duncan MS. 785 (transcription of W. Walker), p. 78, King's College Library, Aberdeen. From Duncan MS., No. 450. (Bain)
9. "Johnnie o' Braidisleys." Greig and Keith, *Last Leaves*, 1925, pp. 95(b) and 93. From Duncan MS., No. 242. (Mackay)
10. "Johnnie o' Braidiesleys." Greig-Duncan MS. 785 (Walker), p. 78. From Duncan MS., No. 306. (Lyall)
11. "John o' Braidiesley." Greig MSS., I, p. 121, and Bk. 717, VII, p. 105. Also in Greig and Keith, *Last Leaves*, 1925, p. 95(a). (Robb)
12. "Johnie Cock." John Strachan, Caedmon recording No. TC 1146(A3). Also by Ewan MacColl, Riverside recording No. RLP 12-623(A3), *The English and Scottish Popular Ballads*, II, ed. Kenneth S. Goldstein.
13. "Johnny o' Breadislea." Jeannie Robertson (singer), Archive, School of Scottish Studies, University of Edinburgh. Collected by Hamish Henderson. Also by Jeannie Robertson, Prestige-International recording No. 13006(B2).
14. "Jockie o' Bridiesland." John Gillon (singer), Archive, School of Scottish Studies. Collected by Hamish Henderson.
15. "Johnnie o' Braidiesleys." Greig MSS., II, p. 69. Also in Greig-Duncan MS. 785 (Walker), p. 78; and *Rymour Club Miscellanea*, I (1910), p. 198. (Quirrie)

TUNES WITH TEXTS

GROUP Aa

1. "Johnie of Breadislee"

Motherwell, 1827, App'x., No. 22; text, App'x., p. xxi. Also in Blaikie MS., NL Scotland MS. 1578, No. 127, p. 39; and Chambers, 1844, p. 13. From A. Blaikie, Paisley.

p π¹

Variants a, b, and c are the readings of the Blaikie MS. It appears to be a bar short in the fourth phrase.

Johnie rose up in a May mornin,
  Called for water to wash his hands—
Gar loose to me the gude gray dogs
  That are bound wi' iron bands.

2. "Johnie o' Braidislee"

Lady John Scott's Sharpe MS., NL Scotland MS. 843, fol. 22.

a I/Ly, ending on the octave

1. Johnie rose up in a May morning,
Sought water to wash his hands;
"Gar loose to me the gude gray dogs,
Weel bound in iron bands,—
Weel bound wi' [*sic*] iron bands."

2. When Johnie's mother heard o' that,
Her hands for dule she wrang:—
"O Johnie! for my benison,
To the greenwood dinna gang—gang,
To the greenwood dinna gang!"

3. But Johnie's busk't his good bend bow,
His arrows one by one;
And he is gane to Durrisdeer
To hunt the dun-deer down—down,
To hunt the dun-deer down.

4. Its down, its down by Merriemass,
Its down among the scrags—
And there ye'll espie a bonnie boy,
Lie asleep amang his dogs—dogs—
Asleep amang his dogs.

5. The first flight of arrows the forresters shot,
They wounded him on the knee;
And out an' spak' the seventh forrester,—
"The next will gar him dee—dee—
The next will gar him dee.["]

6. Johnie's set his back against an aik,
His feet against a stane;
And he has slain the seven forresters,
He has slain them a' but ane—ane—
He has slain them a' but ane.

7. "O is there na a bonnie bird,
Can sing as I can say
Could flee for me to my mother's bower,
And tell to fetch Johnie away—away—
And tell to fetch Johnie away.

8. "Is there na a bonnie bird,
Will do sae mickle for me,
As dip its wing in the wan water,
And straik it on my e'e-bree—bree—
And straik it on my e'e-bree!"

9. The Starling flew to his mother's window,
It whistled and it sang;
And aye the ower-word o' the lay,
Was "Johnie tarries lang—lang!—
Was "Johnie tarries lang!"

* * * * *

10. Now Johnie's gude bent-bow is broke,
And his gude gray dogs are slain—
Green grows his grave in Durrisdeer,—
And his hunting it is done—done—
And his hunting it is done!

3a. "What news, what news my gay old man?"

Hudson MS., No. 704, c. 1840. From Edward Clements.

p M

3b. "Johnny Cox," or "Johnny of Cockalie"

Petrie, 1902-05, No. 743. From Edward Clements.

p M

4. "Johnnie Brod"

Harris MS., No. 18; text, fol. 25. Also in Child, 1882-98, V, p. 419; text, III, p. 8(G). From Mrs. Amelia Harris; learned from an old nurse during childhood in Perthshire, late eighteenth century. Noted by her daughter.

p I/M

As Keith has observed, a variant of this tune is given by Kinloch (1827) for Child No. 110 ("The Shepherd's Dochter").

1. Johnnie Brad, on a May mornin,
 Called for water to wash his hands,
An there he spied his twa blude-hounds,
 Waur bound in iron bands, bands,
 Waur bound in iron bands.

2. Johnnie's taen his gude bent bow,
 Bot an his arrows kene,
An strippit himsel o the scarlet red,
 An put on the licht Lincoln green.

3. Up it spak Johnnie's mither,
 An' a wae, wae woman was she:
I beg you bide at hame, Johnnie,
 I pray be ruled by me.

4. Baken bread ye sall nae lack,
 An wine you sall lack nane;
Oh, Johnnie, for my benison,
 I beg you bide at hame!

5. He has made a solemn aith,
 Atween the sun an the mune,
That he wald gae to the gude green wood,
 The dun deer to ding doon.

6. He luiket east, he luiket wast,
 An in below the sun,
An there he spied the dun deer,
 Aneath a bush o brume.

7. The firsten shot that Johnnie shot,
 He wounded her in the side;
The nexten shot that Johnnie shot,
 I wat he laid her pride.

8. He's eaten o the venison,
 An drunken o the blude,
Until he fell as sound asleep
 As though he had been dead.

9. Bye there cam a silly auld man,
 And a silly auld man was he,
An he's on to the Seven Foresters,
 As fast as he can flee.

10. "As I cam in by yonder haugh,
 An in among the scroggs,
The bonniest boy that ere I saw
 Lay sleepin atween his dogs."

. . . .

11. The firsten shot that Johnnie shot,
 He shot them a' but ane,
An he flang him owre a milk-white steed,
 Bade him bear tidings hame.

The text here printed is from Child. In the tune MS., where the title is "Johnnie Brod," the first stanza is as follows:

Johnnie Brod in a May mornin',
 Got water for his hands,
An' he ca'd on his twa bluid hounds,
 Waur bound wi iron bands, bands,
 Waur bound wi iron bands.

5. "Johnnie o' Braidslie"

Lady John Scott's MS., NL Scotland MS. 840.

p I

1. Johnnie rase up on a May morning,
Called for water to wash his hands
Gae loose to me my gude grey dogs
That are bound wi' iron bands.

2. When Johnnie's Moth[er] got word o' that,
Her hands for dule she wrang
Oh Johnnie for my benison
To the green woods dinna gang.

3. But Johnnie busked up his gude bent bow
Wi' his arrows ane by ane
An' he's awa' to the Duris deer
To hunt the dun deer down.

4. He lookit east, he lookit west
He lookit anaith the sun
And there he saw the dun deer lying
Beneath a bush o' [? whin].

5. The dun deer lap & Johnnie shot
& he skaithed her in the side
An between the water & the brae
His hounds they laid her pride.

6. Johnnie took out the dun deer's liver
An' sae did he her lungs
An he had fed his three grey hounds
As if they had been gude Earls sons.

7. They ate sae muckle of the venison
An drank sae muckle o' the bluid
That Johnnie an' his three gre[y] hounds
Fell asleep as if they had been dead.

8. An by there cam a silly auld carle
(An' an ill death may he die)
An he's awa to the seven foresters
As fast as he can hie.

9. What news, What news, Ye silly auld carle
What news, do you bring to me
Nae news, nae news, gan the silly auld carle
Nae news hae I for thee!

10. But as I cam by yon wan water
Down among the scroggs
There I saw a gentlemen
Lying sleeping amang his dogs.

11. His cheeks were like the roses red
His brow was like the snaw
He was the Bonniest Gentlemen
These E'en they ever saw.

12. Out then spak ane, out then spak twa
Out then spak twa or three
Out spak the Maister Forester
It's Johnnie of Braidslie.

13. It's down, down, it's low down
It's down amang the scroggs
There they found braw Johnnie lying
Sleeping amang his dogs.

14. Out then shot ane, out then shot twa
Out then shot twa or three
Out shot the Maister Forester
& wounded Johnnie above the knee.

15. Oh wae to you seven foresters
I wonder ye dinna think shame
For thee are seven armed men
And I am but ane my lane.

16. But stand ye fast my gude grey hounds
Stand fast & dinna flee
Oh stand by me my noble dogs
An we will gar them dee.

17. He leant his back upon an aik
Set his fit against a stane
An he has slain the seven foresters
He has slain them a' but ane.

18. An he's tossed him up, and he's tossed him down
He's broken his collar bane
He's tied him to the bridle rein
Bid him carry his tidings hame.

19. Oh is there a Bird in a' this bush
Wad sing as I wad say
Wad gae hame, & tell my auld mither
That Johnnie has won the day.

20. Oh is there a bird in a' the wood
Wad dae that muckle for me
Wad drap its wing in the wan water
An' straik it ower my brae!

21. The Starling flew to his mothers window stane
It whistled & it sang
An' aye the oerword o his song
Was Johnnie tarries lang.

22. They striped a rod o' the slae thorn bush
An' anither o' the [? Hagh] tree
An sad, and mony were the men
Seeking Johnnie O' Braidslie.

23. Oh! aft were brought to the Braidslie
The less gear, and the mair
But we never brought to the Braidslie
What grieved my heart sae sair.

24. Now Johnnie's gude bent bow is brake
An' his grey dogs are slain
An' his body it lies wi' the Duris deer
An his hunting it is done.

GROUP Ab

6. "Jock o' Braidiesleys"

Greig MSS., I, p. 155. Also in Greig and Keith, 1925, p. 95(d). Sung by Charles Walker, Brucklay, New Deer, March 1906.

p D (inflected III)

[Johnnie's best bow is broke,
And his twa great dogs are slain,
And his body lies in bonnie Monymusk,
And his huntin' days is deen
And his huntin' days is deen.]

A note in the MS. indicates the words are Mrs. McGilwray's [MacGillivray's?].

7. "Johnnie o' Braidisleys"

Greig MSS., I, p. 155. Also in Greig and Keith, 1925, p. 95(c). Sung by J. W. Spence, Fyvie, April 1906.

p D

Johnnie rose one May morning
Called water to wash his hands
Says loose to me my guid gray dogs
That are bound in iron bands
That are bound wi iron bands.

8. "Johnnie o' Braidiesleys"

Greig-Duncan MS. 785 (Walker transcript), p. 78; from Duncan MS., No. 450. Sung by J. Bain, Echt; learned from his mother.

p Æ

It's Johnnie rose in a May morning
Call'd cold water to wash his hands,
Says, Come lowse to me my twa gray hounds
That lie bound in iron bands
That lie bound in iron bands.

9. "Johnnie o' Braidisleys"

Greig and Keith, 1925, p. 95(b); text, p. 93. From Duncan MS., No. 242. Sung by Alexander Mackay, Alford; learned c. 1860.

p D/Æ

1. Johnnie arose on a May mornin,
Called for water to wash his hands,
Says, "Gae lowse to me thae twa greyhounds
That lie bound in iron bands,
That lie bound in iron bands."

2. When Johnnie's mother she heard o this,
Her hands wi dool she wrang,
Says, "Johnnie, for your venison
To the green woods dinna gang.

3. "We hae plenty o the white bread,
An' plenty o the good red wine,
So, Johnnie, for your venison
To the greenwood dinna gang."

4. But Johnnie has breskit his good benbow,
His arrows one by one,
An' he is on to the gay green woods
For to pull the dun deer doon.

5. As he gaed doon through Merrimoss,
An doon amon yon scroggs,
Twas there he spied a dun deer lie
At the back o a bush o broom.

6. Johnnie shot, an' the dun deer lap,
He had wounded her in the side,
An' atween the water an' the wood,
An' the greyhounds laid her pride.

7. Johnnie has handled the deer so weel,
Taen oot her liver an' lungs,
An' he has fed the dogs wi them
As though they'd been yearl's sons.

8. They ate so much o the raw venison,
An' they drank so much o the blood,
That Johnnie an' his twa greyhounds
Fell asleep as gin they'd been dead.

9. By there cam a silly aul man,
Some ill death may he dee;
An' he is on to the seven foresters
For to tell what he did see.

10. "What news, what news, ye silly aul man,
What news hae ye to gie?"—
"Nae news, nae news," said the silly aul man,
"But what my twa een did see.

11. "As I cam doon through Merriemoss,
An' doon amon yon scroggs,
An' the bonniest youth that ever I saw
Lay a-sleepin atween twa dogs.

12. "The coat he bore upon his back
Was o the Linkum twine,
An' the stock he wore aroon his neck
It was pearl an' precious stone.

13. "The buttons he wore upon his coat
They were o the gold so good,
An' the twa greyhounds that he lay atween,
An' their mouths were a' dyed wi blood."

14. Twas oot then spak the first forester,
An angry man was he,
Says, "An this be Johnnie o Braidisleys,
My faith, we'll gar him dee."

15. Twas oot then spak the second forester,
His sister's son was he,
Says, "An this be Johnnie o Braidisleys,
We'd better lat him be."

16. Twas oot then spak the seventh forester,
He was forester ower them a',
Says, "An this be Johnnie o Braidisleys,
An' to him an' we'll gang."

17. The first shots that the foresters fired,
An' they wounded him in the knee,
An' the second shots that the foresters fired,
An' the red blood blinded his ee'.

18. As Johnnie awakened oot o his sleep,
An angry man was he,
Says, "Ye micht hae waukened me oot o my sleep
Ere the red blood blinded my e'e.

19. "Gin my bow prove true, as she used to do,
An' my courage do not fail,
I'll mak ye dearly rue that day
Ye cam to the Dinspeerhill."

20. He planted his back against an oak,
His foot against a stone,
An' he has shot the seven foresters,
He has shot them a' but one.

21. He has broken three o that one's ribs,
Likewise his collar bone,
An' he laid him twa faul' ower his steed,
Bade him carry the tidings home.

22. "Noo whaur will I get a bonnie little bird
That wad sing as I will say,
That will fly on to my mother's bower,
An' tell them to tak Johnnie away?"

23. The starling flew to his mother's bower,
It whistlèd an' sang,
An' aye the owercome o its sang
Was, Johnnie tarries lang!

24. Some o them pu'd o the hawthorn's bush,
An' some o the hollin tree,
An' mony, mony were the men
At the fetchin o young Johnnie.

25. Noo Johnnie's good benbow is broke,
An' his twa greyhounds they're slain;
Noo Johnnie sleeps in Merriemoss,
An' his huntin days are done.

26. But woe be to yon silly aul man,
An ill death may he dee,
An' the highest tree in Merriemoss
Shall be his gallows tree.

10. "Johnnie o' Braidiesleys"

Greig-Duncan MS. 785 (Walker transcript), p. 78; from Duncan MS., No. 306. Sung by Mrs. Lyall, Skene, who learned it from her mother.

p D/Æ

Johnnie arose in a May morning
Call'd cold water to wash his hands,
Says, Come lowse to me my twa grey hounds
That lie bound in iron bands
That lie bound in iron bands.

11. "John o' Braidiesley"

Greig MSS., I, p. 121; text, Bk. 717, VII, p. 105. Also in Greig and Keith, 1925, p. 95(a). Tune from Alexander Robb, Maud, May 1906; text from James Lawrence, New-castle, December 1906.

p Æ

1. Johnnie arose on a May mornin'
Called cold water to wash his hands
Says, "Come lowse to me my good grey hounds
That lie bound in iron bands.
(Repeat) Bands, that lie bound in iron bands."

2. Johnny shouldered his good bent bow,
His arrows one by one;
And he's gaen doon by the good greenwood
For to ding the din (dun) deer-doon.
(Repeat as above.)

3. The din deer lap (leaped) an' Johnny fired
And wounded her on the side;
And between the waters and the woods
The grey hounds laid her pride.

4. Johnny skinned his good din deer,
Took out her liver and her lungs
And fed his dogs on the venison
As gin they were Earl's sons.

5. They ate so much of the venison
And drank so much of the blood
That they all lay upon the plain
As gin that they were dead.

6. Then by there cam a silly auld man
And an ill death may he die
For he's gaen doon to Islington
Where the seven foresters do lie;

7. Says: "As I cam doon by Monymusk
An doon among the scrogs (bushes)
The fairest youth that ever I saw
Lay sleepin' among his dogs."

8. And then outspake the head forester
He was forester o'er them a'
Gin this be Johnny o' Braidiesleys
It's unto him we'll draw.

9. But then outspake the second forester
A sister's son was he
Gin this be Johnny o' Braidiesleys
We'd better lat him be.

10. The first shot that the hunters fired
It wounded him on the knee
And the second shot that the foresters fired
His heart's blood blinded his e'e.

11. Now Johnny awoke him out of his sleep
And an angry man was he
Says: Ye micht hae awaked me out o' my sleep
Ere my heart's blood blinded my e'e.

12. "But gin my bent bow prove true to me
(An' seldom it proves wrang.)
I'll mak' ye a' rue the day
That I dang the din deer doon."

13. He leaned his back against an oak
His foot against a stone
And fired at the seven foresters
And shot them all but one.

14. An' he's broken three o' this one's ribs
Likewise his collar-bone
And laid him twafauld o'er a steed
Bade him "carry the tidings home."

. . . .

And his body lies in Monymusk
An' his huntin' days are dune.

This tune and text from different singers are cross-referenced to each other in the MS.

12. "Johnie Cock"

Sung by John Strachan, Fyvie, Aberdeenshire, Caedmon rec. No. TC 1146(A3). Also sung by Ewan MacColl, Riverside rec. No. RLP 12-623(A3), ed. K. S. Goldstein. Recorded by Alan Lomax and Hamish Henderson; collected and edited by Peter Kennedy and Alan Lomax.

p D/Æ

1. Johnny rose on a May mornin',
Called for water to wash his hands,
And he call-ed for his twa greyhounds
To be bound in iron chains, chains,
To be bound in iron chains.

2. Johnny shot the dun-deer lap,
She was wounded in the side;
And between the waters and the woods
The greyhounds laid her pride.

3. Now Johnny ate o' the venison
And the dogs drank o' the bluid;
And they all lay doon and fell asleep,
Asleep as though they'd been deid.

4. And by there come a silly aul' man
And a silly aul' man was he;
And he's awa' to the king's foresters
For to tell on young Johnnie.

5. Johnny shot six o' them
And the seventh he wounded sore
An' he swung his hook over his horse' back
An' he swore that he would hunt more.

6. Now Johnny's guid bend-bow is broke
An' his twa grey hounds are slain,
His body lies in Monymusk
An' his hunting days are dein.

13. "Johnny o' Breadislea"

Archive, School of Scottish Studies. Sung by Jeannie Robertson, Aberdeen. Also on Prestige-International rec. No. 13006(B2). Collected by Hamish Henderson for the School of Scottish Studies. Transcribed by Francis M. Collinson.

p D/Æ

1. Johnnie he rase one May mornin',
Called water tae wash his hands;
Roarin', bring tae me my twa grey hounds
That are bound in iron bands, bands
That are bound in iron bands.

2. His aul wife, she wrung her hands:
Tae the green wids dinnae gang!
For the sake o' the venison
Tae the green wids dinnae gang, gang
Tae the green wids dinnae gang.

3. But Johnnie went up through Moneymoss,
An' doon an' through some scroggs,
An' it was there he spied a dun deer leap—
She was lyin' in a bush o' sprogs, sprogs
She was lyin' in a bush o' sprogs.

4. The first arrow he fired at her,
He wounded her on the side;
And between the water and the wids
For the grey hounds laid her pride, pride
For his greyhounds laid her pride.

5. Johnnie and his twa grey hounds
Drank so muckle o' her blood,
That Johnnie and his twa grey hounds
Fell a-sleepin' in the wids, wids
Fell a-sleepin' in the wids.

6. By came a silly aul' man,
And a ill daith may he dee!
He went up an' tellt the first forester,
And he tellt what he did see, see,
And he tellt what he did see.

7. If that be's young Johnnie the Brine,
   Ye'd better leave him a-be;
If that is young Johnnie the Brine,
   Ye'd better leave him a-be, a-be
   Ye'd better leave him a-be.

8. He went up an' tellt the seventh forester;
   He was Johnnie's sister's son.
If that be's young Johnnie the Brine
   Tae the green wids we will gang, gang
   Tae the green wids we will gang.

9. The first arrow they fired at him,
   They wounded him on the thie;
And the second arrow they fired at him
   For his hairt's blood blint his ee,
   For his hairt's blood blint his ee.

10. But Johnnie rose up wi' a angry growl,
   For a angry man was he.
I will kill a' you six foresters,
   An' brak the seventh one's back in three, three
   An' brak the seventh one's back in three.

11. He placed his fit upon a stone,
   An' his back against the tree;
And he killed a' the six foresters,
   And broke the seventh one's back in three, three
   And broke the seventh one's back in three.

12. Johnnie he broke his back in three
   And he broke his collar-bone;
And he tied him on his grey meir's back
   For tae carry the tidings home, home
   For tae carry the tidings home.

14. "Jockie o' Bridiesland"

Archive, School of Scottish Studies. Sung by John Gillon, from Brechin, Angus, 1954; learned as a child. Collected by Hamish Henderson for the School of Scottish Studies. Transcribed by Gillian E. Johnstone.

p D/Æ (with variants, m Æ)

1. O Jockie rose up one May mornin
   Called water tae wash his hands.
Sayin', Bring tae me that twa great hunds
   That is bund in iron bands, ay,
   That is bund in iron bands.

2. Now, the auld wumman hearin' this,
   Commenced tae wring her hands.
Sayin', If that be for the sake o' venison,
   Tae the green woods dinnae gang, gang
   Tae the green woods dinnae gang.

3. Now it's up got that great dun deer,
   And he wounded her through the side.
For he fed his dogs on the livers and the lungs,
   And he drunk so much o' its blood, blood
   And he drunk so much o' its blood.

4. Now it's Jockie and his twa great hunds
   Lay sleepin neath the tree,
For it's fa passed but a silly auld cull,
   And a silly auld cull bein' he.

5. For he ran up to the seven foresters,
   To tell what he did see,
And he ran up to the seven foresters
   To tell what he did see.

6. Now it's up spoke the first forester
   And an angry man bein' he,
For if that be Jock o' Bridiesland,
   This nicht we will gar him dee, ay,
   It's this nicht we will gar him dee.

7. For it's up spoke a young forester,
   And a near friend bein' he,
For if that be Jock o' Bridiesland,
   We'd better lea him be, ay,
   We'd better lea him be.

Spoken: Weel, I cannae mind the rest o' that, but I ken the end o't. It goes like this:

. . . . broke his back,
   Likewise his collar bane,
And threw him over his great white steed
   Tae carry the tidins hame, hame,
   Ay, tae carry the tidins hame.

15. "Johnnie o' Braidiesleys"

Greig MSS., II, p. 69. Also in Greig-Duncan MS. 785 (Walker transcript), p. 78; and *Rymour Club Miscellanea*, I (1910), p. 198. Sung by J. Quirrie, North Mains of Craigston Turriff, August 1906.

p D/Æ

114. JOHNIE COCK

It's Johnnie arose in a May mornin'
  Called for water to wash his hands,
Says, Come lowse to me the twa gray hounds
  That { lie / are } bound in iron bands
  That lie bound in iron bands.

Adam Bell, Clim of the Clough, and William of Cloudesly

CHILD NO. 116

There is no sound clue to a tune for this little gest. But Rimbault discovered on a flyleaf of the unique copy of *Parthenia In-Violata*, printed for John Pyper in oblong quarto, n.d., but c. 1620, a tune that Rimbault gives in his *Musical Illustrations* of Percy's *Reliques*. He does not tell why he feels justified in connecting the tune with the ballad. Possibly the titles corresponded but, in the face of his deductions elsewhere, this is a doubtful supposition. In any case, the tune is apparently closely related with that other which Rimbault says he transcribed from a flyleaf of *Parthenia*, 1611, and gives to "Robin Hood and the Curtal Friar" (No. 123), q.v. It is admitted here on the off-chance that evidence of a connection may be found. Since his book passed into the Drexel Collection in 1877 and thence into the New York Public Library, it should have been a fact easy to ascertain. But the front flyleaf bears no tune, and the back flyleaf, conjecturally conjugate, has vanished. But, again, the front flyleaf has a watermark with the date 1795. Two inferences seem legitimate. The first is that the book was rebound long before Rimbault acquired it, and not after; the second, that *if* the tune, in accordance with his printed statement, *op.cit.*, p. 6, was on the flyleaf torn out or removed, it must have been set there after 1795—shall we say, by a nineteenth-century hand?

LIST OF VARIANTS

"Adam Bell, Clym of the Clough, and William of Cloudesly." Edward F. Rimbault, *Musical Illustrations of Bishop Percy's Reliques*, 1850, p. 48.

TUNE WITH TEXT

"Adam Bell, Clym of the Clough, and William of Cloudesly"

Rimbault, 1850, p. 48.

p I (–VI)

Mery it was in grene forest
Amonge the levès grene,
Wheras men hunt east north and west
Wyth bowes and arrowes kene.

Robin Hood

CHILD NO. 117

The record of tunes for the Robin Hood ballads is disappointingly meager and uncertain. Rimbault's appendix of musical illustrations in Gutch's *Robin Hood*, 1847, contains fifteen tunes, of which five are unconnected by him with any ballad. Research has, so far as I know, been unable to supplement his collection of early tunes by more than one; but later collectors have been able to add nearly a dozen and a half to the total, mostly from twentieth-century traditional sources. About half of these were recovered on the western side of the Atlantic, from Nova Scotia, New England, and the Appalachian region. Scotland, Lincolnshire, Derbyshire, Sussex, Hampshire, and Somerset have contributed the rest.

Rimbault's attributions will be discussed in connection with the particular ballads; it is enough to say here that several are open to question. The earliest surviving tune by the name of our hero, though not associated with a particular ballad, appears to be "Robin hoode" in Giles Lodge's lute-book, now in the Folger Shakespeare Library. It would seem to have been unknown to Rimbault and Chappell. This manuscript may be as early as 1575 and can hardly be later than 1591. With its fifteen bars, the tune raises questions and seems rather an awkward vehicle for ballad-quatrains, though of course it has been slightly adapted for instrumental use at the cadences, and there may be two or three extra bars for a rhetorical effect before the last phrase and at the midpoint. It would at least be a simple matter to *extract* a ballad-tune from it, reducing it to a six-phrase tune, with the first and fourth phrases used, like a refrain, as the fifth and sixth—so simple, in fact, that the present editor has yielded to the temptation to do so. But we shall see the tune reappearing in a different guise in Ravenscroft's *Pammelia* and elsewhere at later dates.

The next earliest Robin Hood tune of record might seem to be that associated with "The Pinder of Wakefield." According to Chappell, two copies of this are to be found under the name "Wakefield on a green" in the Cambridge lute manuscripts D.d.ii.11 and D.d.iii.18. But he appears to be mistaken in the first reference: no tune under that name has been discovered in that manuscript. He prints, on Rimbault's authority, something that will hardly pass for a tune, declared to be drawn out of the bass and inner parts of the two lute versions as identified above (*Popular Music* [1855-59], II, pp. 393-94). He says a third copy is in a virginal book in Dr. Rimbault's possession. But Rimbault himself does not print this putative "tune" in his musical illustrations of the Robin Hood ballads, nor are we anywhere informed of what the title of the piece was in the virginal book. Instead, Rimbault declares in connection with "The Jolly Pinder of Wakefield" that he found the tune he prints (Gutch, *Robin Hood*, 1847, II, p. 434) in a lute manuscript formerly belonging to the Rev. Mr. Gostling, and presumably latterly in his own possession. Again, he does not say what this is called in the manuscript, nor does he mention any *other tunes* for the ballad, either in lute manuscripts, virginal manuscripts, or print; but he does say that the tune he here gives from the Gostling MS., which is certainly (as he notices) a form of "The Bailiff's Daughter" (No. 105), exists in another copy in Cambridge D.d.iii.18—one of Chappell's references a decade later for his "Wakefield on a green" (but bearing no resemblance to the Gostling tune), extracted, from the inner part and base of something or other, by Rimbault himself! Close inspection of David Lumsden's exhaustive thematic catalogue of English lute music from 1540 to 1620[1] has failed to reveal anything like "The Bailiff's Daughter" under any title whatever.

Rimbault prints what he calls "the *ancient* tune of 'Robin Hood'" from (as he says) the Cambridge lute MS. D.d.ix.33 (Gutch, *op.cit.*, II, p. 437). Oddly, again, this manuscript discloses a tune under that title (fol. 81^v) but not the one he gives. But Chappell (*op.cit.*, II, p. 398) tells us that "the same tune [i.e., as printed by Rimbault, p. 437], bears the name of *Robin Reddock* in William Ballet's Lute Book," in Trinity College Library, Dublin. And, indeed, the tune is there to be found. But Ballet's reading proves Rimbault's curiously unbalanced version of the first, repeated phrase to be erroneous. Rimbault's first three bars, doubled, could hardly have accommodated ballad-lines in any case, nor do they match the second half of the tune, which consists of four bars, doubled. Ballet proves that Rimbault (or his source) has omitted what should have been his second bar in each occurrence of the phrase. Restored, the tune is perfectly symmetrical. Whence Rimbault got it, or what it was called, is still uncertain. But its connection with Robin Hood is highly dubious. So, also, is that of the well-known tune now associated with Ophelia's "For bonny sweet Robin is all my joy," and occurring repeatedly in Elizabethan music manuscripts, under various titles: "Robin," "Bonny Sweet Robin," "Robin is to the Greenwood gone." Lumsden's catalogue lists fifteen appearances. Were it not for Ballet's introducing a "hood" into the last of these titles (on p. 113 of his lute-book), there would be no reason to connect Sweet Robin with the outlaw. The title-line goes with no extant ballad, nor easily with the tune itself; the Robin Hood ballads are so wedded (refrains apart) to CM that the LM of this tune would in itself unsuit it for all but (I think) Nos. 132 and 148 (late ballads both); and where had Robin Hood been to be gone *to* the greenwood rather than *out* of it—unless to pay respects to the Sheriff of Nottingham? Not every Robin must wear a hood, though those who love jolly good ale let back and side go bare before they give one up!

In Ravenscroft's *Pammelia*, 1609, is an attractive "Round of three Country dances in one," with a text mentioning Robin Hood and Little John but having no other claim to be connected with a ballad. Yet this tune is the one that also turns up as "Robin hood" in the Cambridge MS. D.d.ix.33, fol. 81^v, in a variant form; and it reappears with the odd title "Trike my wigelo" in the Ballet MS., p. 104, second piece. The tune is given from *Pammelia* by both Rimbault (Gutch, *op.cit.*, II, p. 445) and Chappell (*loc.cit.*). From Professor Claude Simpson comes the valuable information that there are other sets of the tune in a four-voice medley by William Cobbold, Brit. Mus. Add. MS. 18936, fol. 60 (after 1612), and in Will Forster's Virginal Book (before 1624), Brit. Mus. MS., Royal Music 24.d.3, p. 430. The last is again called "Robbin Hood" and is in the major tonality. When this form of the tune is turned from triple into duple time, its relation to the Giles Lodge "Robin hoode" with which we began is inescapable.[2]

[1] "The Sources of English Lute Music, 1540-1620," unpublished Ph.D. dissertation, Cambridge University, 1957, Vol. II.

[2] In F. W. Sternfeld, *Music in Shakespearean Tragedy*, London, 1963,

Next among the early tunes comes the "Three Ravens" (No. 26) tune of 1611, which Rimbault assigns to five Robin Hood ballads, though it cannot be proved to have been used with any one. From flyleaves of books published at about the same time, he has recovered two more, presumably written down not much later; and likewise retrieved the one mentioned above from the Gostling lute MS., of perhaps also the first half of the seventeenth century. This exhausts the record of that century. The earliest copy of "Arthur a Bland" (No. 126), to which a dozen of the seventeenth-century broadsides are directed to be sung, was found by Rimbault in a ballad opera of 1731; but a hundred years earlier the tune may not have been very different. Two copies of "Robin Hood and the Bishop of Hereford" (No. 144), from half-sheets of the early and late eighteenth century, complete the eighteenth-century record. From Scottish tradition of the early nineteenth century the Blaikie MS. yields one tune, not, I believe, hitherto published (No. 134). Rimbault and Chappell print three tunes from Staffordshire tradition of the mid-century, and Jewitt contributes a couple from Derbyshire. In the last decade of the century Kidson and Broadwood glean another pair.

Of the tunes gathered in the present century, several bear traces of a connection with "Arthur a Bland" or other familiar tunes. It cannot be claimed that in the aggregate any very rich musical inheritance has survived in this province. Perhaps that was hardly to be expected, in view of the fact that the muse of Robin Hood was so thoroughly involved with print in the seventeenth and eighteenth centuries. Nevertheless, the broadside press probably kept the outlaw alive—though fallen and changed—a good deal longer than he could have survived without its inky transfusions. It is lamentable that we have no hint of what his proper music was like when he was in his prime.

pp. 76-77, is a bibliographical list of thirty "Robin" songs, *temp.* Elizabeth I, printed and manuscript, of which one called "Robin Hood," in the Euing Book (Glasgow University Library, R.d.43, fol. 46v-47), is not listed above.

LIST OF VARIANTS

1. "Robin hoode." Giles Lodge lute-book, ?1575, MS. V.a.159 (*olim* 448.16), fol. 5r, Folger Shakespeare Library, Washington, D.C.

2a. "A Round of three Country dances in one." Thomas Ravenscroft, *Pammelia*, 1609, No. 74 (American Folklore Society facsimile edition, 1961, p. [34]). Also in Joseph Ritson, *Robin Hood*, 1795, II, p. 208; J. M. Gutch, *A Lytell Geste of Robin Hode*, 1847, II, p. 445 (app'x., ed. Edward F. Rimbault); and W. Chappell, *Popular Music of the Olden Time* [1855-59], II, p. 398.

2b. "Robin hood." Cambridge University MS. Dd.ix.33, fol. 81v, Cambridge University Library.

3. "Robin hood is to the greenwood gone." William Ballet lute-book, MS. D.1.21, p. 113, Trinity College Library, Dublin.

4a. "Robin Reddocke." William Ballet lute-book, Trinity College (Dublin) Library MS. D.1.21, p. 26.

4b. "Robin Hood." Gutch, 1847, II, p. 437 (Rimbault).

TUNES WITH TEXTS

1. "Robin hoode"

Giles Lodge lute-book, ?1575, Folger Shakespeare Library MS. V.a.159 (*olim* 448.16), fol. 5r.

Conjectural reduction by the Editor from the preceding tune:

2a. "A Round of three Country dances in one"

Ravenscroft, 1609, No. 74 (AFS facsimile edition, 1961, p. [34]). Also in Ritson, 1795, II, p. 208; Gutch, 1847, II, p. 445 (Rimbault); and Chappell, [1855-59], II, p. 398.

p D (inflected VII)

Robin Hood, Robin Hood, said Little John,
Come dance before the queene a: (*bis*)
In a red petticote and a greene jacket
A white hose and a greene a (*bis*)

The untitled medley by William Cobbold, mentioned in the headnote above (p. 13), carries the following variant words:

Robin hood Robin hood and little John,
they leand them to a tree a tree,
Frier Tuck and Maid Marrian,
soe turn ye about all three,
frier Tuck and mayd Marrian,
soe turne ye about all three,
about all three.

2b. "Robin hood"

Cambridge University MS. Dd. ix. 33, fol. 81v.

p Minor (–VI)

3. "Robin hood is to the greenwood gone"

William Ballet lute-book, Trinity College (Dublin) Library MS. D.1.21, p. 113. Also in the same MS., p. 27, another copy, titled "Bonny sweet Robin." Transcript by courtesy of Daniel Heartz.

a D

4a. "Robin Reddocke"

William Ballet lute-book, Trinity College (Dublin) Library MS. D.1.21, p. 26. Transcript by courtesy of Daniel Heartz.

a I/M (compass of a sixth)

4b. "Robin Hood"

Gutch, 1847, II, p. 437 (Rimbault). From a MS. lute-book in the Cambridge University Library, Dd.ix.33.

a I/M (–VI) (compass of a fifth)

Robin Hood and Guy of Gisborne

CHILD NO. 118

It would be more than gratifying if we could recover the proper tune of this fine ballad. Unfortunately, there seems not the slightest ground for connecting it with the tune to which Chappell has joined it (*Popular Music*, [1855-59], II, p. 397). Chappell virtually admits this: "I have not found any ballad having particular reference to the song of the lark, and of suitable metre, except 'Robin Hood and Guy of Gisborne.' In that, the story hangs upon Robin Hood's being awakened from a dream by the song of the woodweele, or woodlark; and I have therefore coupled them." Given a tune called "The Chirping of the Lark," or "The Lark" (a country dance tune in Playford's *English Dancing Master*, 1651, ed. Margaret Dean-Smith, 1957, p. 24), find a suitable ballad text. An earlier printing of the same tune, slightly different, is in A. Valerius, *Nederlandtsche Gedenck-Clanck*, 1626, p. 33 (ed. 1943, p. 48), as Chappell has observed. It there bears the name of the "Engelsche Foulle, Walsch Wallinneken." He omits to note that "Muscadin," in the Fitzwilliam Book, set by G. Farnaby, is a version of the same. (See the edition of J. A. Fuller Maitland and W. Barclay Squire, 1899, II, p. 481.) Incidentally, the tune as given in the *Dancing Master* would not fit the ballad without adaptation.

Robin Hood and the Monk

CHILD NO. 119

AGAIN we have a suggestion, but hardly more, for a tune for this very early, and superb, ballad. Chappell observes (*Popular Music* [1855-59], II, p. 541), that Ashmole noted down, about the end of Charles I's reign, a tune with the words of "Under the Greenwood Tree." The text began, "In summer time, when leaves grow green." This song was frequently reprinted, and the tune was used in a number of ballad operas (Chappell, *loc.cit.*). The only reason for connecting it with the "Monk" is that the latter commences "In som*er*, when þe shawes be sheyn*e*," and that the eighth line is "Vnd*er* the grene-wode tre." No one, however, could seriously argue that there was a scintilla of likelihood that the tune and the ballad had any connection.

Robin Hood's Death

CHILD NO. 120

For the Percy Folio text of this ballad, Child A, there is no trace of a refrain, nor any clue to the proper tune, by name or note. Child Ba, nearly a century and a half later (1786), is directed to be sung to the tune of "Robin Hood's last farewel, etc." There is no extant Robin Hood ballad that bears this title, and no tune has survived with the text; so that we are still in the dark. Child Ba has a refrain interpolated as the second and last lines of the stanza: "Down a down a down a down," and "Hey, etc." The latter abbreviation would seem to indicate a repetition of the second line; but the line is given at the end of the ballad as "Hey down a derry derry down." As Child notes after Ritson, however, the last two stanzas are apparently adopted from "Robin Hood and the Valiant Knight" (No. 153), so that this latter form of the refrain may be incorrect for the present ballad. Moreover, the Bb form of the ballad, in other respects textually very close, quite lacks any refrain, as well as any indication of a named tune.

Rimbault says (Gutch, *Robin Hood*, 1847, II, p. 435), on no authority, but obviously on the sole evidence of the refrain, that this ballad, like Nos. 135, 136, 141, and 145, was sung to the tune of the "Three Ravens," which he quotes from Ravenscroft's *Melismata*, 1611, declaring, again upon his own authority, that the tune "is there adapted to" the "Three Ravens" text. This we need not believe unless we choose; but adaptation in one direction or the other there would have to be, for the tune would not fit any extant form of "Robin Hood's Death" without some textual modification. At the least, the further refrain element "with a down," would need to be added after the (proper) second line of the quatrain. Rimbault goes on to remark that this tune is traditionally still current (i.e., c. 1850) in most counties of England, and that he has eight different versions of it; but he does not claim that any of these has been found with this or any other Robin Hood ballad; and it is probable that the texts were in most or all cases some form of the "Three Ravens" ballad. We have, therefore, no very secure ground for associating the tune with the present ballad. For "The Three Ravens," see Child No. 26, *ante*, Vol. I, p. 309.*

Thus we reach the present century without any reliable musical record. In 1913, Miss Martha Davis contributed a version of the ballad, with a tune, current in her family for three generations, apparently thus reaching back to the eighteenth century in American oral tradition. Though found in Virginia, it went back through Maryland to a Pennsylvania settlement of Scotch-Irish.

The tune is interesting, and valuable at any rate as the sole recorded traditional air for this ballad. It is a two-strain melody, a Æ/P, if its final be tonic, but possibly p D/Æ, with its tonic a fourth above the final. Confirmation of its genuine association with Robin Hood comes in the fact that a variant was picked up recently in Kentucky to a text of No. 125, q. v. Furthermore, it may well be a form of "Arthur a Bland," which itself is the proper early tune of No. 126 and found with a considerable number of other Robin Hood ballads, as will presently be seen.

* In printing this tune for that ballad, to which it truly belongs, the editor, not having access to the first edition of Ravenscroft, gave it from Ritson's reprint, which erroneously reads the first-phrase cadence-note as C rather than A. In this misreading, Rimbault followed suit (Gutch, *loc.cit.*). See the facsimile edition of Ravenscroft's *Melismata* in Publications of the American Folklore Society, Bibliographical and Special Series, Vol. XII, ed. MacEdward Leach, 1961, pp. 138-39. Whether Ravenscroft intended the E in bar 4 to be flattened is an open question. In the eighth bar, it is surely a natural.

LIST OF VARIANTS

"Robin Hood's Death." Arthur Kyle Davis, Jr., *Traditional Ballads of Virginia*, 1929, pp. 586 and 390.

TUNE WITH TEXT

"Robin Hood's Death"

Davis, 1929, p. 586; text, p. 390. Contributed by Martha M. Davis, Harrisonburg, Rockingham County, Va., April 8, 1913. Text dictated by her grandmother in 1882.

a Æ/P (or p D/Æ, ending on *V*)

1. As Robin Hood and Little John
 Walked by a bank of broom,
Said Robin in a mournful voice,
 "I fear approaching doom.

2. "And since the day that we did meet,
 Much mirth and joy we saw;
To many a poor man have we given
 Since we became outlaw.

3. "But now, alas! these days are o'er,
 For I am taken ill;
I must away to Kirkley Hall
 To try physician's skill."

4. "Fare thee well," said Little John,
 "O master dear, farewell;
And when I see your face once more,
 Good news I hope you'll tell."

5. He is away to Kirkley Hall
As fast as he could hie,
But ere that he could reach that length
He was nigh like to die.

6. And when he came to Kirkley Hall,
He knocked and made great noise;
His cousin flew to let him in,
Full well she knew his voice.

7. "Will you sit down, dear cousin?" she said,
"And drink some wine with me?"
"I will neither eat nor drink
Until I blooded be."

. . . .

8. When he perceived their treachery,
Away he strove to fly
Out of the window, but could not,
It was so very high.

9. Then he picked up his bugle horn
That hung down by his knee;
He tried with all his might and main
If he could blow blasts three.

10. Then Little John heard his master's call
As he sat under a tree.
"I think," said he, "my master's ill,
He blows so wearily."

11. Then he is away to Kirkley Hall,
Its doors broke open wide,
And when he came to Robin Hood
He knelt down by his side.

12. "What shall I do, dear master?" he said,
"That you avenged may be?
Shall I burn cursed Kirkley Hall
And all its nunnery?"

13. "O nay, O nay," said Robin Hood,
"I ne'er in all my life
Burned any kirk nor any nun,
Nor widow, child, nor wife.

14. "Nor shall it now be said of me
In this my dying hour
Upon the head of Christian folks
Destruction I did pour.

15. "Now bring me here my much-loved bow.
One arrow I'll let fly,
And whereso'er that arrow lights,
There let my body lie.

16. "Let green grass grow upon my grave,
By my side my bow so good,
At my head a stone that all may read,
'Here lies bold Robin Hood.' "

17. Underneath this little stone
Lies Robert, Earl of Huntingdon.

Robin Hood and the Butcher

CHILD NO. 122

CHILD'S A, coming from the Percy Folio, lacks, as usual, both name of tune and refrain. The texts collated under B, broadsides of the second half of the seventeenth century, are all directed to be sung to the tune of "Robin Hood and the Begger" (No. 133). The latter ballad is extant on broadsides of the same era, and these share with the "Butcher" the features of middle rhyme in the (proper) third line and a refrain, "With hey down, down, an a down" (or some close variant) injected after the first line. This pattern, though unusual, is common to about a dozen of the Robin Hood ballads, which are variously directed, in a thoroughly confusing way, to be sung to one another's tunes. But by whatever name, the tune can generally be identified as ultimately that of "Robin Hood and the Tanner" (No. 126), the hero of which, Arthur a Bland, gives his own name as the readiest identification of the tune. Cf. further, No. 126.

Robin Hood and the Curtal Friar

CHILD NO. 123

This ballad comes to us from a mutilated copy in the Percy Folio and a number of broadsides roughly contemporary with the Folio. We know in this case, at least, that a form of the ballad lay behind the *Play of Robin Hood*, printed in the first half of the sixteenth century by Copland. Nothing, however, helps to identify the proper tune, which in the broadsides is called, simply, a "new northern tune." Here again, however, Rimbault steps forward (Gutch, *Robin Hood*, 1847, II, p. 436) with a tune which he found on a flyleaf of a copy of *Parthenia*, 1611. But in his own copy of this work, now in the Huntington Library, the tune is not discoverable; nor is it to be found in another copy inscribed with his autographed comment, in the New York Public Library (Drexel 5608). He does not say what the tune was called in the MS. copy, nor whether the hand was of the same date; Chappell, following him (*Popular Music*, [1855-59], II, p. 392), says it was "written in a contemporary hand." Since Rimbault says that "The Noble Fisherman" is "directed to be sung to the same tune," and since that ballad, Child No. 148, is in all the broadsides actually directed to be sung to "In summer time," or "Summer time," we may infer that Rimbault's MS. copy was so designated. If so, it would appear that Rimbault's sole reason for connecting the tune and the present ballad is that the ballad, in the broadside copies, begins with the words which make the title of his tune—a very shaky premise in view of the fact that a number of other ballads begin with the same words; and that, again, a number of different ballads in other stanzaic patterns are also directed to be sung to the tune of "In Summer time." Cf., e.g., Chappell, *op.cit.*, II, pp. 392-93 and 541.

It is worth observing that the present tune and that given by Rimbault for "Adam Bell" (No. 116), from a kindred flyleaf, appear to be cousins.

LIST OF VARIANTS

"Robin Hood and the Curtall Friar." J. M. Gutch, *A Lytell Geste of Robin Hode*, 1847, II, p. 436 (app'x., ed. Edward F. Rimbault). Text, Francis James Child, *The English and Scottish Popular Ballads*, 1882-98, III, p. 124(B).

TUNE WITH TEXT

"Robin Hood and the Curtall Friar"

Gutch, 1847, II, p. 436 (Rimbault). From the flyleaf of a copy of *Parthenia*, 1611. Text, Child, 1882-98, III, p. 124(B).

p I

1. In summer time, when leaves grow green,
   And flowers are fresh and gay,
Robin Hood and his merry men
   Were disposed to play.

2. Then some would leap, and some would run,
   And some would use artillery:
'Which of you can a good bow draw,
   A good archer to be?

3. 'Which of you can kill a buck?
   Or who can kill a do?
Or who can kill a hart of greece,
   Five hundred foot him fro?'

4. Will Scadlock he killd a buck,
   And Midge he killd a do,
And Little John killd a hart of greece,
   Five hundred foot him fro.

5. 'God's blessing on thy heart,' said Robin Hood,
   'That hath [shot] such a shot for me;
I would ride my horse an hundred miles,
   To finde one could match with thee.'

6. That causd Will Scadlock to laugh,
   He laughed full heartily:
'There lives a curtal frier in Fountains Abby
   Will beat both him and thee.

7. 'That curtal frier in Fountains Abby
   Well can a strong bow draw;
He will beat you and your yeomen,
   Set them all on a row.'

8. Robin Hood took a solemn oath,
   It was by Mary free,
That he would neither eat nor drink
   Till the frier he did see.

9. Robin Hood put on his harness good,
   And on his head a cap of steel,
Broad sword and buckler by his side,
   And they became him weel.

10. He took his bow into his hand,
   It was made of a trusty tree,
With a sheaf of arrows at his belt,
   To the Fountains Dale went he.

11. And comming unto Fountain[s] Dale,
 No further would he ride;
There was he aware of a curtal frier,
 Walking by the water-side.

12. The fryer had on a harniss good,
 And on his head a cap of steel,
Broad sword and buckler by his side,
 And they became him weel.

13. Robin Hood lighted off his horse,
 And tied him to a thorn:
'Carry me over the water, thou curtal frier,
 Or else thy life's forlorn.'

14. The frier took Robin Hood on his back,
 Deep water he did bestride,
And spake neither good word nor bad,
 Till he came at the other side.

15. Lightly leapt Robin Hood off the friers back;
 The frier said to him again,
Carry me over this water, fine fellow,
 Or it shall breed thy pain.

16. Robin Hood took the frier on's back,
 Deep water he did bestride,
And spake neither good word nor bad,
 Till he came at the other side.

17. Lightly leapt the fryer off Robin Hoods back;
 Robin Hood said to him again,
Carry me over this water, thou curtal frier,
 Or it shall breed thy pain.

18. The frier took Robin Hood on's back again,
 And stept up to the knee;
Till he came at the middle stream,
 Neither good nor bad spake he.

19. And coming to the middle stream,
 There he threw Robin in:
'And chuse thee, chuse thee, fine fellow,
 Whether thou wilt sink or swim.'

20. Robin Hood swam to a bush of broom,
 The frier to a wicker wand;
Bold Robin Hood is gone to shore,
 And took his bow in hand.

21. One of his best arrows under his belt
 To the frier he let flye;
The curtal frier, with his steel buckler,
 He put that arrow by.

22. 'Shoot on, shoot on, thou fine fellow,
 Shoot on as thou hast begun;
If thou shoot here a summers day,
 Thy mark I will not shun.'

23. Robin Hood shot passing well,
 Till his arrows all were gone;
They took their swords and steel bucklers,
 And fought with might and maine;

24. From ten oth' clock that day,
 Till four ith' afternoon;
Then Robin Hood came to his knees,
 Of the frier to beg a boon.

25. 'A boon, a boon, thou curtal frier,
 I beg it on my knee;
Give me leave to set my horn to my mouth,
 And to blow blasts three.'

26. 'That will I do,' said the curtal frier,
 'Of thy blasts I have no doubt;
I hope thou'lt blow so passing well
 Till both thy eyes fall out.'

27. Robin Hood set his horn to his mouth,
 He blew but blasts three;
Half a hundred yeomen, with bows bent,
 Came raking over the lee.

28. 'Whose men are these,' said the frier,
 'That come so hastily?'
'These men are mine,' said Robin Hood;
 'Frier, what is that to thee?'

29. 'A boon, a boon,' said the curtal frier,
 'The like I gave to thee;
Give me leave to set my fist to my mouth,
 And to whute whutes three.'

30. 'That will I do,' said Robin Hood,
 'Or else I were to blame;
Three whutes in a friers fist
 Would make me glad and fain.'

31. The frier he set his fist to his mouth,
 And whuted whutes three;
Half a hundred good ban-dogs
 Came running the frier unto.

32. 'Here's for every man of thine a dog,
 And I my self for thee:'
'Nay, by my faith,' quoth Robin Hood,
 'Frier, that may not be.'

33. Two dogs at once to Robin Hood did go,
 The one behind, the other before;
Robin Hoods mantle of Lincoln green
 Off from his back they tore.

34. And whether his men shot east or west,
 Or they shot north or south,
The curtal dogs, so taught they were,
 They kept their arrows in their mouth.

35. 'Take up thy dogs,' said Little John,
 'Frier at my bidding be;'
'Whose man art thou,' said the curtal frier,
 'Comes here to prate with me?'

36. 'I am Little John, Robin Hoods man,
 Frier, I will not lie;
If thou take not up thy dogs soon,
 I'le take up them and thee.'

37. Little John had a bow in his hand,
 He shot with might and main;
Soon half a score of the friers dogs
 Lay dead upon the plain.

38. 'Hold they hand, good fellow,' said the curtal frier,
'Thy master and I will agree;
And we will have new orders taken,
With all the haste that may be.'

39. 'If thou wilt forsake fair Fountains Dale,
And Fountains Abby free,
Every Sunday throughout the year,
A noble shall be thy fee.

40. 'And every holy day throughout the year,
Changed shall thy garment be,
If thou wilt go to fair Nottingham,
And there remain with me.'

41. This curtal frier had kept Fountains Dale
Seven long years or more;
There was neither knight, lord, nor earl
Could make him yield before.

The Jolly Pinder of Wakefield

CHILD NO. 124

ALTHOUGH this ballad was entered in the Stationers' Register in 1558, the earliest copies we have are a very mutilated one in the Percy Folio (about 1640) and similarly defective broadsides (or garlands) of approximately the same date or a little later. Of the latter, two (Child Ab, Ac) are directed to be sung to a northern tune—evidence of the fashion at that time in popular song: one never reads of *southern* tunes being called for. In these broadside texts, every second and fourth line is repeated —a practice so ill in keeping with balladry as to suggest an attempt to adjust the text to a dance measure.

Two copies of a tune called "Wakefield on a green" were noted by Chappell, *Popular Music* [1855-59], II, pp. 393-94, as he says, from lute tablature in Cambridge University Library (D.d.ii.11 and D.d.iii.18), with Rimbault's assistance in extracting the melody from the instrumental *rifacimenti*. It cannot be said that the result is a convincing tune; but it is noteworthy that provision is made in it for the characteristic repetition of lines two and four—which without the textual evidence one would attribute to the common habit of an instrumental echo of a vocal phrase, as in the familiar "Willow Song," with lute accompaniment. The first copy has not been rediscovered. But the copy in D.d.3.18, fol. 11ᵛ bears no resemblance to what Chappell prints. It appears to be a series of divisions for the lute by Jo. Johnson, entitled "Wakefilde on a green," but, although on a single melodic line, it does not state the tune itself, and does not seem to carry its variations beyond a possible second phrase. According to Professor Claude Simpson, however, there is another untitled copy of this in the Marsh lute-book, p. 146, in Archbishop Marsh's Library, Dublin. This I have not seen. Chappell refers, but so far as I know Rimbault publicly does not, to a third copy of the tune in a MS. volume of virginal music, *temp.* Elizabeth, in Rimbault's possession. If actually of the same air, this copy does not appear to have thrown any light on the genuine reading. But Professor Simpson has found a "wakefild on a greene" for virginals in Brit. Mus. Add. MS. 30485, fol. 56. Whether or not this is the same as Rimbault's copy to which Chappell alludes, it too is very reluctant to yield a recognizable tune.

Rimbault does, however, refer to, and transcribe, another tune for the ballad from a third MS. in lute tablature, the Gostling MS., and with this he has been more plausibly successful. The result is, as both he and Chappell note (Gutch, *Robin Hood*, 1847, II, p. 434, and Chappell, *op.cit.*, p. 390), a version of the common tune of the "Bailiff's Daughter of Islington" (No. 105). What seems not to have been observed is that the tune of "Arthur a Bland" (No. 126) is a more elaborate form of this in different metre (cf. that ballad). It might also be mentioned that "Walsingham" ("How should I your true love know") is another of the same family. On the other hand, this tune makes no provision for the repeated lines in the A broadsides. The Percy Folio copy does not indicate repetitions but stanzas four and five contain six lines each, which could be accommodated by repeating the second half of the tune.

We may hazard the observation that the Chappell-Rimbault transcript of "Wakefield on a green" (if transposed) comes close to being a sort of discant or division to the other melody. (The "echo" of course drops out.) Perhaps, for a wild hypothesis, "Walsingham" is behind the whole lot.

LIST OF VARIANTS

1. "The Jolly Pinder of Wakefield." J. M. Gutch, *A Lytell Geste of Robin Hode*, 1847, II, p. 434 (app'x., ed. Edward F. Rimbault). Text, Francis James Child, *The English and Scottish Popular Ballads*, 1882-98, III, p. 131(A).
2. "Wakefield on a green." W. Chappell, *Popular Music of the Olden Time* [1855-59], II, p. 394.

TUNES WITH TEXTS

1. "The Jolly Pinder of Wakefield"

Gutch, 1847, II, p. 434 (Rimbault). Text, Child, 1882-98, III, p. 131(A). From a lute MS. once belonging to Rev. Mr. Gostling of Canterbury.

p Minor

1. In Wakefield there lives a jolly pinder,
   In Wakefield, all on a green; (*bis*)

2. 'There is neither knight nor squire,' said the pinder,
   'Nor baron that is so bold, (*bis*)
   Dare make a trespasse to the town of Wakefield,
   But his pledge goes to the pinfold.' (*bis*)

3. All this beheard three witty young men,
   'T was Robin Hood, Scarlet, and John;
   With that they spyed the jolly pinder,
   As he sate under a thorn.

4. 'Now turn again, turn again,' said the pinder,
   'For a wrong way have you gone;
   For you have forsaken the king his highway,
   And made a path over the corn.'

5. 'O that were great shame,' said jolly Robin,
'We being three, and thou but one:'
The pinder leapt back then thirty good foot,
'T was thirty good foot and one.

6. He leaned his back fast unto a thorn,
And his foot unto a stone,
And there he fought a long summer's day,
A summer's day so long,
Till that their swords, on their broad bucklers,
Were broken fast unto their hands.

* * * * * * * * *

7. 'Hold thy hand, hold thy hand,' said Robin Hood,
'And my merry men euery one;
For this is one of the best pinders
That ever I try'd with sword.

8. 'And wilt thou forsake thy pinder his craft,
And live in [the] green wood with me?
. . . .
. . . .

9. 'At Michaelmas next my covnant comes out,
When every man gathers his fee;
I'le take my blew blade all in my hand,
And plod to the green wood with thee.'

10. 'Hast thou either meat or drink,' said Robin Hood,
'For my merry men and me?
. . . .
. . . .

11. 'I have both bread and beef,' said the pinder,
'And good ale of the best;'
'And that is meat good enough,' said Robin Hood,
'For such unbidden guest.

12. 'O wilt thou forsake the pinder his craft,
And go to the green wood with me?
Thou shalt have a livery twice in the year,
The one green, the other brown [shall be].'

13. 'If Michaelmas day were once come and gone
And my master had paid me my fee,
Then would I set as little by him
As my master doth set by me.'

2. "Wakefield on a green"

Chappell, [1855-59], II, p. 394. Said to be from lute copies in the Dowland MSS., Cambridge Dd.ii.11 and Dd.iii.18.

a Æ

In Wakefield there lives a jolly Pinder
In Wakefield all on a green,
In Wakefield all on a green;
There's neither Knight nor Squire, says the Pinder,
Nor Baron that is so bold,
Nor Baron that is so bold,
Dare make a trespass to the town of Wakefield,
But his pledge goes to the Pinfold,
His pledge goes to the Pinfold.

Robin Hood and Little John

CHILD NO. 125

The earliest copies of this ballad which are now extant are of the eighteenth century, although Thackeray's press is known to have printed it, late in the seventeenth, and doubtless it derives from early materials. The indicated tune is "Arthur a Bland," for which see the next ballad (No. 126).

Child has argued that the present ballad is that which must have been meant in references to "Robin Hood and the Stranger," to which "Robin Hood and the Tanner," "Robin Hood and the Beggar," "Robin Hood and the Bishop" (Nos. 126, 133, and 143) are all directed to be sung. Three other ballads of Robin Hood are to be sung to the tune of "Robin Hood and the Beggar," which therefore is to be equated as to tune; and two others to "Arthur a Bland," the named tune of this present ballad. All the ballads so qualified are alike in having mid-rhyme in line three of the stanza. Child's reason for thinking that the present ballad would be called "Robin Hood and the Stranger" is that in it Robin's antagonist is eleven times called "the stranger." In this feature it is exactly matched by "Robin Hood newly revived" (No. 128). Child thinks, however, that since the last-named ballad does not have the middle rhyme, there is "a slightly superior probability to the supposition that ['Robin Hood and Little John'], or rather some older version of it (for the one we have is in a rank seventeenth-century style), had the secondary title of 'Robin Hood and the Stranger'" (1882-98, III, p. 133). By supposing an older version Child seems inadvertently to have overturned his own argument, for the middle rhyme need not—and in his opinion (cf. *sub* No. 122, his last paragraph of headnote, p. 116) would not—have been a feature of the earlier version. The tune of "Robin Hood newly revived," he grants in a footnote, was likewise "Arthur a Bland." Moreover, not only No. 128, but Nos. 130, 150, and possibly 129, were all to be sung to the same tune, yet 130 and 150 have the middle rhyme, whilst 128 and 129 lack it. And, contrariwise, 137, 151, 152, and 153, none of which goes to this tune, have still the middle rhyme. There is no evidence, then, in either text or tune, to tilt the scales in favor of Child's supposition that the present ballad rather than "Robin Hood newly revived," is "Robin Hood and the Stranger." Ritson gave his judgment in favor of the other (No. 128); and Child has scrupulously acknowledged that it (No. 128) is found in the 1663 garland along with "Robin Hood and the Bishop," "Robin Hood and the Butcher" and the other ballads of the group first mentioned above, but that "Robin Hood and Little John" is not among them—a fact which might finally tip the balance in favor of No. 128.

Very recently, a copy of this ballad was recovered in Kentucky from an oral source, where it could be followed back in family tradition for two generations. The text is somewhat disconcertingly close to the eighteenth-century form. The tune is, as has been remarked, a variant of that found in Virginia with "Robin Hood's Death" (No. 120). Its second strain would seem to be related to the "Jolly Pinder" or "Bailiff's Daughter" tune which Rimbault has produced from the Gostling MS. (Gutch, *Robin Hood*, 1847, II, p. 434). This is reassuring evidence of its traditional authenticity.

LIST OF VARIANTS

1. "Robin Hood and Little John." John Strachan (singer), Archive, School of Scottish Studies, University of Edinburgh. Collected by Hamish Henderson. Also on Caedmon recording No. TC 1146(A4).
2. "Robin Hood and Little John." Mrs. Mariana Schaupp, LC Archive of American Folk Song, recording No. 6081(A). Also in E. C. and M. N. Kirkland, *Southern Folklore Quarterly*, II (1938), p. 72.

TUNES WITH TEXTS

1. "Robin Hood and Little John"

Archive, School of Scottish Studies. Sung by John Strachan, Aberdeenshire. Also on Caedmon rec. No. TC 1146(A4). Collected by Hamish Henderson for the School of Scottish Studies. Transcribed by Francis M. Collinson, 1963.

a I

When Robin Hood was about twenty years old,
He happened to meet little John.
A jolly brisk blade, just fit for the trade,
And he was a sturdy young man.

They happened to meet on Nottingham Bridge,
And neither of them would give way.
Till brave Robin Hood, in right merry mood—
"I'll show ye right Nottingham play."

Robin laid on so thick and so strong,
He made little John to admire;
And every knock, it made his bones smoke
As if he had been in a fire.

2. "Robin Hood and Little John"

Sung by Mrs. Mariana Schaupp, of Ohio, 1941; learned in 1914 from a schoolteacher, who had in turn learned it c. 1865. LC/AAFS, rec. No. 6081(A). Also in E. C. and M. N. Kirkland, *SFQ*, II (1938), p. 72.

a P/Æ

The catch-signature indicates the pitch at which the tune was printed in the *Quarterly*. I have transcribed afresh from tape, and failed to hear the raised seventh in the second, third, and penultimate bars.

1. When Robin Hood was about eighteen years old,
He chanced to meet Little John,
A jolly brisk blade, just fit for his trade,
For he was a sturdy young man.
Although he was Little, his limbs they were large;
His stature was seven feet high.
Wherever he came, he soon quickened his name,
And he presently caused them to fly.

2. One day these two met on a long narrow bridge,
And neither of them would give way,
When Robin stepped up to the stranger and said,
"I'll show you brave Nottingham play."
"You speak like a coward," the stranger he said,
"As there with your long bow you stand,
I vow and protest you may shoot at my breast
While I have but a staff in my hand."

3. "The name of a coward," said Robin, "I scorn,
And so my long bow I lay by.
And then for your sake a staff I will take,
The faith of your manhood to try."
Then Robin he stepped out into a grove,
And pulled up a staff of green oak,
And this being done straight back he did come
And thus to the stranger he spoke.

4. "Behold thou my staff; it is lusty and tough;
On this long narrow bridge let us play;
Then he who falls in, the other shall win
The battle, and then we'll away."
Then Robin hit the stranger a crack on the crown
Which was a most terrible stroke[1]
And then[2] so enraged they more [?][3] engaged
And they laid on the blows most severe.

5. The stranger hit Robin a crack on the[4] crown,
That[5] was a most horrible[6] stroke.
The very next blow laid Robin below
And tumbled him into the brook.
"Oh where are you now?" the stranger he cried.
With a hearty laugh in reply,
"Oh, faith in the flood," quoth[7] bold Robin Hood,
"And floating away with the tide."

6. Then Robin, he waded all out of the deep
And he[8] pulled himself up by a thorn;
And[9] just at the last he blew a loud blast
So merrily on his bugle horn.
The hills they did echo, the vales they did[10] ring,
Which caused his gay men to appear,
All dressed in green, most fair to be seen;
Straight up to the master they steer.

7. "What aileth thee, Master?" quoth William Stutely.
"You seem to be wet to the skin."
"No matter," said he, "this fellow you see,
In fighting hath tumbled me in."
"We'll pluck out his eyes, and duck him likewise."
Then seized they the stranger right there.
"Nay, let him go free," quoth bold Robin Hood,
"For he's a brave fellow. Forbear!

8. "Cheer up, jolly blade, and don't be afraid
Of all[11] these gay men that you see.
There are fourscore and nine, and if you will be mine
You may wear of my own livery."
A brace of fat deer[12] was quickly brought in,
Good ale and strong liquor likewise;
The feast was so good all in the greenwood
Where this jolly babe was baptized.

The footnotes below record different readings in *SFQ* from an earlier singing by Mrs. Schaupp (1937).

[1] Which caused the blood to appear
[2] thus
[3] closely
[4] his
[5] Which
[6] terrible
[7] cries
[8] Omitted in *SFQ*
[9] Then
[10] valleys did
[11] Omitted in *SFQ*
[12] doe

Robin Hood and the Tanner

CHILD NO. 126

ALL the early broadsides of this ballad are directed to be sung to "Robin and the Stranger." If, by that title, "Robin Hood and Little John" (No. 125) be meant, as Child argues, the tune indicated is "Arthur a Bland," which can only be the present ballad! If, as Ritson judged, No. 128, or "Robin Hood newly revived" be intended, the tune indicated is only "a delightful new tune." In any case, and by any name, the characteristic refrain line coming after line one, and the internal rhyme in line three of each stanza, relate it to the group of ballads already mentioned under No. 125. The tune which fits this peculiar pattern was known in the eighteenth century as "Arthur a Bland," so that we rest here on firm ground. The earliest printing of this tune which Chappell succeeded in finding was in the ballad-opera *The Jovial Crew*, 1731. From this source both he and Rimbault reprinted it (see variant 1); perhaps Ritson (*Robin Hood*, 1795, II, p. 37) as well.

The most striking feature of the tune is the extra phrase between the first and (normal) second phrase. It seems to be carrying us to the middle cadence, and we are surprised to find ourselves mistaken, for folktunes are not given to tricks of this kind. The tune is quite complete without it, and its absence would never be missed. In fact, without the interpolated phrase the tune is seen to belong to one of the most favorite of British types. A simpler form of it is seen in the "Jolly Pinder" tune of Rimbault, where phrase three repeats phrase one instead of going on independent adventures. "Goddesses" in Playford's *English Dancing Master* is another form, as is "Fayne wold I wed" in the Fitzwilliam Book. Many other names could be added; but it is clear already that "Arthur a Bland" is made out of folk-stuff. It seems much more probable that the refrain phrase was a happy fancy that caught on than that the tune was originally of this shape. Catch on it did, and was by far the most popular of the Robin Hood tunes so far as we have record, being used for no fewer than ten of the extant ballads: Nos. 122, 125, 126, 128, 131, 133, 142, 143, 146, 150.

The other records are of the present century, though in each case pointing back deep into the nineteenth. Cecil Sharp has put on display a version of great interest for students of variation (*English Folk-Song: Some Conclusions*, 1907, pp. 21-22).

Miss Martha Davis, of Virginia, had from her grandmother a version of this ballad, remarkably close to the seventeenth-century copies, except that the first four stanzas belong rather with Child No. 131 than with the present song. This text was written down from Miss Davis's grandmother's dictation in 1882; but Cecil Sharp took the tune from Miss Davis's own singing, as late as 1918. Whether it, too, is related to "Arthur a Bland" I shall not venture to determine. Sharp thought the presence of the leading-note in this copy due to the singer; but in view of the inflected seventh in "Arthur a Bland" itself—supposing the two related—the fact may be otherwise.

LIST OF VARIANTS

1. "Arthur a Bland." *The Jovial Crew*, 1731, p. 2. Also in J. M. Gutch, *A Lytell Geste of Robin Hode*, 1847, II, p. 433 (app'x., ed. Edward F. Rimbault); and W. Chappell, *Popular Music of the Olden Time*, [1855-59], II, p. 392.
2. "Robin Hood." Sharp MSS., 632/683, Clare College Library, Cambridge. Also in Cecil J. Sharp and Charles L. Marson, *Folk Songs from Somerset*, 2nd series, 1905, p. 34; Sharp, *English Folk-Song: Some Conclusions*, 1907, p. 21; Sharp, *One Hundred English Folksongs*, 1916, p. 8; and Sharp, *English Folk Songs*, Selected Ed., Novello and Co., [1920], I, p. 8. (Larcombe)
3. "Robin Hood." Sharp MSS., 4162/. Also in Arthur Kyle Davis, Jr., *Traditional Ballads of Virginia*, 1929, pp. 586 and 393. (Davis)

TUNES WITH TEXTS

1. "Arthur a Bland"

The Jovial Crew, 1731, p. 2. Also in Gutch, 1874, II, p. 433 (Rimbault); and Chappell [1855-59], II, p. 392. The text is from Child, 1882-98, III, p. 137.

m Minor

1. In Nottingham there lives a jolly tanner,
   With a hey down down a down down
   His name is Arthur a Bland;
   There is nere a squire in Nottinghamshire
   Dare bid bold Arthur stand.

2. With a long pike-staff upon his shoulder,
   So well he can clear his way;
   By two and by three he makes them to flee,
   For he hath no list to stay.

3. And as he went forth, in a summer's morning,
   Into the forrest of merry Sherwood,
   To view the red deer, that range here and there,
   There met he with bold Robin Hood.

4. As soon as bold Robin Hood did him espy,
   He thought some sport he would make;
   Therefore out of hand he bid him to stand,
   And thus to him he spake:

5. Why, what art thou, thou bold fellow,
That ranges so boldly here?
In sooth, to be brief, thou lookst like a thief,
That comes to steal our king's deer.

6. For I am a keeper in this forrest;
The king puts me in trust
To look to his deer, that range here and there,
Therefore stay thee I must.

7. 'If thou beest a keeper in this forrest,
And hast such a great command,
Yet thou must have more partakers in store,
Before thou make me to stand.'

8. 'Nay, I have no more partakers in store,
Or any that I do need;
But I have a staff of another oke graff,
I know it will do the deed.'

9. 'For thy sword and thy bow I care not a straw,
Nor all thine arrows to boot;
If I get a knop upon thy bare scop,
Thou canst as well shite as shoote.'

10. 'Speak cleanly, good fellow,' said jolly Robin,
'And give better terms to me;
Else I'le thee correct for thy neglect,
And make thee more mannerly.'

11. 'Marry gep with a wenion!' quoth Arthur a Bland,
'Art thou such a goodly man?
I care not a fig for thy looking so big;
Mend thou thyself where thou can.'

12. Then Robin Hood he unbuckled his belt,
He laid down his bow so long;
He took up a staff of another oke graff,
That was both stiff and strong.

13. 'I'le yield to thy weapon,' said jolly Robin,
'Since thou wilt not yield to mine;
For I have a staff of another oke graff,
Not half a foot longer then thine.

14. 'But let me measure,' said jolly Robin,
'Before we begin our fray;
For I'le not have mine to be longer then thine,
For that will be called foul play.'

15. 'I pass not for length,' bold Arthur reply'd,
'My staff is of oke so free;
Eight foot and a half, it will knock down a calf,
And I hope it will knock down thee.'

16. Then Robin Hood could no longer forbear;
He gave him such a knock,
Quickly and soon the blood came down,
Before it was ten a clock.

17. Then Arthur he soon recovered himself,
And gave him such a knock on the crown,
That on every hair of bold Robin Hoods head,
The blood came trickling down.

18. Then Robin Hood raged like a wild bore,
As soon as he saw his own blood;
Then Bland was in hast, he laid on so fast,
As though he had been staking of wood.

19. And about, and about, and about they went,
Like two wild bores in a chase;
Striving to aim each other to maim,
Leg, arm, or any other place.

20. And knock for knock they lustily dealt,
Which held for two hours and more;
That all the wood rang at every bang,
They ply'd their work so sore.

21. 'Hold thy hand, hold thy hand,' said Robin Hood,
'And let our quarrel fall;
For here we may thresh our bones into mesh,
And get no coyn at all.

22. 'And in the forrest of merry Sherwood
Hereafter thou shalt be free:'
'God-a-mercy for naught, my freedom I bought,
I may thank my good staff, and not thee.'

23. 'What tradesman art thou?' said jolly Robin,
'Good fellow, I prethee me show:
And also me tell in what place thou dost dwel,
For both these fain would I know.'

24. 'I am a tanner,' bold Arthur reply'd,
'In Nottingham long have I wrought;
And if thou'lt come there, I vow and do swear
I will tan thy hide for naught.'

25. 'God a mercy, good fellow,' said jolly Robin,
'Since thou art so kind to me;
And if thou wilt tan my hide for naught,
I will do as much for thee.

26. 'But if thou'lt forsake thy tanners trade,
And live in green wood with me,
My name's Robin Hood, I swear by the rood
I will give thee both gold and fee.'

27. 'If thou be Robin Hood,' bold Arthur reply'd,
'As I think well thou art,
Then here's my hand, my name's Arthur a Bland,
We two will never depart.

28. 'But tell me, O tell me, where is Little John?
Of him fain would I hear;
For we are alide by the mothers side,
And he is my kinsman near.'

29. Then Robin Hood blew on the beaugle horn,
He blew full lowd and shrill,
But quickly anon appeared Little John,
Come tripping down a green hill.

30. 'O what is the matter?' then said Little John,
'Master, I pray you tell;
Why do you stand with your staff in your hand?
I fear all is not well.'

31. 'O man, I do stand, and he makes me to stand,
The tanner that stands thee beside;
He is a bonny blade, and master of his trade,
For soundly he hath tand my hide.'

32. 'He is to be commended,' then said Little John,
'If such a feat he can do;
If he be so stout, we will have a bout,
And he shall tan my hide too.'

33. 'Hold thy hand, hold thy hand,' said Robin Hood,
'For as I do understand,
He's a yeoman good, and of thine own blood,
For his name is Arthur a Bland.'

34. Then Little John threw his staff away,
As far as he could it fling,
And ran out of hand to Arthur a Bland,
And about his neck did cling.

35. With loving respect, there was no neglect,
They were neither nice nor coy,
Each other did face, with a lovely grace,
And both did weep for joy.

36. Then Robin Hood took them both by the hand,
And danc'd round about the oke tree;
'For three merry men, and three merry men,
And three merry men we be.

37. 'And ever hereafter, as long as I live,
We three will be all one;
The wood shall ring, and the old wife sing,
Of Robin Hood, Arthur, and John.'

2. "Robin Hood"

Sharp MSS., 632/683. Also in Sharp and Marson, 2nd series, 1905, p. 34; Sharp, 1907, p. 21; Sharp, 1916, p. 8; and Sharp, Selected Ed., [1920], I, p. 8. Sung by Henry Larcombe (82), Haselbury-Plucknett, Somerset, September 2 and 3, 1905.

a D

1. Bold Arden walked forth one summer morning
For to view the merry green woods
For to hunt for the deer that run here & there
And there he espied bold Robin Hood
Aye & there he espied bold Robin Hood.

2. What a fellow art thou? quoth bold Robin Hood
And what business hast thou here?
I'll tell thee now brief thou dost look like a thief
And thou come for to steal the king's deer
Aye and thou etc.

3. I am the keeper of this Parish
And the king hath a put me in trust
And therefore I pray thee must pray take thy way
Or else upstanding [?] I must,
Aye etc.

4. And thou must be more in particular of store
Before thou canst make me stand
For I have a staff he's made of ground graff [?]
And I warrant he shall do my deed
Aye etc.

5. And I have another said bold Robin Hood
He's made of an oaken tree
He's eight feet and a half & would knock down a calf
And why shouldn't a knock down thee
Aye [etc.]

6. Let us measure our staffs said bold Robin Hood
Before we do begin a way
For if mine should be half a foot longer than thine
Then that will be counted foul play
Aye [etc.]

7. Then at it they went for bang for bang
And the space of two hours or more
Every blow made the grove for to ring
And they played our game so sure
Aye [etc.]

3. "Robin Hood"

Sharp MSS., 4162/. Also in Davis, 1929, p. 586; text, p. 393. Sung by Miss Martha M. Davis, Harrisonburg, Va., April 18, 1918; learned from her grandmother, who dictated the ballad in 1882.

m Minor (–VI, sharp VII)

"As sung by her grandmother a Scotch woman. The F♯'s are no doubt Miss Davis' addition. I sang the tune with and without the sharps to Miss Davis and she was unable to detect any difference!" [*Sharp's MS. note.*]

Robin he took them both by the hand
And danced all around the oak tree
And three merry men and three merry men
And three merry men are we.

Miss Davis' full text is given in Davis, 1929, as follows:

1. When Phoebus had melted the shackles of ice
And likewise the mountains of snow,
Bold Robin Hood, that archer so good,
Went frolicking abroad with his bow.

2. He left his merry men all behind,
As through the green woods he passed.
There did he behold a forester bold
Who cried out, "Friend, whither so fast?"

3. "I'm going," said Robin, "to kill a fat buck
For me and my merry men all,
And likewise a doe before that I go,
Or else it will cost me a fall."

4. "You'd best have a care," the forester said,
"For these are His Majesty's deer.
Before that you shoot, that thing I'll dispute,
For I am head forester here."

5. ". . . . .
And you have such great command,
You must have more partakers in store
Before that you make me to stand."

6. "I have no more partakers in store,
Nor any at all do I need;
But if I get a knock on your bare scalp
. . . .

7. "Let us measure our weapons," said bold Robin Hood,
"Before we begin the affray;
I wouldn't have mine any longer than thine
For that would be counted false play."

8. "I pass not for length," the stranger replied,
"For mine is of oak so free;
Six foot and a half will knock down a calf,
And I'm sure it will knock down thee."

9. About and about they lustily dealt
For almost two hours and more;
At every bang the woods they rang,
They plied their work so sore.

10. And Robin he raged like a wild boar
As soon as he saw his own blood.
Bland was in haste and laid on so fast,
As if he was cleaving of wood.

11. "Hold your hand," said jolly Robin,
"And let our quarrel fall.
Here we might thrash our bones to smash
And get no money at all."

12. "And what is your name?" said jolly Robin.
. . . .
. . . .
. . . .

13. . . . .
"In Nottingham long have I wrought;
And if you come there, I vow and declare,
I'll tan your hide for naught."

14. . . . .
"If you'll be so kind and free,
If you'll tan my hide for naught,
I'll do the same for thee."

15. "Tell me, O tell me, where is Little John?
Of him fain would I hear,
For we are related by the mother's side,
And he is my kinsman near."

16. Then Robin he put his horn to his mouth
And blew both loud and shrill,
And quickly and soon appeared Little John
Tripping over the hill.

17. "What's the matter?" said Little John,
"O master, I pray thee me tell?
Why do you stand with your staff in your hand?
I fear that all isn't well."

18. "O man, I stand, and he makes me to stand,
The tanner who stands by my side;
He is a bold blade and master of his trade
And sorely he's tanning my hide."

19. "He is to be commended," said Little John,
"If such a thing he can do;
If he is so stout we must have a bout,
And he shall tan my hide too."

20. "Hold your hand," said jolly Robin;
"As I do understand,
He's a yeoman good and of your own blood,
His name it is Arthur O'Bland."

21. Then Little John flung his staff away
As far as he could fling,
Then out of hand to Arthur O'Bland,
And about his neck he did cling.

22. For love and respect there was no neglect,
They neither were nice nor coy;
Each other did face with a comely grace,
And both did weep for joy.

23. Then Robin he took them both by the hand
And danced all around an oak tree,
And said, "Three merry men, and three merry men,
And three merry men are we.

24. "And ever hereafter, as long as we live,
We three shall be as one;
The woods they will ring and the old wives sing
Of Robin Hood, Arthur, and John."

Robin Hood and the Tinker

CHILD NO. 127

This ballad, like No. 148, is directed to be sung to the tune of "In Summer time." But if we are to regard the refrain as a clue and not merely a whimsy of the redactor, the present ballad and the other could not be sung to the same tune. This one is in iambic ballad quatrains, with a "Down a down a down" refrain inserted between every two lines of text. No. 148 is in *tetrameter* quatrains, predominantly anapaestic. Now, if "Robin Hood and the Curtal Friar" (No. 123) is also, as Rimbault and Chappell allege, to be sung to the tune of "In summer time"—the first line of all three ballads beginning with an identical line ("In summer time, when leaves grow green") —we have still another pattern to reconcile, for that ballad is in straight ballad quatrains *without any refrain*. Cf. also the discussion under No. 123. A fair guess would be that the plethora of refrain in the present ballad (No. 127) was tossed there without regard to an actual tune. At any rate, no tune of "Summer Time" which has been discovered could accommodate this amount of refrain; nor does any other text of any ballad directed to be sung to "Summer Time" have this stanzaic pattern.

Robin Hood Newly Revived

CHILD NO. 128

THIS ballad is directed to be sung "to a delightful new tune." The refrain after line one, "With a hey down down a down down," places it in the "Arthur a Bland" group. For that tune, cf. under No. 126. As to whether the present ballad or "Robin Hood and Little John" (No. 125) is the one which should be called "Robin Hood and the Stranger," cf. under No. 125. It is, after all, possible that there was another Robin Hood ballad which has not survived that bore the name in question as its own.

Robin Hood and the Prince of Aragon

CHILD NO. 129

THIS vapid, pseudo-chivalrous romance, as Child calls it, is directed to be sung to the "tune of Robin Hood, or, Hey down, down a down." Although Chappell (*Popular Music* [1855-59], II, p. 391) says that "Hey down a down" (that is, the tune "Arthur a Bland") is sometimes referred to as "Robin Hood" simply—in itself a probable statement, in view of the popularity of that tune for ballads of Robin Hood—I have myself not seen any old copy of the *tune* with that title. Here, moreover, it is remarkable that the print does not carry the characteristic refrain, or any refrain at all. It is not obligatory to read the direction as a reference to one tune under two names; the second could be an alternative tune.

Strangely enough, this ballad has turned up in recent oral tradition in New Brunswick—forty-six rather deplorable stanzas of it! The tune was recorded by the scrupulous hand and ear of George Herzog. It does not sound very convincing as a ballad tune: it has two strains, and modulates.

LIST OF VARIANTS

"Robin Hood and the Prince of Aragon." Phillips Barry, Fannie H. Eckstorm, and Mary W. Smyth, *British Ballads from Maine*, 1929, p. 233. (Nesbitt)

TUNE WITH TEXT

"Robin Hood and the Prince of Aragon"

Barry, Eckstorm, and Smyth, 1929, p. 233. Text recited by J. P. A. Nesbitt, St. Stephen, New Brunswick, October 1927; his tune recorded in 1928 by George Herzog. Learned from his father sixty years before.

a Major (inflected VII) with modulation

1. Robin Hood and Will Scarlot and Little John
   Was roamin' over the plain;
   A good fat buck Will Scarlot
   By his own bow had slain.

2. "Jog along, jog along," quayth Robin Hood,
   "The day has run full fast;
   My nephew's not a breakfast gave,
   So I've not broke my fast."

3. Wi' geestern an' jokin' they spent their day,
   Till Phoebe sunk into the deep,
   And each man to their own quarters went
   Their own guard for to keep.

4. They hadn't travelled the greenwood long
   Till Robin Hood did spy
   A beautiful damsel come jogging along,
   All on her black palfrey did ride.

5. Her ridin' suit was the saddle-hue black,
   A sypress over her face,
   A red rosee her cheek did blush,
   All with a comerly grace.

6. "Where are you goin'?" says Will Scarlot,
   "Pretty maid, come tell me right;
   Where are you from, or whither thou goest,
   All in such a mournful plight?"

7. "From Dublin City," the damsel cries,
   "From London all on those towns;
   It is a grievious thing to tell,
   Likewise 'tis a foryen arms.

8. "For the Prince of Oregon
   Sware by his masked hand
   He has a princess as his spouse
   Or else he'll spoil this land,

9. "Unless those champions can be found
   To dare to fight three and three,
   Against those twins, though giants two,
   So horrible to see.

10. "The grevi looks and eyes that burned
    Strike terror from whence they come,
    And serpent hissin' on their heads
    Instead of feather plume.

11. "We are three damsels sent abroad
    From East, West, North and South
    To see what fortune could be great
    To bring those champions forth.

12. "But all in vain we set about
    Where none so brave they are
    That would dare venture flesh and blood
    To free a lady fair."

13. "When is the day," quayth Robin Hood,
    "Tell me and no more."
    "On midsummer next," the damsel cries,
    "On June the twenty-four."

14. And as the tears trickled down her cheeks
And silent was her tongue,
The sigh and grief she took her leaf,
And away her palfrey sprung.

15. The news struck Robin to the heart,
He fell down on the grass,
His actions and his troublèd mind
Show how deplex he was.

16. "What is the matter?" said Will Scarlot,
"Dear master tell to me;
If the damsel's eyes have pierced your heart,
I'll bring her back to thee."

17. "No nay, no nay," quayth Robin Hood,
"Not her that caused my smart;
It is the poor distressed princess,
She's wounded to the heart.

18. "I will fight those giants all
To set this lady free."
"Bad luck to me," said Little John,
"If I part with my companee."

19. "Shall I stay behind?" said Will Scarlot;
"Oh, nay, that will not be,
I'll make you third man in the fight,
So we'll be three and three."

20. The news struck Robin to the heart,
Love shinèd in his face,
And with his arms he hugged them both
And kindly them embraced.

21. "We'll put on our mantles grace,
With long staves in our hands,
Scrips and bottles from our side,
Like them from the Holy Land.

22. "So we'll march along the highway,
No one would ask us whence we come;
They'd take us pilgrims for to be,
Or else some holy men."

23. Now they're on their journey gone
As fast as they could speed;
But all the haste that they had made,
The princess forth was led,

24. To deliver unto the prince,
Who in the list did stand,
Ready to fight or else receive
His lady by the hand.

25. The prince he walked around the list
With the giants by his side;
"Bring me the champions," he cries,
"Or bring me forth my bride;

26. "For this is the four and twentieth day,
The day we pitched upon;
Bring me my bride, or London burns,
I swear by archerin'!"

27. Then up stepped the king and queen,
Weepin' as they spake,
"Here we bring our daughter dear,
Her we're forced to forsake."

28. And then upspeakèd Robin Hood:
"For my pledge it is not so;
As pretty as the fair princess is
She's not for tyrants small."

29. "You infidel, you tyrant Turk,
You frantic fool barboon,
How dare you stop my victor's prize,
I would kill you with a frown!"

30. "You infidel, you tyrant Turk,"
Robin Hood replies,
"Your frown I scorn, lo! here's my gage,
And that I will defy.

31. "And as for your two G'liers there
That stand on either side,
Here is two little Davids
They will soon tame their pride."

32. Then the prince for armor sent,
For sword, lances and shields,
And all those three with armor bright
Came marching to the field.

33. The trumpets commenced to sound each charge,
Each singled out their man,
Arms in pieces was hewn,
Blood sprung from every vein.

34. At length the prince reached Robin a blow,
He struck with might and main,
Caused him to kneel about the field,
As though he had been slain.

35. "God crave mercy for that blow,"
Robin Hood replies,
"That blow shows a fair dispose
Between you and your bride."

36. Then from his shoulders he cut his head
And to the ground did fall,
With a grumbling sound of Robin Hood
Would be redealt with all.

37. He saw the giants in their rage
To see their prince lie dead.
"You'll be the next," said Little John,
"If you don't guide your head."

38. And with his sword he turned about
A bin keen and sharp;
He closed the giant by the belt
And he cut between his heart.

39. Now Will Scarlot he played his part,
He brought his to the knee;
He says, "The devil will break his heart,
So it will take all three."

40. Now the field with joy was filled,
The sky did renoun;
He's brought the princess to herself,
She's lying in a swound.

41. "The princess as she the victors spies,
She can't have all three;"
"She shall choose," says Will Scarlot;
Little John says, "She ain't for me."

42. The princess she lookt on those three
With a calm and comely grace;
She took Will Scarlot by the arm,
And says she: "I've made my choice."

43. Then up stepped a Maxler,
And a Maxler was he;
He looked Will Scarlot in the face
And he wept most bitterly.

44. He says, "I had a son like thee,
Who I liked wondersome well,
He's either gone, or else he's dead;
His name was Youngham Well."

45. Will Scarlot fell on his knees,
Said, "Father, father dear,
Here is your son, your Youngham Well,
You said you liked so dear."

46. How more embracin' could there be
When all those friends were met;
They're gone to the weddin', they're now to the beddin',
And I'll bid them all farewell.

Robin Hood and the Scotchman

CHILD NO. 130

The A form of this ballad constitutes the conclusion of No. 128 in the broadsides. It has the "Arthur a Bland" pattern of refrain, together with middle rhyme, and whether an independent ballad or not, would doubtless be sung to that tune. The B form, from a late eighteenth-century Irish broadside, lacks the refrain, but has internal rhyme. There is no indication of a tune; but apart from refrain, the first three stanzas are nearly identical with those of A, and one cannot see here any evidence of variation in tradition. Presumably, therefore, the refrain was dropped out by editorial agency.

Robin Hood and the Ranger

CHILD NO. 131

THIS ballad, though perfectly in the broadside style, seems to have had some oral currency in the past two centuries. The eighteenth-century form was to be sung to "Arthur a Bland," with one noticeable exception. Child's copy d, a garland printed without date, in York, lacks the characteristic refrain after the first line, and also the direction. In this it anticipates all known later copies. Rimbault (Gutch, *Robin Hood*, 1847, II, p. 440) gives a traditional tune from Staffordshire. This tune is of the four-phrase variety, ABCD, a major plagal tune in 6/8 time, conventional in form, except that the first phrase suggests the relative minor. The middle cadence is on the fifth, and the third phrase divides in two, underlining the internal rhyme. In these features it resembles "Arthur a Bland," as also in rhythm. Cf. No. 126.

The only other musical record was recovered by Kidson, toward the close of the nineteenth century, in the north of England. This is a two-strain, modulating tune, still further extended by a sort of bridge refrain and repetition of the last two phrases. It has no very popular ring, and Kidson seems not to have thought well enough of it to revive it in any later publication. The text clearly derives from the earlier broadsides or garlands, though the singer knew it not.

N.B. that the first four stanzas of this ballad are combined with the Virginia version of No. 126, q.v.

LIST OF VARIANTS

GROUP A

1. "Robin Hood and the Ranger." J. M. Gutch, *A Lytell Geste of Robin Hode*, 1847, II, p. 440 (app'x., ed. Edward F. Rimbault).

GROUP B

2. "Robin Hood and the Keeper." Frank Kidson, *JFSS*, I, No. 5 (1904), p. 247.

TUNES WITH TEXTS

GROUP A

1. "Robin Hood and the Ranger"

Gutch, 1847, II, p. 440 (Rimbault). From Staffordshire tradition.

p I

[He left all his merry men waiting behind,
  Whilst through the green vallies he passd;
There did he behold a forester bold,
  Who cry'd out, Friend, whither so fast?]
                                        [*Etc.*]

The text here is from Child, 1882-98, III, p. 152.

GROUP B

2. "Robin Hood and the Keeper"

Kidson, *JFSS*, I, No. 5 (1904), p. 247. Sung by a farmer near Huddersfield, who learned it as a boy.

p I (–VI and inflected IV)

1. When Phoebus had melted the ic'les of ice
   And dissolved all the mountains of snow,
   Bold Robin Hood in a frolicsome mood
   Went wand'ring about with his bow,
   He had left all his merry men waiting behind,
   And travelled the woods far and near,
   When by the woodside the game-keeper he spied
   Who questioned him how he came there,
   How he came there,
   When by the woodside the game-keeper he spied,
   Who question'd him how he came there.

2. "I'm coming," said Robin, "to shoot a fat buck
For me and my men in the wood,
And besides, e'er I go, I must have a young doe
For I think they are tender and good."
"You had best have a care," said the keeper in wrath,
"For these are his majesty's deer,
Before you do shoot your right I dispute,
For I am chief forester here."

3. "These thirteen long summers," bold Robin replied,
"I've thus let my arrows all fly;
So freely I've ranged and to me it seems strange
That you should have more right than I!
These woods and these valleys I count as my own,
And so does the nimble deer too,
I therefore declare, and solemnly swear,
That I'll not be commanded by you."

4. The keeper had got a large staff in his hand,
Like wise a broadsword by his side,
Without more ado his scabbard he drew,
And swore that the truth should be tried.
Bold Robin likewise had a sword of the best,
He swore he would suffer no wrong;
His courage was flush, and he long'd for a brush,
For to prove if that it was strong.

5. The keeper struck first and he gave such a bang,
That he made his broad weapon cry "twang";
He struck Robin's head, and he fell down for dead,
For he'd never received such a bang.
But soon he recovered and jumped to his feet,
And quickly maintained his own ground.
The very next stroke both weapons were broke
Without either giving a wound.

6. Their large oaken cudgels they next took in hand,
Because they would have a new bout,
Bold Robin Hood in jeopardy stood,
Unwilling to yield or give out.
At length the bold keeper became quite in a rage,
He cudgelled poor Robin so sore,
Till he scarcely could stand, so, shaking his hand
Cries Robin, "Let's fairly give o'er!"

7. "For thou art a good fellow, bold, skilful, and brave,
I never knew any so good,
A very fit man to be one of my clan
And dwell in yon merry greenwood.
I'll give thee a ring as a token of love,
If thou to my wish art inclined
For a man that can fight, I behold with delight,
For I love them with heart and with mind."

8. Robin then took his horn to assemble his men,
And loudly he made it to blow.
His archers soon heard and in order appeared,
And each of them had his long bow.
Little John was their leader, he marched at their head,
And wore a rich mantle of blue;
The rest were all seen, dressed in garments of green,
A beautiful prospect to view.

9. "These are my bowmen," bold Robin he cried,
"And thou shalt be one of my train,
A quiver and bow and a dress I'll bestow
On those whom I thus entertain."
The keeper survey'd them with pleasant surprise,
They made such an excellent show;
At length in his mind he became quite inclined
Along with bold Robin to go.

10. What singing and dancing there was in the wood
For the joy of another new mate!
With mirth and delight they employed the whole night
And they lived at a plentiful rate.
Next day Robin gave him a mantle of green,
A quiver and curious long bow,
And when he was dressed quite as gay as the rest
Robin ranged all his men in a row.

11. "So all my brave comrades be true to your trust,
And then we have nothing to fear,
We'll range the woods wide with our arms by our side,
And live without sorrow or care."
They all with a shout made the elements ring,
And swore they would ever be true,
So he marched them away, looking gallant and gay,
Their pastimes and sports to renew.

The Bold Pedlar and Robin Hood

CHILD NO. 132

This ballad was regarded by Child as a traditional variation of "Robin Hood Revived" (No. 128). I confess, this seems to me a very hasty assertion. The names Young Gamwell and Gamble Gold may be allowed a resemblance, especially if some version of the earlier ballad gave Gamwell the epithet of *bold*; and the two men's reasons for leaving home (murder), and their relation to Robin Hood (cousins) are alike. But with this the parallel concludes. Child himself finds more stanzas reminiscent of No. 136. The conduct of the present narrative is as far from that of No. 128 as it is from any one of the ballads dealing with Robin's meeting his match in a hand-to-hand encounter and thereupon enlisting his adversary in his band. The opponent in No. 128 is a bowman with nothing of the pedlar about him. And so on. Coupled with other differences, it seems not insignificant that No. 128 is formally of the "Arthur a Bland" pattern, while No. 132 not only is in tetrameter quatrains (LM), but also has a two-line refrain or burden. That one ballad may have borrowed from two stanzas of the other might be admitted without prejudice to the dichotomy.

"Robin Hood and the Pedlar," at any rate, has survived in tradition more successfully than most—or, at least, in the *record* of tradition. Copies are available from Derbyshire for the mid-nineteenth century, from Sussex for the latter part of it, and from Vermont and Nova Scotia in recent tradition. All these copies conform to the tetrameter quatrain pattern; but fall apart in the matter of refrains. The Derbyshire copies conform to the earlier shape, having a two-phrase end-refrain. The later copies all lack the burden, and all seem related more closely in melodic pattern. The Derbyshire tunes were also used with No. 164.

LIST OF VARIANTS

GROUP Aa

1. "Robin Hood and the Pedlar." Llewellynn Jewitt, *The Ballads and Songs of Derbyshire*, 1867, p. 2.
2. "Robin Hood and the Pedlar." Jewitt, 1867, p. 3.
3. "Bold Robin Hood and the Pedlar." Helen Hartness Flanders and Marguerite Olney, *Ballads Migrant in New England*, 1953, p. 68. Also in Helen Hartness Flanders, *Ancient Ballads Traditionally Sung in New England*, III, 1963, p. 101.

GROUP Ab

4. "Robin Hood and the Pedlar." Ralph Vaughan Williams MSS., III, p. 90.

GROUP Ba

5. "Robing Wood and the Pedlar." Ralph Vaughan Williams, *JFSS*, II, No. 8 (1906), p. 155. Also in Vaughan Williams MSS., II, p. 114; and A. L. Lloyd, Riverside recording No. RLP 12-624(B4), *The English and Scottish Popular Ballads*, II, ed. Kenneth S. Goldstein.
6. "Robin Hood and the Pedlar." Sharp MSS., 1669/1509, Clare College Library, Cambridge. Also in Cecil J. Sharp, *JFSS*, V, No. 18 (1914), p. 94. (Francis)
7. "Bold Pedlar and Robin Hood." Helen Creighton and Doreen H. Senior, *Traditional Songs from Nova Scotia*, 1950, p. 67.

GROUP Bb

8. "Robin Hood and the Pedlar." Mrs. Carrie Grover, LC Archive of American Folk Song, recording No. 4697(A1). Also in Carrie B. Grover, *A Heritage of Songs*, ed. Ann L. Griggs, privately printed by Gould Academy, Bethel, Maine, n.d., p. 78.
9. "Robin Hood and the Pedlar." Vaughan Williams MSS., I, pp. 486 and 485. Also in Vaughan Williams MSS., III, p. 417.
10. "The Bold Pedlar and Robin Hood." Geordie Robertson (singer), Archive, School of Scottish Studies, University of Edinburgh.

GROUP BC

11. "The Bold Pedlar and Robin Hood." Lucy E. Broadwood, *JFSS*, I, No. 4 (1902), p. 144. Also in Broadwood, *English Traditional Songs and Carols*, 1908, p. 4.
12. "Pedlar Bold." Helen Creighton, *Songs and Ballads from Nova Scotia*, [1933], p. 12.
13. "Robin Wood and the Pedlar." Vaughan Williams MSS., I, p. 30.

GROUP C

14. "Bold Robing Hood." Helen Hartness Flanders and George Brown, *Vermont Folk-Songs & Ballads*, 1931, p. 217. Also in Flanders, *Ancient Ballads*, III, 1963, p. 104.

TUNES WITH TEXTS

GROUP Aa

1. "Robin Hood and the Pedlar"

Jewitt, 1867, p. 2. From tradition in his boyhood.

a I

I'll tell you of a pedlar bold,
A pedlar bold he chanced to be,
[Oh] he roll'd his pack upon his back,
As he came tripping o'er the lea.

Chorus:
Fal de ral de ray,
Fal de ral de ray.

2. "Robin Hood and the Pedlar"

Jewitt, 1867, p. 3. From William Chappell; traditional.

a I

I'll tell you of a pedlar bold,
A pedlar bold he chanced to be,
[Oh] he roll'd his pack upon his back,
As he came tripping o'er the lea.

Chorus:
Down, down, a down,
Down, down, a down.

3. "Bold Robin Hood and the Pedlar"

Flanders and Olney, 1953, p. 68. Also in Flanders, III, 1963, p. 101. Sung by Mrs. Belle Richards, Colebrook, N.H., November 20, 1940; learned from her father, who came from Canada. From *Ballads Migrant in New England*, edited by Helen Hartness Flanders and Marguerite Olney; copyright 1953 by Helen Hartness Flanders.

a I, ending on II

The tune has been re-barred by the present editor.

1. "What have you got, you pedlar trim?
What have you got, pray tell to me?"
"It's seven suits of the gay green silk,
Beside my bow-strings two or three."

2. "If you've seven suits of the gay green silk,
Besides your bow-strings two or three;
Upon my word," said Little John,
"One half of them belong to me."

3. The pedlar then took off his pack,
And laid it down most manfully,
Saying, "The man that can drive me two feet from this,
The pack and all I will give to thee."

4. Then Little John he drew his sword.
The noble pedlar held his hand.
They swaggered swords till the sweat did drop,
Saying, "Noble pedlar, stay your hand."

5. Then Robin Hood, he drew his sword.
The noble pedlar held his hand.
They swaggered swords till the blood did drop,
Saying, "Noble pedlar, stay your hand."

6. "What is your name, you pedlar trim?
What is your name, pray tell to me?"
"Not one bit of it—of my name you'll get
Till both of yours you tell to me."

7. "My name is Bold Robin Hood,
The other Little John so free,
And now it lies within your breast
To tell us what your name can be."

8. "My name is Bold Gammon gay,
And I came far beyond the sea;
For killing a man in my father's court
I was banished from my own country."

9. "Your name it is Bold Gammon gay,
And you came far beyond the sea;
And if we are two sister's sons;
What nearer kindred need we be?"

GROUP Ab

4. "Robin Hood and the Pedlar"

Vaughan Williams MSS., III, p. 90. The singer is not identified in the MSS.

p I

GROUP Ba

5. "Robing Wood and the Pedlar"

Vaughan Williams, *JFSS*, II, No. 8 (1906), p. 155. Also in Vaughan Williams MSS., II, p. 114; and sung by A. L. Lloyd, Riverside rec. No. RLP 12-624(B4), ed. K. S. Goldstein. Sung by Mr. Denny, Billericay, April 25, 1904.

a π^3

References to analogous tunes are given in the *Journal, loc.cit.*

It's of a pedlar, pedlar bold,
A pedlar bold, so bold was he;
He takes his pack all on his back
And merrily trudged o'er the lea.

6. "Robin Hood and the Pedlar"

Sharp MSS., 1669/1509. Also in Sharp, *JFSS*, V, No. 18 (1914), p. 94. Sung by Job Francis (71), Shipley, April 21, 1908.

a M

This melody is very near perfection in its modal kind.

1. Twas of a pedlar stout and bold
As fine a pedlar as ever was seen
He threw his pack all on his back
And away went pedlar right over the lea.

2. The first he met two troublesome men
Two troublesome men he there met him
What have you on your pack cried Robin Hood
What have you on your pack come tell to me.

3. I've several sorts of the gay green silks
Silken bow-strings by one two three
There's not a man in fair Nottingham
That can take one half of this pack from me.

4. The[n] Little John drew out his sword
The pedlar by his pack did stand
They heaved about till they both did sweat
He now cries pedlar pray hold your hand.

5. Bold Robin Hood was standing by
To see them fight so heartily.
When I find a man of smaller skill
Could whop the pedlar & likewise you.

6. Go you try master says Little John
Go you try master do all you can
Go you try master without delay
For the pedlar this night has well whopped me.

7. What is your name cries bold Robin Hood
What is your name come tell to me
My name to you I'll never tell
Till both your names you tell to me.

8. For one of us is bold Robin Hood
The other is Little John so free
So now it lays in my good will
Will you tell me your name or no?

9. I'm Gamble Gold from the merry green woods
I'm Gamble Gold from over the dee
For killing a man in my father's land
From my native country I was forced to flee.

10. If you're Gamble Gold from the merry green woods
If you're Gamble Gold from over the dee
It's you and I are two sister's sons
And here are cousins as ever can be.

11. So they sheathed their swords without delay
Into the tavern they went straightway
Into the tavern they all did dine
Where they cracked their bottles & drinked their wine.

7. "Bold Pedlar and Robin Hood"

Creighton and Senior, 1950, p. 67. Sung by Mrs. Edward Gallagher, Chebucto Head, N.S.

a M (inflected III)

The signature of the original copy is 6/4.

1. There was a pedlar and a pedlar bold,
A pedlar bold he seemed to be,
He put his pack all on his back
And he went clinking all o'er the lea.

2. By chance he met two troublesome men,
Two troublesome men they chanced to be,
And the one of them was bold Robin Hood
And the other Little John so free.

3. "What's in your pack?" said Little John,
"Come speedilee and tell to me."
"I have seven suits of the Spanish silk
And I have bow strings it's two or three."

4. "If you have seven suits of the Spanish silk
And you have bow strings it's two or three,
I'll pledge myself," said Little John,
"That half of them will belong to me."

5. The pedlar then he lowered his pack,
He lowered it down unto his knee,
Saying, "Show me the man will put me two foot back,
The pack and all will be his fee."

6. Then Little John he pulled out his sword
And the pedlar he pulled out his brand
And they swiped their swords till the sweat did run,
He cried, "Lovely pedlar come hold your hand."

7. Now Robin Hood he being standing by,
As angry a man as there could be,
Saying, "I know a man of smaller scale
Who could whip the pedlar and win the fee."

8. "Go try him master," cried Little John,
"Go try him master most speedilee,
For there's not a man in fair Nottingham
Who could whip the pedlar and win the fee."

9. Then Robin Hood he pulled out his sword
And the pedlar he drew out his brand,
And they swiped their swords till the blood did run,
He cried, "Lovely pedlar come hold your hand."

10. "What is your name?" cried Little John,
"Come quickly tell it unto me."
"Oh the devil a bit of my name you'll get
Until both of yours you'll tell to me."

11. Then Robin Hood he being standing by,
As pleasant a man as there could be,
Saying, "The one of us is bold Robin Hood
The other Little John so free."

12. Now the pedlar said, "I have your names,
For both of them you have told to me,
And now it lies within my own breast
I'll tell my name to either he or thee."

13. "*But* my name," he said, "it is young Gamewell,
I have travelled far over land and sea,
For killing a man in my father's court
In my own defence I was forced to flee."

14. Robin Hood he being standing by,
As pleasant a man as there could be,
"We are two sisters' sons," he said,
"And what nearer kindred can we be?"

GROUP Bb

8. "Robin Hood and the Pedlar"

Sung by Mrs. Carrie Grover, Gorham, Me., 1941, LC/AAFS, rec. No. 4697(A1). Also in Grover, n.d., p. 78. Collected by Mrs. Sidney Robertson Cowell.

a π^3

1. 'Tis of a pedlar, a pedlar trim,
A pedlar trim he seemed to be,
He strapped his pack all on his back,
And he went linkin' o'er the lea.

2. He met two men, two troublesome men,
Two troublesome men they seemed to be,
And one of them was bold Robin Hood,
And the other Little John so free.

3. What have you there? cries bold Robin Hood,
What have you there, pray tell to me?
I have six bolts of the gay green silk
And silken bowstrings two or three.

4. If you have six bolts of the gay green silk
And silken bowstrings two or three,
Then, by my faith, cried bold Robin Hood,
The half of them belong to me.

5. The pedlar he took off his pack,
He hung it low down by his knee,
Saying, The man who beats me three feet from that,
The pack and all, it shall go free.

6. Bold Robin Hood drew his nut-brown sword,
The pedlar he drew out his brand,
They fought until they both did sweat:
Oh pedlar, pedlar, stay your hand.

7. O fight him, Master, cried Little John,
O fight him, Master, and do not flee!
Now by my faith, cried the pedlar trim,
'Tis not to either he or thee.

8. What is your name? cried bold Robin Hood,
What is your name, pray tell to me?
No, not one word, cried the pedlar trim,
Till both your names you tell to me.

9. The one of us is bold Robin Hood,
The other Little John so free.
Oh, now I have it at my good will
Whether my name I'll tell to thee.

10. I am Gamble Gold of the Gay Green Woods,
Far far beyond the raging sea.
I killed a man on my father's land,
And was forced to leave my own countery.

11. If you're Gamble Gold of the Gay Green Woods,
Far far beyond the raging sea,
Then you and I are sisters' sons,
What nearer cousins can we be?

12. They sheathed their swords with friendly words,
And so like brothers did agree,
Then unto an ale-house in the town,
Where they cracked bottles merrily.

9. "Robin Hood and the Pedlar"

Vaughan Williams MSS., I, p. 486; text, I, p. 485. Also in Vaughan Williams MSS., III, p. 417. The singer is not identified in the MSS.

a M

And Robin Hood he was standing by [?]
And laughing ready to crack his sides [?]
Saying I'd fight a man as large again [?]
Before a coward I would ever be.

10. "The Bold Pedlar and Robin Hood"

Archive, School of Scottish Studies. Sung by Geordie Robertson. Collected by Hamish Henderson for the School of Scottish Studies. Transcribed by Francis M. Collinson.

a M (inflected VII)

1. A pedlar busk, and a pedlar thrum
   And a pedlar linkin' ower the lea—
   It was there he met wi' two troublesome men,
   Two troublesome men there was, seems to be.

2. What's in your pack, noo my gey fellee
   What's in your pack, noo come tell to me.
   There's seven shirts and three cravats,
   Besides my bow-strings two or three.

3. It's be my saul says Little John,
   The most part o' that shall fa' to me.

4. The pedlar takes the pack noo off his back
   And lays doon low by his knee.
   Any man that'll fight me three steps back,
   The pack and a' shall fa' to thee.

5. Little John drew a broad, broad brand,
   And the pedlar drew the same.
   And they swackit swords till they both did sweit,
   Cryin' noble pedlar, hold your hand.

6. It's what's your name, noo, my gey fellee,
   What's your name noo, come tell to me?
   There's not a bit of my name shall tell
   Till both your names you shall tell to me.
   And it lies in my ain breist-bone
   Whether I'll tell my name or no.

7. But my name it was Stoot Fellee.
   I was pitten far noo across the sea,
   For the killin' of man in my father's land,
   To the merry green woods I was forced to flee.

GROUP BC

11. "The Bold Pedlar and Robin Hood"

Broadwood, *JFSS*, I, No. 4 (1902), p. 144. Also in Broadwood, 1908, p. 4. Sung by Henry Burstow, Horsham, Sussex, 1893.

a D

1. There chanced to be a Pedlar bold,
   A Pedlar bold he chanced to be.
   He put his pack all on his back,
   And so merrily trudgèd o'er the lea.

2. By chance he met two troublesome men,
   Two troublesome men they chanced to be,
   The one of them was bold Robin Hood,
   And the other was little John so free.

3. "O Pedlar, Pedlar, what is in thy pack?
   Come speedily and tell to me."
   "I've several suits of the gay green silks,
   And silken bowstrings by two or three."

4. "If you have several suits of the gay green silk,
   And silken bowstrings two or three,
   Then, by my body," cries little John,
   "One half your pack shall belong to me."

5. "O nay, O nay," said the Pedlar bold,
   "O nay, O nay, that never can be,
   For there's never a man from fair Nottingham
   Can take one half my pack from me."

6. Then the Pedlar he pulled off his pack,
   And put it a little below his knee,
   Saying, "If you do move me one perch from this,
   My pack and all shall gang with thee."

7. Then little John he drew his sword,
   The Pedlar by his pack did stand,
   They fought until they both did sweat,
   Till he cried, "Pedlar, pray hold your hand."

8. Then Robin Hood he was standing by,
   And he did laugh most heartily,
   Saying, "I could find a man of smaller scale,
   Could thrash the Pedlar and also thee."

9. "Go you try, master," says little John,
"Go you try, master, most speedily,
For by my body," says little John,
"I am sure this night you will know me."

10. Then Robin Hood he drew his sword,
And the Pedlar by his pack did stand;
They fought till the blood in streams did flow,
Till he cried, "Pedlar, pray hold your hand.

11. "O Pedlar, Pedlar, what is thy name?
Come speedily and tell to me."
"Come, my name I ne'er will tell
Till both your names you have told to me."

12. "The one of us is bold Robin Hood,
And the other little John so free."
"Now," says the Pedlar, "it lays to my good will,
Whether my name I choose to tell to thee.

13. "I am Gamble Gold of the gay green woods,
And travelled far beyond the sea,
For killing a man in my father's land
And from my country was forced to flee."

14. "If you are Gamble Gold of the gay green woods,
And travelled far beyond the sea,
You are my mother's own sister's son,
What nearer cousins can we be?"

15. They sheathed their swords, with friendly words,
So merrily they did agree,
They went to a tavern and there they dined,
And cracked bottles most merrily.

12. "Pedlar Bold"

Creighton, [1933], p. 12. Sung by Ben Henneberry, Devil's Island, N.S.

a D/Æ

1. There chanced to be a pedlar bold,
A pedlar bold there chanced to be,
He put his pack upon his back
And so merrily trudged o'er the lee.
By chance he met with two troublesome men,
Two troublesome men they chanced to be,
One of their names was bold Robin Hood
And the other Little John so free.

2. "Pedlar, pedlar, what's in thy pack?
Come speedilie and tell to me."
"I have several suits of the gay, green silk,
And silken bow-strings one, two, and three."
"If you have several suits of the gay, green silk,
And silken bow-strings one, two and three,
Then by my body," cried Little John,
"Half your pack belongs to me."

3. The pedlar then took his pack
And placed little below his knee,
And demanded, "Moves me one perch from this
The pack and all shall gang to thee."
Little John he pulled forth the sword
And the pedlar by his pack did stand,
They swaggered swords till the sweat did flow
And he cried, "Pedlar, pray hold your hand."

4. Robin Hood, he being standing by,
He did laugh most heartilie,
"I could find a man of smaller scale
Could whip the pedlar and also thee."
"Go try, master," cried Little John,
"Go try, go try most speedilie,
There is not a man in fair Nottingham
Can beat the pedlar and also me."

5. Bold Robin Hood he drew forth his sword
And the pedlar by his pack did stand,
Where they swaggered swords till the blood did flow,
When he cried, "Pedlar, pray hold your hand.
Oh pedlar, pedlar, what is thy name?
Come speedilie and tell to me."
"The devil a one of ye my name shall know
Before both your names ye have told to me."

6. "One of our names is bold Robin Hood,
The other one Little John so free."
"Now," said the pedlar, "it's my good will
Whether my name I should tell to thee.
I am Gamble Gold of the gay green woods,
I have travelled far and o'er the sea,
And for killing of a man in my father's court
From my country I was forced to flee."

7. "If you'll Gamble Gold of the gay, green woods
And have travelled far and o'er the sea,
You are my mother's own sister's son,
What nearer cousins then can we be?"
They sheathed the swords with friendly words,
So merrilie they did agree,
They went to a tavern and did they dine
And cracked a bottle most merrilie.

8. Then these three they took hold of hand,
Merrilie danced round the green tree.
You drink water while your money lasts,
There's a time you'll die, lads, as well as me.

13. "Robin Wood and the Pedlar"

Vaughan Williams MSS., I, p. 130. The singer is not identified in the MSS.

a D

The eighth dots on the third and fourth cadence-notes omitted in the MS.

GROUP C

14. "Bold Robing Hood"

Flanders and Brown, 1931, p. 217. Also in Flanders, III, 1963, p. 104. Sung by Mr. Sharon Harrington, Bennington, Vt., September 15, 1930. Recorded by George Brown. From *Vermont Folk-Songs & Ballads*, edited by Helen Hartness Flanders and George Brown; copyright 1931 by Arthur Wallace Peach.

a M, ending on V

1. Bold Robing Hood and Little John
Went a-roving the world all o'er.
They met a man in peddler trim
In peddler trim he seemed to be.

2. "What have you in your pack, pray, peddler trim?
What have you in your pack, pray tell to me?"
"I have seven suits of the grey green suits
Besides two bow-strings, two or three."

3. "If you've seven suits of the grey green suits
Besides two bow-strings, two or three,
I will lay my life," says Little John,
"That two of them belong to me."

4. He pulled his pack from off his back
He laid it down so manenly,
Saying, "The man that'll drive me six inches from that,
My pack and all they'll take from me."

5. They swong their swords 'til the blood run down;
"Pray, peddler trim, pray stand your land,
What is your name, pray, peddler trim?
What is your name, pray tell to me?"

6. "Not a divil of a bit of my name you'll git
Til both of yours is told to me.
If you say your name 'tis Will Gamuel Gay,
And come ye far from over the sea,
We are two sister's sons
And was banished from Americee."

A footnote in Flanders and Brown comments that the last verse was practically spoken.

Robin Hood and The Beggar I

CHILD NO. 133

The seventeenth-century printers of this ballad all direct it to be sung to the tune of "Robin Hood and the Stranger." This, as we know, is the tune of "Arthur a Bland" (No. 126), q.v. There are, as usual, very slight variations between copies in the form of the refrain; and in one copy, "Hey derry derry down," instead of the usual "Hey down down and a down."

Robin Hood and The Beggar II

CHILD NO. 134

THERE is no very early copy of this Scottish (or at least northern) ballad, Ritson's reprint in 1795 of a Newcastle copy being our earliest to survive. There is no indication of a tune. The ballad lacks a refrain and is in CM.

The Blaikie MS. has a tune—but no words—with the present title. Since the other ballad called by this name was of the "Arthur a Bland" pattern, the present one ought to be the one belonging to Blaikie's tune. He has given no source; in the absence of specific information we may guess the Paisley region where he did his collecting. No other tune for the ballad has been found.

LIST OF VARIANTS

"Robin Hood and the Beggar." Blaikie MS., National Library of Scotland MS. 1578, No. 94, p. 29.

TUNE WITH TEXT

"Robin Hood and the Beggar"

Blaikie MS., NL Scotland MS. 1578, No. 94, p. 29.

m I

Robin Hood and the Shepherd

CHILD NO. 135

THE seventeenth-century garland and broadside copies of this piece direct it to be sung to the tune of "Robin (Hood) and Queen Katherine." As was remarked *sub* No. 120, Rimbault asserts that that ballad and this, together with three others (Nos. 136, 141, 145), were all sung to the tune of the "Three Ravens." Undoubtedly, his only evidence lies in the form of the refrain, "Down a down," etc., after the first and last lines of the stanza. But no known form of that tune exactly fits any one of these ballads. Cf. No. 120.

Robin Hood's Delight

CHILD NO. 136

THIS ballad is to be sung to "Robin Hood and Queen Katherine," or, "Robin Hood and the Shepheard." These would appear to be the same tune. Cf. under Nos. 135 and 120 for further discussion, and for Rimbault's identification of the "Three Ravens" as the tune intended.

Under the title "Robin Hood's Delight" in his Appendix, seventh item, Ritson printed a dance or fiddle tune from Oswald's *Caledonian Pocket Companion* (*Robin Hood*, 1795, II, p. 219). Besides being unsingable, it does not in the least match the stanza-form of the ballad.

Robin Hood and Allen a Dale

CHILD NO. 138

THE broadsides indicate a "pleasant northern tune, or, Robin Hood in the green wood stood"; or "Robin Hood in the green wood." No tune by that name is known. My own guess, for what it is worth, would be that this ballad is the one intended, even though stanza two in the extant early copies begins "As Robin Hood in the *forrest* stood, All under the green-wood tree." The ballad is in CM, with the last line of the stanza repeated—the only Robin Hood ballad to employ this common type of refrain in the early texts.

Rimbault (Gutch, *Robin Hood*, 1847, II, p. 439) gives as the tune for this ballad the first strain of "Drive the cold winter away," which is to be found in Playford's *English Dancing Master*, 1651 *et seq*. (Chappell, *Popular Music*, [1855-59], I, p. 193). Rimbault gives the tune as from a MS. of James I's time in his own possession. The notes are identical with the *Dancing Master* form, except for the closing cadence. On what ground the tune is connected with this ballad I do not know: Rimbault's own words indicate that it bore another title in his MS. (query if not "Drive the cold winter away"?!), for he writes, "The *original* name . . . appears to be 'Robin Hood in the green-wood stood.' " As he gives it, at any rate, it has no provision for the repeated last line. I suspect that there is no evidence of any connection between ballad and tune.

Possibly—though I doubt it—we are closer to a connection in the tune "Bonny sweet Robin," which is preserved, as Rimbault (*op.cit.*, II, p. 445) says, in the Fitzwilliam Virginal Book, in Dowland's lute MSS. in Cambridge, and in William Ballet's lute-book (Trinity College, Dublin). The last-named contains two copies, one by the name just given, the other titled "Robin Hood is to the greenwood gone" (Ballet's MS., pp. 27, 113). This is a four-phrase tune, in LM dactylic rhythm, and so again unsuitable. See under No. 117, *ante*, for the tune and further discussion.

Robin Hood's Progress to Nottingham

CHILD NO. 139

The tune indicated for this ballad in all copies that mention a tune is "Bold Robin Hood." The stanzaic pattern is uncommon, but it occurs in Nos. 141, 147, and 153, in recent copies of 144, and in a MS. copy of 110 as well.

The ballad must have been popular, as it has contributed a tune's name for both No. 147 (i.e., "Robin Hood was a tall young man") and No. 153 ("Robin Hood and the Fifteen Foresters"). Child is less careful than usual when he says that "Robin Hood and Queen Katherine" (145) may be the ballad meant by "Bold Robin Hood." His reasons are that "this conjunction of words occurs several times in R. H. and Queen Katherine" and that No. 139, to be sung to "Bold Robin Hood," has the same burden (1882-98, III, p. 198). On the latter point he is inaccurate. He refers presumably to the broadsides of his B class in No. 145. But very few of the ballads fail to attach the epithet "bold" more than once. It would be easy to point to half a dozen—and probably more—Robin Hood ballads where the conjunction "bold Robin Hood" occurs as often, or nearly so, as in "Robin Hood and Queen Katherine" (five times); and the disposition of the refrain is quite different in these two (i.e., 139 and 145). If the name refers to an extant ballad, perhaps the likeliest is "Robin Hood's Golden Prize" (No. 147). That ballad has the same stanza pattern, and the phrase "bold Robin Hood" occurs in the first line and a sufficient number of times else (five in all, if we allow "bold Robin" for one). It is typical that the tune-name for that ballad is the first line of the broadside texts of the present one! From that fact, Child argued the priority of the present ballad; and in the Pepys text collated here (e) by Child an extra "bold Robin Hood" occurs, to make up five: so it might be held at a pinch that, as sometimes happens, the ballad names its own tune.

At any rate, we shall hardly argue it back to life. No tune is known by the name of "Bold Robin Hood," and even the resourceful Rimbault fails, I believe, to identify one.

Versions of the ballad, with tunes, have been recently recovered from tradition in Nova Scotia by Helen Creighton. They have a "derry down" last phrase, the fifth; but the refrain line coming after line one is absent.

LIST OF VARIANTS

1. "Robin Hood's Progress to Nottingham." Helen Creighton, *Songs and Ballads from Nova Scotia* [1933], p. 15.
2. "Robin Hood's Progress to Nottingham." Helen Creighton and Doreen H. Senior, *Traditional Songs from Nova Scotia*, 1950, p. 69.

TUNES WITH TEXTS

1. "Robin Hood's Progress to Nottingham"

Creighton [1933], p. 15. Sung by Ben Henneberry, Devil's Island, N.S.

a I

Robin Hood he bent his noble good bow
  And his broad arrow let fly,
Till fourteen of those fifteen foresters
  Dead on the ground did lie.
    Chorus.
  Hi down, hi derry derry down.

Ten men they came from brave Nottingame
  To take up Robin Hood,
Some lost arms and some lost legs
  And more they lost their blood.
    Chorus.

Ten men they came from brave Nottingham
  To take up Robin Hood,
But he picked up his noble good bow
  And he's off to the merry greenwood.
    Chorus.

2. "Robin Hood's Progress to Nottingham"

Creighton and Senior, 1950, p. 69. Sung by Mrs. Annie C. Wallace, Halifax, N.S.

a I/Ly

But bold Robin Hood sent an arrow after him
And split his head in twain,
Bold Robin Hood sent an arrow after him
And brought him back again,
I down, I derry derry down.

Robin Hood Rescuing Three Squires

CHILD NO. 140

THIS ballad has had a vogue which is not yet quite extinct. All the copies found are in CM, without refrain. There are many eighteenth-century printings of a text, but no tune has been recorded as of so early a date. Ritson, in 1795, noted the fact that his friend Edward Williams, a Welsh bard, had told him that the song was well known in South Wales by the name of *Marchog glas* ("Green Knight"), but nobody (I believe) has captured a copy, either text or tune. Rimbault remarks (Gutch, *Robin Hood*, 1847, II, p. 439) of Child's C type that in Staffordshire and Derbyshire it was sung in his day to "Robin Hood and the Curtall Friar's" tune, which he gives not from tradition but from an early MS. (cf. *sub* No. 123). But Rimbault also gives a traditional tune for type B, from the "borders of Staffordshire," collected by himself in 1845 from an old man who remembered little of the words. The tune, as he says, is a variant of "Lord Thomas and Fair Eleanor" (No. 73).

More recently the ballad has been collected by Percy Grainger and Vaughan Williams, in attractive forms; and, still later, it has been surprised in North Carolina and Maine.

LIST OF VARIANTS

GROUP A

1. "Robin Hood Rescuing the Widow's Three Sons from the Sheriff." J. M. Gutch, *A Lytell Geste of Robin Hode*, 1847, II, p. 438 (app'x., ed. Edward F. Rimbault).
2. "Bold Robin Hood Rescuing the Three Squires." Helen Hartness Flanders and Marguerite Olney, *Ballads Migrant in New England*, 1953, p. 69. Also on LP recording, *Eight Traditional British-American Ballads*, New England Folk-Song Series I, Middlebury College, Middlebury, Vt., 1953, ed. Marguerite Olney; in LC Archive of American Folk Song, recording No. 9128; and Helen Hartness Flanders, *Ancient Ballads Traditionally Sung in New England*, III, 1963, p. 111.
3. "Robin Hood and the Three Squires." R. Vaughan Williams, *JFSS*, III, No. 13 (1909), p. 268.
4. "Bold Robing." *The Frank C. Brown Collection of North Carolina Folklore*, IV (*The Music of the Ballads*, ed. Jan P. Schinhan), 1957, p. 81, and II (*Folk Ballads from North Carolina*, ed. Henry M. Belden and Arthur Palmer Hudson), 1952, p. 153. Also in LC Archive of American Folk Song, recording No. 970; and Richard Chase, *American Folk Tales and Songs*, 1956, p. 124.

GROUP B

5. "Robin Hood." Percy Grainger MS., NYPL MS., *MO+ (English), No. 188, New York Public Library.
6. "Robin Hood." Grainger MS., NYPL MS., *MO+(English), No. 188.
7. "Robin Hoods Men." Ralph Vaughan Williams MSS., I, p. 129.

TUNES WITH TEXTS

GROUP A

1. "Robin Hood Rescuing the Widow's Three Sons from the Sheriff"

Gutch, 1847, II, p. 438 (Rimbault). Sung by an old man from the Staffordshire border, summer 1845.

p I

[There are twelve months in all the year,
As I hear many men say,
But the merriest month in all the year
Is the merry month of May.]

[*Etc.*]

Child's text (1882-98, III, p. 180[Ba], from *The English Archer, Robin Hood's Garland*, York, N. Nickson, n.d., p. 65).

2. "Bold Robin Hood Rescuing the Three Squires"

Flanders and Olney, 1953, p. 69. Also on LP rec., New England Folk-Song Series I, from the Helen Hartness Flanders Collection, Middlebury, Vt., 1953, ed. Marguerite Olney; on LC/AAFS, rec. No. 9128; and in Flanders, III, 1963, p. 111. Sung by Charles Finnimore, Bridgewater, Me., September 24, 1942. From *Ballads Migrant in New England*, edited by Helen Hartness Flanders and Marguerite Olney; copyright 1953 by Helen Hartness Flanders.

p I

The variant readings are from the Middlebury recording.

1. Bold Robin Hood marched along the highway,
Along the highway marched he,
Until he met with a lady fair
A-weeping along the highway.

2. "O do you mourn for gold," he says,
"Or do you mourn for fee,
Or do you mourn for any high knight
That deserted your company?"

3. "No, I don't mourn for gold," she said,
"Nor I don't mourn for fee,
Nor I don't mourn for any high knight
That deserted my company.

4. "But I do mourn for my three sons,
Today they're condemned to die;
In Nottingham town so fast they lie bound,
In Nottingham prison they lie."

5. "O have they sat any temple on fire
Or any high knight have they slain
Or have they enticed fair maidens to sin
Or with married men's wives have they lain?"

6. "No they've not sat any temple on fire
Nor any high knight have they slain
Nor they've not enticed fair maidens to sin
Nor with married men's wives they've not lain.

7. "But they have killed the King's fallow deer.
Today they're condemned to die.
In Nottingham town so fast they lie bound,
In Nottingham prison they lie."

8. "Go home, go home," said bold Robin Hood.
"And weep no more to-day
And I will stand hangman this livelong day
To hang the Squires all three."

9. Then Robin Hood called on his merry men all,
By one, by two and by three.
"When you hear three blasts on my bugle horn
You must hasten most speedily."

10. Bold Robin Hood marched along the highway.
Along the highway marched he,
Until he met with an old beggarman
A-begging along the highway.

11. Good morning, good morning, my old beggarman,
What news do you bring to me?"
"There is weeping and wailing in all Nottingham
For the loss of the Squires all three."

12. "Come change your clothing," said bold Robin Hood,
"Come change your clothing for mine.
Here's fifty bright guineas I'll give in exchange.
'Twill buy you cake and wine."

13. Robin Hood put on the beggarman's clothes.
They were made of hemp and tow.
"They will cause me to scrub," said bold Robin Hood,
"But further to-day I must go."

14. Bold Robin Hood marched along the highway,
Along the highway marched he,
Until he met with the Master High Sheriff,
And with him the Squires three.

15. "Good morning, good morning, my old beggarman,
What can I do for thee?"
"I want to stand hangman this livelong day
To hang the Squires three."

16. "Yes you can have all of their gay clothing,
And all of their bright monee,
And you may stand hangman this livelong day,
To hang the Squires three."

17. "I don't want none of their gay clothing,
Nor none of their bright monee;
But I want three blasts on my bugle horn
That their souls in Heaven might be."

18. Bold Robin Hood marched to the gallus so high,
To the gallus so high marched he,
And by his side was the Master High Sheriff
And with him the Squires three.

19. He put the bugle unto his mouth,
He blew it loud and shrill.
A hundred and ten of bold Robin Hood's men
Come trippeling over the hill.

20. "Whose men, whose men?" cried the High Sheriff,
"Whose men? I pray, tell me."
"They are mine and not thine," said bold Robin Hood,
"Come to borrow three Squires of thee."

21. "O take them, O take them," then cried the High Sheriff,
"O take them, O take them," cried he;
"But there's not another beggar in all Nottingham
Could borrow three more from me."

3. "Robin Hood and the Three Squires"

Vaughan Williams, *JFSS*, III, No. 13 (1909), p. 268. Sung by Mrs. Goodyear (75), Axford by Basingstoke, Hampshire, January 1909. Collected by G. B. Gardiner.

a M

Miss Ann Gilchrist cites an analogous major version, from Yorkshire, used with Child No. 4 (*ante*, Vol. I, p. 77, variant 94). Others of that family could be added with ease.

1. Bold Robin Hood rangèd the forest all round,
The forest all round rangèd he,
And the first that he met was a gay lady,
Come weeping along the highway.

2. "Oh, why do you weep, my gay lady?
Oh, why do you weep?" said he.
"Oh, why do you weep, my gay lady?
I pray thee come tell unto me.

3. "Oh, do you weep for gold or fame,
Or do you weep for me
Or do you weep for anything else
Belonging to anybody?"

4. "I don't weep for gold or fame,
Nor I don't weep for thee;
Nor I don't weep for anything else
Belonging to anybody."

5. "Then why do you weep, my gay lady?
Why do you weep?" said he.
"Oh, why do you weep, my gay lady?
I pray thee come tell unto me."

6. "Oh, I do weep for my three sons,
For they are condemned to die."
"Oh, what have they done?" said bold Robin Hood,
"Oh, what have they done?" said he.

7. "What parish church have they robbed?" said bold Robin Hood,
"Or what parish priest have they slain?
Did they ever force a maid against her will,
Or with other men's wives have they lain?

8. "Oh, what have they done," said bold Robin Hood,
"Oh, what have they done?" said he.
"They have stole sixteen of the king's white deer,
To-morrow they are condemned to die."

9. "Go your way home, my gay lady,
Go your way home," said he.
"Oh, go your way home, my gay lady,
To-morrow I set them quite free."

10. "What men are all those?" said bold Robin Hood,
"What men are all those?" said he.
"They are all of them mine and none of them thine,
They are come for the squires all three."

11. "Go and take them, go and take them," says the master sheriff,
"Go and take them all," said he;
"Never no more in fair Nottingham town
Shall borrow three more of me."

4. "Bold Robing"

Schinhan, *Music*, *Brown Collection*, IV, 1957, p. 81; text, Belden and Hudson, *Folk Ballads*, *Brown Collection*, II, 1952, p. 153. Also in LC/AAFS, rec. No. 970; and Chase, 1956, p. 124. Sung by Mrs. Calvin Hicks, Mast's Gap, Watauga County, N.C., September 30, 1940.

a I/M

The variant readings are from a second recording.

Brown Collection, II, prints the following version of Mrs. Hicks's text, one of four written copies (plus a recording) available to the editors. The variants noted below are drawn from their full collation, q.v.

1. Bold Robing hood one morning he stood
With his back against a tree,
And he was the war of a fine young man,
As fine as fine could be.

2. Bold Robing hood put out to Nouttongain town
As fast as he could ride,
And who should he meet but a poor old woman
As she came weeping by.

3. 'Are you weeping for my gold?' he said,
'Or are you weeping for my store?
Or are you weeping for your three heads[1]
Been taking from your Bodye?'

4. 'I'm not weeping for your gold,' she said,
'Nor neather for your store;
I am just a-weeping for my three sons
That has to be hung today.'

5. Bold Robing put on to Nouttongain town
As fast as he could ride;
But who should he meet but a poor old boobager[2]
As he came walking by.

6. 'Change clothing, change clothing,' Bold Robing he said,
'Pray change your clothing with me.
Hear is 40 bright guinnes I'll give you to boot
If you will change your clothing with me.'

7. Bold Robing put on the boobegars coat;[3]
It was patched on every side good.
'Faith to my soul,' bold Robing he said,
'They'll think I'll just wear this for pride.'

8. Bold Robing put on to Nouttongain town
As fast as he could ride;
But who should he see but the old town Sheriff
As he stood there close by.

9. 'Which way, which way,' the old town Sheriff said,
'Which way, I say to thee?'
'I heard there was three sons to be hung here today,
And the hangman I want for to be.'

10. 'Quick granted, quick granted,' the old town Sheriff said,
'Quick granted I say to three.[4]
And you can have all their gay goo[5] clothing
And all their bright money.'

11. 'It's I want none of their gay goo[5] clothing
Or none of their bright money.
I want three blast from my bugle horn
As happy as soldiers[6] can be.'

12. He wund his horn unto his mouth
And he lowed blasted.
Five hundred and ten of Bold Robins men come,
Came marching all up in a row.

13. 'Whose men, whose men,' the old town Sheriff said,
'Whose men, I pray to thee?'
'They are brave men of mine,' Bold Robing he said,
'Come to borrow three sons from thee!'

14. 'Oh take them! oh take them!' the old town Sheriff said,
'Oh take them, I pray to thee!
No lord nor knight, nor no Christendome,[7]
Can borrow three more from me.'

[1] One copy has "your three son's heads"; another has "your three sons."
[2] *Sic* two copies; the third has "beggar." Belden and Hudson suggest the word may be "a corruption of 'bullbeggar,' a bogie."
[3] *Sic* the same two copies, the third reading "the old beggar's coat."
[4] ". . . a slip of the pencil; all the other texts have 'thee.'" [*Belden and Hudson's note.*]
[5] Normalized to "good" in two copies.
[6] Two copies read "a soldier."
[7] One copy has "christes sone," the two others "brave men of yourn" and "brave men of yours."

GROUP B

5. "Robin Hood"

Grainger MS., NYPL MS. *MO+(English), No. 188. Sung by Dean Robinson at Brigg, July 26, 1906. Transcribed by Grainger stanza by stanza from the phonograph recording.

m I

The text following is that sung by Mr. Robinson in 1906. The variant readings, listed in Grainger's MS., are from Mr. Robinson's singing in 1905 (for the tune, see the next variant) and from a handwritten copy made for Grainger by him.

1. As Robin Hood rangèd the woods all round,
All round rangèd he;
He saw a young lady in very deep grief,
Weeping against a large tree.

2. "O why weepest thou, my fair lady;
O why weepest thou?" said he.
'Well, I've got 3 brothers, young squires, in Nottingham jail,
All hangèd this day must be.'[1]

3. "O what have they done then, my fair lady,
O what have they done?" sād (said) he.
'Why they have killed 3 of the King's faller (fallow) deer,[2]
& this day all hangèd must be.'

4. "O weep not, O weep not, my fair lady.
O weep not, O weep not" said he.
"And I'll away down to fair Nottinggum,
The High Sheriff for to see."

5. Then Robin Hood hastened to fair[3] Nottinggum,
The High Sheriff for to see.

6. "One favor, one favor I have to beg;
One favor to beg of thee;
That thou wilt reprieve the 3 young squires,
That's doomed this day hangèd to be."[4]

7. 'O no, O no, that never can be,
O no, that never can be;
For they have shot[5] 3 of the King's faller deer,[6]
& this day all hangèd must be.'

8. "One favor more I have to beg,
One favor more of thee;
That I may have 3 blows on my old bugle horn,
That the[7] spirits to heaven may flee."

9. 'O granted, O granted,' the High Sheriff sād (said);
'O granted, O granted,' said he.
'Thou can have 3 blows on thy old bugle horn,
That the[7] spirits to heaven may flee.'

10. Then Robin Hood mounted the gallows so high,
& he blēú (blew) both loud & shill (shrill);[8]
When 3 hundred & 10 of old Robin Hood's men
All came marching across the green hill.

11. 'O whose men are those?' then the High Sheriff said,
'O whose men are those?' said he.
"Why, they're all mine, & they're none of them thine,
And they've come for the squires all 3."

12. 'O take them, O take them,' the High Sheriff said;
'O take them, O take them,' said he.
'For there's not a man not in all Nottinggam[9]
That can do the like of thee.'

[1] 1905: This day all hangèd must be.
[2] Robinson's MS.: "dears" instead of "deer" [3] Omitted in 1905.
[4] 1905: And this day set them free. Robinson's MS.: That this day all hangèd must be.
[5] 1905: killed [6] Robinson's MS.: deere
[7] Robinson's MS.: these [8] Robinson's MS.: loude & chill
[9] 1905: For there's not a man in fair Nottingham,

6. "Robin Hood"

Grainger MS., NYPL MS. *MO+(English), No. 188. Sung by Dean Robinson at Scawby Brook, September 3 and 4, 1905.

a D (inflected VI and VII)

For the text, see the preceding variant.

7. "Robin Hood's Men"

Vaughan Williams MSS., I, p. 129. The singer is not identified.

a D

Three hundred and ten of bold Robin Hood's men
Came trippeling over the hill, came trippeling over the hill
"Whose men are all they?" the gentleman said.
"Those men are all mine, there's not a one thine
They come for the squires all three,
They come for the squires all three."

Robin Hood Rescuing Will Stutly

CHILD NO. 141

This ballad has the same stanza-pattern in the early copies as that of No. 139, q.v. The tune indication, however, is "Robin Hood and Queen Katherine" (No. 145). None of the three types of the latter ballad would sing to a tune that would carry the present text as it stands, and the direction would seem to be a reckless one. Rimbault's mating of the ballad to the "Three Ravens" tune (Gutch, *Robin Hood*, 1847, II, p. 435) is therefore equally ill-considered.

This is one of three Robin Hood ballads that was recovered from Martha Davis's grandmother in 1882, and deposited in the Virginia archive in 1913. It is noteworthy that her first line is "As Robin Hood in the green wood stood," which is—minus *As*—the same as the named tune of "Robin Hood and Allen a Dale" (No. 138). Unless, however, the repeated last line of the latter were omitted, that ballad could not be sung to this tune. But, since the last phrase of the tune here apparently ends on the second degree, it is possible that the tune originally did repeat the last phrase, with a final cadence on the tonic. Sharp found other examples of tunes which by dint of repeating many stanzas with a circular inconclusive ending had lost their true conclusions. In any case, the Davis tune is of a different pattern from the ones quoted by Child: it is CM as it stands. It suggests a tune in D'Urfey, *Wit and Mirth: Or Pills to Purge Melancholy*, 1719, I, p. 126 ("In Kent I hear").

LIST OF VARIANTS

"The Rescue of Will Stutly." Arthur Kyle Davis, Jr., *Traditional Ballads of Virginia*, 1929, pp. 587 and 397.

TUNE WITH TEXT

"The Rescue of Will Stutly"

Davis, 1929, p. 587; text, p. 397. Contributed by Martha M. Davis, Harrisonburg, Rockingham County, Va., April 8, 1913. Dictated by her grandmother in 1882; from Scots-Irish family tradition.

If C tonic, a I/Ly
If D tonic, a M/D

1. As Robin Hood in the green wood stood
 Under a green wood tree,
Sad tidings came to him with speed,
 Tidings for certainty.

2. That Stutly he surprised was,
 In Aiken* prison lay.
Three varlets whom the king had hired
 Did basely him betray.

3. When Robin Hood these news did hear,
 He grievèd was full sore,
And likewise his brave bowmen bold,
 Who all together swore

4. That Stutly he should rescued be,
 Unto the woods again
Return with them to hunt the deer,
 Or in his cause be slain.

5. "Will send one forth the news to hear
 From yonder palmer there,
Whose cell is near the castle wall;
 Some news he may declare."

6. Then stepped forth a brisk young man,
 Of courage stout and bold,
And straight unto the palmer went,
 Saying, "Ye palmer old,

7. "Tell me, if you can rightly tell,
 When must Will Stutly die,
Who is of Robin Hood's brave men
 That here in prison lie?"

8. "Alas, alas," the palmer said,
 "That ever woe is me,
This day Will Stutly must be hung
 Upon yon gallows tree.

9. "But did his noble master know,
 He soon would succor send;
A few of his brave bowmen bold
 Would save him from this end."

10. "That is true," the young man said,
 "He soon would set him free;
So fare thee well, thou good old man,
 With many thanks to thee."

11. Then Robin dressed himself in red,
 His merry men all in green,
With swords and buckles and long bows
 Most glorious to be seen.

12. Not long from jail the young man went,
 The gates were open wide,
When from the castle Stutly came,
 Guarded on every side.

13. Not far from castle they had gone,
When appeared Little John,
And straight unto the sheriff went
And said to him, "Anon,

14. "Mr. Sheriff, with your leave,
I'll speak with him a while."
"No," said the sheriff, "you'll me seize;
Thou art an outlaw vile.

15. "I'll not consent," the sheriff said,
"But hangèd he shall be,
And so shall his vile master be
When in my custody."

16. Then in haste did Little John
Away cut Stutly's bands,
And from a man he twisted soon
The sword out of his hands.

17. Saying, "Will, take you this sword a while,
You can it better sway,
And now defend thy life from harm
For aid will come straight way."

18. And then they turned them back to back
And fought with valor good,
Until at length approachèd near
The valiant Robin Hood.

19. Then quick an arrow Robin sent
Which near the sheriff flew,
And quickly made him for to run,
And all his coward crew.

20. "O stay a while," said Will Stutly,
"And do not from us start;
O stay and hang up Robin Hood
Before you do depart.

21. "Thanks, O thanks, my master dear,
We'll in the green woods meet,
Where we will make our bow strings twang
Music for us most sweet."

* "Aiken," Davis shrewdly suggests, is a corruption of *eke in*. Presumably, "In" is subsequent, for *An(d)*.

Little John a Begging

CHILD NO. 142

The Percy Folio version of this ballad has no refrain. The copies of Child's B type are to be sung to "Robin Hood and the Begger" (No. 133), which see. The tune, therefore, is "Arthur a Bland," for which cf. No. 126. The declension goes as follows: No. 142 is to be sung to the tune of No. 133, which is to be sung to No. 128, or 125 (according to Child), which is to be sung to "Arthur a Bland," which is No. 126, which is to be sung to "Robin Hood and the Stranger," which is No. 125 (or 128)! Cf. Rimbault (Gutch, *Robin Hood*, 1847, II, p. 433) and Chappell (*Popular Music* [1855-59], II, p. 391). The copies of the ballad which are Roxburghe III, i. 10, and Pepys II, p. 119, No. 105, name the tune, respectively, as "Robin Hood and the Begger" and "Robin Hood, &c."

Robin Hood and the Bishop

CHILD NO. 143

THIS ballad is of the same stanza-type as that immediately preceding, i.e., "Arthur a Bland." In this case, again, the tune is named as "Robin Hood and the Stranger." Cf. No. 126.

Robin Hood and the Bishop of Hereford

CHILD NO. 144

THE early copies of this ballad have neither refrain nor tune name. They are all in CM. Luckily, the ballad has survived in tradition. Three records of a tune are known. The first was printed by Rimbault (Gutch, *Robin Hood*, 1847, II, p. 441) from a broadside printed for Daniel Wright, and later by Chappell (*Popular Music* [1855-59], II, p. 395), presumably from the same broadside (early eighteenth century?) with insignificant differences. The next was printed by Moffat and Kidson, 1901, p. 143, from a British Museum half-sheet engraved by T. Straight, c. 1780. It is the same tune, with slight differences. These have no refrains or provisions therefor.

The last copy was collected in 1906, in Dorset, by Mr. Hammond. It has a double refrain—after every first and fourth line, of the "Derry down" type. Cf. also No. 139. There may be a relation here to the Derbyshire variants of No. 132.

LIST OF VARIANTS

GROUP A

1. "The Bishop of Hereford's Entertainment." J. M. Gutch, *A Lytell Geste of Robin Hode*, 1847, II, pp. 441 (app'x., ed. Edward F. Rimbault) and 277. Also in W. Chappell, *Popular Music of the Olden Time*, [1855-59], II, p. 395.
2. "Robin Hood and the Bishop of Hereford." Alfred Moffat and Frank Kidson, *The Minstrelsy of England*, 1901, p. 143. Also in Joseph Ritson, *Robin Hood*, 1795, II, p. 150.

GROUP B

3. "Robin Hood and the Bishop of Hereford." H. E. D. Hammond, *JFSS*, III, No. 11 (1907), p. 61. Also in Cecil J. Sharp, ed., *Folk Songs of England*, 1908-12, I (*Folk Songs from Dorset*, ed. Cecil J. Sharp and H. E. D. Hammond), p. 4.

TUNES WITH TEXTS

GROUP A

1. "The Bishop of Hereford's Entertainment"

Gutch, 1847, II, p. 441 (Rimbault); text, p. 277. Also in Chappell, [1855-59], II, p. 395. From a broadside printed for Daniel Wright, Holborn.

a I, ending on the octave

1. Some they will talk of bold Robin Hood,
 And some of barons bold;
But I'll tell you how he serv'd the bishop of Hereford,
 When he robb'd him of his gold.

2. As it befel in merry Barnsdale,
 All under the green-wood tree,
The bishop of Hereford was to come by,
 With all his company.

3. Come, kill me a ven'son, said bold Robin Hood,
 Come, kill me a good fat deer,
The bishop of Hereford is to dine with me to-day,
 And he shall pay well for his cheer.

4. We'll kill a fat ven'son, said bold Robin Hood,
 And dress it by the highway side;
And we will watch the bishop narrowly,
 Lest some other way he should ride.

5. Robin Hood dress'd himself in shepherd's attire,
 With six of his men alsò;
And, when the bishop of Hereford came by,
 They about the fire did go.

6. O what is the matter? then said the bishòp,
 Or for whom do you make this a-do?
Or why do you kill the king's ven'son,
 When your company is so few?

7. We are shephèrds, said bold Robin Hood,
 And we keep sheep all the year,
And we are disposed to be merry this day,
 And to kill of the king's fat deer.

8. You are brave fellows! said the bishòp,
 And the king of your doings shall know:
Therefore make haste, and come along with me,
 For before the king you shall go.

9. O pardon, O pardon, said bold Robin Hood,
 O pardon, I thee pray!
For it becomes not your lordship's coat
 To take so many lives away.

10. No pardon, no pardon, said the bishòp,
 No pardon I thee owe;
Therefore make haste, and come along with me,
 For before the king you shall go.

11. Then Robin set his back 'gainst a tree,
And his foot against a thorn,
And from underneath his shepherd's coat
He pull'd out a bugle horn.

12. He put the little end to his mouth,
And a loud blast did he blow,
Till threescore and ten of bold Robin's men
Came running all on a row:

13. All making obeysance to bold Robin Hood,
'Twas a comely sight for to see.
What is the matter, master, said Little John,
That you blow so hastilie?

14. "O here is the bishop of Hereford,
And no pardon we shall have."
Cut off his head, master, said Little John,
And throw him into his grave.

15. O pardon, O pardon, said the bishòp,
O pardon, I thee pray;
For if I had known it had been you,
I'd have gone some other way.

16. No pardon, no pardon, said bold Robin Hood,
No pardon I thee owe;
Therefore make haste, and come along with me,
For to merry Barnsdale you shall go.

17. Then Robin he took the bishop by the hand,
And led him to merry Barnsdale;
He made him to stay and sup with him that night,
And to drink wine, beer, and ale.

18. Call in a reckoning, said the bishòp,
For methinks it grows wond'rous high.
Lend me your purse, master, said Little John,
And I'll tell you bye and bye.

19. Then Little John took the bishop's cloak,
And spread it upon the ground,
And out of the bishop's portmantua
He told three hundred pound.

20. Here's money enough, master, said Little John,
And a comely sight 'tis to see;
It makes me in charity with the bishòp,
Tho' he heartily loveth not me.

21. Robin Hood took the bishop by the hand,
And he caused the music to play;
And he made the [old]* bishop to dance in his boots,
And glad he could so get away.

* *Sic* Gutch.

2. "Robin Hood and the Bishop of Hereford"

Moffat and Kidson, 1901, p. 143. Also in Ritson, 1795, II, p. 150. From a British Museum half-sheet, engraved c. 1780 by Thomas Straight.

a I, ending on the octave

1. O some they do talk of bold Robin Hood,
And some of the barons bold;
But I'll tell you of the Bishop of Hereford,
How they robb'd him of all his gold.

2. Robin Hood dress'd himself in shepherd's attire,
With six of his men also;
When the Bishop of Hereford he passed by,
They about the fire did go.

3. "You are brave fellows all," the Bishop he said,
"The King of your doings shall know;
And make ye therefore haste, and come with me,
For before the King you shall go."

4. Then Little John took the Bishop's cloak,
And spread it upon the ground;
And from the Bishop's portmanteau
He took three hundred pound.

5. Robin Hood took the Bishop by the hand,
And caused the horn to play;
And he made the old Bishop to dance in his boots,
And glad he could so get away.

GROUP B

3. "Robin Hood and the Bishop of Hereford"

Hammond, *JFSS*, III, No. 11 (1907), p. 61. Also in Sharp, 1908-12, I, p. 4. Sung by George Stone, Wareham, Dorset, November 1906; learned sixty years before.

a I

1. Some will talk of bold Robin Hood,
Derry derry down!
And some of the barons so bold;
But I'll tell you how they served the Bishop,
When they robbed him of his gold.
Derry down! Hey! derry derry down!

2. Robin Hood he dressed himself in shepherd's attire
And six of his men also,
And, when the Bishop he did come by,
They round the fire did go.

3. "Oh! we are shepherds," said bold Robin Hood,
"And keep sheep all the year,
And we are resolved to make merry to-day,
And to eat of our King's fat deer."

4. "You are a brave fellow," said the old Bishop,
"And the King of your doings shall know,
Therefore make haste and come along with me
And before the King you shall go."

5. Robin Hood set his back against an oak
And his foot against a thorn,
And out underneath his shepherd's cloak
Pulled out his bugle-horn.

6. He put the small end to his mouth,
And a loud blast he did blow.
Six score and ten of bold Robin's men
Came tripping along in a row.

7. "Oh! what is the matter?" said Little John,
"Oh! why do you blow so hastily?"
"Oh! the Bishop of Hereford he has come by,
And a pardon he shall have."

8. "Here's the Bishop," said bold Robin Hood,
"No pardon I shall have."
"Cut off his head, Master," says Little John,
"And bundle him into his grave."

9. "Oh! pardon me, Oh! pardon me," says the Bishop,
"Oh! pardon me I pray.
If I had a-known it had been you,
I'd a-gone some other way."

10. Robin Hood he took the Bishop by the hand,
And led him to merry Barnsdale,
And made him sup with him that night,
And drink wine, beer, and ale.

11. "Call in the reckoning," the old Bishop said,
"For I'm sure 'tis going very high."
"Give me your purse, Master" said Little John,
"I'll tell you by and bye."

12. Little John he took the Bishop's cloak,
And spread it on the ground,
And out of the Bishop's portmanteau
He pulled five hundred pound.

13. "There's money enough, master" said Little John,
"'Tis a comely sight to see.
It makes me in charity with the Bishop;
In his heart he don't love me."

14. Little John he took the Bishop by the hand,
And he caused the music to play,
And he made the old Bishop dance till he sweat.
And he was glad to get so away.

Robin Hood and Queen Katherine

CHILD NO. 145

THREE different stanza-forms are presented by the various copies of this ballad. The Percy Folio version is in CM quatrains, as usual without refrain. Broadside copies of Child's B group have a "Down a down a down" refrain after the first, second, and last lines of each CM quatrain. This is sufficient to persuade Rimbault that the "Three Ravens" is the tune intended (Gutch, *Robin Hood*, 1847, II, p. 435); but in strict accuracy, the old tune which he prints for this and other ballads will not go to the words. The copies themselves are to be sung "to a new tune." What, it may be asked, would have been meant by a "new" tune in the seventeenth century? If we were sure we had the earliest broadside copy, what might be *meant* in Charles I's time could be a current, recently invented tune. But what would probably be *used* with an old-fashioned narrative song of this kind—the kind of tune the broadside poet would have in mind —would be a simpler, more popular, traditional tune. If the broadside continued thereafter to be reprinted, whether by the same or different printers, the old direction would in all probability be repeated, and the "new tune," of course, would carry exactly as much meaning as the customer cared to import. It is further to be remarked that when the practice became common, after the Restoration, particularly in the 1680's and 1690's, of printing a tune on the broadsides, the tunes chosen—when they were not a mere meaningless jumble of notes scattered for decoration—were almost never popular, traditional tunes, but recent theatre tunes, composed by men like Banister or Purcell. It is practically never the case that anything like a Robin Hood broadside, or semi-popular ballad of the narrative sort, is given the compliment of a musical score. Such things are expected to be sung to the tunes that everybody knows. To argue for priority, therefore, as Child and Rimbault occasionally do (Child, 1882-98, III, pp. 198, 208, and Gutch, *loc.cit.*), on the ground that one ballad, e.g., "Robin Hood and Queen Katherine," is to be sung "to a new tune," and others, e.g., "Robin Hood and the Shepherd" (No. 135), "Robin Hood Rescuing Will Stutly" (141), and "Robin Hood's Delight" (136), are to be sung to the tune of "Robin Hood and Queen Katherine," is to argue on flimsy evidence. To put a hypothetical case, extreme, but by no means impossible, suppose a ballad of Robin Hood + x printed by Thackeray in the 1680's, the only survivor of its kind, to be sung to a "new tune"; suppose a ballad, Robin Hood + y, printed by Grove in the 1630's, to be sung to Robin Hood + x; and suppose the ballad of Robin Hood + y were entered in the Stationers' Register in 1579: what inferences should be drawn about priorities? The limits of assurance are only that when one ballad, (a), is directed to be sung to the tune of another, (b), that other is known and supposed current by the earliest circulator of (a) in the form in question. Moreover, in the present instance, not one of the three ballads directed to be sung to "Robin Hood and Queen Katherine" has the same stanza-pattern as any of the three styles of this last ballad, and could only be sung to the same tune if we simply ignored the interlaced refrain and followed the tune. I am not prepared to justify such a proceeding.

Of the whole series of Robin Hood ballads, the one which comes closest to the refrain pattern of "Robin Hood and Queen Katherine" (B) is "Robin Hood and the Tinker" (No. 127), which goes our present ballad precisely one better in putting a triple "down a down" between *every* line of text. Of that style, Rimbault has written: "The 'Down a down' after every line seems to have been arbitrary, and was sung or not, at the pleasure of the singer. If used in the present instance, it would require another tune"—than the one he now prints as "In Summer time" (Gutch, *op.cit.*, pp. 440 and 436). The possibility may certainly be allowed that in pieces so carelessly and irresponsibly printed as the broadsides, not everything needs to be given equal weight. Yet I think we ought not to jettison all ballast for mere momentary convenience. There is usually *some* meaning behind these tune directions, for in the majority of cases it proves to be true that where one ballad is said to be sung to the tune of another which is extant, the two will be found to have the same stanza-form, as, for example, in the case of "Arthur a Bland." The changes of name where the same tune is meant can only mean that one or another ballad sung to that tune is sufficiently in vogue to be of likely familiarity when the new effort is put into printed circulation, or that the broadside redactor, at least, used it for a pattern. The failure in correspondence of the ballads directed to be sung to "Robin Hood and Queen Katherine" is unusual. Slight variations, as in the number of "downs" in a single line, are of common occurrence between different copies even of the same ballad, but the presence or absence of a whole line of refrain is important. The "Will Stutly" (No. 141) ballad seems to me a case of erroneous tune-naming. The "Shepherd" (135) and "Robin Hood's Delight" (136), however, are identical in pattern, and since the second is to be sung, according to direction, either to "Queen Katherine" or to the "Shepherd" tune, there seems little likelihood of inadvertence. The different copies of No. 136 agree, I believe, absolutely in the details of their refrain. So do the different copies of Child's B-type in No. 146 agree among themselves. No. 135, on the contrary, shows variety: Child's b and c both read "Down a down a down a down"; a, according to Child's note, does not print a third *a down* after the first line, but does so after the last; and d has "Down a down down." But since elsewhere we often find simply, "Down, etc.," to indicate the refrain line, these fluctuations are not disturbing. Other and later copies than those collated by Child, such as I have seen, throw no new light. In view of the fact that "Robin Hood and Queen Katherine" is, as it stands, a unique pattern, and that Nos. 135 and 136 are in agreement with each other—to which we may add No. 120b—we may argue the weight of numbers, augmented besides in the additional copies of the several ballads, for concluding that the B-form of "Katherine" is mistakenly printed and the other form correct for a tune known variously as "Robin Hood's last farewel," "Robin Hood and Queen Katherine," and "Robin Hood and the Shepherd." We may also, if we wish, suppose that the B-form of No. 145 is directed to be sung "to a new tune," because the sponsor of it knew it would not go to the old—though why he should have altered the form in this way would remain a mystery.

Still a third type, Child's C, which comes from the same garland as one exemplar of B (that of 1663), is to be sung to

"The Pinder of Wakefield" (cf. No. 124), and here there is no difficulty: a noteworthy confirmation of the all-but-unique stanza-pattern of that ballad.

Child's conjecture that the present ballad is the one meant by the title "Bold Robin Hood," to which tune "Robin Hood's Progress to Nottingham" is directed to be sung, has been discussed adversely in connection with No. 139.

Robin Hood's Chase

CHILD NO. 146

This ballad is, in all the old copies, directed to be sung to "Robin Hood and the Begger." The stanza-pattern, with the tell-tale refrain after the first line, and the mid-rhyme in line three, shows that No. 133, not 134, is meant. No. 133, as we have seen, went to the tune of "Robin Hood and the Stranger," which could be either No. 125 or 128, both of which have the same pattern; and of these last, the former goes to "Arthur a Bland," which we know to be No. 126, q.v.

There are slight variations in the verbal form of the refrain, but not enough to disturb the singing of the tune.

Robin Hood's Golden Prize

CHILD NO. 147

THIS ballad, according to the old copies, goes to the tune of "Robin Hood was a tall young man," that being the first line of "Robin Hood's Progress to Nottingham" (No. 139). The two have identical patterns. In discussing the former ballad, I have suggested the possibility that by "Bold Robin Hood" might be meant the present ballad; and have rejected, on grounds of internal evidence, Child's suggestion that No. 145 might be intended.

The Noble Fisherman, or, Robin Hood's Preferment

CHILD NO. 148

The tune named for this ballad in the early copies is "In summer time" or "Summer time." There is no indication of any kind of refrain. We have met this tune-name before, in No. 127; and there, the stanza was split up in a unique fashion, with a "Down a down a down" after every first and third line, and "Hey down a down a down" after every second and fourth. Such a plethoric refrain seems in itself a suspicious circumstance. Now, Rimbault (Gutch, *Robin Hood*, 1847, II, p. 436) prints a tune written, he says, on a flyleaf of a copy of *Parthenia*, 1611, which, it is to be assumed, bore the title "In Summer time." (Such, also, one gathers, is Chappell's understanding; and he may have seen the MS. by favor of Rimbault; cf. Chappell, *Popular Music* [1855-59], II, pp. 392-93.) This tune, it is important to observe, is a four-phrase tune in CM. Rimbault prints the tune as for No. 123 (q.v.)—doubtless on account of the opening words of the B type of that ballad—and remarks that our present No. 148 is also directed to be sung to the same tune. It is, however, to be noticed that No. 123B is in CM, while the present ballad is in LM and would not go appropriately to the tune. It should be recalled that No. 123B does not name the tune, but indicates "a new northern tune." On the other hand, Nos. 127 and 148 both name "In Summer time." No. 127 is in CM if we ignore the refrain lines, and, without them, would go easily to Rimbault's discovery.

We have, then, three Robin Hood ballads beginning with the words "In summer time," two of them bearing that name for the tune, the third not. Each of the three has a different stanza-form. On the other hand, we have a tune presumably named "In summer time," roughly contemporary and on the face of it a ballad tune. The only one of the three ballad texts which it perfectly fits is the one which does not name it. That there was a tune of the same name, and in LM, is shown by Chappell, *op.cit.*, II, p. 393: his reference is Pepys, I, p. 463 (for I, p. 464). Other references to ballads employing a tune so named are given, with further comment, in Rollins, *A Pepysian Garland*, 1922, pp. 161-62; *The Pack of Autolycus*, 1927, p. 133; *Pepys Ballads*, II, 1929, p. 43. Rollins's suggestion in the first of these that the tune may be "Maying-time" (Chappell, *op.cit.*, I, p. 377) I think quite unlikely. As he remarks, most of the ballads to which the tune "In summer time" is to be sung are in LM iambics. But the Pepys ballad (I, p. 464) of which Chappell quotes the first stanza is anapaestic; and the "Noble Fisherman" is anapaestic at will. The tune of "Maying-time" is a two-strain, modulating piece in trochaic movement, and no ballad-tune in any popular sense.

The tune of "In summer time" to which the present ballad was intended to be sung has not yet been identified.

Robin Hood and Maid Marian

CHILD NO. 150

THIS ballad is another of the "Arthur a Bland" family, with the characteristic refrain and middle rhyme in line three. The only broadside copy is directed to be sung to "Robin Hood Reviv'd" (No. 128), q.v. For the tune, cf. No. 126.

Robin Hood and the Valiant Knight

CHILD NO. 153

This ballad is to the tune of "Robin Hood and the Fifteen Foresters." It thus joins the company of Nos. 139 and 147. There are some differences in the copies: Child's c gives the refrain in full as "Derry down down" after line one, and "Hey down derry derry down" after line four. Copy b omits the refrain altogether, but is otherwise roughly the same. Copy a writes merely "Derry, etc." after line one, and "Hey, etc." after line four. It was not unusual for the eighteenth-century garland copies to omit the refrain of the ballads they reprinted. See, further, Nos. 139, 144, 147.

Sir Hugh, or, The Jew's Daughter

CHILD NO. 155

The connection of this ballad with the legend of Hugh of Lincoln seems deep-rooted and genuine, but the main tradition of the ballad nevertheless appears to be Scottish, passing thence to Ireland and the U.S.A.

Of Child's twenty-one variants, the only one with a refrain (a repeated last line) is that from Motherwell's Appendix, which alone has a tune. Among the variants with tunes—Scots, Irish, Nova Scotian, and U.S.—refrains of some kind occur more often than not.

The inappropriate rainy opening occurs in the earliest text to reach print, Child's B (Percy); and again in G (Philadelphia, c. 1800), H (Baltimore, c. 1825), I (E. Brydges, c. 1810), J (Northamptonshire, c. 1800-1850), K (Shropshire, c. 1810), L (Buckinghamshire, c. 1825), M (Gypsy, 1872), N (New York from Ireland, 1885 dating from 1850?), O (London, c. 1850), S (London, c. 1850). But it is *not* in Child A (Mrs. Brown), nor C (Paton-Percy, 1768), nor D (Herd MSS.), nor E (Motherwell, 1827). Perhaps it came in through contamination with "The Unquiet Grave" (No. 78), also concerned with a revenant and mourning for the dead. There are also apparent crossings with "Twa Brothers" (No. 49) at the beginning and end; and with "Lamkin" (No. 93)—cf. Linkim, Lincoln, Lankin—in the bloodletting passage.

It seems quite probable that the ballad has its roots in a story of ritualistic murder by Jews. There is in the earliest chronicles no reference to a miracle of Our Lady: the corpse is not resuscitated in any way, but itself performs miracles. There is no mention of a woman among the Jews, but the mother of the boy figures prominently. If this story were taken up by superstitious Protestants, there would be no tendency for accretions to grow upon it of the religious sort, and the miracles of the corpse would naturally drop out. In folk-story (although not in "Lamkin") the evil-doer is frequently a woman or witch, and it is natural for such a figure to appear as villainess. The ballad first comes to light in Scotland, the stronghold of Protestantism. The event seems, from the name Hugh, to have been originally localized at Lincoln, but already when it appears in the eighteenth century the name is beginning to be blurred out of recognition. Child A mentions "merry Lincoln" four times; D "merry Linkim"; but B and C have dissolved this to "Mirryland toun"; and E further to Scottish "Maitland town." F (Irish) does not localize, nor N (American-Irish), nor P and R (both fragments). G, H, I, J, M, O (all English and American) carry back to "Scotland" and Scotland is echoed by Shropshire K's "Merry-Cock land." (J, though placing the action in Scotland, mentions Lincoln in stanza ten.) Scottish Q has "Lincolnshire." This would indicate a Scottish tradition with original proper attribution to Lincoln, fading out; carried thence into England, where a sense of its Scottishness would throw back localization upon Scotland. The ballad appears to have no continental history, though there are widespread legends on the theme, and verses (early) in Anglo-Norman and English.

The ballad-makers certainly worked at a considerable remove from any dependence on chronicle or pious legend, and seem to have kept nothing more than the nucleus: that Hugh of Lincoln was murdered by a Jew, thrown into a well, sought by his mother, and discovered, "for murder, though it have no tongue, will speak/ With most miraculous organ." The event is alleged to have occurred in 1255. In 1290, Edward I officially expelled the Jews from England; and they were not readmitted till Cromwell's era.

Except for Percy, 1765, the best Scottish texts are very much alike, and thus point either to a strong and continuous tradition or one controlled by recent dissemination or narrow distribution. The Percy text seems already sufficiently corrupted or sophisticated for it to have gone some way in popular handling: e.g., stanzas 1, 2, 6, 10, 11, 12, and the general abridgment. But some of this could have been done by Lord Hailes or his donor.

The musical tradition cannot be taken very far back, and for the most part it is fairly homogeneous, keeping to the I-π^1-I/M region, and using the "Lady Isabel" B, or "Lord Lovel," style of tune. (See *ante*, Vol. I, No. 4, and Vol. II, No. 75.) This, however, allows for a good deal of variety, and runs all the way from "St. Valentine's Day" to "Cowdenknowes."

Before examining the minuter varieties of difference, however, it will be well to note two or three departures from the main current of tradition. These occur among the earlier records, and also in the Irish line. The tune given in Johnson's *Museum* (variant 1 below) is, as printed, a six-phrase one. Glen is "doubtful if it ever appeared in any collection prior to the Museum"; he considers it, he says, "of the mongrel species, compounded from 'The Mason's Anthem, Merrily danced the Quaker,' &c." (Glen, *Early Scottish Melodies*, 1900, p. 237). To me it appears that the first two phrases would properly be repeated (ABAB) to form an eight-phrase tune. As it stands, the last two verbal lines are repeated to fill out the last four phrases (CDEB) of the tune—a way not followed in any other copy of this ballad. The tune is plagal and virtually I/M, but with the leading-note introduced twice as a passing note. It is not certain that this tune is of stuff quite alien from the main melodic stream. Its claim in tradition is strengthened by the suggestion of an inverted form of the tune in a Nova Scotian variant (2 below) and a *zersungen* Virginian copy (variant 3).

A tune set down in the Blaikie MS. (early nineteenth century) and probably never printed, is solitary, like most of those after Group C, but of sound Scottish material (Group F, variant 58).

J. Stafford Smith, in *Musica Antiqua*, c. 1812, I, p. 65, gives as from tradition the only early copy in a minor mode—a 6/8, eight-phrase tune, probably Æolian originally, but modulating, and with an inflected seventh (see variant 62). The first two phrases repeat to form the first strain, and in this the sixth is lacking. Provenience is not given.

Motherwell (variant 56) gives a 4/4, five-phrase, I/M plagal tune, off the beaten track for this ballad, but suggestive of the "Islington" or "Johnny Cock" pattern. (See *ante*, Vol. II, No. 105, and No. 114 of the present volume.)

James Joyce, in *Ulysses*, provides one of the few fully Mixolydian tunes (variant 60). It is a rather florid version, full of repetition, the second and fourth lines repeating, and then the whole second half again; added to which is a second strain, of which the second half reverts to a restatement of the second half of the first strain. Joyce's tune may be related to another Irish version, Honoria Galwey's, in *Old Irish Croonauns*, 1910, from

Donegal, mid-nineteenth century (variant 59). This is I plagal, five-phrase, in duple time.

A curious Vermont version (variant 65), probably much disordered, changes from 3/4 to 2/4 time and shifts to another form in a later stanza. It has been sung to tatters and perhaps is only a vague approximation to the genuine tune, possibly influenced by "Lord Bateman" (No. 53). But a more shapely Vermont copy (variant 66) seems related. The singer of the first version used his tune also for "The Twa Brothers" (No. 49; *ante*, Vol. I, p. 387, variant 7)—a natural association.

The central singing tradition of the ballad (C) is represented in variants from Somerset, New York, Southern Pennsylvania, Ohio, Indiana, Missouri, and most strongly in the Appalachian region. Here it takes the "Lord Lovel" pattern, or that of "Lady Isabel" B, with a 6/8 metre. All examples are in the major area, and all except a couple of disordered copies are five-phrase, the last phrase repeating. But not Somerset and Indiana.

In Group B, Mason's Northumbrian version (I/M) is also four-phrase and duple in metre. This is closely followed, text and notes, in a variant (25) got by Sharp in Somerset. Another Somerset tune (26) seems to have been affected by "The Mermaid" (Child No. 289).

Of the total number of tunes now in hand, the greater portion seems to be built of familiar melodic stock. The geographical range is unusually extensive, although—perhaps through the chances of collecting—the great majority is Appalachian. Dates of record run from 1803 to the present, but not many examples were collected before the present century. The Scottish tunes recorded in the early nineteenth century seem somewhat apart, as do the English one of the same time and Irish tunes of the late nineteenth and early twentieth century.

Within the largest groups, A and C, there is much variety of form, crystallizing into fairly well-marked sub-groups at certain points, with distinct affiliations among other ballads. Duple rhythm with 6/8 metre is by far the most favored measure. There is a nearly even division between plagal and authentic tunes. It is impossible to discern any *Ur*-pattern from which others have developed. The Kentucky and Tennessee variants are fairly homogeneous, favoring π^1 plagal, and 4/4 or 2/2 metre. The largest homogeneous group is Appalachian chiefly, but runs into Pennsylvania, Indiana, New York, Ohio, and is found once in Somerset. It is 6/8, with mid-cadence on V, is always authentic, mostly major, but with I/Ly, π^1, I/M forms; and almost universally repeats the last line to make a five-phrase tune.

LIST OF VARIANTS

GROUP Aa

1. "The rain rins down &c." James Johnson, *The Scots Musical Museum*, VI [1803], No. 582, p. 602 (repr. 1853). Also in H. E. Krehbiel, *New York Tribune*, August 17, 1902, Pt. II, p. 2, col. 1.
2. "Sir Hugh," or "The Jew's Daughter." Helen Creighton, *Songs and Ballads from Nova Scotia* [1933], p. 16.
3. "A Little Boy Threw His Ball So High." Arthur Kyle Davis, Jr., *Traditional Ballads of Virginia*, 1929, pp. 588(E) and 406. Also in Dorothy Scarborough, *On the Trail of Negro Folk-Songs*, 1925, p. 53; and Scarborough, *A Song Catcher in Southern Mountains*, 1937, pp. 403 and 172.

a. "The Jewses' Daughter." Arthur Kyle Davis, Jr., *More Traditional Ballads of Virginia*, 1960, p. 236(DD).

GROUP Ab

4. "Little Sir Hugh." Sharp MSS., 701/787, Clare College Library, Cambridge. Also in Cecil J. Sharp and Charles L. Marson, *Folk Songs from Somerset*, 3rd series, 1906, p. 39, Sharp, *English Folk-Song: Some Conclusions*, 1907, p. 75; Sharp, *One Hundred English Folksongs*, 1916, p. 22; Sharp, *JFSS*, V, No. 20 (1916), p. 255; and Sharp, *English Folk Songs*, Selected Ed., Novello and Co. [1920], I, p. 22. (Ree).
5. "Little Harry Hughes and the Duke's Daughter." William Wells Newell, *Games and Songs of American Children*, 1883, p. 76. Also in Newell, *JFSS*, IV, No. 14 (1910), p. 36; and C. Alphonso Smith, *The Musical Quarterly*, II (1916), p. 123(A).
6. "Sir Hugh," or "Little Harry Hughes." Davis, *Traditional Ballads of Virginia*, 1929, pp. 589(I) and 411(I). Also in Smith, *The Musical Quarterly*, II (1916), p. 123(B).
7. "Little Saloo." Lester A. Hubbard and LeRoy J. Robertson, *JAF*, LXIV (1951), p. 47. Also in Lester A. Hubbard, *Ballads and Songs from Utah*, 1961, p. 24.
8. "Little Sir Hugh." Sharp MSS., 3866/. Also in Cecil J. Sharp and Maud Karpeles, *English Folk Songs from the Southern Appalachians*, 1932, I, p. 229(I). (N. A. Hensley)
9. " 'Twas on a Cold and Winter's Day." Mrs. Pearl Jacobs Borusky, LC Archive of American Folk Song, recording No. 4987.

10a. "Sir Hugh." Sharp MSS., 4266/3066. Also in Sharp and Karpeles, *Appalachians*, 1932, I, p. 227(F). (Small)

10b. "Sir Hugh." Dol Small, LC Archive of American Folk Song, recording No. 10,003(A1).

11. "The Jeweler's Daughter." Alton C. Morris, *Folksongs of Florida*, 1950, p. 302.
12. "Fatal Flower Garden." Nelson and Touchstone (Nelstone's Hawaiians), Victor recording No. V-40193(B). Also on Folkways LP recording No. FP 251(A3), ed. Harry Smith.

GROUP Ac

13. "Christmas Carol." Marian Arkwright, *JFSS*, I, No. 5 (1904), p. 264.
14. "Little Sir Hugh." Sharp MSS., 3867/. Also in Sharp and Karpeles, *Appalachians*, 1932, I, p. 229(H). (S. A. Hensley)
15. "Sir Hugh." Sharp MSS., 3839/2811. Also in Sharp and Karpeles, 1932, I, p. 226(E). (Finlay)
16. "Sir Hugh." Sharp MSS., 3896/2840. Also in Sharp and Karpeles, 1932, I, p. 228(G). (Bishop)

GROUP Ad

17. "Sir Hugh." Sharp MSS., 3943/2852. Also in Sharp and Karpeles, 1932, I, p. 229(J). (Creech)
18. "Sir Hugh." Sharp MSS., 4749/3308. (Boone)
19. "Sir Hugh." Sharp MSS., 3579/. (J. Maples)
20. "Sir Hugh." Sharp MSS., 3583/2645. Also in Sharp and Karpeles, *Appalachians*, 1932, I, p. 222(B). (Campbell)
21. "Sir Hugh." Sharp MSS., 3585/2648. Also in Sharp and Karpeles, 1932, I, p. 223(C). (W. M. Maples)
22. "Sir Hugh." Sharp MSS., 3509/2592. Also in Sharp and Karpeles, 1932, I, p. 222(A). (Sawyer)

23. "Sir Hugh." Sharp MSS., 3655/2719. Also in Sharp and Karpeles, 1932, I, p. 225(D). (Broghton)

GROUP B

24. "Little Sir William." M. H. Mason, *Nursery Rhymes and Country Songs* [1878], p. 46. Also in Lucy E. Broadwood and J. A. Fuller Maitland, *English County Songs*, 1893, p. 86.
25. "Little Sir Hugh." Sharp MSS., 2085/1946. (Sister Emma)
26. "Little Sir Hugh." Sharp MSS., 1232/1200. Also in Sharp, *JFSS*, V, No. 20 (1916), p. 254(2).
27. "The Jew's Daughter." Krehbiel, *New York Tribune*, August 17, 1902, Pt. II, p. 2, col. 3.

GROUP C

28. "The Jew's Daughter." B. Floyd Rinker, *JAF*, XXXIX (1926), p. 213.
29. "The Jew's Daughter." Captain Pearl R. Nye, LC Archive of American Folk Song, recording No. 1609(A2).
30. "Sir Hugh." Walter McCraw, *North Carolina Folklore*, VII (July 1959), p. 35.
31. "Little Sir Hugh." Florence Shiflett, LC Archive of Amercan Folk Song, recording Nos. 12,004(B21)-12,005(A1).
32. "Sir Hugh." Romney Pullen, LC Archive of American Folk Song, recording No. 9980(A3).
33. "It Rained a Mist." Mrs. Bertha Basham Wright, LC Archive of American Folk Song, recording No. 11,453 (A15).
34. "It Rained a Mist." Davis, *Traditional Ballads of Virginia*, 1929, pp. 589(F) and 407.
b. "The Jewish Lady." *The Frank C. Brown Collection of North Carolina Folklore*, IV (*The Music of the Ballads*, ed. Jan P. Schinhan), 1957, p. 83(D).
c. "The Jew's Daughter." Davis, *More Traditional Ballads of Virginia*, 1960, p. 231(AA).
d. "The Jewish Lady." Davis, 1960, p. 233(BB).
35. "It Rained a Mist." Mrs. Ollie Gilbert, Prestige-International recording No. INT-DS 25003(A7).
36. "Sir Hugh," or "The Jew's Daughter." Winston Wilkinson MSS., 1935-36, p. 78, University of Virginia.
37. "The Jew's Daughter." Krehbiel, *New York Tribune*, August 17, 1902, Pt. II, p. 2, col. 2.
38. "The Jew's Garden." Vance Randolph, *Ozark Folksongs*, I, 1946, p. 149(A).
39. "The Jew's Daughter." Davis, *Traditional Ballads of Virginia*, 1929, pp. 587(A) and 401. Also in Smith, *The Musical Quarterly*, II (1916), p. 124(C).
40. "Jewish Lady." Mrs. Crockatt Ward, LC Archive of American Folk Song, recording No. 5228(B2).
41. "Little Sir Hugh." Viola Cole, LC Archive of American Folk Song, recording No. 12,006(B2).
42. "Little Sir Hugh." Rebecca Jane Collins, LC Archive of American Folk Song, recording No. 12,006(A29).
43. "Little Sir Hugh." Sharp MSS., 528/601. Also in Sharp, *JFSS*, V, No. 20 (1916), p. 253(1); and by A. L. Lloyd, Riverside recording No. RLP 12-624(A2), *The English and Scottish Popular Ballads*, I, ed. Kenneth S. Goldstein. (Swain)
44. "The Jew's Garden." Paul G. Brewster, *JAF*, XLVIII (1935), p. 297. Also in Brewster, *Ballads and Songs of Indiana*, 1940, p. 130.
e. "It Rained a Mist." Schinhan, *Music, Brown Collection*, IV, 1957, p. 82(B).
45. "It Rained, It Mist." Byron Arnold, *Folksongs of Alabama*, 1950, p. 42.
46. "Hugh of Lincoln." Mellinger Edward Henry, *JAF*, XLIV (1931), p. 65. Also in Henry, *Folk-Songs from the Southern Highlands*, [1938], p. 103.
47. "The Jew's Daughter." Davis, *Traditional Ballads of Virginia*, 1929, pp. 589(K) and 412.
48. "The Jew's Garden." Mary O. Eddy, *Ballads and Songs of Ohio*, 1939, p. 66. Also in Albert H. Tolman and Mary O. Eddy, *JAF*, XXXV (1922), p. 344.
49. "It Rained a Mist." Foster B. Gresham, *JAF*, XLVII (1934), pp. 361 and 358.
50. "Sir Hugh," or "The Jew's Daughter." Maurice Matteson and Mellinger Edward Henry, *Beech Mountain Folk-Songs and Ballads*, 1936, p. 22.
51. "Sir Hugh of Lincoln." Elsie C. Parsons and Helen H. Roberts, *JAF*, XLIV (1931), p. 296.
52. "The Two Playmates." Reed Smith, *South Carolina Ballads*, 1928, p. 148.
53. "Sir Hugh." Davis, *Traditional Ballads of Virginia*, 1929, pp. 590(L) and 413.
54. "It Rained a Mist." Davis, 1929, pp. 588(C) and 404.
55. "The Jew's Garden." Cecilia Costello, Caedmon recording No. TC 1146(A5). Also in Marie Slocombe, *JEFDSS*, VII, No. 2 (1953), p. 102.

GROUP D

56. "Sir Hew." William Motherwell, *Minstrelsy: Ancient and Modern*, 1827, App'x., No. 7 and p. xvii.

GROUP E

57. "Little Sir Hugh." Donald Whyte (singer), Archive, School of Scottish Studies, University of Edinburgh.

GROUP F

58. "The Jew's Daughter." Blaikie MS., National Library of Scotland MS. 1578, No. 57, p. 20.

GROUP G

59. "Little Sir Hugh." Honoria Galwey, *Old Irish Croonauns*, 1910, p. 15.

GROUP H

60. "Little Harry Hughes." James Joyce, *Ulysses*, New York, 1934, p. 675.

GROUP I

61. "Fair Scotland." George Korson, *Pennsylvania Songs and Legends*, 1949, p. 36.
f. "Little Boy and the Ball." Davis, *More Traditional Ballads of Virginia*, 1960, p. 234(CC).

GROUP J

62. "Little Sir Hugh." J. Stafford Smith, *Musica Antiqua* [1812], I, p. 65. Also in Edward F. Rimbault, *Musical Illustrations of Bishop Percy's Reliques*, 1850, p. 46; and Johnson, *The Scots Musical Museum*, 1853, IV (William Stenhouse, *Illustrations*), No. 582, p. 500.

GROUP K

63. "Sir Hugh and the Jew's Daughter." Margaret Stewart (singer), Archive, School of Scottish Studies.

GROUP L

64. "The Jew's Garden." Mrs. Allie Long Parker, LC Archive of American Folk Song, recording No. 11,903(B1).

GROUP M

65. "Sir Hugh," or "The Jew's Daughter." Phillips Barry, *BFSSNE*, No. 5 (1933), p. 7. Also in Helen Hartness Flanders, Elizabeth Flanders Ballard, George Brown, and Phillips Barry, *The New Green Mountain Songster*, 1939, p. 254; and Helen Hartness Flanders, *Ancient Ballads Traditionally Sung in New England*, III, 1963, p. 124.

66. "Little Harry Huston." Helen Hartness Flanders and Marguerite Olney, *Ballads Migrant in New England*, 1953, p. 30. Also in Flanders, III, 1963, p. 121.

TUNES WITH TEXTS

GROUP Aa

1. [The rain rins down &c.]

Johnson, VI [1803], No. 582, p. 602 (repr. 1853). Also, with editorial changes, in Krehbiel, *N. Y. Tribune*, August 17, 1902, Pt. II, p. 2, col. 1.

p I (–VII, except in grace-note)

1. The rain rins down thro' Mirry-land toune,
   Sae does it down the Pa:
   Sae does the lads of Mirry-land town,
   When they play at the ba.
   Sae does the lads of Mirry-land town
   When they play at the ba.

2. Then out and cam the Jew's dochter,
   Said, will ye com in and dine!
   I winnae cum in, I winnae cum in,
   Without my play feres nine.

3. She pow'd an apple reid and white,
   To intice the young thing in:
   She pow'd an apple white and reid,
   And that the sweet bairn did win.

4. And she has taine out a little pen-knife,
   And low down by her gair,
   She has twin'd the young thing o' his life,
   A word he ne'er spake mair.

5. And out and cam the thick thick bluid,
   And out and cam the thin;
   And out and cam the bonny herts bluid;
   Thair was nae life left in.

6. She laid him on a dressing borde,
   And drest him like a swine,
   And laughing said, gae now and play
   With your sweet play-feres nine.

7. She row'd him in a cake of lead,
   Bade him ly still and sleep.
   She cast him in a deep draw-well,
   Was fifty fathom deep.

8. When bells wer rung, and mass was sung,
   And every lady went hame:
   Than ilk lady had her young son,
   But Lady Helen had nane.

9. She row'd her mantil her about,
   And sair sair gan she weep:
   And she ran into the Jewis castle,
   When they wer all asleep.

10. My bonny Sir Hew, my pretty Sir Hew,
    I pray thee to me speak:
    "O lady rinn to the deep draw-well
    "Gin ye your son wad seek."

11. Lady Helen ran to the deep draw well,
    And knelt upon her knee,
    My bonny Sir Hew, and ye be here,
    I pray thee speak to me.

12. The lead is wondrous heavy, mither,
    The well is wondrous deep,
    A keen pen-knife sticks in my hert,
    A word I downae speak.

13. Gae hame, gae hame, my mother dear,
    Fetch me my winding-sheet,
    And at the back o' Mirry-land toune,
    Its there we twa sall meet.

2. "Sir Hugh," or "The Jew's Daughter"

Creighton, [1933], p. 16. Sung by Mrs. William McNab, Halifax, N.S.

a π^4; but if tonic F, p π^1 with fallen close

1. It rains, it rains in merry Scotland,
   It rains in bower and ha',
   And all the boys in merry Scotland
   Are playing of the ba'.

2. They tossed it high, so very high,
   They tossed it high and low,
   They tossed it into a Jew's garden
   Where many a flower did grow.

3. Then out came one of the Jew's daughters,
    She was all dressed in green,
 "Come in, come in, my little boy,
    And get your ball again."

4. "I won't come in; I daren't come in;
    I won't come in at all.
 I can't come in; I won't come in
    Without my schoolfellows all."

5. She gave him an apple green as the grass,
    She gave him a gay, gold ring,
 She gave him a cherry as red as the blood
    Until she enticed him in.

6. She sat him on a golden chair
    And gave him sugar sweet,
 She laid him on a dresser board
    And stabbed him like a sheep.

7. She threw him in a deep, cold well
    Where it was deep and cold.
 . . . .
    . . . .

3. "A Little Boy Threw His Ball So High"

Davis, 1929, p. 588(E); text, p. 406. Also in Scarborough, 1925, p. 53; and Scarborough, 1937, p. 403; text, p. 172. Contributed by Mrs. L. R. Dashiell, Richmond, Va., April 11, 1921, as sung by herself.

p I (–VI)

1. A little boy threw his ball so high,
    He threw his ball so low;
 He threw it into a dusky garden
    Among the blades of snow.

2. "Come hither, come hither, my sweet little boy,
    Come hither and get your ball."
 "I'll neither come hither, I'll neither come there,
    I'll not come get my ball."

3. She showed him an apple as yellow as gold,
    She showed him a bright gold ring,
 She showed him a cherry as red as blood,
    And that enticed him in.

4. Enticed him into the drawing-room
    And then into the kitchen,
 And there he saw his own dear nurse,
    A-pick-i-ing a chicken!

5. "I've been washing this basin this live-long day,
    To catch your heart's blood in."
 "Pray spare my life, pray spare my life,
    Pray spare my life!" cried he.
 "I'll not spare your life,
    I'll not spare your life," cried she.

6. "Pray put my Bible at my feet,
    My parer-book at my feet,
 If any of my playmates should ask for me,
    Oh, tell them I'm dead and asleep!"

7. She dragged him on his cooling board,
    And stabbed him like a sheep.
 She threw him into a dusky well
    Where many have fallen asleep.

GROUP Ab

4. "Little Sir Hugh"

Sharp MSS., 701/787. Also in Sharp and Marson, 3rd series, 1906, p. 39; Sharp, 1907, p. 75; Sharp, 1916, p. 22; Sharp, *JFSS*, V, No. 20 (1916), p. 255; and Sharp, Selected Ed. [1920], I, p. 22. Sung by Mrs. Joseph Ree, Hambridge, Somerset, December 26, 1905.

p I/M

1. Do rain, do rain in American corn
 Do rain both great and small
 When all the boys came out to play
 They played all with their ball.

2. They tossed their ball so high so low
 They tossed their ball so low
 They tossed it over in the Jew's garden
 When all the fine Jews below.

3. The first that came out was a Jew's daughter
 Was dressèd all in green
 Come in, come in, my little Sir Hugh
 Shall have your ball again.

4. I cannot come there, I will not come there
 Without my playmates all
 For if my mother should chance to know
 'Twould cause my blood to flow.

5. The first she offered him was a fig
 The next a finder thing
 The third a cherry as red as blood
 And that enticed him in.

6. She set him down in a chair of gold
 And gave him sugar sweet
 She laid him on a dresser board
 And stabbed him like a sheep.

7. And when the school was over
His mother came out for to call
With a little rod under her apron
To beat her son withal.

8. Go home, go home my heavy mother
Prepare a winding-sheet
And if my father should ask of me
You tell him I'm fast asleep.

9. My head is so heavy I cannot get up
My grave it is so deep
Besides a penknife struck into my heart,
So up I cannot get.

Many editorial changes were made in the printed versions of the text.

5. "Little Harry Hughes and the Duke's Daughter"

Newell, 1883, p. 76. Also in Newell, *JFSS*, IV, No. 14 (1910), p. 36; and Smith, *MQ*, II (1916), p. 123(A). Sung by some New York children.

p I

1. It was on a May, on a midsummer's day,
When it rained, it did rain small;
And little Harry Hughes and his playfellows all
Went out to play the ball.

2. He knocked it up, and he knocked it down,
He knocked it o'er and o'er;
The very first kick little Harry gave the ball,
He broke the duke's windows all.

3. She came down, the youngest duke's daughter,
She was dressed in green;
"Come back, come back, my pretty little boy,
And play the ball again."

4. "I won't come back, and I daren't come back,
Without my playfellows all;
And if my mother she should come in,
She'd make it the bloody ball."

5. She took an apple out of her pocket,
And rolled it along the plain;
Little Harry Hughes picked up the apple,
And sorely rued the day.

6. She takes him by the lily-white hand,
And leads him from hall to hall,
Until she came to a little dark room,
That none could hear him call.

7. She sat herself on a golden chair,
Him on another close by;
And there's where she pulled out her little penknife
That was both sharp and fine.

8. Little Harry Hughes had to pray for his soul,
For his days were at an end;
She stuck her penknife in little Harry's heart,
And first the blood came very thick, and then came very thin.

9. She rolled him in a quire of tin,
That was in so many a fold;
She rolled him from that to a little draw-well
That was fifty fathoms deep.

10. "Lie there, lie there, little Harry," she cried,
"And God forbid you to swim,
If you be a disgrace to me,
Or to any of my friends."

11. The day passed by, and the night came on,
And every scholar was home,
And every mother had her own child,
But poor Harry's mother had none.

12. She walked up and down the street,
With a little sally-rod in her hand;
And God directed her to the little draw-well,
That was fifty fathoms deep.

13. "If you be there, little Harry," she said,
"And God forbid you to be,
Speak one word to your own dear mother,
That is looking all over for thee."

14. "This I am, dear mother," he cried,
"And lying in great pain,
With a little penknife lying close to my heart,
And the duke's daughter she has me slain.

15. "Give my blessing to my schoolfellows all,
And tell them to be at the church,
And make my grave both large and deep,
And my coffin of hazel and green birch.

16. "Put my Bible at my head,
My busker at my feet,
My little prayer-book at my right side,
And sound will be my sleep."

6. "Sir Hugh," or "Little Harry Hughes"

Davis, 1929, p. 589(I); text, p. 411(I). Also in Smith, *MQ*, II (1916), p. 123(B). Sung by Miss Charlotte Rodé, near Rustburg, Campbell County, Va.; learned in childhood from poor white tenants and Negroes on her father's farm. Contributed by Juliet Fauntleroy, March 1, 1914.

a I

1. A little school boy, he bounced his ball,
He bounced his ball so high,
He bounced his ball into the Queen's garden,
Where the lilies and roses lie.

2. "Come over, come over, you little school boy,
   And you shall have your ball."
   "I won't come over, I can't come over,
   I won't come over at all."

3. She called up her servants one by one,
   She called them three by three.
   She said, "Oh, there's a little school boy,
   I pray you bring him to me."

4. And some they took him by the hair of his head,
   And others by his feet,
   And they carried him and threw him into a well
   That was ten thousand feet deep.

5. "Oh, put my Bible at my head,
   My prayer-book at my feet,
   And if my playmates ask for me,
   Tell them I'm fast asleep."

7. "Little Saloo"

Hubbard and Robertson, *JAF*, LXIV (1951), p. 47. Also in Hubbard, 1961, p. 24. Sung by Mrs. Mabel J. Overson; learned long before from Mrs. Anna McKellar, Leamington, Utah.

p π^1

1. Yesterday was a holiday,
   A holiday in the year;
   And all the school boys had leave to play,
   And little Saloo was there, was there,
   And little Saloo was there.

2. He had an aunt who held him spite;
   She lived in castle hall.
   She said, "Come here, my little Saloo,
   To you I will give this ball, this ball,
   To you I will give this ball."

3. She took a ball out of her pocket
   And threw it in the hall.
   And little Saloo he picked it up,
   The prettiest one of all, of all,
   The prettiest one of all.

4. She took him by his little white hand
   And led him through the hall,
   And led him into a cold dark room
   Where none could hear him call, call,
   Where none could hear him call.

5. She took a penknife out of her pocket
   And pointed it to his breast.
   "Oh aunt, oh aunt, oh cruel aunt,
   Please don't disturb my rest, my rest,
   Please don't disturb my rest."

6. She cut and cut through thick and thin
   Until she came to skin,
   Until she came to his little heart's blood,
   Where life it lies within, within,
   Where life it lies within.

7. Then she wrapped him up in a sheet of lead,
   Which weighed a many a pound,
   And threw him into a dark, cold well
   Way down deep under ground, ground,
   Way down deep under ground.

8. "Little Sir Hugh"

Sharp MSS., 3866/. Also in Sharp and Karpeles, 1932, I, p. 229(I). Sung by Mrs. Nancy Alice Hensley, Oneida, Clay County, Ky., August 17, 1917.

a π^2 (or p π^1, ending on *V*)

Up in a dark hollow,
Where the dew drops never fall,
Every scholar in that school
Went out to playing ball, ball,
Went out to playing ball.

9. "'Twas on a Cold and Winter's Day"

Sung by Mrs. Pearl Jacobs Borusky, Pearson, Wis., 1941; learned from her mother, who heard it sung formerly in West Virginia. LC/AAFS, rec. No. 4987. Collected by Robert F. Draves.

p I

1. 'Twas on a cold and winter's day,
   The children had all gone to school,
   And they were all a-playing ball,
   And dancing all around.[1]

The intonation was not very certain. The B's in bar one were quite flat, as was the F♯ in the second bar. In the sixth bar, the first C was decidedly high. For another interpretation of Mrs. Borusky's tune, made from her singing in Bryant, Wis., July 15, 1938, see the copy given by Asher E. Treat in *JAF*, LII (1939), p. 43.

2. They knocked it high and they knocked it dry,
And they knocked against[2] the Jew's castle-wall.
Go in, go in, my little boy Hugh,
Go in and get your ball.

3. I mustn't go in, I da'sn't go in,
My school-bell doth me call,
And if my master knew of this,
He would surely make my blood fall.

4. Out stepped the Jew's daughter
With apples in her hand,
Come in, come in, my little boy Hugh,
I will give you one or two.

5. She took him by his little white hand
And led him through the hall,
She laid (led?) him in to a stone wall
Where no one could hear him call.

6. She pierced him with a little pen-knife
Which was both sharp and keen.
La-la-la-la-la-la-la-la.
Le-la-la-la-la-la.[3]

7. She wrapped him in a shirt[4] of lead,
One fold or two.
And threw him into a draw well
Which was both[5] cold and deep.

8. The day had fled and night came on,
The children had all gone home;
And every mother had her son,
But little Hugh's mother had none.

9. She broke her a switch all off of the birch
And through the streets she ran.
She ran till she came to the Jews' gate
And the Jews were all asleep.

10. She ran till she came to the draw-well
Which was so[6] cold and deep,
Saying, If you are here, my little boy Hugh,
Speak one word to your Mother dear.

11. Oh, here I am, dear Mother, he cried,
And here I've lain so long,
With a little pen-knife pierced to my heart,
And the blood is still running strong.

12. Oh take me out of this draw-well,
And make me a coffin (out) of birch,
Oh take me out of this draw-well
And bury me in yonders church.

[1] Only the first line of this stanza is given in *JAF*.
[2] *JAF*: knocked it 'gainst
[3] The singer could not remember these lines in 1938 either.
[4] *JAF*: sheet [5] *JAF*: so [6] *JAF*: both

10a. "Sir Hugh"

Sharp MSS., 4266/3066. Also in Sharp and Karpeles, 1932, I, p. 227(F). Sung by Mr. Dol Small, Nellysford, Va., May 22, 1918.

a M (–IV, VI) (compass of a sixth)

"This was sung by Mr. Small and his two daughters and they one and all sang the F's full natural, and without any hesitancy." [*Sharp's MS. note.*]

1. O she tossed it high, she tossed it low,
She tossed it in yonders wall,
Saying: Come along, my little boy Hugh,
And get your silken ball.

2. I can't come in, I daren't come in
To get my silken ball,
For if my master knew it all
He'd let my life's blood fall.

3. She took him by his lily-white hand,
She led him through the hall,
And in that silver basin clear
She let his life's blood fall.

4. She wound him up in a lily-white sheet,
Three or four times four,
And tossed him in her draw-well,
It were both deep and cold.

5. The day had passed and the evening come,
The scholars going home.
Every mother had a son,
Little Hugh's had none.

6. She broke a switch all off that birch,
And through the town she run,
Saying: I'm going to meet my little boy Hugh,
I'm sure for to whip him home.

7. She run till she came to the old Jew's gate,
The old Jews all so* sleep.
She heard a voice in that draw-well,
It were both cold and deep.

8. Cheer up, dear mother, it's here I've lain,
It's here I've lain so long,
With a little penknife pierced through my heart,
The stream do run so strong.

9. Go take me out of this draw-well
And make me a coffin of birch;
O take me out of this draw-well
And bury me at yonders church.

* 1932: do

10b. "Sir Hugh"

Sung by Mr. Dol Small (81), Nellysford, Va., September 10, 1950. LC/AAFS, rec. No. 10,003(A1). Collected by Maud Karpeles and Sidney Robertson Cowell.

a M (–IV, VI) (compass of a sixth)

1. She tossed it high, she tossed it low,
She tossed it in yonders hall,
Saying, Come along, my little boy Hugh,
And get your silken ball.

2. I can't come in and I won't come in
To get my silken ball,
For if my master knew it all
He'd let my life's blood fall.

3. She took him by his lily-white hand,
She led him through the hall,
And in that silver basin clear
She let his life's blood fall.

4. She wound him up in a lily-white sheet,
Three or four times four,
And tossed him into her draw-well,
'Twere both deep and cold.

5. The day had passed and the even had come,
Scholars going home,
Every mother had her son,
Little Hugh's had none.

6. She broke a switch all off that birch,
Through the town she run:
I'm going to meet my little boy Hugh,
I'm sure for to whip him home.

7. She ran till she came to the old Jews' gate
The old Jews all so asleep.
She heard a voice in that draw-well
'Twere both cold and deep.

8. Cheer up, dear Mother, it's here I've lain,
It's here I've lain so long,
With a little pen-knife pierced through my heart,
The stream did run so strong.

9. O take me out of this draw-well,
Make me a coffin of birch;
O take me out of this draw-well
Bury me at yonders church.

11. "The Jeweler's Daughter"

Morris, 1950, p. 302. Sung by Mrs. G. A. Griffin, Newberry, Fla.; learned from her father, of Georgia.

p I (–VI)

There must be some obscure connection between this and the following variant. The tune arouses suspicion as traditional melody, but it turns up again with a New England version of "Edom o Gordon"; cf. No. 178, variant 6.

1. It rains, it pours, it rains, it pours,
It rains both night and day.
The prettiest boy in our whole town
Came down there playing ball.

2. They tossed the ball so high, so low,
And then again so low;
They tossed it onto the jeweler's garden,
Where man was daredn't to go.

3. Down stepped the jeweler's daughter,
Dressed in green and yellow,
"Come in, come in, my pretty little boy,
And get your ball again."

4. "I can't and I shan't and I won't come in,
Without my playmates all,
For that would get to my mother's ears;
Her tears would surely fall."

5. She showed to him an apple seed,
And then a gay gold ring;
She showed him a cherry rose red,
And that's what 'ticed him in.

6. She takened him by his lily-white hand,
And led him through the wall;
She led him into the chamber room,
Where none could hear him call.

7. She pinned him in a silver chair;
She pinned him with a pin;
She shined a basin both bright and brass
For to catch his heart's blood in.

8. "O nurse me, nurse me, now or never,
O nurse me now or never;
If I ever live to be a man,
I'll give you a veil forever."

From *Folksongs of Florida* by Alton C. Morris. Published by the University of Florida Press, 1950. Used by permission.

12. "Fatal Flower Garden"

Sung by Nelson and Touchstone (Nelstone's Hawaiians). Victor rec. No. V-40193(B), c. 1930. Also on Folkways LP rec. No. FP 251(A3), ed. Harry Smith.

p I (–VI)

1. It rained it poured it rained so hard
(It) rained so hard all day
But all the boys in our school
Came out to toss and play.

2. They tossed their ball again so high
Then again so low
They tossed it into a flower-garden
Where no one was allowed to go.

3. Out stepped this Gipsy lady
All dressed in yellow and green
Come in, come in, my pretty little boy
And get your ball again.

4. I won't come in, I shan't come in
Without my playmates all.
I'll go to my father, tell him about it,
That I cause tears to fall.

5. She first showed him an apple-seed,
Then again a gold ring,
Then she showed him a diamond,
That enticed him in.

6. She took him by his lily-white hand
She led him through the hall
She put him into an upper room
Where no one could hear him call.

7. O take those finger-rings off my fingers,
Smoke them with your breath.
If any of my friends should call for me,
Tell 'em that I'm at rest.

8. Bury the Bible at my head,
The Testament at my feet.
If my dear mother should call for me,
Tell her (that) I'm asleep.

9. Bury the Bible at my feet
The Testament at my head.
If my dear father should call for me,
Tell him that I am dead.

GROUP AC

13. "Christmas Carol"

Arkwright, *JFSS*, I, No. 5 (1904), p. 264. Sung by children from Ecchinswell, Hampshire, and noted by Miss Arkwright at Adbury, Newbury, in 1900.

p I

1. Oh down, oh down in rosemerry Scotland
It rained and snowed both hard.
Two little boys went out one day,
For to play with their ball.

2. They tossèd it up so very high,
They tossèd it down so low,
They tossèd it over in they Jews' garden,
Where they Jews laid down by law.

3. Up steps one of the Jews' daughters,
Clothèd all in green,
Said, "You come here, my fair pretty boy,
And you shall have your ball."

4. "Oh no, no, no, my fair pretty maid,
My playmate is not well."
They showed him an apple as green as grass,
And 'ticed him in at last.

5. They showed him a cherry as red as blood,
They gave him sugar sweet,
They laid him on some dresser drawer,
And stabbed him like a sheep.

6. "Oh, put a Bible at my head,
And a Testament at my feet,
If my poor mother was to pass by me,
Oh, pray to tell her I am asleep."

14. "Little Sir Hugh"

Sharp MSS., 3867/. Also in Sharp and Karpeles, 1932, I, p. 229(H). Sung by Mrs. Sophie Annie Hensley, Oneida, Clay County, Ky., August 17, 1917.

m π^1

Up in a dark hollow
Where the dew drops never fall,
Every scholar in that school
Went out to playing ball, ball,
Went out to playing ball.

15. "Sir Hugh"

Sharp MSS., 3839/2811. Also in Sharp and Karpeles, 1932, I, p. 226(E). Sung by Ben J. Finlay, Manchester, Ky., August 10, 1917.

m π^1

1. Low and low and low holiday
   When dew drops they do fall,
   And ev'ry scholar of that school
   Went out to playing ball, ball, ball,
   Went out to playing ball.

2. Along comes the Jewress lady gay
   With some apples in her hand.
   She says: Come along, my littly son 'Ugh-ey (Hughie)
   And one of these shall ha'.

3. I'm not a-going to come,
   Nor I won't a-come,
   For if my parents knew,
   It would make my red blood run.

4. She took him by his little white hand,
   She led him for a while;
   She led him down to that cold well
   Where it were so cold and deep.

5. Sink, O sink, my little son 'Ugh-ey,
   And don't you never swim.
   If you do it'll be a scandal
   To me and all my kin.

6. The day passed off and the night came on,
   The parents went to seek their son;
   And every parent had a son,
   But Urie's (Hughie's?) she had none.

16. "Sir Hugh"

Sharp MSS., 3896/2840. Also in Sharp and Karpeles, 1932, I, p. 228(G). Sung by Mrs. Dan Bishop, Teges, Clay County, Ky., August 21, 1917.

p π^1

1. 'Twas on a dark and holiday
   When the dew drops they did fall
   And all the scholars of the school
   Went out to playing ball, ball,
   Went out to playing ball.

2. Out stepped that Jewish lady
   With apples in her hand.
   Come here, come here, my little son Hugh,
   And one of those shall have.

3. I cannot come nor I will not come,
   For if my mother knew,
   She'd make my red blood run.

4. She took him by his lily-white hand,
   She led him from porch to hall,
   She locked him up in a tight little room
   Where no one could hear his call.

5. She sat him down in a golden arm-chair
   And scratched him with a pin,
   With a bowl and basin in her hand
   To catch his heart's blood in.

. . . .

GROUP Ad

17. "Sir Hugh"

Sharp MSS., 3943/2852. Also in Sharp and Karpeles, 1932, I, p. 229(J). Sung by Mrs. Berry Creech, Pine Mountain, Harlan County, Ky., August 29, 1917.

p π^1 (–VI)

1. Down come a Jewess
With some apples in her hand,
Saying: Come here, my little son Hugh,
And you shall have one them, them, them,
And you shall have one them.

2. I can't come there,
Nor I won't come there at all,
If my mother was to knew I was here,
My red blood she'd make fall.

3. She picked him up all in her arms,
And carried him to her hall,
She set him down in a big arm-chair,
And scratched him with a pin.

4. In her hands she held a little basin
To catch his heart's blood in.

5. She carried him down to yonders well
Where it's both cold, winding deep.
Lie there, my little son Hugh,
I hope you will never swim.

6. When the sun went down all the children went home.
Every mother had a little son,
But little Hugh's mother had none.

7. She picked up her little birch-rod
And after him did go,
Saying: If I meet him on the road,
I'll whip him home.

8. She went down to yonders gate,
Whiles the Jews were all asleep;
She went down to yonders well,
Where it's both cold, winding deep.

9. Saying: If you're in here, my little son Hugh,
Answer when I call.

. . . .

. . . .

10. Here I am in this cold place,
Where it's both cold, winding deep;
My soul is high up in Heaven above,
While here is low down in hell.

18. "Sir Hugh"

Sharp MSS., 4749/3308. Sung by Mrs. Julia Boone, Micaville, Yancey County, N.C., October 3, 1918.

a I/M (compass of a sixth)

"First verse corrupt: second verse gives the normal form of the tune." [*Sharp's MS. note.*]

She pulled out a pretty yellow apple,
A gay gold ring,
A bunch of cherries as red as a rose
To 'tice that little boy in.

Some took him by his pretty yellow locks,
Some took him by his heels;
Turned him over a slippery plane,
And stabbed him like a pig.

. . . .

Lay my prayer-book at my head,
My bible at my feet;
If my mammy calls for me,
Tell her I'm asleep.

19. "Sir Hugh"

Sharp MSS., 3579/. Sung by Miss Julia Maples, Sevier County, Tenn., April 19, 1917.

p π^1 (–VI)

Go bury my Bible at my head,
My hymn book at my feet,
And if all the scholars ask about me,
Pray tell them I'm asleep, sleep,
Pray tell them I'm asleep.

20. "Sir Hugh"

Sharp MSS., 3583/2645. Also in Sharp and Karpeles, 1932, I, p. 222(B). Sung by Luther Campbell, Bird's Creek, Sevier County, Tenn., April 19, 1917.

p π^1 (–VI)

1. As I walked out one holiday
Some drops of dew[1] did fall,
All the scholars in the school
Were out a-playing ball, ball,
Were out a-playing ball.

2. They tossed the ball both to and fro,
To the Jews's garden it flew.
No one was so ready to bring it out
But our little son Hugh.

3. The Jews's daughter come stepping out
With apples in her hand:
Little son Hugh, come go with me
And I will give you them.

4. I cannot go, I will not go,
I cannot go at all,
For if my mother were to know
The red buds[2] she'd make fall.

5. His mother broke a birch-rod in her hand,
She walked all through the town,
Saying: If I find my little son Hugh,
O I will whip him home.

6. She walked up to the Jews's gate,
And they were all asleep,
And there she spied a great big well
Which was fifty fathoms deep.

7. Little son Hugh, O are you here,
Which I suppose you to be?
Yes, dear mother, I am here
Who stands in the need of thee.

8. Go bury my bible at my head,
My prayer book at my feet,
If any of the scholars ask about me,
Pray tell them I'm asleep.

[1] 1932: rain [2] 1932 footnote: blood?

21. "Sir Hugh"

Sharp MSS., 3585/2648. Also in Sharp and Karpeles, 1932, I, p. 223(C). Sung by W. M. Maples, Sevierville, Sevier County, Tenn., April 20, 1917.

p π^1 (–VI)

1. As I walked out one holiday
The drops of dew did fall,
And every scholar in the school
Was out a-playing ball, ball,
Was out a-playing ball.

2. They tossed the ball to and fro,
In the Jews's garden it did go,
There was no one ready to get it out,
There stood little son Hugh.

3. The Jews's daughter come stepping along
With some apples in her hand,
Saying: Little son Hugh, come go with me
And I will give you them.

4. I cannot go, I will not go,
I cannot go at all,
For if my mamma she knew it,
The red blood she'd make fall.

5. She took him by the lily-white hand,
She drug him from hall to hall,
And took him to a great stone wall
Where none could hear his call.

6. She set him down in a little arm-chair
And pierced his heart within.
She had a little silver bowl,
His heart blood she let in.

7. She took him into the Jews's garden,
The Jews was all asleep,
And she threw him into a great deep well
Was fifty fathoms deep.

8. His mother then she started out
With a birch-rod in her hand,
Walked the streets through and through.
If I find little son Hugh,
I'd avowed she'd whip him home.

9. When she come to the Jews's gate,
The Jews was all asleep;
She walked on to a great deep well
Was fifty fathoms deep.

10. Saying: Little son Hugh, if you be,
As I suppose you to be.
Dear mother, I am here
And stand in the need of thee.

11. With a little penknife pierced through my heart
And the red blood running so free.
Mother, O mother, dig my grave,
Dig it long, wide and deep.

12. And bury my bible at my head,
My prayer book at my feet.
And if any of the scholars ask for me,
Pray tell them I'm asleep.

22. "Sir Hugh"

Sharp MSS., 3509/2592. Also in Sharp and Karpeles, 1932, I, p. 222(A). Sung by Mrs. Swan Sawyer, Black Mountain, N.C., September 19, 1916.

p π^1 (–VI)

All the scholars in the school
As they are a-playing ball,
They knocked it high, they knocked it through,
Through the Jew's garden it flew.

She took him by his lily white hand
And she drug him from wall to wall,
She drug him to a great, deep well,
Where none could hear his call.
She placed a pen-knife to his heart,
The red blood it did fall.

Bury my bible at my head,
My prayer book at my feet.
When the scholars calls for me,
Pray tell 'em I'm asleep.

23. "Sir Hugh"

Sharp MSS., 3655/2719. Also in Sharp and Karpeles, 1932, I, p. 225(D). Sung by Mrs. Mollie Broghton, Barbourville, Knox County, Ky., May 7, 1917.

p I/M

1. Dark and dark some drizzling day,
 Some apples in her hand,
 The Jewish lady in the town
 Walked out with apples in her hand.
 Come here, come here, my little son Hugh,
 Some apples you may have, have,
 Some apples you may have.

2. She took him by the lily-white hand,
 She led him through the hall,
 She sat him down on a winding chair,
 Where none could hear his call, call,
 Where none could hear his call.

3. She held a basin in her hand
 That catched his own heart's blood,
 She picked him up in a winding-sheet,
 She walked with him for a while,
 She took him down to the deepest well
 And there she splunged him in.

4. She went to the well next day
 To see what she could see,
 And there she saw her little Son Hugh
 Come swimming around to thee.

5. O take me out of this deep well,
 O take me out, says he,
 O take me out of this deep well
 And bury me in yonders yard.

6. Sink, O sink, my little son Hugh,
 Sink, O sink, said she.
 Sink, O sink and don't you swim,
 You are an injury to me and my kin.

GROUP B

24. "Little Sir William"

Mason [1878], p. 46. Also in Broadwood and Maitland, 1893, p. 86. From Lincolnshire.

a I/M

This version has been set by Benjamin Britten.

1. Easter Day was a holiday,
 Of all days in the year;
 And all the little school fellows went out to play,
 But Sir William was not there.

2. Mamma went to the Jew's wife's house,
 And knocked at the ring,
 Saying, "Little Sir William, if you are there,
 Oh! let your mother in!"

3. The Jew's wife opened the door and said,
 "He is not here to-day;
 He is with the little schoolfellows out on the green,
 Playing some pretty play."

4. Mamma went to the Boyne water,
 That is so wide and deep,
 Saying, "Little Sir William, if you are there,
 Oh! pity your mother's weep!"

5. "How can I pity your weep, mother,
 And I so long in pain?
 For the little penknife sticks close in my heart,
 And the Jew's wife has me slain."

6. "Go home, go home, my mother dear,
 And prepare my winding sheet;
 For to-morrow morning before eight o'clock,
 You with my body shall meet.

7. "And lay my Prayer-book at my head,
   And my grammar at my feet;
That all the little schoolfellows, as they pass by,
   May read them for my sake."

By permission of J. B. Cramer & Co., Ltd., London, England.

25. "Little Sir Hugh"

Sharp MSS., 2085/1946. Sung by Sister Emma (about 70), at Clewer, February 27, 1909.

a I/M

1. Yesterday was a high holiday
   Of all the days in the year
   And all the little schoolfellows went out to play
   But Sir William was not there

2. His mother she went to the Jew's wife's house
   And knocked loud at the ring
   O little Sir William if you are here
   Come let your mother in

3. He is not here the Jew's wife said
   He is not here today
   He's with his little schoolfellows out on the green
   Keeping this high holiday.

4. His mother she went to the Boyne Water
   That flows so dark & deep.
   O little Sir William if you are here
   O pity your mother's weep.

5. O how can I pity your weep mother
   And I so full of pain
   For the little pen knife sticks close to my heart
   And the Jew's wife has me slain

6. Go home go home my mother dear
   And prepare me a winding sheet
   For tomorrow morning before it is day
   Your body and mine shall meet.

7. And lay my prayer book at my head
   And my grammar at my feet
   That all the little schoolfellows as they pass by
   May read them for my sake.

26. "Little Sir Hugh"

Sharp MSS., 1232/1200. Also in Sharp, *JFSS*, V, No. 20 (1916), p. 254(2). Sung by James Chedgey, Bincombe-over-Stowey, January 23, 1907.

a I/M

1. It rains it rains in merry Scotland
   When the boys did play at ball
   They tossed them high they tossed them low
   They tossed them over the Jew's castle wall

2. Out come one of the Jew's daughters
   She was dressed in a gown of green
   Come here come here my pretty little boy
   You shall have your ball again

3. O no, O no, I dare not a come
   Without my playmates too,
   For if my mother should be standing at the door
   She would cause my poor heart to rue.

4. She showed him an apple as green as grass
   She showed him a gay gold ring
   She showed him a cherry as red as red
   And enticed this little boy in

5. She took him to the parlour door
   And led him through the kitchen
   And then he saw his own mother dear
   She were picking of her chicken

6. Down on his bended knees he fell
   Mother pardon me
   For if I live to be a man
   I will give thee gold in three (fee?).

7. She placed a prayer-book at his head
   And a testament at his feet
   She placed the Bible at his heart
   And a penknife in so deep.

8. She wrapped him up in blankets warm
   And tooked him to a well
   Saying good bye good bye my pretty little boy
   I hope you are quite well.

27. "The Jew's Daughter"

Krehbiel, *N.Y. Tribune*, August 17, 1902, Pt. II, p. 2, col. 3. From a "gentle spinster" in Waterbury, Conn., "some years" previous to its publication; learned from her mother.

m I/M

There was a little boy,
   He tossed his ball so high—
There was a little boy,
   He tossed his ball so low—
He tossed his ball so high,
   He tossed his ball so low—
He tossed it into a merry Jew's garden,
   Where all the Jews did go.

Then out came the merry Jew's daughter,
All dressed up in green;
"Come here, come here, my little boy,
And fetch your ball again."
She enticed him with an apple,
She enticed him with a pear;
She enticed him with a cherry red,
And so she enticed him there.

She led him through the parlor,
She led him through the hall,
She led him to the kitchen,
Among the servants all;
She sat him down in a chair of gold
And gave him sugar sweet—
She laid him on the dresser,
And killed him like a sheep.

She took him to the bedroom,
And laid him on the bed;
She placed a Bible at his feet,
And a prayer book at his head:
She placed a prayer book at his head,
And a Bible at his feet,
And all the neighbors that came in
Thought the little boy was asleep.

GROUP C

28. "The Jew's Daughter"

Rinker, *JAF*, XXXIX (1926), p. 213. From Mrs. Samantha E. Rinker, Huntingdon County, Pa.; learned from her mother, c. 1872.

a I/Ly

1. It rained, it hailed, it snowed, it blowed,
It stormed all over the land;
And all the boys from our town
Came out to toss their ball, ball, ball,
Came out to toss their ball.

2. First they tossed it too high,
And then again too low,
And over into the Jew's garden it went,
Where no one dared to go, go, go,
Where no one dared to go.

3. Out came the Jew's daughter,
Dressed up in silk so fine,
She said, "Come in, my pretty little boy,
And toss your ball with me, me, me,
And toss your ball with me."

4. "I can't come in, nor I shan't come in,
Unless my playmates do,
For if I come in I'll never get out,
I'll never get out any more, more, more,
I'll never get out any more."

5. First a mellow apple,
And then a gay gold ring,
And next a cherry as red as blood,
To coax this little boy in, in, in,
To coax this little boy in.

6. She took him by the lily-white hand,
And into the cellar she ran;
And called for a bowl as yellow as gold,
To catch his heart's blood in, in, in,
To catch his heart's blood in.

7. "O place my prayer book at my head,
My hymn book at my feet,
And when my mother calls for me,
Tell her I am asleep, sleep, sleep,
Tell her I am asleep."

29. "The Jew's Daughter"

Sung by Captain Pearl R. Nye, Akron, Ohio, 1937. LC/AAFS, rec. No. 1609(A2). Collected by Alan and Elizabeth Lomax.

a I

It rained a mist, it rained a mist,
It rained, rained, rained all around
But all the boys in our town
Went out to toss their ball—
Went out to toss their ball.

They tossed one up, they tossed one high,
One went into the Jew's garden by
Where no one was just (?) to go nigh—
Where no one was just to go nigh.

Out came the Jew's daughter dressed in red
To 'tice the little boy in:
Come in, come in, you dear little boy,
You can have your ball again—
You can have your ball again.

She called for a charger and a knife
For to catch his heart's blood in,
All the boys were sad and knew
He'd never come out again—
He'd never come out again.

30. [Sir Hugh]

McCraw, *North Carolina Folklore*, VII (July 1959), p. 35. Sung by Miss Irene Rush, Burlington, N.C. Learned from her mother, who had learned it from her own mother during childhood in Carroll County, Va.

a π^1

1. It rained a mess, it rained a mess,
It rained all over the town,
And three little children went out to play,
To toss the ball around, around,
To toss the ball around.

2. They tossed it high, they tossed it low,
They tossed it all over the ground,
But one tossed it over in a hard woman's yard
Where no one was allowed to go, oh, go,
Where no one was allowed to go.

3. "Come in, little boy, you shall have your ball,
Come in, you shall have your ball."
. . . .

4. "I shan't come in, I shan't come in,
Unless my playmates come too,
For I have been told that if once you go in,
You'll never come out any more, any more,
You'll never come out any more."

5. She showed him a bright red apple,
And then she showed him a chain,
And then she showed him a diamond ring,
To invite the little one in, oh, in,
To invite the little one in.

6. She took him by his lily white hand
And led him through the hall
And then into the dining room
Where no one could hear him call, oh, call,
Where no one could hear him call.

7. "Oh, please spare my life, oh, please spare my life,
Oh, please spare my life," he cried,
"And if I live to be forty years old,
My treasures will all be thine, oh, thine,
My treasures will all be thine."

8. "Please put my prayer book at my feet,
The Bible to my head,
And when my playmates call for me,
Please tell them that I am dead, oh, dead,
Please tell them that I am dead."

9. She pinned a napkin over his face,
She pinned it with a pin,
And then she took a carving knife,
And carved his little heart in, oh, in,
And carved his little heart in.

10. She put the prayer book at his feet,
The Bible at his head,
And when his playmates called for him,
She told them that he was dead, oh, dead,
She told them that he was dead.

31. "Little Sir Hugh"

Sung by Florence Shiflett, Wyatt's Mountain, near Dyke, Va., June 5, 1962. LC/AAFS, rec. Nos. 12,004(B21)-12,005(A1). Collected by George Foss.

a I/Ly

1. *Spoken*: It rained o mist, it rained o mist,
It rained all over the city
Sung: Till all those boys in Marlborough Town
Came out to toss the ball, ball, ball,
Came out to toss the ball.

2. First they tossed it . . . too high,
   And then again too low
And then over in Duty Garden
   Where any one das'nt to go, go, go,
   Where any one das'nt to go.

3. Come in, my lad, come in, my lad,
   You can have your ball again.
I won't come in, I shan't come in,
   I've heard of you befo', befo',
   I've heard of you befo'.

4. First she offered him a ripe mellow apple,
   And then a gay gold ring,
And then a cherry as red as blood,
   She enticen'd this little boy in, in, in,
   She enticen'd this little boy in.

5. She taken him by his little white hand,
   And through the cellar she went
She pinned him down to the cellar door door
   Where no one could hear him layment, layment,
   Where no one could hear him layment.

[*In the following stanza the singer got quite confused, and although prompted, failed to make it out.*]

6. Go dig my grave [both wide and deep]
   And put my ?Bible (?marbles) at my head and feet,
And at my head a gay gold ring
   And when my playmates call for me
   Pray tell them I am dead.

32. "Sir Hugh"

Sung by Romney Pullen, Sperryville, R.I. LC/AAFS, rec. No. 9980(A3). Collected by MacEdward Leach and Horace P. Beck.

a I/Ly

It rained a mist, it rained a mist,
   It rained all over that land,
And every boy was into this town,
   Went out to toss a ball, a ball.

And first they tossed it up too high,
   And then again too low,
And they cast it over in the Jews' garding,
   Where no one was da'st to go, to go,
   Where no one was da'st to go.

33. "It Rained a Mist"

Sung by Mrs. Bertha Basham Wright, Franklin County, Ohio. LC/AAFS, rec. No. 11,453(A15). Collected by Anne Grimes.

a I

1. It rained a mist, it rained a mist,
   It rained all over this town,
When two little children went out to play,
   To toss the ball around, around,
   To toss the ball around.

2. At first too low and then too high,
   And then up over the wall,
And then into the maiden's room,
   Where no one was allowed to go, to go,
   Where no one was allowed to go.

3. Then at the door the maiden came,
   All dressed in silk so fine,
Saying, Come in, come in, you shall have your ball,
   You shall have your ball again, again,
   You shall have your ball again.

4. I can't come in, I won't come in,
   Unless my playmates comes, too;
I've often heard of little ones coming in,
   And never coming out again, again,
   And never coming out again.

5. At first she showed them a red rosy apple
   And then she showed them a chain,
And then she showed them a diamond ring
   To entice the little ones in, ay-in,
   To entice the little ones in.

6. She tuck him by the lily-white hand,
   And led him through the hall,
And taken him into the dining-room,
   Where no one could hear his call, his call,
   Where no one could hear his call.

7. She placed a napkin o'er his face,
   And pinned it with a pin,
And then she taken a little penknife,
   And taken his little heart in, ay-in,
   And taken his little heart in.

8. O spare my life, O spare my life,
   O spare my life, he cried,
And if I live to be a man,
   My treasures shall be ay-thine, ay-thine,
   My treasures shall be ay-thine.

9. Please place the prayer-book at my feet,
The Bible at my head,
And if my playmates call for me,
You can tell them that I am dead, am dead,
You can tell them that I am dead.

34. "It Rained a Mist"

Davis, 1929, p. 589(F); text, p. 407. Sung by Jesse Burgess, Altavista, Va. Contributed by Juliet Fauntleroy, April 30, 1915.

a π^1

1. It rained a mist, it rained a mist,
It rained all over the town,
When two little boys went out to play,
To toss their ball around, around,
To toss their ball around.

2. Then first they tossed the ball too high,
And then they tossed it too low;
They tossed it into the Union yard
Where no one was 'lowed to go, to go,
Where no one was 'lowed to go.

3. Here came young Miss, all dressed in silk,
All dressed in silk so fine;
"Come in, come in, my pretty little boys,
You shall have your ball again, again,
You shall have your ball again."

4. Then first she showed him a red rosy apple,
And then she showed him a peach,
And then she showed him a charming gold ring
Which charmed the little one in, one in,
Which charmed the little one in.

5. She took him by his little white hand,
She led him across the hall;
She took him into the dining room
Where none could hear him call, him call,
Where none could hear him call.

6. She pinned a napkin over his face,
She pinned it with a pin;
Then she took up a carving knife
And cut his little heart in, heart in,
And cut his little heart in.

7. "O spare my life, O spare my life,"
The little one he cried;
"If ever I come to a joyous man,
My joys will all be there, be there,
My joys will all be there."

8. "O place a prayer-book at my feet,
A Bible at my head,
And when my playmates call for me,
Pray tell them I am dead, am dead,
Pray tell them I am dead."

9. She placed the Bible at his head,
The prayer-book at his feet.
And when his playmates called for him,
She told them he was asleep, asleep,
She told them he was asleep.

35. "It Rained a Mist"

Sung by Mrs. Ollie Gilbert. Prestige-International rec. No. INT-DS 25003(A7). Recorded by Alan Lomax.

a π^1 (IV once)

1. It rained a mist, it rained all day,
Two little boys went out to play,
Went out on the grass to play, play, play,
Went out on the grass to play.

2. The first ball tossed, it was too high,
The next one was too low,
The next one was in Jew's room,
Where no one's allowed to go, go, go,
Where no one's allowed to go.

3. Out stepped the Jew, all dressed so fine,
"Come in, come in," she calls,
"Come in, come in, you brave little lad,
And you may have your ball, ball, ball,
And you may have your ball."

4. "I won't come in, I'll not come in,
I won't come in your hall.
For he who passes through your hall
Will never get out at all, all, all,
Will never get out at all."

5. The first she showed him was gold rings,
The next one was gold pins,
The next one was all fine gold things
To invite the little lad in, in, in,
To invite the little lad in.

6. She taken him by his little white hand,
And led him through the hall,
And down in a cellar dark and deep,
Where no one hear him call, call, call,
Where no one hear him call.

7. She pinned a napking o'er his face,
And pinned it with gold pin,
Then called for a vessel of gold
To catch his heart-blood in, in, in,
To catch his heart-blood in.

8. "Go dig my grave both wide and deep,
Go dig my grave for me.
And when my playmates calls for me,
Tell them that I do sleep, sleep, sleep,
Tell them that I do sleep."

9. "Go place my psalm-book at my feet,
My Bible at my head;
And when my parents calls for me
Tell them their little boy's dead, dead, dead,
Tell them their little boy's dead."

36. "Sir Hugh," or "The Jew's Daughter"

Wilkinson MSS., 1935-36, p. 78. Sung by Miss Julia Coleman, Richmond, Va., December 5, 1935.

a I

1. It rained a mist, it rained a mist,
It rained all over the town.
And all the boys in our town
Went out to toss their balls, their balls,
Went out to toss their balls.

2. They tossed their balls so very high,
And then so very low.
And then so very high again,
Right over Jew's garden did go, did go,
Right over Jew's garden did go.

3. Out comes the Jew's daughter,
Out comes the Jew's daughter,
All dressed in green.
Come in my pretty boy and get your ball again, again,
And get your ball again.

4. I won't come in, I shan't come in,
For I'll never come out any more.
I'll never come out any more, any more,
I'll never come out any more.

5. She took him by his lily white hand,
And led him through the hall.
And put him in a dark cellar
Where none could hear his call, his call,
Where none could hear his call.

6. She wrapped him in a new napkin,
And in a towel too.
And pinned him all around with pins
To keep his life blood in, blood in,
To keep his life blood in.

37. "The Jew's Daughter"

Krehbiel, *N.Y. Tribune*, August 17, 1902, Pt. II, p. 2, col. 2. From Clyde Fitch; learned from his mother, who had it from her mother during childhood in Hagerstown, Md.

a I

1. It rained a mist, it rained a mist,
It rained all over the town;
And all the boys in our town,
Went out to toss their balls, balls, balls,
Went out to toss their balls.

2. At first they tossed their balls too high,
And then again too low,
And then into the garden,
Where no one had dare [*sic*] to go, go, go,
Where no one had dare to go.

3. Out came the Jewish lady,
All dressed in silk and green;
"Come in, my little boy," she said,
"You shall have your ball again, 'gain, 'gain,
You shall have your ball again."

4. "I won't come in, I shan't come in,
Without my playmates too,
For I've often heard who would come in,
Should never come out again, 'gain, 'gain,
Should never come out again."

5. At first she showed him a rosy, red apple
And then, again, a gold ring;
And then a cherry red as blood,
To entice the little boy in, in, in,
To entice the little boy in.

6. She led him in the parlor,
And then into the hall;
And then into the dining room,
Where no one would hear his call, call, call,
Where no one would hear his call.

7. She wrapped him in a napkin,
   And pinned it with a pin,
And called out for the carving knife,
   To stab his little heart in, in, in,
   To stab his little heart in.

8. "Oh, save me, Oh, save me!"
   The little boy did cry;
"If ever I live to be a man,
   My treasure shall all be thine, thine, thine,
   My treasure shall all be thine.

9. "Pray lay the Bible at my head,
   The prayer book at my feet;
And if my parents ask for me,
   Pray tell them that I'm asleep, 'sleep, 'sleep,
   Pray tell them that I'm asleep.

10. "Pray lay the Bible at my feet,
   The prayer book at my head;
And if my playmates ask for me,
   Pray tell them that I am dead, dead, dead,
   Pray tell them that I am dead."

38. "The Jew's Garden"

Randolph, I, 1946, p. 149(A). Sung by Mrs. Guy Bosserman, Pineville, Mo., October 17, 1927.

a I

1. It rained a mist, it rained a mist,
It rained right over th' lea,
An' two little boys from our town,
Come over to play with me.

2. One tossed too high, one tossed too low,
One tossed right over the wall,
One tossed right into the Jew's garden
Where no one could enter at all.

3. Out come a maid all dressed so fine,
All dressed in silk so gay,
Come in, little boy, come in, she says,
An' you shall have your ball.

4. I won't come in, I can't come in,
An' I won't come in, he says,
For oft-times I have heard them say
That they wouldn't get out till death.

5. She took him by the lily white hand
An' drew him into the hall,
She placed him into the dark dungeon
Where no one could enter at all.

6. She spread a handkerchief over his face,
An' pinned it with a gold pin,
An' called for a case as pure as gold
For to catch his heart blood in.

7. Oh put the prayer-book at my head,
The bible at my feet,
An' when my playmates call for me,
Tell them that I'm asleep.

8. Oh put the prayer-book at my feet,
The bible at my head,
An' when my parents call for me,
Tell them that their little one's dead.

39. "The Jew's Daughter"

Davis, 1929, p. 587(A); text, p. 401. Also in Smith, *MQ*, II (1916), p. 124(C). Contributed by Martha M. Davis, Harrisonburg, Va., April 26, 1913.

a π^1

1. It rained a mist, it rained a mist,
   It rained all over the land.
Some little boys of our town
   Went out to toss a ball, ball, ball,
   Went out to toss a ball.

2. At first they tossed it up too high,
   And then again too low,
Then over into a Jew's garden
   Where no one dared to go, go, go,
   Where no one dared to go.

3. Out came the Jew's daughter into the garden
   All in her golden array,
"Come in, come in, my pretty little man
   And you shall have your ball, ball, ball,
   And you shall have your ball."

4. "I won't come in, I can't come in,
   I have heard of you before;
Whoever goes in to your garden
   Will never come out any more, more, more,
   Will never come out any more."

5. At first she offered an apple so red,
   And then again her ring,
And then she offered a cherry so ripe,
   To entice this little boy in, in, in,
   To entice this little boy in.

6. She took him by his lily-white hand,
   And led him through the hall
Down into a cellar so dark and deep,
   Where no one could hear him call, call, call,
   Where no one could hear him call.

7. She bound him down on the floor of stone
. . . .
Where no one could hear him moan.

8. She bound him down on the floor so cold,
Where none could see his tears,
She called for a basin as bright as gold
To catch his heart's blood in, in, in,
To catch his heart's blood in.

. . . .

9. "O place my Bible at my head,
My prayer-book at my feet,
And if my mother asks for me,
O tell her that I am asleep, sleep, sleep,
O tell her that I am asleep.

10. "O place my prayer-book at my feet,
My Bible at my head,
And if my playmates ask for me,
O tell them that I am dead, dead, dead,
O tell them that I am dead."

40. "Jewish Lady"

Sung by Mrs. Crockatt Ward, Galax, Va., 1941. LC/AAFS, rec. No. 5228(B2). Collected by Alan Lomax.

a I

1. It rained a mist, it rained a mist,
It rained all over the town
When two little boys went out to play,
To toss their ball around, around,
To toss their ball around.

2. At first they tossed their ball too high,
And then they tossed it too low.
It rolled into a Jewish girl's yard
Where no one was allowed to go, to go,
Where no one was allowed to go.

3. Out came a Jewish lady,
All dressed in white linen so fine.
Come in, little boy, you shall have your ball.
I can't come in, I shan't come in,
Unless my school-mates comes too,
I've heard of little boys comin' in, comin' in,
And never come out any more, any more,
And never come out any more.

4. At first she showed him a red rose(y) apple,
Then she showed him a chain,
Then she showed him a diamond gold ring,
To entoice the little one in, O in,
To entoice the little one in.

5. She took him by his little white hand,
She led him in the hall,
She led him in a great high room,
Where no one could hear him call, O call,
Where no one could hear him call.

6. She pinned a napkin over his face,
She pinned it with a pin,
She took her ruby (?) carving-knife
And carved his little heart in, O in,
And carved his little heart in.

7. She wrapped him up in a linen white sheet,
As she did them all.
She throwed him in a great deep well
Where it was both deep and cold, O cold,
Where it was both deep and cold.

8. If my school-mates comes and calls for me,
Pray tell them I'm asleep, asleep,
Pray tell them I'm asleep.

41. "Little Sir Hugh"

Sung by Viola Cole, Fancy Gap, Va., July 10, 1962. LC/AAFS, rec. No. 12,006(B2). Collected by George Foss.

a I/Ly

1. It rained a mist, it rained a mist,
It rained all over the town
And two little boys went out to play
To toss the ball around, around,
To toss the ball around.

2. 'Twas first too high and then too low,
Till they tossed it into the Jury room
Where no one was let to go, to go,
Where no one was let to go.

3. Pretty soon, pretty soon, out came a pretty miss,
All stylish and dressed in green.
Come in, come in, my dear little one,
You shall have your ball again, again,
You shall have your ball again.

4. At first she showed him a red rosy apple,
And then she showed him a chain,
And then she showed him a diamond ring,
To entice the little one in, O in,
To entice the little one in.

5. She took him by the lily-white hand,
She led him through the hall
She led him into the dining-room,
Where no one could hear his call, his call,
Where no one could hear his call.

6. She pinned a napkin over his face,
She pinned it with a pin,
And then she took a little penknife
And took his little heart in, O, in,
And took his little heart in.

7. O spare my life, O spare my life,
O spare my life, he cried,
If ever I live to be a man,
My treasure shall all be thine, O thine,
My treasure shall all be thine.

42. "Little Sir Hugh"

Sung by Rebecca Jane Collins, Mount Airy, N.C., July 10, 1962. LC/AAFS, rec. No. 12,006(A29). Collected by George Foss.

a I

It rained, it mist, it rained, it mist,
It rained all over the town,
When the two little babes went out to play,
To toss their ball around, 'round, 'round,
To toss their ball around.

The first they tossed it . . .
And then they tossed it too low
And then they tossed it in the gray goose's yard,
For no one 'lowed to go, go, go,
For no one 'lowed to go.

43. "Little Sir Hugh"

Sharp MSS., 528/601. Also in Sharp, *JFSS*, V, No. 20 (1916), p. 253(1); and by A. L. Lloyd, Riverside rec. No. RLP 12-624(A2), ed. K. S. Goldstein. Sung by John Swain, Donyatt, Somerset, August 7, 1905.

a I

1. Send out, send out, her daughter dear,
An apple and a ring
And twenty more fine things beside
To toll the little boy in.

2. I can't come in that little boy said,
Without my fellows do
My mother she bates me black & blue
And I shall be first to rue.

3. O she set him up in a gilty chair
So gilty and so fine
And put a penknife in his heart
And kill him just like a swine.

4. Bring hither, bring hither a white winding sheet
All on a Marland cross
All by a rose mother } *(sic)*
All by my her desire }

5. O she put him up all by the fire
She scorched (his kerchief) by the sun
All that will shine like any fine gold
Against the morning sun.

44. "The Jew's Garden"

Brewster, *JAF*, XLVIII (1935), p. 297. Also in Brewster, 1940, p. 130. Sung by Mrs. Hiram Vaughan, Oakland City, Ind., March 3, 1935; learned from her mother. Noted by Mrs. I. L. Johnson.

a π^1

In the 1940 printing, bars 6 and 7 are omitted.

155. SIR HUGH, OR, THE JEW'S DAUGHTER

1. It rained a mist, it rained a mist
All o'er, all o'er the town,
When all the girls and boys went out
To toss their ball around, -round, -round,
To toss their ball around.

2. It was first too low and then too high,
And then again too low,
And then into the Jew's garden
Where none was allowed to go, go, go,
Where none was allowed to go.

3. "Come in, little boy, and get your ball,
And get your ball again."
"I won't come in; I shan't come in;
. . . .
. . . .

4. ". . . . .
For I've ofttimes heard it said,
If anyone entered the Jew's garden,
They'd never come out again, -gain, -gain,
They'd never come out again."

5. She first offered him a mellow apple
And then a golden ring
And then a cherry as red as blood,
Which enticed the little boy in, in, in,
Which enticed the little boy in.

6. She took him by the lily-white hand
And led him through the hall,
And seated him down at the end of the table
Where no one could hear him call, call, call,
Where no one could hear him call.

7. She called then for a napkin,
She pinned it with a pin,
And then she called for a tin basin
To catch his heart's blood in, in, in,
To catch his heart's blood in.

8. "Place my prayer book at my head,
My bible at my feet,
And if my schoolmates call for me,
Just tell them that I'm asleep, -sleep, -sleep,
Just tell them that I'm asleep."

9. "Place my prayer book at my feet,
My bible at my head,
And if my parents call for me,
Just tell them that I am dead, dead, dead,
Just tell them that I am dead."

45. "It Rained, It Mist"

Arnold, 1950, p. 42. Sung by Nell Young, Huntsville, Ala.

a I/Ly

1. It rained, it mist,
It rained all over the town
Where no one was allowed to play
But on the playing ground, ground, ground,
But on the playing ground.

2. First too high and then too low
All over St. Johns's ground
Where no one was allowed to play
But on the playing ground, ground, ground,
But on the playing ground.

3. Out stepped a lady
All fairly dressed in green.
"Come in, come in, my little one;
You shall have your ball again, gain, gain
You shall have your ball again."

4. "I will come in, I won't come in,
I will not enter your door,
I've often heard little ones come in
And never come out any more, more, more
And never come out any more."

5. First she showed him a red rosy apple
And then she showed him a chain,
Then she showed him a gold diamond ring
To 'vite the little one in, in, in
To 'vite the little one in.

6. She took him by the lily white hand,
She led him through the hall,
She led him to the far back room
Where no one could hear his call, call, call,
Where no one could hear his call.

7. She placed a napkin over his face
She pinned it with a pin
And then she taken a little pen knife
And jobbin' his little heart in, in, in,
And jobbin' his little heart in.

8. "Oh spare my life, oh spare my life
Oh spare my life," said he;
"If you will only spare my life
Some gold I'll give to thee, thee, thee,
Some gold I'll give to thee."

9. "Oh, place a marble at my feet
And a prayer book at my head,
And when my playmates call for me
Just tell them that Willie is dead, dead, dead
Just tell them that Willie is dead."

"Verses five through eight were supplied by Mrs. Young's sister, Edith Proctor. . . ." [*Arnold's note.*]

46. "Hugh of Lincoln"

Henry, *JAF*, XLIV (1931), p. 65. Also in Henry [1938], p. 103. Obtained from M. M. Hoover of New York City, who learned it from his mother in southeastern Pennsylvania.

a I

1. It rained a mist, it rained a mist;
It rained all over the town;
Till every boy in Scotland
Went out to toss his ball.

2. At first he tossed his ball too high;
And then again too low;
Till over into the Jew's garden it went
Where no one had dared to go.

3. Out came the Jew's daughter, all dressed, all dressed;
All dressed in the finest of jewels;
Come in, come in, you little lambkin,
You shall have your ball back again.

4. I will not come in, I shall not come in,
Unless my playmates do;
For whoever comes in will never come back
Will never come back any more.

5. At first she showed him a gay gold ring;
And then a yellow, mellow apple;
And then a cherry as red as blood,
Which enticed the little boy in.

6. And then she took him by the hand;
And through the castle she went;
And pitched him into a cellar below,
Where no one could hear his lament.

7. Oh, spare me, oh, spare me; the little boy cried;
That little boy cried he;
And if ever I live to be a man,
My treasures shall be thine.

8. Then she took him out again;
And pinned him in a napkin;
And called for a basin washed with gold,
To catch his heart's blood in.

9. Oh, lay my prayer book at my head;
My Bible at my heart;
And if my playmates should ask for me,
Oh, tell them that we must part.

10. Oh, lay my prayer book at my heart;
My Bible at my head;
And if mother should ask of me,
Oh, tell her that I am dead.

47. "The Jew's Daughter"

Davis, 1929, p. 589(K); text, p. 412. Sung by Ed Davis and Mrs. Marion Browning, Shipman, Va. Contributed by John Stone, November 15, 1916.

a I

It rained a mist, it rained a mist,
It rained all over the land,
It rained three days in the Jew's garden,
And no one could understand, -stand, -stand,
And no one could understand.

The boys went out to toss the ball,
To toss the ball, to toss the ball,
The boys went out to toss the ball
Upon the queen's highway, -way, -way,
Upon the queen's highway.

And first they tossed it up too high,
And then it went too low;
It went into the Jew's garden,
Where no one dared to go, go, go,
Where no one dared to go.

Out came the Jew's daughter, out came the Jew's daughter,
All dressed in finest of silk,
Saying, "You may come in, my pretty boy,
And you your ball shall win, win, win,
And you your ball shall win."

48. "The Jew's Garden"

Eddy, 1939, p. 66. Also in Tolman and Eddy, *JAF*, XXXV (1922), p. 344. Sung by Mrs. Charles Wise, Perrysville, Ohio.

a I

1. It rains, it mists, it rains, it mists,
It sprinkles all over the plain,
And all of the boys in our town
Went out to toss their ball, ball, ball,
Went out to toss their ball.

2. At first they tossed it a little too high,
   And then a little too low;
Over in the Jew's garden flew one of the balls,
   Where no one dared to go.

3. Out came the Jew's daughter all dressed in silk,
   Crying; "Come in, little boy,
Come in, come in, my pretty little boy,
   You shall have your ball again."

4. "No, I won't come in, no, I shan't come in,
   Unless my playmates do;
For ofttimes have I heard it said
   Whoever went in should never come out again."

5. At first she showed him a ripe, yellow apple,
   And then a gay, gold ring,
And next a cherry as red as blood
   To entice the little boy in.

6. She took him by his lily-white hand,
   And drew him across the hall;
Down in the dark cellar she went with him,
   Where no one could him amid.

7. And there she laid him upon a table,
   Beside a great bow knife,
And called for a basin all lined with gold
   To catch his heart blood in.

8. "Lay my Bible at my head,
   My prayer-book at my feet,
And when my playmates call for me,
   Pray tell them I'm asleep.

9. "Lay my prayer-book at my feet,
   My Bible at my head,
And when my parents call for me,
   Pray tell them that I'm dead."

49. "It Rained a Mist"

Gresham, *JAF*, XLVII (1934), p. 361; text, p. 358. Sung by Mrs. Ruth Jones, Prince George County, Va., February 23, 1933.

a I

1. It rained a mist, it rained a mist,
   It rained all over the town;
Two little boys came out to play,
   They tossed their ball around, around,
   They tossed their ball around.

2. They tossed the ball too high at first,
   And then they tossed it too low;
And then it fell in a Jewish yard
   Where no one was allowed to go, to go,
   Where no one was allowed to go.

3. A pretty fine miss, she came to the door,
   All dressed in silk so fine.
"Come in, come in, my pretty little boy,
   You shall have your ball again, again,
   You shall have your ball again."

4. "I won't come in, I won't come in,
   Unless my playmate comes too;
For they say when little boys go in,
   They'll never come out again, again,
   They'll never come out again."

5. She showed him a rosy red apple
   And then a blood red peach,
And then she showed him a diamond ring
   That urged his little heart in, oh in,
   That urged his little heart in.

6. She took him by his lily white hand,
   And led him through the hall,
She led him to her dining room,
   Where no one could hear him call, oh call,
   Where no one could hear him call.

7. And then she took a red white towel
   And tied it 'round his chin,
And then she took a carving knife,
   And cut his little heart in, oh in,
   And cut his little heart in.

8. "Oh, spare my life, oh, spare my life!"
   And then the little boy cried,
"If ever I should grow to be a man,
   My pleasure shall all be thine, oh thine,
   My pleasure shall all be thine.

9. "Oh, place a Bible at my head
   And a prayer book at my feet;
And ever my playmate call for me,
   Pray tell him that I am asleep, asleep,
   Pray tell that I am asleep.

10. "Oh, place a prayer book at my feet
   And a Bible at my head;
And ever my mother call for me,
   Pray tell her that I am dead, oh dead,
   Pray tell her that I am dead."

50. "Sir Hugh," or "The Jew's Daughter"

Matteson and Henry, 1936, p. 22. Sung by Mrs. J. E. Schell, Banner Elk, N.C., July 15, 1933.

a I/M

1. It rained, it rained, it rained, it rained,
It rained all over the town.
Two little boys came out to play
For to toss their balls and play, play, play,
For to toss their balls and play.

2. At first they tossed it too high
And then they tossed it too low,
And then they tossed it in a vacant yard
Where no one was allowed to go, go, go,
Where no one was allowed to go.

3. A lady came out all dressed in silk,
All dressed in silk so fine,
"Come in, come in, my little boy,
And you shall have your ball, ball, ball,
And you shall have your ball."

4. At first she showed him a fine gold watch,
And then she showed him a chain,
And then she showed him a diamond ring,
Which fit his little hand so neat, neat, neat,
Which fit his hand so neat.

5. She pinned a napkin around his head,
She pinned it with a pin;
And in her hand was a carving knife—
She stabbed his little heart in, in, in,
She stabbed his little heart in.

6. "Oh, spare my life, Oh, spare my life,
Oh, spare my life," he cried;
"If ever I grow up to be a man,
I'll do some labor for you, you, you,
I'll do some labor for you.

7. "Please place the Testament at my head,
And the Bible at my feet;
If mother and father should call for me
Please tell them that I'm asleep, sleep, sleep,
Please tell them that I'm asleep.

8. "Please place the Testament at my feet
And the Bible at my head;
If any of my friends should call for me,
Please tell them that I'm dead, dead, dead,
Please tell them that I'm dead."

51. "Sir Hugh of Lincoln"

Parsons and Roberts, *JAF*, XLIV (1931), p. 296. Sung by May F. Hoisington, Rye, N.Y.; learned in Pennsylvania from her nurse, of Welsh extraction.

a I

1. One day it rained in our town,
The rain did softly fall,
And all the boys in our town,
Went out to toss the ball, ball, ball,
Went out to toss the ball.

2. And first it went too high
And then it went too low
And then it fell in the Jew's garden
Where nobody dared to go.

3. Then out and came the Jew's daughter
All dressed in silk so fine.
Says she, Sir Hugh, oh pretty Sir Hugh,
Come get that ball of thine.

4. And first she gave him an apple
And then she gave him a pear
And then she gave him a pretty gold ring
Which coaxed the poor little boy in.

5. She rolled him up in a napkin,
She pinned him with a pin,
And then she took out her little pen knife
And stuck his poor little heart in,
In, in, in,
And stuck his poor little heart in.

6. "Oh put the prayer book at my head,
The Bible at my feet.
If any my people call for me,
Pray tell um that I am asleep.

7. "Oh put the prayer book at my feet
The Bible at my head
If any my people call for me
Pray tell um that I am dead."

52. "The Two Playmates"

Smith, 1928, p. 148. Sung by Mrs. E. L. Bolin, McCormick County, S.C.; learned in childhood from a playmate's grandmother in Spartanburg County.

a I/Ly

1. It rained, alas! it rained, alas!
 It sprinkled all over the town.
Two little boys went out to toss a ball;
 To toss a ball.

2. At first they tossed the ball too high;
 And then too low;
And then they tossed it into a yard
 Where no one was allowed to go.

3. A Jewish Lady came to the door,
 All dressed in silk so fine;
"Come in, come in, my pretty little boys, come in."

4. "Oh, no! Oh, no! I can't come in,
 Unless my playmate comes too;
For when little boys come in your door
 They never come out any more."

5. At first she showed him a bright red apple,
 And then a pretty red peach;
And then she showed him a diamond ring,
 That called his little heart in.

6. And then she led him to the dining room,
 Where no one could hear his cry;
And then she took a carving knife
 To carve his little heart in.

7. "Oh spare my life, oh spare my life,"
 The little boy cried.

. . . .

8. "Well, place a Bible at my head,
 And a prayer book at my feet;
And when my playmate calls for me,
 Pray tell him that I'm asleep.

9. "And place a prayer book at my feet,
 And a Bible at my head;
And when my mother calls for me,
 Pray tell her that I am dead."

53. "Sir Hugh"

Davis, 1929, p. 590(L); text, p. 413. Contributed by Mr. and Mrs. George D. McLaughlin, Benicia, Calif., May 15, 1916. Learned in Rockbridge County, Va.

a I/M

1. It rained a mist, it rained a mist,
It rained all over the town, town, town,
It rained all over the town.

2. And all the boys in our town
Went out to toss their balls.
Went out to toss their balls, balls, balls,

3. Some tossed too high, some tossed too low,
And one in the old Jew's garden did go,
In the old Jew's garden did go.

4. "Come in, my boy, come in, my boy,
Your ball you shall have again, 'gain, 'gain,
Your ball you shall have again."

5. And then she took his lily-white hand,
And led him in the hall, hall, hall,
And led him in the hall.

6. And then she called for the butcher knife
To stab his little heart in, in, in,
To stab his little heart in.

7. And then she called for the gold basin
To catch his heart's blood in, in, in,
To catch his heart's blood in.

54. "It Rained a Mist"

Davis, 1929, p. 588(C); text, p. 404. Contributed by Alfreda M. Peel, April 24, 1923, from the singing of Miss Marie Hatfield, Vinton, Va.

a I/M

1. It rained a mist, it rained a mist,
 It rained all over the town;
And two little boys came home from school
 To toss their balls around, around,
 To toss their balls around.

2. At first they tossed their balls too high,
 The second they tossed too low,
The third they tossed in the Jew's daughter's garden
 Where no one was 'lowed to go, to go,
 Where no one was 'lowed to go.

3. The Jew's lady came to the door,
 All dressed in silk so fine,
"Come in, come in, my only son,
 You may have your ball again, again,
 You may have your ball again."

4. "I can't come in, and I won't come in.
 I'll tell you the reason why:
I've heard of so many little boys coming in,
 But never coming out alive, alive,
 But never coming out alive."

5. At first she showed him a red rose apple,
 And then a diamond ring;
And then she showed him a watch and chain
 To toss the ball again, again,
 To toss the ball again.

6. She took him by his little white arm,
   And led him through the hall,
   And took him in a little dark room,
   Where no one could hear him call, him call,
   Where no one could hear him call.

7. She pinned a napkin to his neck,
   She pinned it with a pin;
   And she took out her carving knife,
   To carve his little heart in, oh in,
   To carve his little heart in.

8. "Now place a Bible at my head,
   A prayer-book at my feet,
   And when my school-mates call for me,
   Tell them I'm fast asleep, oh sleep,
   Tell them I'm fast asleep."

9. She placed a Bible at his head,
   A prayer-book at his feet.
   "And when my father calls for me,
   You may tell him I am dead, am dead,
   You may tell him I am dead."

55. "The Jew's Garden"

Sung by Mrs. Cecilia Costello (65), Birmingham, England. Caedmon rec. No. TC 1146(A5); collected and edited by Peter Kennedy and Alan Lomax. Recorded by Marie Slocombe, BBC. Also in Slocombe, *JEFDSS*, VII, No. 2 (1953), p. 102.

m M (inflected VII)

It 'ails, it rains in merry Scotland,
It 'ails all over the sea,
When all the children in the town,
They like to play at ball.

They throwed the ball so high and so low,
They throwed it into the (h)air,
They throwed it into the Jew's garden,
The Jew he lay below.

'E showed 'im an apple as green as grass,
'E showed 'im a prettier thing;
'E showed 'im a cherry as red as blood,
Until he 'ticed 'im in.

'E laid 'im in a chair of gold
Till 'e went fast asleep;
'E laid 'im on the Jew's bo-ard,
And stabbed him like a sheep.

GROUP D

56. "Sir Hew"

Motherwell, 1827, App'x., No. 7; text, App'x., p. xvii. From A. Blaikie, Paisley.

p I/M

It was in the middle o' the midsimmer tyme
   When the scule weans play'd at the ba', ba',
Out and cam the Jew's dochter
   And on little Sir Hew did ca', ca',
   And on little Sir Hew did ca'.

GROUP E

57. "Little Sir Hugh"

Archive, School of Scottish Studies. Sung by Donald Whyte. Collected by Hamish Henderson for the School of Scottish Studies. Transcribed by Francis M. Collinson.

a M

This tune is more typical of "The Gaberlunzie Man" (Child No. 279A).

I wont come back or I shall not come back;
I winna come back at all aye at all;
I fear your(e) daddy might come out;
He would make it a bloody ball, ball;
He would make it a bloody ball.

GROUP F

58. "The Jew's Daughter"

Blaikie MS., NL Scotland MS. 1578, No. 57, p. 20.

a π^3

GROUP G

59. "Little Sir Hugh"

Galwey, 1910, p. 15. Learned from a servant in childhood, Innishewen, Donegal.

p I

The last bar is short a beat in the original.

GROUP H

60. "Little Harry Hughes"

Joyce, *Ulysses*, N.Y., 1934, p. 675.

p M

1. Little Harry Hughes and his schoolfellows all
Went out for to play ball.
And the very first ball little Harry Hughes played
He drove it o'er the jew's garden wall.
And the very second ball little Harry Hughes played
He broke the jew's windows all.

2. Then out came the jew's daughter
And she all dressed in green.
"Come back, come back, you pretty little boy.
And play your ball again."

3. "I can't come back and I won't come back
Without my schoolfellows all.
For if my master he did hear
He'd make it a sorry ball."

4. She took him by the lilywhite hand
And led him along the hall
Until she led him to a room
Where none could hear him call.

5. She took a penknife out of her pocket
And cut off his little head,
And now he'll play his ball no more
For he lies among the dead.

GROUP I

61. "Fair Scotland"

Korson, 1949, p. 36. Sung by Perry Gump, Greene County, Pa., 1929. Recorded by Samuel P. Bayard.

p M (inflected III; or bi-modal)

1. There was some children in fair Scotland
A-playing at school ball.[1]

2. They throwed their ball so high, so high,
They throwed their ball so low;
They throwed their ball into the Jew's garden
Where no one dares for to go.

3. One of the Jew's daughters came out,
Her doddle [*sic*] all dressed in green:
Come in, come in, you little Sir Hugh,
And get your ball again.

4. I will not do it, I shall not do it,
Without my schoolmates all,
For if I would, my mammy would whip
Till the red blood down would fall.

5. She showed him an apple so round, so round,
She showed him a cherry so red;
And then she showed him a gay gold ring
Which enticed this poor boy in.

6. She tuck him by his little hand
And led him through the room,
And then she led him in the kitchen,
And there he saw his own dear nurse[2]
A-cooking of a chicken.

7. And then she says, I'll do more for you
Than any of your kin:
I'll scour this basin of the bright silver
To ketch your heart's blood in.

8. She laid him on her lap, her lap,
And fed him sugar sweet,
And then she laid him on her dressing board,
And stuck him like a sheep.

1 "The first stanza is sung to the second half of the air." [*Bayard's note.*]
2 "Fourth line is sung to music of third line." [*Bayard's note.*]

GROUP J

62. [Little Sir Hugh]

Smith, [1812], I, p. 65. Also in Rimbault, 1850, p. 46; and Johnson, 1853, IV (Stenhouse), No. 582, p. 500. Sung by Elizabeth Linley (Mrs. Richard Brinsley Sheridan).

a Æ (inflected VII)

The rain rins doun through Mirry-land toune,
Sae dois it doune the Pa:
Sae dois the lads of Mirry-land toune,
Quhan they play at the ba'.

Than out and cam the Jewis dochtèr,
Said, Will ye cum in and dine?
I winnae cum in, I cannae cum in,
Without my play-feres nine.
[*Etc.*]

The text is from Percy's *Reliques*, ed. Henry B. Wheatley, 1910, I, p. 59.

GROUP K

63. "Sir Hugh and the Jew's Daughter"

Archive, School of Scottish Studies. Sung by Margaret Stewart, and also by Maggie Whyte. Collected by Hamish Henderson for the School of Scottish Studies. Transcribed by Francis M. Collinson.

m π^1

1. Young Hugh he was the best of all,
   Went out to kick the playboy's ball.
   He kicked that ball so very high
   He clinched it with his knee
   And at the back o' some windin' wall
   Young Hugh he caused his ball to flee.

2. Fling out my ball, fair maiden he cried—
   Fling out my playboy's ball—
   I daur not fling out your ball, young Hugh,
   It's till you came and talk to me—

3. I daur not came, I cannot came,
   Fling out my playboy's ball.
   For she pulled an apple both reid and green
   Off her father's garden wall
   To welcome bonnie young Hughie in.

4. She welcomed him in to one big room;
   She welcomed him in tae two,
   And she welcomed him in to her own bedroom
   Where many a Duke and Earl had dined.

5. Her little pen knife bein' lang and sharp,
   She bid him take a sleep;
   And she wrapped him up and a caik of leid
   And put him in to yon draw-wall
   Which is fifty fadoms deep.

6. And at the back o' some windin' wall
   It's there it's my young Hugh shall sleep:
   When cockle shells grows silver bells
   It's there that me and young Hugh shall meet.

GROUP L

64. "The Jew's Garden"

Sung by Mrs. Allie Long Parker, near Eureka Springs, Ark., c. September 1958. LC/AAFS, rec. No. 11,903(B1). Collected by Max Hunter(?).

p π^1

1. It rained one day in old Scotland
   As hard as rain could fall
   And all the boys of our town
   Were out a-playing ball, ball,
   Were out a-playing ball.

2. They threw their ball so swift and high,
   They threw their ball so low
   They threw their ball in the Jew's garden
   Where there they dare not go, go, go,
   Where there they dare not go.

3. The Jew's daughter came walking out,
 Dressed up in silk so gay
Saying, Come in, come in, my pretty little boy,
 And get your ball away, 'way, 'way,
 And get your ball away.

4. I can't come in nor I won't come in
 Without my playmates all,
Or without the leave of my mother dear:
 You'd cause my heart's blood to fall, fall, fall,
 You'd cause my heart's blood to fall.

5. She shewed him her mantle as green as grass,
 She shewed him her gay gold ring,
She shewed him a cherry as red as a plum(?)
 To entice this little boy in, in, in,
 To entice this little boy in.

6. She took him by the lily-white hand
 And led him across the hall,
And with a broad sword cut off his head
 And kicked it against the wall, wall, wall,
 And kicked it against the wall.

7. She threw him in a new drawing-well
 Just fifty-five feet deep
With a catechism at his head
 And a Bible at his feet, feet, feet,
 And a Bible at his feet.

8. Dear Mother, dear Mother, don't weep for me,
 For I have gone to sleep.
If you come here at ten o'clock,
 You'll find me in the deep, deep, deep,
 You'll find me in the deep.

GROUP M

65. "Sir Hugh," or "The Jew's Daughter"

Barry, *BFSSNE*, No. 5 (1933), p. 7. Also in Flanders *et al.*, 1939, p. 254; and Flanders, III, 1963, p. 124. Sung by Josiah S. Kennison, of Townshend, Vt., at Cambridge, Mass., April 6, 1932. Recorded and transcribed by George Brown.

a I/M (–VI)

1. A little boy about five years old
 Came up and broke a staging window;
And then he up and run,
 And then he up and run.

2. "Come back, come back, my little boy,
 And play your game of ball,—"
"I won't, I shan't come back
 And play my game of ball,
For if your mother was here,
 She'd make it a bloody ball."

3. She took an apple from her pocket,
 And laid it on the ground:
The little boy stooped to pick it up,—
 She caught him by the lily white hand.

4. . . . .
 She led him from room to room,
She led him into a little dark room,
 Where none could hear his call.

5. She took a penknife from her pocket,
 And pierced it to his heart;
The little fresh blood came trinckling down,
 So cold and dark he sleeps.

6. "Go dig my grave on yonders hill,
 And there you may bury me,
Place my Bible at my head,
 My prayer book at my feet,
And swing my little bow arrow to my side,
 And on yonders hill you may bury me."

The text in Flanders *et al.*, *The New Green Mountain Songster*, is essentially the same but has a slightly different stanzaic arrangement.

66. "Little Harry Huston"

Flanders and Olney, 1953, p. 30. Also in Flanders, III, 1963, p. 121. Sung by Mrs. John Fairbanks, North Springfield, Vt.; learned from her mother, Margaret Kelley, of County Limerick, Ireland. From *Ballads Migrant in New England*, edited by Helen Hartness Flanders and Marguerite Olney; copyright 1953 by Helen Hartness Flanders.

a I/M

1. Yesterday was a very fine day,
The finest day in the year, year,
When little Harry Huston and schoolboys all
Went out to play at ball, ball,
Went out to play at ball.

2. The first little tip Harry Huston gave the ball,
It was not good at all, all,
The second little tip Harry Huston gave,
He broke the window all, all,
He broke the window all.

3. A Jewess, she came down the stairs
And she all dressed in green, green,
Saying, "Little Harry Huston, if you come here"
. . . .
. . . .

4. "I'll not go back, and I won't go back
And I'll not go back at all, all,
For if my mama came to know
She would" . . . . . .
. . . .

5. She coaxed him back with an apple so red
And with a cherry so sweet, sweet,
And took him to her own dressing room
Where she slew him like a sheep, sheep,
Where she slew him like a sheep.

6. She rolled him up in a winding sheet,
It was her own winding sheet, sheet,
And she took him to Saint Simon's well
Which was seven fathoms deep, deep,
Which was seven fathoms deep.

7. Five o'clock was past and gone,
And all schoolboys gone home, home.
Every mama had her boy
Harry Huston's mama had none, none,
Harry Huston's mama had none.

8. When she went to the Jewess' house
And kneels down on a stone, stone,
Saying, "Little Harry Huston, if you be there,
Will you pity your mama's moan, moan,
Will you pity your mama's moan?"

9. "He is not here, nor he was not here
And he's not been here all day, day,
But if you go to Saint Simon's well
You might have seen him there, there,
You might have seen him there."

10. She went unto Saint Simon's Well
And knelt down on a stone, stone,
Saying, "Little Harry Huston, if you be there,
Will you pity your mama's moan, moan,
Will you pity your mama's moan?"

11. "How can I pity your moan, mama,
When I am here so long, long,
The little pen-knife she stuck through my heart;
The Jewess, she did me wrong, wrong,
The Jewess, she did me wrong.

12. "But come tonight at twelve o'clock
And there you'll see my ghost, ghost;
Place my schoolbooks at my feet
And my Bible at my head
That my schoolmates they may read, read,
That my schoolmates they may read."

Queen Eleanor's Confession

CHILD NO. 156

This ballad first appeared in broadsides of the last quarter of the seventeenth century, "to a pleasant new tune." It was included in the collection of 1723 and in Percy's *Reliques*, 1765 and all subsequent editions. The oral circulation of it in Scotland seems to have followed in the wake of the *Reliques*. Child thinks that print lies behind all his recited copies; but that oral currency may be presumed behind the earliest printed copies. Such an assumption is very plausible: it is just the little roughnesses of narrative, arising from oral transmission, that Percy was usually at pains to smooth out; and his adjustments are still reflected in Motherwell's later traditional copy. Motherwell, at any rate, secured the sole surviving traditional tune, through Andrew Blaikie's good offices, and Rimbault reprinted it in 1850, with insignificant alterations and the remark that he had often heard it in Derbyshire and Staffordshire. Rimbault was followed by Chappell, who places it in the reign of Queen Elizabeth, doubtless on textual considerations. It is a sturdy English-sounding tune, like the first strain of the "British Grenadiers." Motherwell notes that "in singing, the two last lines of each stanza are repeated"; but, oddly, in his appendix the repetition is not indicated (1827, p. 1, and App'x., p. xxii, No. xxvii). Neither is it marked in Rimbault. All the other versions of the ballad are CM quatrains, without refrain.

Further references may be added on the authority of the Gray-Muir MS., NL Scotland MS. 2254: Bunyan MS., 1877, p. 6; Strathearn, p. 78; Na. Gow, I, p. 28. These I have not been able to verify.

LIST OF VARIANTS

"Earl Marshall." William Motherwell, *Minstrelsy: Ancient and Modern*, 1827, App'x., No. 27, and p. 1. Also in Edward F. Rimbault, *Musical Illustrations of Bishop Percy's Reliques*, 1850, p. 65; and W. Chappell, *Popular Music of the Olden Time* [1855-59], I, p. 174.

TUNE WITH TEXT

"Earl Marshall"

Motherwell, 1827, App'x., No. 27; text, p. 1. Also in Rimbault, 1850, p. 65; and Chappell, [1855-59], I, p. 174. Andrew Blaikie, Paisley.

p I

1. Queene Eleanor was a sick woman,
And sick just like to die;
And she has sent for two fryars of France
To come to her speedilie.
And she has sent, &c.

2. The king called downe his nobles all,
By one, by two, by three:
"Earl Marshall I'll go shrive the queene,
And thou shalt wend with mee."

3. "A boone, a boone," quoth Earl Marshall,
And fell on his bended knee;
"That whatsoever the queene may say,
No harm thereof may bee."

4. "O you'll put on a gray friar's gowne,
And I'll put on another;
And we will away to fair London town,
Like friars both together."

5. "O no, O no, my liege, my king,
Such things can never bee;
For if the Queene hears word of this,
Hanged she'll cause me to bee."

6. "I swear by the sun, I swear by the moon,
And by the stars so hie,
And by my sceptre, and my crowne,
The Earl Marshall shall not die."

7. The King's put on a gray friar's gowne,
The Earl Marshall's put on another,
And they are away to fair London towne,
Like fryars both together.

8. When that they came to fair London towne,
And came into Whitehall,
The bells did ring and the quiristers sing,
And the torches did light them all.

9. And when they came before the Queene,
They kneeled down on their knee;
"What matter! what matter! our gracious Queene,
You've sent so speedilie?"

10. "Oh, if you are two fryars of France
Its you that I wished to see;
But if you are two English lords
You shall hang on the gallowes tree."

11. "Oh, we are not two English lords,
But two fryars of France we bee,
And we sang the Song of Solomon,
As we came over the sea."

12. "Oh, the first vile sin I did commit,
Tell it I will to thee:
I fell in love with the Earl Marshall,
As he brought me over the sea."

13. "Oh, that was a great sin," quoth the king,
"But pardon'd it must bee."
"Amen! Amen!" said the Earl Marshall,
With a heavie heart spake hee.

14. "Oh the next sin that I did commit,
I will to you unfolde:
Earl Marshalle had my virgin dower
Beneath this cloth of golde."

15. "Oh, that was a vile sin," said the King,
"May God forgive it thee."
"Amen! Amen!" groaned the Earl Marshall,
And a very frightened man was hee.

16. "Oh, the next sin that I did commit,
Tell it I will to thee:
I poisoned a lady of noble blood
For the sake of King Henrie."

17. "Oh, that was a great sin," said the King,
"But pardoned it shall bee."
"Amen! Amen!" said the Earl Marshall,
And still a frightened man was hee.

18. "Oh, the next sin that ever I did,
Tell it I will to thee:
I have kept strong poison this seven long years
To poison King Henrie."

19. "Oh, that was a great sin," said the King,
"But pardoned it must bee."
"Amen! Amen!" said the Earl Marshall,
And still a frightened man was hee.

20. "Oh, dont you see two little boys
Playing at the football;
Oh, yonder is the Earl Marshall's son,
And I like him best of all.

21. "Oh, dont you see yon other little boy
Playing at the football;
Oh, that one is King Henrie's son,
And I like him worst of all.

22. "His head is like a black bull's head—
His feet are like a bear"—
"What matter! what matter!" cried the King,
"He's my son and my only heir!"

23. The King plucked off his fryar's gowne,
And stood in his scarlet soe red:
The Queen she turned herself in bed,
And cryed that she was betrayde.

24. The King lookt o'er his left shoulder,
And a grim look looked he:
"Earl Marshall," he said, "but for my oath,
Thou hadst swung on the gallowes tree."

Gude Wallace

CHILD NO. 157

References in the fifteenth and seventeenth centuries inform us that there were wandering ballads on the subject of Wallace in early days (cf. Child, 1882-98, III, p. 266). But there is no evidence that the present ballad has its roots in any of these. Judging by the close correspondence of the versions which Child has assembled, the subject took a new and late start, and Child asserts that Blind Harry's *Wallace* is "clearly" the parent of this second crop. Child's G and H, which add a second episode out of the same original, are, as he says, "plainly a late piece of work, very possibly of this century, much later than the other [i.e., A-F], which itself need not be very old" (*ibid.*). Now, the first recorded appearance of the older part is in a chapbook of about 1745; and why may we not suppose that the reinvention was an offshoot of Jacobite enthusiasm in the first half of the eighteenth century? Certainly it has been carried out by some one steeped in the traditional style—and of such persons eighteenth-century Scotland had store.

Only two musical records have been found, one recovered by Robert Burns, the other of approximately the same era but set down a little later by C. K. Sharpe. The two have nothing in common—further evidence that the ballad had no rooted singing tradition. Burns's is the more homely tune; and Sharpe's seems to have been crossed with "The White Cockade" (cf. Johnson's *Museum*, III, [1790], No. 272). The Gray-Muir MS. (NL Scotland MS. 2254) states that a tune is in the Bunyan MS., 1877, pp. 110 and 132.

LIST OF VARIANTS

1. "Gude Wallace." James Johnson, *The Scots Musical Museum*, V, [1796], No. 484, p. 498 (repr. 1853).
2. "Gude Wallace." C. K. Sharpe MS. (William Macmath transcript, Harvard College Library, p. 32). Also in Francis James Child, *The English and Scottish Popular Ballads*, 1882-98, V, pp. 419 and 242.

TUNES WITH TEXTS

1. "Gude Wallace"

Johnson, V, [1796], No. 484, p. 498 (repr. 1853). From Robert Burns; traditional.

p D/Æ

1. O for my ain king, quo gude Wallace,
   The rightfu' king of fair Scotland.
   Between me and my soverign blude
   I think I see some ill seed sawn.

2. Wallace out over yon river he lap,
   And he has lighted low down on yon plain,
   And he was aware of a gay ladie,
   As she was at the well washing.

3. What tydins, what tydins, fair lady, he says,
   What tydins hast thou to tell unto me
   What tydins, what tydins, fair lady, he says,
   What tydins hae ye in the south Countrie.

4. Low down in yon wee Ostler house,
   There is fyfteen Englishmen,
   And they are seekin for gude Wallace,
   It's him to take and him to hang.

5. There's nocht in my purse, quo gude Wallace,
   There's nocht, not even a bare pennie,
   But I will down to yon wee Ostler house
   Thir fyfteen Englishmen to see.

6. And when he cam to yon wee Ostler house,
   He bad bendicite be there;
   . . . .
   . . . .

7. Where was ye born, auld crookit Carl,
   Where was ye born in what countrie,
   I am a true Scot born and bred,
   And an auld crookit carl just sic as ye see.

8. I wad gie fifteen shillings to onie crookit carl,
   To onie crookit carl just sic as ye,
   If ye will get me gude Wallace,
   For he is the man I wad very fain see.

9. He hit the proud Captain alang the chafft blade,
   That never a bit o' meal he ate mair;
   And he sticket the rest at the table where they sat,
   And he left them a' lyin sprawlin there.

10. Get up, get up, gudewife, he says,
    And get to me some dinner in haste;
    For it will soon be three lang days
    Sin I a bit o' meat did taste.

11. The dinner was na weel readie,
    Nor was it on the table set,
    Till other fyfteen Englishmen
    Were a' lighted about the yett.

12. Come out, come out, now gude Wallace
    This is the day that thou maun die;
    I lippen nae sae little to God, he says,
    Altho' I be but ill wordie.

13. The gudewife had an auld gudeman,
    By gude Wallace he stiffly stood,
Till ten o' the fyfteen, Englishmen,
    Before the door lay in their blude.

14. The other five to the greenwood ran,
    And he hang'd these five upon a green,
And on the morn wi' his merry men a'
    He sat at dine in Lochmaben town.

2. "Gude Wallace"

C. K. Sharpe MS. (Macmath transcript, p. 32). Also in Child, 1882-98, V, p. 419; text, V, p. 242.

a P/Æ (or if C tonic, a I/Ly, ending on III)

1. "I wish I had a king," brave Wallace he said,
    "That every brave Scotsman might leave by his oun,
For between me and my sovreign leige
    I think I see some ill [seed] sowen."

2. Brave Wallace out-oer yon river he lap,
    And he lighted low down on the plain,
And he came to a gay lady,
    As she was at the well washing.

3. "Some tidings, some tidings," brave Wallace he said,
    "Some tidings ye most tell unto me;
Now since we are met here togither on the plain,
    Some tidings ye most tell unto me."

4. "O go ye down to yon wee ale-house,
    And there is fifeteen Englishmen,
And they are seeking for good Wallace,
    And him to take and him for to hang."

5. "I wish I had a penny in my pocket," he says,
    "Or although it were but a bare baubee,
And I wad away to the wee ale-house,
    The fifeteen Englishmen to see."

6. She's put hir hand in hir left pocket,
    And fifeteen shillings to him she told down:
"If ever I live to come back this way,
    The money's be well paid agein."

7. He louted twafauld oer a stick,
    And he louted threefauld oer a tree,
And he 'es gane awa to the wee ale-house,
    The fifeteen Englishmen to see.

8. When he came to the wee ale-house,
    He walked ben, says, Decencey be there!
The Engilish proud captain he awnsered him,
    And he awnsered him with a graid domineer.

9. "Why, where wast thou born, thou old crooked carle?
    Where and of what country?"
"I am a true Scotsman bred and born,
    And an auld crooked carle, just sic as ye may see."

10. "I wad gee fifeteen shillings," the captain he said,
    "To an auld crooked carle, just sic a ane as thee,
If ye wad tell me of Willie Wallace,
    For he's the man I wad fain see."

11. "O hold your hand," brave Wallace he said,
    "And let me see if yeer coin be good;
If ye wad give fifeteen shillings more,
    Ye never bade a better boad."

12. He's tean the captain out-oer the chaft-blade,
    Till a bitt of meat he never did eat mair;
He stickit a' the reste as the sat aroun the table,
    And he left them all a spraulling there.

13. "Get up, get up, goodwife," he says,
    "Get up and get me some denner in haste,
For it is now three days and nights
    Since a bit of meat my mouth did taste."

14. The denner was not well made ready,
    Nor was it on the table sett,
Till other fifeteen English men
    Were a' perading about the yett.

15. "Come out, come out now, Wallace," they crys,
    "For this is the place ye 'es sure for [to] die;"
"I lippen not sae little to good," he says,
    "Although I be but ill-wordie."

16. The goodman ran butt, the goodwife ran ben,
    They put the house in such a fever!
Five of them he sticket where they stood,
    And other five he smoddered in the gitter.

17. Five of them he folowd to the merry greenwood,
    And these five he hangt on a grain,
And gin the morn at ten o'clock
    He was wi his mirry men at Lochmaben.

The text is given as in Child.

The Battle of Otterburn

CHILD NO. 161

The Battle of Otterburn, fought (probably) August 19, 1338, was a Scottish victory. Child declares that "it would be against the nature of things that there should not have been a ballad as early as 1400" on the event (1882-98, III, p. 293). Allusions in *The Complaynte of Scotlande*, 1549, indicate that a Scottish ballad on the subject was current in the sixteenth century. The earliest surviving text, however, is of about 1550; and its narrative is from the English point of view. It is likely, Child thinks, to have been modernized from an early predecessor. But this, too, would probably be an English ballad; and of the late eighteenth century Scottish versions and fragments, B-E, Child infers that they have borrowed from the English where correspondences occur. If, as seems altogether probable, "Chevy Chase" (No. 162) celebrates the same battle in later and more romantic fashion, there is no extant ballad from the Scots point of view that can stand comparison with the English. It seems peculiarly unjust that the English should have stolen the bays as well as a victory which they did not win. But justice is a commodity even scarcer in the ballad-world than in history.

Possibly on the musical side the palm may rest with the Scots. We have no knowledge of what the tunes may have been like that went to the earliest texts, known or unknown; and, speaking of "Otterburn" as distinct from "Chevy Chase," there is in fact no record or hint of an English tune at all. The musical record is thus a blank until the Scottish forms of the ballad emerge toward the end of the eighteenth and early nineteenth century. (And by that time the English ballad seems to have vanished forever from tradition—had in fact departed a hundred and fifty years previously.)

The two musical records which have been preserved are both of about the end of the first quarter of the nineteenth century. There may be a very distant relationship between them, appearing now chiefly in the rhythm; but the tunes are distinct. It is important to note that, contrary to the English tradition, which is consistently CM, the Scottish appears—if we may generalize on so scanty a record—greatly to prefer LM. The present tunes reflect this preference. Of the two, Sharpe's has to our ears the more archaic and plaintive character. Scott's is a form of the tune most generally associated with the famous "Lines" of the Marquis of Montrose, "My dear and only love." A more extended form of this tune, appearing in the *Orpheus Caledonius* in 1725, we have already met in connection with No. 74, q.v. Other connections are with the "Lowlands of Holland" (Johnson's *Museum*, II, [1788], No. 115), the tune of Burns's "Of a' the airts." Chappell (*Popular Music*, [1855-59], I, p. 380) gives the tune from John Gamble's MS., c. 1659 (now Drexel 4257, New York Public Library), No. 274; and Glen, with mordant comment, from the Blaikie MS. of 1692 (*Early Scottish Melodies*, 1900, p. 31). Chappell, probably too hastily, has claimed the tune as English. The earliest appearance of any form of it is that in the Skene MS., c. 1627, entitled "Alace I lie my alon, I'm lik to die awld" (transcribed in Dauney, *Ancient Scotish Melodies*, 1838, No. 28, p. 227).

A tune is said to be in the Bunyan MS., 1877, p. 111. Cf. Gray-Muir MS., NL Scotland MS. 2254.

LIST OF VARIANTS

1. "The Battle of Otterburn." C. K. Sharpe MS. (William Macmath transcript, Harvard College Library, p. 32). Also in Francis James Child, *The English and Scottish Popular Ballads*, 1882-98, V, pp. 419 and 243.
2. "The Battle of Otterbourne." Sir Walter Scott, *The Poetical Works of Sir Walter Scott*, 1833-34, I, opp. p. 368, and p. 354. Also in Edward F. Rimbault, *Musical Illustrations of Bishop Percy's Reliques*, 1850, p. 45.

TUNES WITH TEXTS

1. "The Battle of Otterburn"

C. K. Sharpe MS. (Macmath transcript, p. 32). Also in Child, 1882-98, V, p. 419; text, V, p. 243.

m M/D

Cf. the MacColl version of "Hughie the Graeme" (No. 191).

1. It was about the Lammes time,
   When moorland men do win their hay,
   Brave Earl Douglass, in armer bright,
   Marchd to the Border without delay.

2. He hes tean wi him the Lindseys light,
   And sae hes he the Gordons gay,
   And the Earl of Fife, without all strife,
   And Sir Heugh Montgomery upon a day.

3. The hae brunt Northumberland,
   And sae have [the] Northumbershire,
   And fair Cluddendale they hae brunt it hale,
   And he's left it all in fire fair.

4. Ay till the came to Earl Percy's castle,
   Earl Percey's castle that stands sae high:
   "Come dowen, come dowen, thou proud Percey,
   Come down and talk one hour with me.

5. "Come down, come down, thou proud Percey,
Come down and talk one hour with me;
For I hae burnt thy heritage,
And sae will I thy building high."

6. "If ye hae brunt my heritage,
O dule, O dule, and woe is me!
But will ye stay at the Otter burn
Untill I gather my men to me?"

7. "O I will stay at the Otter burn
The space of days two or three,
And if ye do not meet me there,
I will talk of thy coardie."

8. O he hes staid at the Otter burn
The space of days two or three;
He sent his page unto his tent-door,
For to see what ferleys he could see.

9. "O yonder comes yon gallent knight,
With all bonny banners high;
It wad do ony living good
For to see the bonny coulers fly."

10. "If the tale be true," Earl Douglass says,
"The tidings ye have told to me,
The fairest maid in Otterburn
Thy bedfellow sure shall she be.

11. "If the tale be false," Earl Douglass says,
"The tidings that ye tell to me,
The highest tree in Otterburn,
On it high hangëd shall ye be."

12. Earl Douglass went to his tent-door,
To see what ferleys he could see;
His little page came him behind,
And ran him through the fair body.

13. "If I had a little time," he says,
"To set in order my matters high,
Ye Gordons gay, to you I say,
See that ye let not my men away.

14. "Ye Linseys light, both wise and wight,
Be sure ye carry my coulers high;
Ye Gordons gay, again I say,
See that ye let not my men away.

15. "Sir Heugh Montgomery, my sistir's son,
I give you the vangaurd over all;
Let it neer be said into old England
That so little made a true Scot fall.

16. "O lay me dowen by yon brecken-bush,
That grows upon yon liley lea;
Let it neer be said into old England
That so little made a true Scot die."

17. At last those two stout knights did meet,
And O but they were wonderous keen!
The foght with sowards of the temperd steel,
Till the drops of blood ran them betwen.

18. "O yeald thee, Percie," Montgomery crys,
"O yeald ye, or I'll lay the low;"
"To whome should I yeald? to whom should I yeald?
To whom should I yeald, since it most be so?"

19. "O yeald ye to yon breckan-bush,
That grows upon yon lilley lea;
And if ye will not yeald to this,
In truth, Earl Percey, I'll gar ye die."

20. "I will not yeald to a breckan-bush,
Nor yet will I yeald to a brier;
But fain wad I yeald to Earl Douglass,
Or Sir Heugh Montgomery, if he were here."

21. O then this lord begun to faint,
And let his soward drop to the ground;
Sir Heugh Montgomery, a courtious knight,
He bravely took him by the hand.

22. This deed was done at the Otter burn,
Betwen the sunshine and the day;
Brave Earl Douglass there was slain,
And they carried Percie captive away.

The text is given from Child.

2. "The Battle of Otterbourne"

Scott, 1833-34, I, opp. p. 368; text, p. 354. Also in Rimbault, 1850, p. 45.

m I

1. It fell about the Lammas tide,
When the muir-men win their hay,
The doughty Douglas bound him to ride
Into England, to drive a prey.

2. He chose the Gordons and the Græmes,
With them the Lindesays, light and gay;
But the Jardines wald not with him ride,
And they rue it to this day.

3. And he has burn'd the dales of Tyne,
And part of Bambrough shire;
And three good towers on Reidswire fells,
He left them all on fire.

4. And he march'd up to Newcastle,
And rode it round about;
"O wha's the lord of this castle,
Or wha's the lady o't?"—

5. But up spake proud Lord Percy, then,
And O but he spake hie!
"I am the lord of this castle,
My wife's the lady gay."

6. "If thou'rt the lord of this castle,
Sae weel it pleases me!
For, ere I cross the Border fells,
The tane of us shall die."—

7. He took a lang spear in his hand,
Shod with the metal free,
And for to meet the Douglas there,
He rode right furiouslie.

8. But O how pale his lady look'd,
Frae aff the castle wa',
When down before the Scottish spear
She saw proud Percy fa'.

9. "Had we twa been upon the green,
And never an eye to see,
I wad hae had you, flesh and fell;
But your sword sall gae wi' me."

10. "But gae ye up to Otterbourne,
And wait there dayis three;
And, if I come not ere three dayis end,
A fause knight ca' ye me."—

11. "The Otterbourne's a bonnie burn;
'Tis pleasant there to be;
But there is nought at Otterbourne,
To feed my men and me.

12. "The deer rins wild on hill and dale,
The birds fly wild from tree to tree;
But there is neither bread nor kale,
To fend my men and me.

13. "Yet I will stay at Otterbourne,
Where you shall welcome be;
And, if ye come not at three dayis end,
A fause lord I'll ca' thee."—

14. "Thither will I come," proud Percy said,
"By the might of Our Ladye!"—
"There will I bide thee," said the Douglas,
"My troth I plight to thee."

15. They lighted high on Otterbourne,
Upon the bent sae brown;
They lighted high on Otterbourne,
And threw their pallions down.

16. And he that had a bonnie boy,
Sent out his horse to grass;
And he that had not a bonnie boy,
His ain servant he was.

17. But up then spake a little page,
Before the peep of dawn—
"O waken ye, waken ye, my good lord,
For Percy's hard at hand."—

18. "Ye lie, ye lie, ye liar loud!
Sae loud I hear ye lie:
For Percy had not men yestreen
To dight my men and me.

19. "But I have dream'd a dreary dream,
Beyond the Isle of Sky;
I saw a dead man win a fight,
And I think that man was I."

20. He belted on his guid braid sword,
And to the field he ran;
But he forgot the helmet good,
That should have kept his brain.

21. When Percy wi' the Douglas met,
I wat he was fu' fain!
They swakked their swords, till sair they swat,
And the blood ran down like rain.

22. But Percy with his good broad sword,
That could so sharply wound,
Has wounded Douglas on the brow,
Till he fell to the ground.

23. Then he call'd on his little foot-page,
And said—"Run speedilie,
And fetch my ain dear sister's son,
Sir Hugh Montgomery.

24. "My nephew good," the Douglas said,
"What recks the death of ane!
Last night I dream'd a dreary dream,
And I ken the day's thy ain.

25. "My wound is deep; I fain would sleep;
Take thou the vanguard of the three,
And hide me by the braken bush,
That grows on yonder lilye lee.

26. "O bury me by the braken bush,
Beneath the blooming brier,
Let never living mortal ken,
That ere a kindly Scot lies here."

27. He lifted up that noble lord,
Wi' the saut tear in his ee;
He hid him in the braken bush,
That his merrie-men might not see.

28. The moon was clear, the day drew near,
The spears in flinders flew,
But mony a gallant Englishman
Ere day the Scotsmen slew.

29. The Gordons good, in English blood,
They steep'd their hose and shoon;
The Lindsays flew like fire about,
Till all the fray was done.

30. The Percy and Montgomery met,
That either of other were fain;
They swapped swords, and they twa swat,
And aye the blood ran down between.

31. "Now yield thee, yield thee, Percy," he said,
"Or else I vow I'll lay thee low!"—
"To whom must I yield," quoth Earl Percy,
"Now that I see it must be so?"—

32. "Thou shalt not yield to lord nor loun,
    Nor yet shalt thou yield to me;
But yield thee to the braken bush,
    That grows upon yon lilye lee!"—

33. "I will not yield to a braken bush,
    Nor yet will I yield to a brier;
But I would yield to Earl Douglas,
    Or Sir Hugh the Montgomery, if he were here."

34. As soon as he knew it was Montgomery,
    He struck his sword's point in the gronde;
The Montgomery was a courteous knight,
    And quickly took him by the honde.

35. This deed was done at the Otterbourne
    About the breaking of the day;
Earl Douglas was buried at the braken bush,
    And the Percy led captive away.

The Hunting of the Cheviot

CHILD NO. 162

It was this ballad, rather than the preceding, which, Child thinks, evoked the familiar praise of Sir Philip Sidney. Since Sidney called it only "the olde song of Percy and Duglas," it could, as Child admits, have been either; Child gives his vote for the present ballad on grounds of superior merit alone. Our earliest text is the one written down about the middle of the sixteenth century by Richard Sheale, a minstrel from Tamworth. Child supposes that Sidney knew a much older form of it than this, for reasons which I cannot follow. Sheale's version, he writes, "if heard by Sidney, could not have seemed to him a song of an uncivil age, meaning the age of Percy and Douglas, two hundred years before his day. It would give no such impression even now, if chanted to an audience three hundred years later than Sidney" (1882-98, III, p. 305). Elsewhere, Child points out that the grammatical forms of this text are older than those of "Otterburn" (c. 1550), the plural of nouns often keeping a syllabic ending—e.g. *lordes, bowys*; and it is incontrovertible—not to dispute about the reaction of an audience of today—that the ballad seemed so antiquated to the men of the early seventeenth century that it was thoroughly overhauled by the broadside poets, not for its content, but to modernize its old-fashioned style; and in the later form it was everywhere perpetuated with enthusiasm. One can easily suppose that Sidney himself might have felt something antiquated, quite apart from the spelling, about a stanza such as Sheale's forty-seventh:

> Ther was neu*er* a freake wone foot wolde fle,
> but still in stour dyd stand,
> Heawyng on yche othar, whyll*e* the myghte dre,
> w*ith* many a balfull brande.—

Speaking as the courtly, modern author of his own poetry, might he not refer to such verse as "being so evill apparrelled in the dust and cobwebbes of that uncivill age," especially if he had only heard it sung "by some blinde crouder, with no rougher voyce then rude stile?" Generally speaking, the language of a ballad transmitted by word of mouth keeps rough pace with the language of the transmitters; and it seems unlikely that any street-singer of Sidney's day would have proved more of an antiquary than Sheale, a quarter of a century earlier. I must therefore demur at supposing that Sidney had any opportunity to attend an older form of "Chevy Chase" than what has actually, by a miracle, been saved to us, from such a crowder as he describes, and of his own day.

In connection with this ballad, the names of three tunes appear early in the record, though it is not till the beginning of the eighteenth century, so far as I have learned, that words and a tune appear together. Child's collated copies, presumably the earliest and best, indicate the tune of "Flying Fame." Other ballads to be sung to this tune prove that it was in favor as early as 1600; and, with few exceptions, they are in CM.

Chappell remarks (*Popular Music* [1855-59], I, p. 196) that the earlier printed copies of the ballad of "Chevy Chase" direct it to be sung to "In Pescod Time." This tune is preserved in several Elizabethan instrumental MSS., and under that name. I have not seen the copies of the ballad, however, to which Chappell refers, and cannot vouch for the connection alleged. But Rimbault says (*Musical Illustrations*, 1850, p. 15) that the earliest copy he has seen, printed by T. Passenger on London Bridge, is directed to be sung to this tune; so that the reference appears sufficiently definite. The earliest copies of "The Lady's Fall," a ballad much favored in the seventeenth century, are also to the tune of "Peascod Time," and this ballad seems to have supplanted the older name of the tune with its own name. But neither have I seen any copies of "Chevy Chase" to be sung to the tune of "The Lady's Fall."

Already, by the middle of the seventeenth century, a tune called "Chevy Chase" was being indicated for other ballads; but if there were more than one tune commonly associated with the ballad, any such would serve, and we cannot safely conclude that a single tune had superseded all rivals. It is, however, fairly clear that the *ballad* of "Peascod Time" (which was in *England's Helicon*, 1600) was no longer in circulation, and that its tune was going about under other names, if at all. By the eighteenth century, and throughout its length, "Chevy Chase" was one of the most popular tunes in use for ballads in CM, and copies of the tune under that name, in ballad-operas, etc., are usually found to be one and the same familiar air.

Not always, however. As Chappell remarks (*op.cit.*, I, p. 200), the single-sheets with music, printed about the beginning of the eighteenth century, carry the tune of the "Children in the Wood," which is the same as that of "O Ponder well" in *The Beggar's Opera*, and which is used also in various other ballad operas: *Penelope*, 1728; R. Fabian's *Trick for Trick*, 1735; *The Plot*, 1735. This, too, has Elizabethan roots. Cf. Chappell, *loc.cit.*

Lastly, some later broadsides direct the ballad to be sung to "Rogero," which appears in Elizabethan records perhaps earlier than all the rest, at least by name (Chappell, *op.cit.*, I, pp. 93-94; Rimbault, *op.cit.*, pp. 37-38 and 108). This is the tune, says Rimbault, to which *all* the black letter copies of the "Children" are directed to be sung. Whether these were originally the same tune I cannot decide.

According to Bruce and Stokoe, *Northumbrian Minstrelsy*, 1882, p. 2, the tune of "Ponder Well," or "The Children in the Wood," "is the tune which has been identified with and sung and played to Chevy Chase by all Northumberland minstrels and pipers without exception from time immemorial." Cf. also W. G. Whittaker, "The Folk-music of North-eastern England," in his *Collected Essays*, 1940, p. 36, where he prints the "magnificent melody," calls it "the national anthem of Northumberland," and praises its "simple grandeur and ruggedness" as summarizing the Northumbrian character.

To me it appears that the "Ponder Well" tune is a first cousin of "Peascod Time," with the rhythm stretched in folk fashion. I have not been able to find any early copy of the tune of "Flying Fame" and cannot justly challenge Rimbault's and Chappell's identification of it with the common tune of "Chevy Chase" printed, e.g., by Ritson, 1783, III, pt. 4, sig. I 2^v, "God prosper long our noble king" with the tune-title "Flying Fame." The earliest copy I have seen is of the later seventeenth century in a MS. in the Edinburgh University Library, where it is called "Chevy Chase." The MS. in which it is found has only three traditional tunes, written at the back; the rest is filled with pieces by William Lawes, J. Wilson, and others; so that the MS. is not peculiarly Scottish in character. The Scottish tradition for this ballad, as for the preceding one, appears involved with the tune of Montrose's "Lines." That familiar but variable tune has been printed with the words of Montrose, in Johnson's *Museum*, in the notes to which Stenhouse calls it "the ancient tune of 'Chevy Chase'" (*Museum*, 1853, IV, p. 400); in Maver, *Genuine Scottish Melodies*, 1866; in Eyre-Todd's *Ancient Scots Ballads* [1894], with the words of "Otterbourne," and in Dale's *Collection* [1794]; also R. Bremner, *Second Set of Scots Songs* [1757], and Oswald's *Collection of Scottish Airs*, c. 1760. Bruce and Stokoe print the tune with "Derwentwater's Farewell," with a note on p. 73. It may be that originally these tunes were more closely related; or it may be that the rhythm has worked an associative influence. According to J. C. Dick, *Songs of Burns*, 1903, p. 483, a black letter broadside of the Scottish form of "Chevy Chase" in the Pepysian Library is to be sung to the "Isle of Kell," which is another tune in kindred rhythm, associated with "Hardyknute," as well. It is clear that, whatever the relations, there is a persistent Scottish tendency toward a slow triple rhythm for this ballad's tunes, either:

or else:

One line of the English tradition appears to have followed a triple rhythm of the following type:

Another has taken the 6/8 path, a scheme mainly compound duple, long and short alternating.

The ballad seems not to have flourished outside Britain. From a MS. of c. 1790, coming from Newburyport, Mass., Barry recovered an unusual copy, with affiliations unrecognizable by the present editor; but in this case it was the tune, not the words, that was valued and saved. Nevertheless, the ballad has been found traditionally circulating in this country, and was also printed as a broadside. Cf. Davis, *Traditional Ballads of Virginia*, 1929, pp. 416-18, with references; and Barry, Eckstorm, and Smyth, *British Ballads from Maine*, 1929, pp. 243-48, with a valuable note saying that the "tune" (whichever it was) was a favorite in eighteenth-century New England. Lately, in *More Traditional Ballads of Virginia*, 1960, Davis has printed the tune of the Virginia copy. It appears to me to be a traditional reshaping of "Peascod Time"; but I suspect that 6/8 rather than 2/4 was what the singer may have sung. The difference would be slight.

LIST OF VARIANTS

GROUP A

1. "Chevy-chase." Joseph Ritson, *A Select Collection of English Songs*, 1783, III, Pt. 4, sig. I 2ᵛ.
2. "Chivy Chase." Engraved sheet, Harvard College Library 2710.900.860.
3. "Chevy Chase." Edinburgh University Library MS. Dc. 1.69, p. 4.

GROUP B

4. "The More Modern Ballad of Chevy Chace." Edward F. Rimbault, *Musical Illustrations of Bishop Percy's Reliques*, 1850, p. 56.
5. "The Battle of Chevy Chase." Arthur Kyle Davis, Jr., *More Traditional Ballads of Virginia*, 1960, p. 242.

GROUP C

6. "Chevy Chase." John Collingwood Bruce and John Stokoe, *Northumbrian Minstrelsy*, 1882, p. 3.
7. "Chevy Chace." Frank Kidson, *Traditional Tunes*, 1891, p. 19.

GROUP D

8. "Chevy Chace." James Johnson, *The Scots Musical Museum*, V, [1796], No. 452, p. 464 (repr. 1853). Also in Robert Maver, *Genuine Scottish Melodies*, 1866, No. 267, p. 134; and George Eyre-Todd, *Ancient Scots Ballads*, [1894], p. 184.

GROUP E

9. "Isle of Kell." James Oswald, *The Caledonian Pocket Companion*, V [c. 1753], p. 31. Also in James C. Dick, ed., *The Songs of Robert Burns*, 1903, No. 324, p. 483.

GROUP F

10. "Chevy Chase." Phillips Barry, *JAF*, XVIII (1905), p. 294.

TUNES WITH TEXTS

GROUP A

1. ["Chevy-chase"]

Ritson, 1783, III, Pt. 4, sig. I 2ᵛ ("Flying Fame").

p I

God prosper long our noble king,
Our lives and safeties all,
A woefull hunting once there did
In Chevy-chase befall.

2. "Chivy Chase"

On an engraved sheet containing satirical verses on Dr. Sacheverell, Harvard College Library 2710.900.860 (one of the Gay broadsides).

p I

3. "Chevy Chase"

Edinburgh University Library, MS. Dc. 1.69, p. 4. From the time of Charles II.

p M (?)

O prosper longe our noble Kinge,
Our lives & safetyes all
A woefull Hunting once ther did
In Chevy chase befall.

GROUP B

4. "The More Modern Ballad of Chevy Chace"

Rimbault, 1850, p. 56. From a Virginal book of the time of Elizabeth in Rimbault's possession.

p I (inflected I)

God prosper long our noble king,
Our lives and safetyes all;
A woful hunting once there did
In Chevy Chase befall.

5. "The Battle of Chevy Chase"

Davis, 1960, p. 242. Sung by Miss Martha M. Davis, Harrisonburg, Va., in whose family it is traditional. The text was written down for Miss Davis by her uncle living in California, so far as he could recall it from his mother's singing; and was contributed to the Virginia Archive on January 8, 1914. Tune noted by Eunice Kettering in 1931.

p I/M (–VI)

1. God prosper long our noble king,
   Our lives and safeties all,
   A woeful hunting once there did
   In Chevy Chase befall.

2. Earl Percy of Northumberland
   A vow to God did make
   His pleasure in the Scottish woods
   Two summer days to take,

3. The chiefest harts in Chevy Chase
   To kill and bear away.
   The child may rue that was unborn
   The hunting of that day.

A forgotten verse which tells about the men who were his followers.

4. To chase the dear with hound and horn
   Earl Percy took his way;
   Like tidings to Earl Douglas came
   In Scotland where he lay,

5. Who sent Earl Percy present word
   He would prevent his sport;
   The English Earl not fearing this
   Did to the woods resort.

6. And long before the noon they had
   A hundred fat bucks slain,
   And having dined the drovers went
   To rouse them up again.

7. Earl Percy to the quarry went
   To view the nimble deer.
   He says, "Earl Douglas promisèd
   This day to meet me here.

8. "And if I thought he would not come,
   No longer would I stay,
   For we now have plenty killed
   For us to bear away."

Just then Douglas and his clansmen come into view.

9. Earl Douglas on a milk-white steed,
   Most like a baron bold,
   Rode foremost of his company;
   His armor shone like gold.

Another verse missing, hot words and a challenge from Douglas that they two fight it out, while the men looked on. They fought with swords. At last Douglas saw that Percy was weakening.

10. "Yield, yield, Earl Percy," Douglas said,
 "For faith I will thee bring,
And thou shalt high renownèd be
 By James our Scottish King."

11. "Nay, nay, Earl Douglas," Percy said,
 "Thy proffer do I scorn,
I would not yield to any Scot
 That ever yet was born."

They fought on until Percy fell dead. Then an arrow from an English bow struck Douglas. The song says,

12. With such vehement force and might
 It did his body gore,
The spear went through the other side
 A good cloth yard or more.

Then the fighting became general—a hand to hand fight—neither side would yield until night came when there were only a few left. These deeds of valor of the men with their names were given in the song, but I cannot recall any more of the verse.

GROUP C

6. "Chevy Chase"

Bruce and Stokoe, 1882, p. 3. From Northumbrian tradition.

a I/M

7. "Chevy Chace"

Kidson, 1891, p. 19. From William Cheetham, of Horsforth.

a I/Ly

God prosper long our noble king,
 Our lives, and safeties all;
A noble hunting did there once
 In Chevy Chace befall.

To drive the deer with hound and horn,
 Earl Percy took his way:
The child may rue that is unborn
 The hunting of that day.
  Etc. etc.

GROUP D

8. [Chevy Chace]

Johnson, V [1796], No. 452, p. 464 (repr. 1853) ("I'll never love thee more"). Also in Maver, 1866, No. 267, p. 134; and Eyre-Todd [1894], p. 184.

p I

The variant readings are from Maver.

GROUP E

9. "Isle of Kell"

Oswald, V [c. 1753],* p. 31. Also in Dick, ed., 1903, No. 324, p. 483.

m π^4

* Date according to Dick, *op.cit.*, p. xli.

GROUP F

10. "Chevy Chase"

Barry, *JAF*, XVIII (1905), p. 294. From the Perkins MS., c. 1790, Newburyport, Mass.

a I

The Battle of Harlaw

CHILD NO. 163

The dependable singing tradition of this ballad is confined to the last century and the present, and, as is natural, is narrowly circumscribed in locality. The musical records are surprisingly close to one another; the chief variation lying in the elaboration of the refrain or burden, which varies from one to four phrases in length, but always comes at the end of the stanza and makes play with kindred vocables. The textual record, as we have it, is also confined to the last two centuries.

There is, however, evidence enough that the Scots have long sung about this battle, which occurred in July 1411.[1] Such a song, "The battel of the Hayrlau," is mentioned in *The Complaynt of Scotland*, 1549; and again in the macaronic *Polemo-Middinia*, ascribed to Drummond of Hawthornden:

> Interea ante alios dux piperlarius heros
> Praecedens, magnamque gestans cum burdine pipam,
> Incipit *Harlai* cunctis sonare *Batellum*.

At about the date when these verses were probably written, was set down in the lute-book of Sir Wm. Mure of Rowallan a piece called "Battel of Harlaw" (transcribed and reprinted in Dauney, *Ancient Scotish Melodies*, 1838, p. 349). Dauney regards this as the "march, or rather pibroch," which the piper would have played (*ibid*., p. 139n.), but I must confess my own skepticism. To me it looks more like a lute accompaniment or obbligato to a tune not recorded in the MS. But perhaps something can be coaxed from it.

In Johnson's *Museum*, No. 512, is a pipe or fiddle tune called "The Battle of Harlaw" and set to the words of the poem which was printed by Allan Ramsay, in *The Ever Green*, 1724, I, p. 78, and by Robert Foulis in 1748, as Child has noted. The tune, which was reprinted by R. A. Smith, c. 1824, by Maver in 1866, and by Eyre-Todd in 1894, is all that concerns us at present. According to John Glen, *Early Scottish Melodies*, 1900, p. 218, Johnson took the tune from Dow's *Ancient Scots Tunes* [1775], "The Battle of Hara Law"; and Glen notes that Stenhouse (*Museum*, 1853, IV, p. 447) gives a bagpipe version of the same as from a "folio manuscript of Scots tunes of considerable antiquity," then in his possession, where it was called "Battle of Hardlaw."

It is obvious that this tune is a close variant of one in the McFarlan MS. (dated c. 1740) of fiddle tunes, NL Scotland MS. 2084-85, No. 158 (pp. 158-59), called "Gray Steel." Moreover, I suspect that this same tune is to be found in the Skene MS., c. 1625, under the name "Pitt on your shirt on Monday" (Dauney, *op.cit.*, No. 58, p. 240). The Skene piece is written for the mandora, like all the tunes in that MS. Quite clearly, none of the tunes so far mentioned is feasible for singing, but it is very possible that a song-tune lies behind them. It happens that there is in the Skene MS. a second copy of "Pitt on your shirt on Monday," quite unlike the other superficially, and although somewhat disguised by the instrumental figuration, still, I believe, showing enough of the tune for it to be made out with tolerable assurance. (Cf. *ibid*., No. 59, p. 240.) When that has been accomplished (cf. variant No. 19b, below), we find that the latter part of the tune is none other than the Jacobite tune popular in the next century as "Up and waur them a" (cf., e.g., *Museum*, II [1788], No. 188, p. 195), which later was put to use (in combination with "John come kiss me now"[2]) in the popular "There's nae luck about the House" (e.g., G. F. Graham, *Songs of Scotland*, 1848-49, II, p. 64; Alfred Moffat, *Minstrelsy of Scotland*, 2nd ed. [1896], p. 12). It should be added that Chappell prints a tune, "Put on thy smock on Monday," from the fourth (or a later) edition of the *English Dancing Master*. Cf., *Popular Music* [1855-59], I, p. 193. There is another variant, "Put on your sark on Monenday" (*sic*), in the Panmure MS., early seventeenth century, closely resembling the first Skene copy (Dauney, No. 58).

It appears likely, therefore, that the Rowallan "Battle of Harlaw" is the instrumental surrogate of a version of the same tune. If so, we may have succeeded in tracing, by "windlasses and with assays of bias," a singing version of the "Battle of Harlaw" similar to those of the seventeenth and perhaps eighteenth century, though unfortunately we cannot recover a verbal text in anything like so early a state.

There is said to be a tune in the Bunyan MS., 1877, p. 11 (according to Gray-Muir MS., NL Scotland MS. 2254).

[1] Cf. William Mackay, "The Battle of Harlaw: Its true Place in History," *Transactions of the Gaelic Society of Inverness*, XXX (1919-22), pp. 267-85.

[2] This incidentally is known to have circulated in Scotland in the sixteenth century—witness the parody of it in *Ane Compendious Book of Godly and Spirituall Sangis*, 1567.

LIST OF VARIANTS

GROUP Aa

1. "Battle o' the Harlaw." Lady John Scott's MS., National Library of Scotland MS. 840.
2. "Battle of Harlaw." Child MSS., XXVI, No. 1921, Harvard College Library.

GROUP Ab

3. "The Battle of Harlaw." Gavin Greig and Alexander Keith, *Last Leaves of Traditional Ballads and Ballad Airs*, 1925, p. 105(d). From Duncan MS., No. 394. (Lyall)
4. "Harlaw." Greig MSS., IV, p. 81, King's College Library, Aberdeen. (Johnstone)
5. "The Battle o' Harlaw." Greig MSS., I, p. 15. Also in Greig and Keith, *Last Leaves*, 1925, p. 105(c). (Forbes)
6. "The Battle of Harlaw." Greig MSS., II, p. 8. Also in Greig and Keith, 1925, p. 105(e). From Duncan MS., No. 22. (Gillespie)

GROUP AC

7. "The Battle of Harlaw." Francis James Child, *The English and Scottish Popular Ballads*, 1882-98, V, p. 419.
8. "The Battle of Harlaw." Greig and Keith, *Last Leaves*, 1925, pp. 105(b) and 102. From Duncan MS., No. 371. (Troup)

9. "Harlaw." Greig MSS., III, p. 64. (Robb)
10. "Harlaw." Greig MSS., IV, p. 182. (Duncan)
11. "The Battle of Harlaw." Greig MSS., I, p. 161, and Bk. 734, XXIV, p. 9. (Spence)

GROUP Ad

12. "Harlaw" ("Sit doon my weary workin' man"). Greig MSS., I, p. 14. Also in Greig and Keith, *Last Leaves*, 1925, p. 104(a). (Knox)
13. "The Battle of Harlaw." Ludy Stewart, Caedmon recording No. TC 1146(A6).
14. "The Battle of Harlaw." Jeannie Robertson (singer), Archive, School of Scottish Studies, Edinburgh University. Also sung by Ewan MacColl, Riverside recording No. RLP 12-625(A1), *The English and Scottish Popular Ballads*, III, ed. Kenneth S. Goldstein.

GROUP B

15. "The Battle of Harlaw." James Johnson, *The Scots Musical Museum*, VI [1803], No. 512, p. 528 (repr. 1853). Also in Robert Archibald Smith, *The Scottish Minstrel* [1820-24], IV, p. 36; Robert Maver, *Genuine Scottish Melodies*, 1866, No. 377, p. 189; and George Eyre-Todd, *Ancient Scots Ballads* [1894], p. 204.
16. "Gray Steel." David Young, McFarlan MS., National Library of Scotland MS. 2084-85, c. 1740, No. 158, p. 158.
17. "Battle of Hardlaw." Johnson, *The Scots Musical Museum*, 1853, IV (William Stenhouse, *Illustrations*), No. 500, p. 447.
18. "Pitt on your Shirt on Monday." Skene MS., National Library of Scotland Adv. MS. 5.2.15, No. 44; transcribed in William Dauney, *Ancient Scotish Melodies*, 1838, No. 58, p. 240.
19a. "Pitt on your Shirt on Monday." Skene MS., NL Scotland Adv. MS. 5.2.15, No. 65; transcribed in Dauney, 1838, No. 59, p. 240.
19b. "Pitt on your Shirt on Monday." Skene MS., NL Scotland Adv. MS. 5.2.15, No. 65; transcribed in Dauney, 1838, No. 59, p. 240, reduced by Editor.
20. "Battle of Harlaw." Rowallan MS., [1620], Edinburgh University Library MS. La. III. 47; transcribed in Dauney, 1838, p. 349.

TUNES WITH TEXTS

GROUP Aa

1. "Battle o' the Harlaw"

Lady John Scott's MS., NL Scotland MS. 840.

m I

1. As I cam in by Garioch's land
An down by Netherha
There was fifty thousand hieland men
A marching to Harlaw.
Wi' a drie arie dredie drum dree drie

2. As I cam on & farther on
And down by Balquhaim
Oh there I met Sir James the Ross
Wi' him Sir John the Grahame
Wi' a drie &c.

3. Oh cam ye frae the hielands man
Oh cam ye a' the way
Saw ye McDonald and his men
As they cam frae the Skye

4. Yes we cam frae the hielands man
An we cam a' the way
An' we saw McDonnell & his men
As they cam in frae Skye.

5. Oh was you near McDonells men
Did ye their numbers see
Come tell to me John hielandman
What might their numbers be

6. Yes, we were near & near eneuch
An' we their numbers saw
There was fifty thousand hielandman
A marching to Harlaw.

7. Gin that be true, said James the Ross
We'll no come muckle speed
We'll cry upon our merry men
An' turn our horses head.

8. Oh na, Oh na, says John the Graeme
That thing maun never be
The gallant Grahames were never beat
We'll try what we can die.

9. As I cam on & farther on
An down & by Harlaw
They fell fu close on ilka side
Sic fun you never saw.

10. They fell sic close on ilka side
Sic fun ye never saw.
For ilka sword gaid clash for clash
At the Battle o' Harlaw.

11. The Hielandmen wi' their lang swords
They laid on us fu sair
An they drave back our merry men
Their Armsbredgth & mair

12. Brave Forbes to his brother did say
O' brither dinna ye see
They beat us back on ilka side
And we'll be bound to flee

13. Oh no, oh no, my brother dear
That thing maun never be.
You'll tak your guid sword in your hand
An ye'll gang in wi' me.

14. Then back to back the brothers have
Gaed in amang the throng
An' they swept down the Hielandmen
Wi' swords baith sharp & long.

15. The first ae stroke that Forbes straik
He garred McDonnell well
An' the next ae straik that Forbes straik
The brave McDonnell fell.

16. An' sic cam a pitturichie
I'm sure you never saw
As was amang the Hielandmen
When they saw McDonnell fa.

17. And when they saw that he was dead
They turned & ran awa
An' they buried him [in] Syate's Den
A large mile frae Harlaw

18. Some rade, some ran, & some did gang
Some went & some . . .
But Forbes an' his merry men
They slew them on the road

19. On Monday at morning
The Battle it began
On Saturday at gloamin
Ye'll sure kent wha had won

20. An sic a weary burying
I'm sure ye never saw
As was the Sunday after that
On the muirs aneath Harlaw

21. If anybody speir at ye
For them ye took awa
Ye may tell them plain & very plain
There sleepin at Harlaw

2. "Battle of Harlaw"

Child MSS., XXVI, No. 1921. From Lt.-Col. Lumsden, London, 1889.

m I

O cam ye frae the Hielands man
Cam ye a' the way
Saw ye Macdonald and his men
A' marchin' frae the Skye
Wi a dree dree drum de dra dy dree.

GROUP Ab

3. "The Battle of Harlaw"

Greig and Keith, 1925, p. 105(d). From Duncan MS., No. 394. Sung by Mrs. Lyall, Skene; learned from her mother in the Garioch.

m I/Ly

. . . .
. . . . . .
. . . .

Wi' a dree a dree a dronalie,
A dree a dree a day,
Wi' a dree a dree a dronalie,
A dree a dree a day.

4. "Harlaw"

Greig MSS., IV, p. 81. From John Johnstone, New Deer, Aberdeenshire.

p I/M

5. "The Battle o' Harlaw"

Greig MSS., I, p. 15. Also in Greig and Keith, 1925, p. 105(c). Communicated by William Forbes, Newark, Ellon, December 1902.

p I

Oh, cam' ye frae the Highlands, man,
Or cam' ye a' the wye?
Or did ye see Macdonald's men
Come frae the Isle o' Skye?
Wi' a da-di-um a derry doo,
A da-di-um a dee,
Wi' a da-di-um a derry doo,
A da-di-um a dee!

6. "The Battle of Harlaw"

Greig MSS., II, p. 8. Also in Greig and Keith, 1925, p. 105(e). From Duncan MS., No. 22. From Mrs. Gillespie, Glasgow.

p I

As I cam' in by Geery's lan'
An' doon by Netherha'
It was there I saw the Hielan'men
Come marchin' to Harlaw.
Oh was ye very near them,
Or did their numbers see?
Or could ye tell, John Hielan'man,
What micht their numbers be?
Wi' a dirrum dirrum, dow dum dirrum, dirrum
dow dum dee,
Wi' a dirrum dirrum, dow dum dirrum, dirrum
dow dum dee.

Greig and Keith, p. 106, substitute for lines 5-8 in the MS. the following:

As I cam on an' farther on,
Till I cam to Balquhain,
An' there I met Sir James the Rose,
An' Hielan Geordie Gryme.

GROUP AC

7. "The Battle of Harlaw"

Child, 1882-98, V, p. 419. From W. Walker, who had it "from a residenter in the Garioch."

m π^1

8. "The Battle of Harlaw"

Greig and Keith, 1925, p. 105(b); text, p. 102. From Duncan MS., No. 371. Sung by Isaac Troup, Ythanwells.

m I

1. As I cam in the Geerie lan's,
An' in by Netherha',
I saw sixty thoosan redcoats
A' marchin to Harlaw.
Wi my derry dey, dumpty dow,
A daddle um a dee.

2. As I cam on, an' farther on,
Till I cam to Balquhain,
Wha was there but James the Rose,
An' wi him was John Graeme.

3. "O did ye fae the Hielans come,
Or did ye come that wye?
Or did ye see Macdonal's men
As they cam fae the Skye?"

4. "O yes, me fae the Hielans cam
An' me cam a' the wye,
An' I did see Macdonal's men
As they cam fae the Skye.

5. "O was ye very near them?
Did ye their numbers see?
Or could ye tell, John Hielanman,
What might their number be?"

6. "O yes, me was near them,
An' me their number saw;
There was ninety thoosan Hielanmen
A' marchin to Harlaw."

7. "If that be true," says James the Rose,
"We'll sheath our swords wi speed,
An' then call in our merry young men,
An' lightly mount our steed."

8. "O no, O no," said John the Graeme,
"O no, that must not be;
The Rose's clans was never cowards,
What man can do we'll try."

9. So they rode on, an' farther on,
Till they cam to Harlaw;
They baith fell fast on every side,
Sic fun ye never saw.

10. The Hielanmen they were behind,
The redcoats before,
An' they beat back the redcoats
Twa acres' breadth an' more.

11. Brave Forbes to his brother said,
"O brother, don't you see
How they beat our men on every side,
An' we'll be forced to flee?"

12. "O no, O no, my brother dear,
O no, that must not be;
Ye'll tak your broadsword in your han,
Go in the ranks wi me."

13. "O no, O no, my brother,
Their clans they are too strong,
Don't ye see that cursèd Hielanmen
Wi heavy swords an' long?"

14. Brave Forbes to his merry men called,
"Ye'll tak your breath a while,
Till I do put my servant
To bring my coat o mail."

15. His servant to Drumminor rode,
His horse he didna fail;
In twa oors an' a quarter
He brought his coat o mail.

16. Noo back to back this twa fierce lords
They went amongst the throng,
They hewèd doon the Hielanmen
Wi heavy swords an' long.

17. Brave Forbes, he bein young an' stoot,
Made the Hielanmen to yield,
As a scythe doth the green grass
That grows upon the field.

18. Macdonal, he being young an' stoot,
Had on his coat o mail,
An' he went swiftly through the ranks
To fecht wi him himsel.

19. The first stroke that Macdonal gave,
He wounded him a dell,
But the next stroke that brave Forbes gave,
The proud Macdonal fell.

20. O there was sic a lamrachie,
The like ye never saw,
As there was amongst the Hielanmen
When they saw Macdonal fa'.

21. But when they saw Macdonal fa'
They lookit lion-like;
But brave Forbes, wi his heavy sword,
He made them fidge an' fyke.

22. An' when they saw their chief was deid,
Wi him they ran awa,
An' buried him at Leggat's den,
A lairge mile fae Harlaw.

23. This battle began on Monday,
Wi the risin o the sun,
An' on Setterday, at twelve o'clock,
Ye wad scarce kent wha had won.

24. Out o sixty thoosan redcoats
Went hame but thirty-twa,
An' ninety thoosand Hielanmen
Went hame but forty-three.

25. O there was sic a burial,
The like ye never saw,
As there was upon the Sabbath day,
The leas aneth Harlaw.

26. If anyone did ask at you,
Where's the men ye had awa?
Ye may tell him plain an' very plain,
They're sleepin at Harlaw.

9. "Harlaw"

Greig MSS., III, p. 64. Sung by A. Robb, New Deer, Aberdeenshire, December 1907.

m I/M

Oh cam' ye frae the Hielans, man,
Or cam' ye a' the wye?
Or did ye see Macdonald's men
As they cam' frae the Skye?
Wi' my dirrum dow, dumpty dow,
Da di dumpti dee.

10. "Harlaw"

Greig MSS., IV, p. 182. Sung by James Duncan, who learned it from his mother, of Keith-hall.

p I

11. "The Battle of Harlaw"

Greig MSS., I, p. 161; text, Bk. 734, XXIV, p. 9. Sung by J. W. Spence, Rosecroft, Fyvie, April 1906.

m I/M

1. As I cam in by Denniedeer
An doon by Netherha
There was fifty thousand Hielandmen
A' marchin' to Harlaw.
Wi my dirrum doo dirrum doo
daddie dirrum dey.

2. As I cam on and farther on
And doon and by Balquhain
It's there I met Sir James the Rose
And wi' him Sir John the Graham

3. Oh cam ye frae the Highlands man
Oh cam ye a' the wey?
Saw ye McDonald and his men
As they came in frae Skye.

4. Yes we cam frae the Highlands man
An' we cam a' the wey.
And we saw McDonald & his men
As they cam in frae Skye.

5. Oh was ye near McDonald's men
Did ye their numbers see
Come tell me Johnnie Hielandman
What micht their numbers be

6. Yes we was near & near eneuch
And we their numbers saw
There was fifty thousand Hielandmen
A marchin' to Harlaw.

7. Gin that be true says Sir James the Rose
Will come nae muckle speed
We'll cry upon our merry men
An' turn oor horses head

8. Oh na, oh na, says John the Graham
That thing can never be
The gallant Grahams were never beat
We'll try what we can dee.

9. As I cam on and farther on
And doon and by Harlaw
They fell fu close on ilka side
Sic strokes ye never saw.

10. They fell fu' close on ilka side
Sic strokes ye never saw
For ilka sword gaed clash for clash
At the battle o' Harlaw.

11. The Hielandmen wi' their lang swords
They laid on us fu' sair
And they drove back oor merry men
Three acres breadth and mair

12. Brave Forbes to his brother said
Oh brither don't ye see
They've beat us back on ilka side
And we'll be forced to flee.

13. Oh na, oh na, my brother said
That thing can never be
You'll tak your sword into your hand
And ye'll come on wi' me

14. Then back to back the brithers twa
Gaed in among the throng
And they laid doon the Hielandmen
Wi' swords baith sharp & lang

15. The first ae stroke that Forbes struck
He gart McDonald reel
And the neist ae stroke that Forbes struck
The brave McDonald fell.

16. And siccan a Pitlarichie
I'm sure ye never saw
As was among the Hielandmen
When they saw McDonald fa'.

17. And when they saw that he was dead
They turned and ran awa
And they turned him in Leggat's den
A mile abeen Harlaw.

18. Some rade, some ran and some did gang
They were o' sma record
But Forbes and his merry men
They slew them a' the road.

19. On Mononday at mornin'
The battle it began
On Saturday at gloamin'
Ye'd kentna wha had won.

20. Gin onybody spier at you
For them that cam awa
Ye can tell them plain & plain enough
They're sleepin' at Harlaw.

GROUP Ad

12. "Harlaw" ("Sit doon my weary workin' man")

Greig MSS., I, p. 14. Also in Greig and Keith, 1925, p. 104(a). Taken down by James Knox, and communicated December 1903; from the singing of an old woman on the streets of Peterhead.

p I

Sit doon, my weary workin man,
And rest yersel a while;
An' I'll send oot my servant lass
To carry your coat a mile.—
Wi' my dirrum-a-dum,
Dirrum-a-dum,
Dirrum-a-dum a-day.

2. O I come frae the hielands, man,
An' I come a' the way.
I spied MacDonald and a' his men
As they come frae the Skye.

3. O was you near MacDonald's men
Their numbers did ye see?
Come tell to me, John-hieland man,
What might their numbers be?

4. O I was near an' near enough
Their numbers I did spy;
There was fifty-thousand hielan' men
A-marching tae Harlaw.

5. "If that be the case," Lord Forbes cried,
"We'll make a muckle speed.
We'll cry upon our merry men
An' turn our horses' heid."

6. "O no, o no, o brother dear,
Such things could never be,
You'll tak' your good sword in your hand
And come along wi' me."

7. The first stroke Lord Forbes struck
He gar MacDonald reel;
The next strike Lord Forbes struck
The brave MacDonald he fell.

8. O when they saw that he was dead
They turned and run awa';
They buried him at Leggett's Den
A lang mile f'ae Harlaw.

13. "The Battle of Harlaw"

Sung by Ludy Stewart, Fetterangus, Aberdeenshire, Scotland, Caedmon rec. No. TC 1146(A6). Recorded by Peter Kennedy; collected and edited by Alan Lomax.

m π^1

1. Did ye come frae the hielands, man,
Or come ye a' the way?
Spied ye MacDonald and a' his men
As they come frae the Skye?
Wi' me durrum doo, me fol-the-day,
My diddy and my day.

14. "The Battle of Harlaw"

Archive, School of Scottish Studies. Sung by Jeannie Robertson, Aberdeen. Also sung by Ewan MacColl, Riverside rec. No. RLP 12-625(A1), ed. K. S. Goldstein. Collected by Hamish Henderson for the School of Scottish Studies. Transcribed by Francis M. Collinson.

m π^1

1. As I cam by the Garioch land
And doon by Netherha'
There were fifty thoosan Hielanmen
A-marchin' tae Harlaw.

Chorus

Singin' didee-i-o
Sing fal la do
Sing didee-i-o-i-ay

2. It's did ye come frae the Hielans, man,
Or did ye come a' the wey,
And did ye see MacDonald and his men
As they marched frae Skye?

3. For I've come frae the Hielans, man,
And I've come a' the wey—
An' I saw MacDonald an' his men
As they marched frae Skye.

4. It's wis ye near and near enough,
Did ye their number see?
Come tell to me, John Hielanman,
What might their number be?

5. For I was near and near enough
An' I their number saw:
There were fifty thoosan Hielanmen
A-marchin' tae Harlaw.

6. For they went on an' furder on
An' doon an' by Balquhain:
It's there they met Sir James the Rose,
Wi' him Sir John the Graham.

7. If that be's true, said Sir James the Rose
We'll no come muckle speed.
We'll call upon wer merry men
And we'll turn wer horses' heids.

8. Oh nay, oh nay, said Sir John the Graham,
Sic things we maunna dee:
For the gallant Grahams were never bate
An' we'll try fit they can dee.

9. For they went on an' furder on
An' doon an' by Harlaw:
They fell full close on ilkae side,
Sic strikes ye never saw.

10. But the Hielanmen wi' their lang swords
They laid on us fu' sair;
They drove back wer merry men
Three acres breadth an' mair.

11. Lord Forbes tae his brother did say
O brither, dinna ye see?
They beat us back on every side,
And we'll be forced to flee.

12. O nay, O nay, my brither dear,
O nay, that maunna be.
Ye'll tak your guid sword in your hand
And ye'll gang in wi' me.

13. For the twa brothers brave
Gaed in amangst the thrang;
They swope doon the Hielanmen
Wi' swords baith sharp an' lang.

14. The first strike Lord Forbes gied
The brave MacDonald reeled;
The second strike Lord Forbes gied
The brave MacDonald fell.

15. What a cry amongst the Hielanmen
When they seed their leader fa';
They lifted him an' buried him
A lang mile frae Harlaw.

GROUP B

15. "The Battle of Harlaw"

Johnson, VI, [1803], No. 512, p. 528 (repr. 1853). Also in Smith, [1820-24], IV, p. 36; Maver, 1866, No. 377, p. 189; and Eyre-Todd [1894], p. 204.

a I/Ly, ending on V

1. Frae Dunidier as I cam through,
Doun by the hill o' Banochie,
Alangst the lands of Garioch:
Grit pitie 'twas to hear and see.
The noys and dulesum harmonie,
That e'er that dreiry day did daw,
Cryand the Corynoch on hie,
Alas! alas! for the Harlaw.

2. I marvlit quhat the matter meint,
All folks war in a fiery fairy:
I wist nocht qua was fae or friend;
Zit quietly I did me carrie.
But sen the days of auld king Hairie,
Sic slaughter was not herde nor sene,
And thair I had nae tyme to tairy,
For bissiness in Aberdene.

3. Thus as I walkit on the way,
To Inverury as I went,
I met a man, and bad him stay,
Requeisting him to make me quaint.
Of the beginning and the event,
That happenit thain at the Harlaw;
Then he entrited me tak tent,
And he the truth sould to me chaw.

4. Grit Donald of the Yles did claim,
Unto the lands of Ross sum richt,
And to the Governour he came,
Thaim for to haif gif that he micht;
Quha saw his interest was but slicht:
And thairfore answert with disdain;
He hastit hame baith day and nicht,
And sent nae bodward back again.

5. But Donald richt impatient
Of that answer Duke Robert gaif,
He vowed to God omnipotent,
All the hale lands of Ross to haif,
Or ells be graithed in his graif.
He wald not quat his richt for nocht,
Nor be abusit lyk a slaif,
That bargin sould be deirly bocht, &c. &c. &c.

16. "Gray Steel"

David Young, McFarlan MS., NL Scotland MS. 2084-85, c. 1740, No. 158, p. 158.

a I/Ly

17. "Battle of Hardlaw"

Johnson, 1853, IV (Stenhouse), No. 500, p. 447. From a folio MS. of Scots tunes owned by Stenhouse.

a I/Ly

18. "Pitt on your Shirt on Monday"

Skene MS., NL Scotland Adv. MS. 5.2.15, No. 44; transcribed in Dauney, 1838, No. 58, p. 240.

19a. "Pitt on your Shirt on Monday"

Skene MS., NL Scotland Adv. MS. 5.2.15, No. 65; transcribed in Dauney, 1838, No. 59, p. 240.

19b. "Pitt on your Shirt on Monday"

Skene MS., NL Scotland Adv. MS. 5.2.15, No. 65; transcribed in Dauney, 1838, No. 59, p. 240. Reduced by Editor to approximate the tune "Up and Waur them a'."

20. "Battle of Harlaw"

Rowallan MS. [1620]; transcribed in Dauney, 1838, p. 349.

King Henry Fifth's Conquest of France

CHILD NO. 164

THE musical record for this ballad is fuller than one might have expected, and fairly continuous for the last century and a quarter. The earliest variants are Scottish, of the early nineteenth century; those of the mid-century belong to England; and the latest are from New England.

All these belong to the same family, and are of a fairly common type. All except the American versions have an end refrain of one phrase.

This group of tunes is so steeped in the common stuff of British folk-melody that it is very difficult to follow it back with any assurance. It may have a not too distant relative in the tune of the "Oxfordshire Tragedy," which Chappell found in several ballad operas of around 1730. He was "strongly impressed" that it might be an old minstrel tune, and he prints it among tunes of the Elizabethan era. Cf. Chappell, *Popular Music,* [1855-59], I, pp. 190-91. Greig collected a typical variant (9) with a text of "The Beggar Wench." For comparison, this is admitted to the appendix, along with the broadside version printed by D'Urfey and mentioned in Child's headnote (1882-98, III, p. 321).

One American version, that from Tennessee (variant 7), is exceptional in that, while it brings back end-refrain and much of the English text, it handles the melodic material too independently to feel comfortable in the family group. It has therefore been separately placed.

LIST OF VARIANTS

GROUP A

1. "The Battle of Agincourt." C. K. Sharpe MS. (William Macmath transcript, Harvard College Library, p. 32). Also in Francis James Child, *The English and Scottish Popular Ballads*, 1882-98, V, p. 420, III, p. 323, and V, p. 245.

2a. "King Henry Fifth's Conquest of France." Phillips Barry, *BFSSNE*, No. 4 (1932), p. 10. Also in Helen Hartness Flanders, Elizabeth Flanders Ballard, George Brown, and Phillips Barry, *The New Green Mountain Songster*, 1939, p. 192; and Helen Hartness Flanders, *Ancient Ballads Traditionally Sung in New England*, III, 1963, p. 146.

2b. "King Henry Fifth's Conquest of France." Helen Hartness Flanders, *Country Songs of Vermont*, 1937, p. 36.

3. "King Henry V's Conquest of France." Llewellynn Jewitt, *The Ballads and Songs of Derbyshire*, 1867, pp. 2 and 4.

4. "King Henry V and the King of France." Sabine Baring-Gould and Cecil J. Sharp, *English Folk-Songs for Schools*, [1906], No. 14, p. 30.

5. "King Henry V's Conquest of France." Jewitt, *The Ballads and Songs of Derbyshire*, 1867, p. 3.

6. "The King lay musing on his bed." Harris MS., No. 26, Harvard College Library. Also in Child, *The English and Scottish Popular Ballads*, 1882-98, V, p. 420.

GROUP B

7. "King Henry Fifth's Conquest of France." Mellinger Edward Henry, *JAF*, XLV (1932), p. 19(B). Also in Henry, *PMLA*, XLVIII (1933), pp. 308 and 309(B); and Henry, *Folk-Songs from the Southern Highlands*, [1938], p. 107.

APPENDIX

8. "King Henry the 5th; his Victory over the French at Agencourt." Thomas D'Urfey, *Wit and Mirth: Or Pills to Purge Melancholy*, 1719-20, V, p. 49.

9. "The Beggar Wench." Greig MSS., IV, p. 168, King's College Library, Aberdeen. (Spence)

TUNES WITH TEXTS

GROUP A

1. "The Battle of Agincourt"

C. K. Sharpe MS. (Macmath transcript, p. 32). Also in Child, 1882-98, V, p. 420; text, III, p. 323, and V, p. 245.

a I

1. As our king lay musing on his bed,
   He bethought himself upon a time
   Of a tribute that was due from France,
   Had not been paid for so long a time.
   Fal, lal, etc.

2. He called for his lovely page,
   His lovely page then called he,
   Saying, You must go to the king of France
   And bring home the tribute that's due to me.

3. O then went away this lovely page,
   This lovely page then away went he;
   And when he came to the king of France,
   Low he fell down on his bended knee.

4. "My master the king salutes thee well,
   Salutes thee well, most graciously;
   You must go send him his tribute home,
   Or in French land you soon will him see."

5. "Your master's young and of tender years,
And darna come to my degree;
Go bid him play with his tenish balls,
For in French lands he dare no me see."

6. O then returned this lovely page,
This lovely page then returned he,
And when he came to our gracious king,
Low he fell down on his bended knee.

7. "What news, what news, my trusty page?
What is the news you have brought to me?"
"Such tidings from the king of France
As I'm sure with him you can ner agree.

8. "He says you're young and of tender years,
Not fit to come into his degree,
He bids you play with these tenish balls,
That with them you may learn to play."

9. "Recruit me Cheshire and Lancashire,
And Derby Hills that are so free;
No marryd man nor no widow's son;
For no widow's curse shall go with me."

10. They recruited Cheshire and Lancashire,
And Derby Hills that are so free:
No marryd man, nor no widow's son;
They were a jovial good company.

11. He counted oer his merry men,
Told them by thirty and by three,
And when the[y] were all numberd oer
He had thirty thousand brave and three.

12. O then we marchd into the French land,
With drums and trumpets so merrily;
And then bespoke the king of France,
"Lo, yonder comes proud King Henry."

13. The first that fird, it was the French,
Upon our English men so free,
But we made ten thousand of them fall,
And the rest were forc'd for there [*sic*] lives to flee.

14. Soon we entered Paris gates,
With drums and trumpets sounding high.
O then bespoke the king of France,
"Have mercy on [my] men and me.

15. "Take home your tribute, the king he says,
And three tons of gold I will give to thee,
And the finest flower that is in all France
To the Rose of England I will give free."

The text above is conflated from Child's a text (III, p. 323) and the variant readings from C. K. Sharpe's MS. which he lists on V, p. 245.

2a. "King Henry Fifth's Conquest of France"

Barry, *BFSSNE*, No. 4 (1932), p. 10. Also in Flanders *et al.*, 1939, p. 192; and Flanders, III, 1963, p. 146. Sung by E. C. Green, Springfield, Vt., October 20 and 21, 1931; learned from his grandmother, of Turner, Me.

m M (–IV)

1. A king was sitting on his throne,
And on his throne was sitting he;
He bethought himself of a tribute due,
Been due in France so many years.

2. Then he called up his little page,
His little page then called he;
Saying, "You must go to the king of France,
And demand that tribute due to me."

3. Away, away went that little page,
Away, away and away went he,
Until he came to the king of France,
Then he fell down on his bended knee.

4. "My master's great as well as you,
My master's great as well as you;
He demands that tribute, tribute due,
Or in French land you will him see."

5. "Your master's young, of tender age,
Not fit to come to my degree;
To him I send five tennis balls,
That in French land he dare not be."

6. Away, away went that little page,
Away, away and away went he,
Until he came to his master dear,
Then he fell down on his bended knee.

7. "What news, what news, my little page?
What news, what news do you bring to me?"
"Such news, such news, my master dear,
The king and you will not agree."

8. "He says you're young, of tender age,
Not fit to come to his degree;
To you he sends five tennis balls,
That in French land you dare not be."

9. The king he numbered up his men,
One by two and two by three,
Until he got thirty thousand men,
A noble jolly bold company.

10. "No married men, no widow's son,
No married men can follow me;
No married men, no widow's son,
A widow's son can't follow me."

11. Now he's marched off to the king of France,
With drums and trumpets so merrily;
And the first that spoke was the king of France,
Saying "Yonder comes proud King Henry!"

12. The first broadside those Frenchmen gave,
They slew our men so bitterly;
And the next broadside our English gave,
They killed five thousand and thirty three;
And the next that spoke was the King of France,
Saying: "Lord, have mercy on my men and me!"

13. "Now if you'll march back from whence you came,
With drums and trumpets so merrily,
The finest flower in all French land,
Five tons of gold shall be your fee."

14. Now he's marched back from whence he came,
With drums and trumpets so merrily,
And the finest flower in all French land,
Five tons of gold now is his fee.

2b. "King Henry Fifth's Conquest of France"

Flanders, 1937, p. 36. Sung by E. C. Green (d. 1931), August 20, 1931; learned from his grandmother, of Turner, Me. From *Country Songs of Vermont*, collected by Helen Hartness Flanders; copyright 1937 by Helen Hartness Flanders.

a I/M

There are no material differences in text between this and the preceding variant (2a) apart from the omission of the eighth stanza.

3. "King Henry V's Conquest of France"

Jewitt, 1867, p. 2; text, p. 4. Traditional.

a I

This tune and that of variant 5 were also used for Child No. 132, q.v.

1. As our king lay musing on his bed,
He bethought himself upon a time,
Of a tribute that was due from France,
Had not been paid for so long a time.
Fal de ral de ray,
Fal de ral de ray.

2. He called for his lovely page,
His lovely page then called he;
Saying, "You must go to the King of France,
To the King of France, sir, ride speedily."
Fal, lal, &c.

3. O then away went this lovely page,
This lovely page then away went he;
Lo he came to the King of France,
And then he fell down on his bended knee.
Fal, lal, &c.

4. "My master greets you, worthy Sir,
Ten ton of gold that is due to he,
That you will send him his tribute home,
Or in French land you soon will him see."
Fal, lal, &c.

5. "Your master's young, and of tender years,
Not fit to come into my degree;
And I will send him three Tennis-Balls,
That with them he may learn to play."
Fal, lal, &c.

6. O then returned this lovely page,
This lovely page then returned he,
And when he came to our gracious King,
Low he fell down on his bended knee.
Fal, lal, &c.

7. "What news? What news? my trusty page,
What is the news you have brought to me?"
"I have brought such news from the King of France,
That he and you will ne'er agree.
Fal, lal, &c.

8. "He says, you're young, and of tender years,
Not fit to come into his degree;
And he will send you three Tennis-Balls,
That with them you may learn to play."
Fal, lal, &c.

9. "Recruit me Cheshire and Lancashire,
And Derby Hills that are so free;
No marry'd man, or widow's son,
For no widow's curse shall go with me."
Fal, lal, &c.

10. They recruited Cheshire and Lancashire,
And Derby Hills that are so free;
No marry'd man, nor no widow's son,
Yet there was a jovial bold company.
Fal, lal, &c.

11. O then we march'd into the French land,
With drums and trumpets so merrily;
And then bespoke the King of France,
"Lo! yonder comes proud King Henry."
Fal, lal, &c.

12. The first shot that the Frenchmen gave,
They kill'd our Englishmen so free;
We kill'd ten thousand of the French,
And the rest of them they run away.
Fal, lal, &c.

13. And then we marched to Paris gates,
With drums and trumpets so merrily,
O then bespoke the King of France,
"The Lord have mercy on my men and me!
Fal, lal, &c.

14. "O I will send him his tribute home,
Ten ton of gold that is due to he,
And the finest flower that is in all France,
To the Rose of England I will give free."
Fal, lal, &c.

4. "King Henry V and the King of France"

Baring-Gould and Sharp [1906], No. 14, p. 30.

a I

1. As our King lay dreaming upon his bed
A happy thought came into his head,
That he would send to the King of France,
And cause his tribute to be paid.
Ri fol de rol, ri fol de ray.

2. Come here to me, my trusty page,
My trusty page, come here to me!
And you shall go to the King of France
To fetch the tribute due to me.

3. O then uprose that trusty page,
That trusty page then uprose he,
Until he came to the King of France,
And he went down on bended knee.

4. "What news, what news, my trusty page,
From English King what news to me?"
"O I have come from the English King
To fetch the tribute due from thee."

5. "Your King is young, of tender years,
And is not come to my degree,
So I will send him three tennis balls
That with them he may play, may he."

6. "Now come to me, my trusty page,
My trusty page, now come to me,
And we will send him such English balls
As in fair France they ne'er did see."

7. "Recruit me Cheshire and Lancashire,
And Derby men that are so free.
No married man and no widow's son,
For no widow's curse shall light on me."

8. They recruited Cheshire and Lancashire,
And Derby men that are so free,
And when the numbers were counted o'er,
'Twas fifty thousand men and three.

9. They fought the French, they fought the King,
Until they gained the victory,
They fought the King until he cried—
"Have mercy on my men and me."

10. "O I will send the tribute home,
Ten tons of gold is due from me,
And the fairest lily that is in France
To the Rose of England give I free."
Ri fol de rol, ri fol de ray.

5. "King Henry V's Conquest of France"

Jewitt, 1867, p. 3. From W. Chappell; traditional.

a I

The words for this tune are the same as those for variant 3 above, but with the following refrain:

Down, down, a down.
Down, down, a down.

6. "The King lay musing on his bed"

Harris MS., No. 26. Also in Child, 1882-98, V, p. 420.

a I

The King lay musing on his bed,
He thought himself upon a time,
Of tribute that was due from France,
Had not been paid, for so long a time,
Fal-al the day,
Fal the taddy day.

GROUP B

7. "King Henry Fifth's Conquest of France"

Henry, *JAF*, XLV (1932), p. 19(B). Also in Henry, *PMLA*, XLVIII (1933), p. 308; text, p. 309(B); and Henry [1938], p. 107. Sung by Sam Harmon, Cade's Cove, Tenn., 1930.

a π^2

The tune has been re-barred by the present editor.

1. As the King lay musing on his bed,—
The King of France owed a tribute due—
A tribute due was due to him;
It hadn't been paid for so long a time.
Far laldry lol dalla, for lol de day.

2. He called for his lovely page,
His lovely page then called he;
Saying, "You must go to the King of France,
To the King of France, sir, ride speedily."
Far laldry lol dalla, for lol de day.

3. Oh, then went away this lovely page,
This lovely page then away sent he,
And when he came to the King of France,
Low he fell down on his bending knee.
Far laldry lol dally, for lol de day.

4. "My master greets you, worthy sir,
Ten ton of gold that is due to he,
That you will send him his tribute home,
Or in French land you soon will him see."
Far laldry lol dalla, for lol de day.

5. "Your master's young and of tender years,
Not fitten to come into my degree,
And I will send him three tennis balls,
That with them he may learn to play."
Far laldry lol dalla, for lol de day.

6. Oh, there returned this lovely page,
This lovely page then returned he,
And when he came to our gracious king,
Low he fell down on his bending knee,
Far laldry lol dalla, for lol de day.

7. "What news, what news you brung to me?
What news you brung to me?"
"No news, no news," says he,
"For with its news you'll never agree."
Far laldry lol dalla, for lol de day.

8. "He says you're young and of tender years,
Not fitten to come into his degree;
And he will send you three tennis balls,
That with them you may learn to play."
Far laldry lol dalla, for lol de day.

9. "Not a married man,
Not a widow's son;
Nor a widow's curse shan't go with me."
Far laldry lol dalla, for lol de day.

10. And then we marched into French land,
With drums and trumps so merrily;
And bespeaks the King of France,
"Yonder comes proud King Henery."
Far laldry lol dalla, for lol de day.

11. The first shot that the Frenchmen gave,
They killed our Englishmen so free;
We killed ten thousand of the French,
And the rest of them they ran away.
Far laldry lol dalla, for lol de day.

APPENDIX

8. "King Henry the 5th; his Victory over the French at Agencourt"

D'Urfey, 1719-20, V, p. 49.

a I/M (compass of a sixth)

The tune is a wrenched version of "Chevy Chase" or "Oh Ponder Well." Cf. No. 162.

1. A Councel grave our King did hold,
With many a Lord and Knight:
That he might truly understand,
That *France* did hold his Right.

2. Unto the King of *France* therefore,
Embassadors he sent;
That he might truly understand,
His Mind and whole Intent.

3. Desiring him in friendly sort,
His lawful Right to yield;
Or else he swore bỷ dint of Sword,
To win it in the Field.

4. The King of *France* with all his Lords,
Did hear this Message plain;
And to our brave Embassador,
Did answer with Disdain.

5. And said our King was yet too young,
And of but tender Age;
Therefore they pass not for his Threats,
Nor fear not his Courage.

6. His Knowledge yet in Feats of Arms,
As yet is very small;
His tender Joints more fitter are,
To toss a Tennis-ball.

7. A Tun of Tennis-balls therefore,
In Pride and great Disdain;
He sent unto this Royal King,
To recompence his Pain.

8. Which Answer when our King did hear,
He waxed wroth in Heart;
And swore he would provide such Balls,
Should make all *France* to smart.

9. An Army then our King did hold,
Which was both good and strong;
And from *Southampton* is our King,
With all his Navy gone.

10. In *France* he landed safe and sound,
Both he and all his Train;
And to the Town of *Husle* then
He marched up amain.

11. Which when he had besieg'd the Town,
Against the fenced Walls;
To batter down the stately Towers,
He sent his English Balls.

12. When this was done our King did march,
Then up and down the Land;
And not a *Frenchman* for his Life,
Durst once his Force withstand.

13. Until he came to *Agencourt*,
Whereas it was his chance;
To find the King in readiness,
With all the Power of *France*.

14. A mighty Host he had prepar'd,
Of Armed Soldiers then;
Which were no less by just Account,
Than Forty Thousand Men.

15. Which sight did much amaze our King,
For he and all his Host;
Not passing Fifteen Thousand had,
Accounted with the most.

16. The King of *France* who well did know,
The Number of our Men;
In vaunting Pride and great Disdain,
Did send an Herald then:

17. To understand what he would give,
For Ransom of his Life,
When they in Field had taken him,
Amongst the bloody strife.

18. And when our King with cheerful Heart,
This answer then did make;
Before that it does come to pass,
Some of your Hearts will ake.

19. And to your proud presumptuous King,
Declare this thing, quoth he;
My own Heart's-blood will pay the Price,
Nought else he gets of me.

20. Then spake the noble Duke of *York*,
O noble King, quoth he,
The Leading of this Battle brave,
It doth belong to me.

21. God-a-mercy Cousin *York*, he said,
I grant thee thy Request;
Then lead thou on couragiously,
And I will lead the rest.

22. Then came the bragging *Frenchmen* down,
With cruel Force and Might;
With whom our Noble King began,
A fierce and dreadful Fight.

23. The Archers they discharg'd their Shafts,
As thick as Hail from Skie;
And many a *Frenchman* in the Field,
That happy Day did die.

24. Their Horses tumbled on the Stakes,
And so their Lives they lost;
And many a *Frenchman* there was ta'en,
As Prisoners to their cost.

25. Ten Thousand Men that Day was slain,
As Enemies in the Field:
And eke as many Prisoners,
Were forc'd that Day to yield.

26. Thus had our King a happy Day,
And Victory over *France*;
And brought them quickly under foot
That late in Pride did prance.

27. God save our King, and bless this Land,
And grant to him likewise;
The upper-hand and Victory,
Of all his Enemies.

9. "The Beggar Wench"

Greig MSS., IV, p. 168. Sung by J. W. Spence.

a I

Sir Andrew Barton

CHILD NO. 167

In accordance with the chances of tradition, which include refashioning into print and out of it again, and willful alteration by individuals as well as unconscious change, the life history of this ballad cannot justly be separated from that of its avatar, "Henry Martin" (No. 250). The present division is made only out of deference to Child's example and for the sake of consistency of method.

Apparently "Sir Andrew Barton" was already a very popular song in the sixteenth century; and this favor it retained, as many broadsides remain to testify, throughout the seventeenth, and well into the eighteenth, century.

The earlier copies are all in tetrameter quatrains or double quatrains. Where a direction for a tune is given, it is always, "Come follow my Love, &c.," which, I believe, can only be the tune of the "Fair Flower of Northumberland" (No. 9), a song that Deloney liked well enough to include in his *Jacke of Newbrie*, c. 1597. The musical tradition for the "Fair Flower," so far as it is now known, is late, and Scottish, but quite consistent and uniform. Its metre is 6/8, and perfectly suited to "Barton." But no copy of the tune as early as the seventeenth century appears to have survived.

Other broadsides of the seventeenth century are extant, directed to be sung to the tune of "Sir Andrew Barton," which would suggest that the present song supplanted the other in familiar use and in turn gave its name to the tune. (Cf., e.g., Roxburghe Collection, I, 44, "A Comparison of the Life of Man"; Huth Collection, Harvard College Library, II, 291, "A Warning for all Lewd Livers," printed W. O. for A. M., sold by J. Deacon.) White-letter copies of "Sir Andrew" carry no indications of a tune.

A number of versions have turned up in recent tradition in this country which seem to preserve more elements of the earlier form of the ballad than of the commoner "Henry Martin" variety; but they are impossible to disentangle—if in fact we ought to try—and will be dealt with more conveniently under the latter head, q.v. (*post*, No. 250).

The tunes here gathered are all from New England, with one exception. The exception was brought to California by a migratory worker from Wisconsin, and may have been carried thither from Maine along the lumberman's trail. All bear pretty clear marks of a single melodic tradition.

There is said to be a tune in the Bunyan MS., 1877, p. 119 (cf. Gray-Muir MS., NL Scotland MS. 2254). For the tune of "Come follow my Love," cf. under No. 9. Cf. also H. E. Rollins, ed., *The Pepys Ballads*, III, 1930, p. 118 and references there given.

LIST OF VARIANTS

1. "Andrew Bardee." Ezra Barhight, LC Archive of American Folk Song, recording No. 11,689(B15).
2. "Andrew Bardeen." Helen Hartness Flanders, *Country Songs of Vermont*, 1937, p. 8.
3. "Andrew Bardeen." Hiram M. Cranmer, LC Archive of American Folk Song, recording No. 11,689(A21).
4. "Andrew Bardan." Phillips Barry Dictaphone Cylinders, No. 78, cutting 2, Harvard College Library. (Harding)

5a. "Sir Andrew Barton." Barry Dictaphone Cylinders, No. 144, cutting 2; transcribed by Samuel P. Bayard. (Forbuss)

5b. "Andrew Briton," or "The Three Brothers." Phillips Barry, *The Maine Woods Songster*, 1939, p. 64.

6. "Andy Bardeen." John Pennington, LC Archive of American Folk Song, recording No. 11,887(A34).
7. "Andrew Bardan." Barry Dictaphone Cylinders, No. 143, cutting 2; transcribed by Samuel P. Bayard. (Merry)
8. "Andrew Batann." Warde H. Ford, LC Archive of American Folk Song, recording No. 4194(B1). Also in LC/AAFS, recording No. L58(A2); and on Folkways LP recording No. P 4001(B2).
9. "Andrew Battam." Phillips Barry, Fannie H. Eckstorm, and Mary W. Smyth, *British Ballads from Maine*, 1929, pp. 483 and 248.

TUNES WITH TEXTS

1. "Andrew Bardee"

Sung by Ezra Barhight (85), Niel's Creek, N.Y., July 17, 1959. LC/AAFS rec. No. 11,689(B15). Recorded by Frank A. Hoffmann and Ellen Stekert.

a I

1. Three brothers, three brothers in Scotland did dwell,
   Three loving brothers were they,
   And they did cast lots to see which of the three
   Would go robbing all round the salt sea,
   And they did cast lots to see which of the three
   Would go robbing all round the salt sea.

2. The lot it fell on And'a Ba'dée,
   The youngest one of the three
   And he to maintain the other two
   Went robbing all round the salt sea,
   And he to maintain the other two
   Went robbing all round the salt sea.

3. He hadn't sailed but two or three weeks,
Three vessels he espied,
A-sailing far off and a-sailing far off
T'll at length they came sailing 'longside,
A-sailing far off and a-sailing far off
T'll at length they came sailing 'longside.

4. Who's there, who's there? cries And'a Ba'dee,
Who's there that sails so nigh?
We are three merchant vessels from Old England
And 'uth(?) [? if ? with] no offense let us pass by.
We are three merchant vessels from Old England
And 'uth(?) no offense let us pass by.

5. O no, O no! cries And'a Ba'dee
Such thing shall never be,
But I'll have your ship and your cargo, boys,
And your body I'll carry with me,
(But) I'll have your ship and your cargo, boys,
And your body I'll carry with me.

6. Go home! go home! cried And'a Ba'dee
Go tell your King for me,
That if he reigns king upon the dry land
That I will reign king at sea,
That if he reigns king upon the dry land
That I will reign king at sea.

[*A false start here*: Broadside broadside they quick did turn, Loud]

7. When these news reached King Henery
The man that wore their crown,
His three merchant vessels had all been taken
And his merry men they were all drowned,
His three merchant vessels had all been taken
And his merry men they were all drowned.

8. Go build a ship, said King Henry,
And build it strong and sure,
And if And'a Ba'dee you do not bring in,
Your life I'll no longer endure,
And if And'a Ba'dee you do not bring in,
Your life I'll no longer endure.

9. That ship was built both stout and strong,
I'll have you understand,
And Captain Charles Stewart he was placed thereon
To take the bold command,
And Captain Charles Stewart he was placed thereon
For to take the bold command.

10. Well he hadn't sailed but two or three days,
Three vessels he espied,
They were sailing far off and a-sailing far off
Till at length they came sailing 'longside.
[*No repeat*]

11. Who's there, who's there, cried And'a Ba'dee, [*corrected to* Captain Charles Stewart]
Who's there that sails so nigh?
We are three bold robbers from merry Scotland
And ? 'out no offense let us pass by,
We are three bold robbers from merry Scotland
And ? 'out no offense let us pass by.

12. O no, O no! cried Captain Charles Stewart,
Such things shall never be;
But I'll have your ship and your cargo, boys,
And your body I'll carry with me,
I'll have your ship and your cargo, boys,
And your body I'll carry with me.

"That's the limit!" [*Singer's conclusion.*]

2. "Andrew Bardeen"

Flanders, 1937, p. 8. Sung by Euclid I. Williams, Lower Waterford, Vt., c. 1934. From *Country Songs in Vermont*, collected by Helen Hartness Flanders; copyright 1937 by Helen Hartness Flanders.

p I

1. Three loving brothers in Scotland did dwell
And loving were the three.
They each cast lots to see which of the three
Should go robbing around the salt sea,
They each cast lots to see which of the three
Should go robbing around the salt sea.

2. The lot it fell upon Andrew Bardeen,
The youngest of all the three,
And for to maintain his two older brothers
Went robbing around the salt sea.

3. He had not sailed but one summer night,
When daylight did appear:
He saw a ship sailing very far off,
And at last it came sailing quite near.

4. "Who's there, who's there?" cried Andrew Bardeen.
"Who's there that sails so nigh?"
"We are the rich merchants from Merrie England
And no offense. Let us by!"

5. "Oh no! Oh no!" said Andrew Bardeen,
"Oh no! That never can be.
Your ship I'll have, and your cargo, too,
And your bodies I'll sink in the sea."

6. Now when this news reached Merrie England
(King George he wore the crown)
That his ship and his cargo were taken away,
And his brave men they were all drowned,

7. "Go build me a ship," says Captain Charles Stewart,
"A ship both stout and sure,
And if I don't fetch this Andrew Bardeen,
My life shall no longer endure."

8. He had not sailed but one summer's night
When daylight did appear.
He saw a ship sailing very far off—
At last it came sailing quite near.

9. "Who's there? Who's there?" cried Captain Charles Stewart,
"There that sails so nigh?"
"We are the bold brothers from Merrie Scotland
And no offense. Let us by."

10. "Oh no! Oh no!" cried Captain Charles Stewart,
"Oh no! that never can be;
Your ship I'll have and your cargo, too,
And your bodies I'll carry with me."

11. Then they drew up a full broadside
And each to the other let pour.
They had not fought but a very short time
When Captain Charles Stewart gave o'er.

12. "Go home, go home," says Andrew Bardeen,
"And tell your king for me
That he may reign king of the merrie dry land,
But that I will be king of the sea."

3. "Andrew Bardeen"

Sung by Hiram M. Cranmer (69), Hammersley Fork, Pa., August 20, 1959. LC/AAFS rec. No. 11,689(A21). Recorded by Frank A. Hoffmann.

a I/M

1. There were three brothers in Old Scotland
Three loving brothers were they,
And they all cast lots to see which of them
Should go robbing around the salt sea.

2. The lot it fell to Andrew Bardeen,
The youngest of the three,
That he should maintain the other two brothers,
By robbing around the salt sea.

3. He had not sailed long till they spied two ships sailing,
Come sailing and sailing far off till at length they came sailing 'longside.

4. Who's there, who's there? cries Andrew Bardeen,
Who's there that's sailing so nigh?
We are the rich vessels from Old England
And {[? it's now thou've ans(wer)] / [? if no offense]} let us pass by.

5. O no, O no, cries Andrew Bardeen,
That thing it never shall be;
Your ship and your cargo I'll have, my brave boys,
And your men I will drown in the sea.

6. This news it reached to Old England,
Young Georgie wearing the crown,
He found that his two noble vessels were sunk
And his merry men all were drowned.

7. Go build me a ship, cries Captain Charles Stewart,
Go build it safe and sure,
And I will bring this Andrew Bardeen
Or my life I'll no longer endure.

8. The ship was built both safe and sure,
Was built at his command,
And Captain Charles Stewart was placed on deck,
To take the whole command.

9. He had not sailed more than a week or ten days,
When he spied a ship sailing and sailing and sailing far off
Till at length she came sailing 'longside.

10. Who's there, who's there? cried Captain Charles Stewart,
Who's there that's sailing so nigh?
We are the bold robbers from Old Scotland,
If it's ?no offense let us pass by.

11. O no! O no! cried Captain Charles Stewart,
This thing it never shall be.
Your ship and your cargo I'll have, my brave boys,
And your men I'll take home with me.

12. Fire on, fire on, says Andrew Bardeen,
I fear you not a pin.
If you have good brass all on the outside,
It's I have good steel within.

13. They had not fought more than two hours,
Till Captain Charles Stewart gave o'er.

14. Go home, go home, says Andrew Bardeen,
And tell your King for me,
If he will reign King all on the dry land,
It's I will reign King at sea.

4. "Andrew Bardan"

Barry Dict. Cyl., No. 78, ctg. 2. Sung by Mrs. S. Harding, Hampden, Me. Transcribed by the Editor.

a I/M; or a D (-VII, inflected III)

Oh what now says Andrew Bardan
What now my friends? says he
The ?lot is ready for Andrew Bardan
To go robbing a-round the salt sea salt sea,
To go robbing a-round the salt sea.

Go home my friends says Andrew, he,
And . . . .
And tell my brothers as they pass by
I'm gone robbing around the salt sea, salt sea,
I'm gone robbing a-round the salt sea.

5a. "Sir Andrew Barton"

Barry Dict. Cyl., No. 144, ctg. 2. Sung by Lamont Forbuss. Transcribed by S. P. Bayard, simplified by Editor.

a M

The text was not obtainable from the cylinder. Cf. variant 5b.

5b. "Andrew Briton," or "The Three Brothers"

Barry, 1939, p. 64. Sung by Lamont Forbuss, Monson, Me.

a M (inflected VII)

1. There were three brothers in old Scotland,
   Three brothers and only three;
   And they did cast lots, and they did cast lots,
   To see who should maintain the whole three.

2. The lot it fell to young Andrew Britón,
   The youngest of the three,
   That he should turn robber upon the salt sea,
   To maintain his two brothers and he.

3. They had not been sailing past two in the night,
   Before a loft ship they did spy;
   At length she came sailing far off and far on,
   And at length she came sailing close by.

4. "Who's there, who's there?" cries Andrew Britón,
   "Who's there a-sailing so nigh?"
   "It's a rich merchant ship from old merry England,
   Will you please, sir, to let us pass by?"

5. "O no, O no," cries Andrew Britón,
   "O no, such a thing ne'er can be;
   We'll take your ship, your cargo too,
   And your mariners drown in the sea!"

6. When the news went back to old merry England,
   King George was wearing the crown;
"A rich merchant ship has been taken and robbed,
   And the mariners all of them drowned."

7. "Go build me a ship," cries Captain Charles Stewart,
   "Go build it firm and secure;
And if I don't show you young Andrew Britón,
   My life I'll no longer endure!"

8. He had not been sailing past two in the night,
   Before a loft ship he did spy;
At length she came sailing far off and far on,
   And at length she came sailing close by.

9. "Who's there, who's there?" cries Captain Charles Stewart,
   "Who's there a-sailing so nigh?"
"It's two bold pirates from old Scotland,
   Will you please, sir, to let us pass by?"

10. "O no, O no," cries Captain Charles Stewart,
   "O no, such a thing ne'er can be;
We'll take your ship, your cargo too,
   And your mariners drown in the sea."

11. "Fire on, fire on," says Andrew Britón,
   "I value you not one pin;
If you're good brass on the outside,
   We'll show you bright steel within."

12. They fought, they fought full four hours long
   While cannon like thunder did roar;
They fought, they fought full four hours long,
   When Captain Charles Stewart gave o'er.

13. "Send word right back to old merry England,
   And tell King George for me,
If he reigns king o'er old England,
   Young Andrew reigns king o'er the sea!"

6. "Andy Bardeen"

Sung by John Pennington, Fayetteville, Ark., May 8, 1952. LC/AAFS, rec. No. 11,887(A34). Collected by Irene Carlisle.

a M

1. Three younger brothers all cast lots
   The youngest one of three
To maintain the others two older boys,
   He went robbing all round the salt sea.

2. He hadn't not sailed mo'n three cold nights,
   Till a ship a-sailing did spy
A-sailing far off, a-sailing far off,
   At length she came sailing nearby.

3. Who's there, who's there? cried Andy Bardeen,
   Who's there that sails so nigh?
We three merchant vessels from Old Scotland,
   Will you please, Sir, let us pass by?

4. O no, O no! cried Andy Bardeen,
   That never, never can be.
Your ship we will sink and your body, boys,
   But your cargo we'll carry with us.

5. Broadcast, broadcast those ships did roll,
   Like thunder the cannons did roar,
Till they give 'em a death wound and were forced to draw off,
   They returned to Old England's fair land.

6. The King he fixed up vessels three,
   Charles Stewart put in command:
Go capture those robbers that sails upon sea
   And bring them to England's fair land.

7. They had'n not sailed mo'n three cold nights
   Till a ship a-sailing did spy
A-sailing far off, a-sailing far off,
   At length she came sailing near by.

8. Who's there, who's there? cried Captain Charles Stewart,
   Who's there that sails so nigh?
We're three bold robbers from Old Scotland,
   Will you please, Sir, let us pass by?

9. O no, O no, cried Captain Charles Stewart,
   That never, never can be.
Your ship we will sink, and your cargo, boys,
   But your bodies we'll carry with us.

10. Broadcast, broadcast those ship did roll,
   Like thunder the cannons did roar,
Till they gave 'em a death-wound and they were forced to draw off,
   They returned to Old England's fair land.

11. Go tell your king these words for me,
   Go tell him this for me:
That he remains king of Old England's fair land,
   But I'll remain king of the sea.

7. "Andrew Bardan"

Barry Dict. Cyl., No. 143, ctg. 2. Sung by H. L. Merry, Thorndike, Me. Transcribed by S. P. Bayard.

p M

8. "Andrew Batann"

Sung by Warde H. Ford, Central Valley, Calif., Christmas Day, 1938. Learned from his uncle, Charles Walker, of Crandon, Wis., who had it from a Scottish logger in Coeur d'Alene, Idaho, in 1906. LC/AAFS, rec. No. 4194(B1). Also in LC/AAFS, rec. No. L58(A2); and on Folkways rec. No. P4001(B2). Collected by Mrs. Sidney Robertson Cowell.

a M/D

1. There once were three brothers from merry Scotland,
   From merry Scotland were they;
   They cast a lot to see which of them
   Would go robbing all o'er the salt sea.

2. The lot it fell to Andrew Batan,
   The youngest one of the three,
   That he should go robbing all o'er the salt sea
   To maintain his three brothers and he.

3. He had not sailed but one summer's eve,
   When a light it did appear;
   It sailed far off and it sailed far on
   And at last it came sailing so near.

4. Who art, who art, cried Andrew Batan,
   Who art that sails so nigh?
   We are the rich merchants from old Eng-a-land
   And I pray you will let us pass by.

5. O no, O no, cried Andrew Batan,
   O no, that never can be;
   Your ships and your cargo I'll take them away
   And your merry men drown in the sea.

6. When the news reached old Eng-a-land
   What Andrew Batan had done,
   Their ships and their cargo he'd taken away
   And all of their merry men drowned.

7. Build me a boat, cried Captain Charles Stuart,
   And build it strong and secure,
   And if I don't capture Andrew Batan
   My life I'll no longer endure.

8. He had not sailed but one summer's eve,
   When a light it did appear;
   It sailed far off and it sailed far on
   And at last it came sailing so near.

9. Who art, who art, cried Captain Charles Stuart,
   Who art that sails so nigh?
   We're the jolly Scots robbers from merry Scotland
   And I pray you will let us pass by.

10. O no, O no, cried Captain Charles Stuart,
    O no, that never can be.
    Your ship and your cargo I'll take it away,
    And your merry men drown in the sea.

11. What ho, what ho, cried Andrew Batan,
    I value you not one pin,
    For while you show me fine brass without
    I'll show you good steel within.

12. Then broadside to broadside these ships they stood
    And like thunder their cannon did roar;
    They had not fought but two hours or so,
    Till Captain Charles Stuart gave o'er.

13. Go home, go home, cried Andrew Batan,
    And tell your king for me,
    While he remains king upon the dry land,
    I'll remain king of the sea.

9. "Andrew Battam"

Barry, Eckstorm, and Smyth, 1929, p. 483; text, p. 248. Text contributed by Mrs. Annie V. Marston, West Gouldsboro, Me., 1926; tune, 1929.

a D

1. There were three brothers in Merry Scotland,
   Three loving brothers were they;
   They all drew lots to see which should go
   A-robbing all on the salt sea.

2. The lot it fell to Andrew Battam,
   The youngest of the three,
   That he should go a-robbing all on the salt sea
   To maintain his two brothers and he.

3. He had not sailed for two winter's nights,
   For two winter's nights or more,
   When they saw a ship sailing far off and far on,
   Till at length she came sailing close by.

4. "Who's there? who's there?" cried Andrew Battam,
   "Who's there that sails so nigh?"
   "We are the rich merchants of Old England,
   And it's won't you please let us pass by?"

5. "O, no! O, no!" cried Andrew Battam,
"Such things can never be;
We will take away all your rich merchandise,
And your mariners drown in the sea."

6. "Go home, go home!" cried Andrew Battam,
"King Henry he wears the crown;
It is now that he offers a large sum of gold,
If this Andrew Battam can be found."

7. "Go build me a ship," cried Captain Charles Stewart,
"Go build it strong and sure,
And I will bring you this Andrew Battam,
Or my life I'll no longer endure."

8. They had not sailed for two winter nights,
For two winter nights or more,
When they saw a ship sailing far off and far on,
Till at length they came sailing close by.

9. "Who's there? who's there?" cried Captain Charles Stewart,
"Who's there that sails so nigh?"
"We are the bold robbers of Merry Scotland,
And it is won't you please let us pass by?"

10. "O, no, O, no," cried Captain Charles Stewart,
"Such things can never be;
We will take away all your rich shining gold,
And your mariners drown in the sea."

11. And then the battle it did begin,
The cannon loud did roar,
They had not fought but an hour or two,
When this Captain Charles Stewart gave o'er.

12. "Go home, go home!" cried Andrew Battam,
"And tell your King for me,
If he reigns King upon dry land,
It is *I* who reigns King on the sea."

Johnie Armstrong

CHILD NO. 169

WHETHER or no "Ihonne Ermistrangis dance," mentioned in *The Complaynt of Scotland*, 1549, had anything to do with the extant tune, no musical record has survived with this ballad which is not probably related to a single tune-family. The first record of a tune, called 'Good night and God be with you," appears in the Skene MS., No. 109, transcribed in Dauney, *Ancient Scotish Melodies*, 1838, No. 16, p. 222. All our melodic records with clear textual connections are early nineteenth-century Scottish ones. The tune exists under a variety of later names. Cf. Stenhouse, *The Scots Musical Museum*, 1853, IV, No. 356, p. 335. Stenhouse observes that the tune is in Oswald's *Caledonian Pocket Companion* (Bk. IX, p. 13, according to Glen), and "would appear to be the progenitor of that class of airs so frequently noticed under the name of *Todlen Hame—Lament for the Chief—Robidh donna gorradh*, and several others." Miss Gilchrist refers to *The Scots Musical Museum*, No. 275, for "Todlen Hame," and notes that the air is now familiar as "My Ain Fireside," and in Ireland as "The Old Head of Denis" (*JEFDSS*, III, No. 3 [1938], p. 191).

The tune indications in the early broadsides are not very serviceable: "To a pretty northern tune called, Fare you well, guilt Knock-hall," "To a pretty new northern tune," "To a Northern Tune." Douce Ballads, II, fol. 151^{v}, Bodleian Library, Oxford ("The married wives Complaint of her unkind husband &c.") has "jonny armstrong" for its tune—along with "True love rewarded with loyalty," and "a very pleasant new tune." The metre is consistently that of LM quatrains.

The Gray-Muir MS. (NL Scotland MS. 2254) mentions tunes in Bunyan MS., 1877, pp. 70 and 113, and Finlay Dun, c. 1840, V, p. 46.

LIST OF VARIANTS

GROUP A

1. "Johnie Armstrang." James Johnson, *The Scots Musical Museum*, 1853, IV (William Stenhouse, *Illustrations*), No. 356, p. 336.
2. "Johnie Armstrang." Johnson, *The Scots Musical Museum*, IV [1792], No. 356, p. 367 (repr. 1853). Also in Joseph Ritson, *Scotish Songs*, 1794, II, p. 7; and George Eyre-Todd, *Ancient Scots Ballads* [1894], p. 162.
3. "Johnie Armstrang." Sir Walter Scott, *The Poetical Works of Sir Walter Scott*, 1833-34, I, opp. p. 416, and p. 407.
4. "Johnny Armstrong." Blaikie MS., National Library of Scotland MS. 1578, No. 117, p. 36.
5. "Johnnie Armstrong." Blaikie MS., NL Scotland MS. 1578, No. 116, p. 36.
6. "Johnie Armstrong." C. K. Sharpe MS. (William Macmath transcript, Harvard College Library, p. 32). Also in Francis J. Child, *The English and Scottish Popular Ballads*, 1882-98, V, p. 420.
7. "Johnnie Armstrong." Harris MS., No. 19, Harvard College Library. Also in Child, 1882-98, V, p. 420.
8. "Johnnie Armstrong." Anne G. Gilchrist, *JEFDSS*, III, No. 3 (1938), p. 190.

APPENDIX A

9. "Good Night and God be With You." Skene MS., National Library of Scotland Adv. MS. 5.2.15, No. 109; transcribed in William Dauney, *Ancient Scotish Melodies*, 1838, No. 16, p. 222.

GROUP B

10. "Johnie Armstrong." Lady John Scott's MS., National Library of Scotland MS. 840.

TUNES WITH TEXTS

GROUP A

1. "Johnie Armstrang"

Johnson, 1853, IV (Stenhouse), No. 356, p. 336. Tune learned by Stenhouse from Robert Hastie, Jedburgh town piper.

m I/M

2. "Johnie Armstrang"

Johnson, IV, [1792], No. 356, p. 367 (repr. 1853). Also in Ritson, 1794, II, p. 7; and Eyre-Todd [1894], p. 162.

p π^1 (m I in second strain)

3. "Johnie Armstrang"

Scott, 1833-34, I, opp. p. 416; text, p. 407. Words from Allan Ramsay, *The Ever Green*, 1724 (Child's C); Ramsay learned them from "a gentleman called Armstrong."

m I

1. Sum speikis of lords, sum speikis of lairds,
   And sick lyke men of hie degrie;
   Of a gentleman I sing a sang,
   Sum tyme called Laird of Gilnockie.

2. The King he wrytes a luving letter,
   With his ain hand sae tenderly,
   And he hath sent it to Johnie Armstrang,
   To cum and speik with him speedily.

3. The Eliots and Armstrangs did convene;
   They were a gallant cumpanie—
   "We'll ride and meit our lawful King,
   And bring him safe to Gilnockie.

4. "Make kinnen and capon ready, then,
   And venison in great plentie;
   We'll wellcum here our royal King;
   I hope he'll dine at Gilnockie!"—

5. They ran their horse on the Langholme howm,
   And brak their spears wi' mickle main;
   The ladies lukit frae their loft windows—
   "God bring our men weel hame agen!"

6. When Johnie cam before the King,
   Wi' a' his men sae brave to see,
   The King he movit his bonnet to him;
   He ween'd he was a King as weel as he.

7. "May I find grace, my sovereign liege,
   Grace for my loyal men and me?
   For my name it is Johnie Armstrang,
   And a subject of yours, my liege," said he.

8. "Away, away, thou traitor strang!
   Out o' my sight soon mayst thou be!
   I grantit never a traitor's life,
   And now I'll not begin wi' thee."—

9. "Grant me my life, my liege, my King!
   And a bonny gift I'll gie to thee—
   Full four-and-twenty milk-white steids,
   Were a' foal'd in ae yeir to me.

10. "I'll gie thee a' these milk-white steids,
    That prance and nicker at a speir;
    And as mickle gude Inglish gilt,
    As four o' their braid backs dow bear."—

11. "Away, away, thou traitor strang!
    Out o' my sight soon mayst thou be!
    I grantit never a traitor's life,
    And now I'll not begin wi' thee!"—

12. "Grant me my life, my liege, my King!
    And a bonny gift I'll gie to thee—
    Gude four-and-twenty ganging mills,
    That gang thro' a' the yeir to me.

13. "These four-and-twenty mills complete
    Sall gang for thee thro' a' the yeir;
    And as mickle of gude reid wheit,
    As a' thair happers dow to bear."—

14. "Away, away, thou traitor strang!
    Out o' my sight soon mayst thou be!
    I grantit never a traitor's life,
    And now I'll not begin wi' thee."—

15. "Grant me my life, my liege, my King!
    And a great great gift I'll gie to thee—
    Bauld four-and-twenty sisters' sons,
    Sall for thee fecht, tho' a' should flee!"—

16. "Away, away, thou traitor strang!
    Out o' my sight soon mayst thou be!
    I grantit never a traitor's life,
    And now I'll not begin wi' thee."—

17. "Grant me my life, my liege, my King!
    And a brave gift I'll gie to thee—
    All between heir and Newcastle town
    Sall pay their yeirly rent to thee."—

18. "Away, away, thou traitor strang!
Out o' my sight soon mayst thou be!
I grantit never a traitor's life,
And now I'll not begin wi' thee."—

19. "Ye lied, ye lied, now, King," he says,
"Altho' a King and Prince ye be!
For I've luved naething in my life,
I weel dare say it, but honesty—

20. "Save a fat horse, and a fair woman,
Twa bonny dogs to kill a deir;
But England suld have found me meal and mault,
Gif I had lived this hundred yeir!

21. "She suld have found me meal and mault,
And beef and mutton in a' plentie;
But never a Scots wyfe could have said,
That e'er I skaith'd her a puir flee.

22. "To seik het water beneith cauld ice,
Surely it is a greit folie—
I have asked grace at a graceless face,
But there is nane for my men and me!

23. "But had I kenn'd ere I cam frae hame,
How thou unkind wadst been to me!
I wad have keepit the Border side,
In spite of all thy force and thee.

24. "Wist England's King that I was ta'en,
O gin a blythe man he wad be!
For anes I slew his sister's son,
And on his breist bane brak a trie."—

25. John wore a girdle about his middle,
Imbroider'd ower wi' burning gold,
Bespangled wi' the same metal,
Maist beautiful was to behold.

26. There hang nine targats at Johnie's hat.
And ilk ane worth three hundred pound—
"What wants that knave that a King suld have,
But the sword of honour and the crown?

27. "O where got thou these targats, Johnie,
That blink sae brawly abune thy brie?"—
"I gat them in the field fechting,
Where, cruel King, thou durst not be.

28. "Had I my horse, and harness gude,
And riding as I wont to be,
It suld have been tauld this hundred yeir,
The meeting of my King and me!

29. "God be with thee, Kirsty, my brother,
Lang live thou Laird of Mangertoun!
Lang mayst thou live on the Border syde,
Ere thou see thy brother ride up and down!

30. "And God be with thee, Kirsty, my son,
Where thou sits on thy nurse's knee!
But an thou live this hundred yeir,
Thy father's better thou'lt never be.

31. "Farewell! my bonny Gilnock hall,
Where on Esk side thou standest stout!
Gif I had lived but seven yeirs mair,
I wad hae gilt thee round about."

32. John murder'd was at Carlinrigg,
And all his gallant companie;
But Scotland's heart was ne'er sae wae,
To see sae mony brave men die—

33. Because they saved their country deir
Frae Englishmen! Nane were sa bauld,
Whyle Johnie lived on the Border syde,
Nane of them durst cum neir his hauld.

4. "Johnny Armstrong"

Blaikie MS., NL Scotland MS. 1578, No. 117, p. 36.

a I, ending on the octave

5. "Johnnie Armstrong"

Blaikie MS., NL Scotland MS. 1578, No. 116, p. 36.

a I/Ly, ending on the octave

6. "Johnie Armstrong"

C. K. Sharpe MS. (Macmath transcript, p. 32). Also in Child, 1882-98, V, p. 420.

a I/M, ending on the octave

This tune is worth comparing with those for Child No. 24.

7. "Johnnie Armstrong"

Harris MS., No. 19. Also in Child, 1882-98, V, p. 420. From Mrs. Amelia Harris; learned from an old nurse during childhood in Perthshire, late eighteenth century. Noted by her daughter.

a I/Ly, ending on the octave

There liv'd a man in the northwest land,
His name was Johnnie Armstrong,
He had neither lands nor rents,
But he keepit eight score o' gallant men.

8. "Johnnie Armstrong"

Gilchrist, *JEFDSS*, III, No. 3 (1938), p. 190. From Shapansey Island in the Orkneys. Collected by Col. David Balfour in *Ancient Orkney Melodies*, privately printed, Edinburgh, 1885.

a I, ending on the octave

Miss Gilchrist sees a likeness here to "Henry V's Conquest of France" (No. 164).

[There dwelt a man in fair Westmore-land
And Johnny Armstrong men did him call;
He'd neither lands nor rents coming in,
Yet he kept eight-score men in his hall.]

(Words supplied by Miss Gilchrist.)

APPENDIX A

9. "Good Night and God be With You"

Skene MS., NL Scotland Adv. MS. 5.2.15, No. 109; transcribed in Dauney, 1838, No. 16, p. 222.

p I/M, ending on *VI*

GROUP B

10. "Johnnie Armstrong"

Lady John Scott's MS., NL Scotland MS. 840.

a M

The text in the MS. follows Scott's quite closely, with a little abridgment and slight verbal differences. Cf. variant 3 above.

The Death of Queen Jane

CHILD NO. 170

All the tunes of this ballad are comparatively recent—so, indeed, are the texts as well—and all are closely related. Nearly all are in genuinely triple rhythm. The earliest record, full of accidentals, is that of Kinloch, 1827. Gilchrist has recovered one that goes back to c. 1845; and Gordon has recorded a version (9 below) that can be traced to Ireland, c. 1880. The rest are later, and come from Devon, Somerset, and Dorset; and from Kentucky and Virginia. It should be observed that three of the Appalachian variants are in common time; but this would appear to be a local idiosyncrasy, stretching the basic triple time in the drawling mountain fashion.

One may suspect that nursery influence has been at work here upon a carol tune (perhaps "When Joseph and Mary"). The melodic tradition, in any case, relates to that of Child No. 54.

In an appendix (1882-98, V, p. 293), Child has printed a version of "The Duke of Bedford," certain stanzas of which, depicting the funeral ceremonies, he declares to be a plagiarism from the present ballad. The same song, under various titles, has been picked up on both shores of the Atlantic: cf., e.g., Sharp, *One Hundred English Folksongs*, 1916, pp. 50-51, and the references he gives on pp. xxvi-xxvii of the same work. A Vermont copy may be added: Flanders and Brown, *Vermont Folk-Songs and Ballads*, 1931, p. 219 ("Two Dukes"). The tunes of these are rhythmically like the ballad on Queen Jane and may perhaps be related; but since the textual connection is very slight, it has not been thought necessary to reprint more than two copies as examples.

LIST OF VARIANTS

GROUP A

1. "Queen Jane." Sabine Baring-Gould, *JFSS*, II, No. 9 (1906), p. 222. Text, Francis James Child, *The English and Scottish Popular Ballads*, 1882-98, V, p. 245.
2. "The Death of Queen Jane." H. E. D. Hammond, *JFSS*, III, No. 11 (1907), p. 67.
3. "Queen Jane." Sharp MSS., 959/1001, Clare College Library, Cambridge. Also in Cecil J. Sharp, *JFSS*, V, No. 20 (1916), p. 257; Sharp, *One Hundred English Folksongs*, 1916, p. 68; and Sharp, *English Folk Songs*, Selected Ed., Novello and Co. [1920], II, p. 30. (Sweet)
4. "The Death of Queen Jane." Sharp MSS., 3988/2868. Also in Cecil J. Sharp and Maud Karpeles, *English Folk Songs from the Southern Appalachians*, 1932, I, p. 230(A). (Thomas)
5. "Queen Jane." Sharp MSS., 4152/2994. Also in Sharp and Karpeles, 1932, I, p. 231(B). (Dunagan)
6. "The Death of Queen Jane." "Peasie" (singer), Archive, School of Scottish Studies, University of Edinburgh.
7. "Death of Queen Jane." Bascom Lamar Lunsford, LC Archive of American Folk Song, Album 21, record No. 104(B6). Also in LC/AAFS, recording No. 9476(A2); on Argonaut pressing, private dubbing, 1947; and in Dorothy Scarborough, *A Song Catcher in Southern Mountains*, 1937, pp. 422 and 254.

APPENDIX A

8. "Queen Jean." Anne G. Gilchrist, *JFSS*, II, No. 9 (1906), p. 221.
9. "Jane was a neighbor." Phillips Barry, *BFSSNE*, No. 2 (1931), p. 7.

GROUP B

10. "Queen Jeanie." George R. Kinloch, *Ancient Scottish Ballads*, App'x. to p. 116, and p. 118.

APPENDIX B

11. "Six Lords went a-hunting." Sharp, *JFSS*, V, No. 18 (1914), p. 79. Also in Sharp, *One Hundred English Folksongs*, 1916, p. 50; and Sharp, *English Folk Songs*, Selected Ed. [1920], II, p. 10. (Atkinson)
12. "Two Dukes." Helen Hartness Flanders and George Brown, *Vermont Folk-Songs & Ballads*, 1931, p. 219. Also in Helen Hartness Flanders, *Ancient Ballads Traditionally Sung in New England*, III, 1963, p. 160.

TUNES WITH TEXTS

GROUP A

1. "Queen Jane"

Baring-Gould, *JFSS*, II, No. 9 (1906), p. 222; text, Child, 1882-98, V, p. 245. Sung by Sam Fone, Dartmoor, March 1893. Noted by F. W. Bussell.

p I

3 3 3 3 3

1. Queen Jane, O! Queen Jane, O! what a lady was she!
And six weeks and a day in labour was she;
Queen Jane was in labour for six weeks and more,
Till the women grew weary and fain would give oer.

2. 'O women, O women, good wives as ye be,
Go send for King Henry and bring him to me.'
King Henry was sent for, and to her he came:
'Dear lady, fair lady, your eyes they look dim.'

3. King Henry came to her, he came in all speed,
In a gown of red velvet, from the heel to the head:
'King Henry, King Henry, if kind you will be,
Send for a good doctor, and let him come to me.'

4. The doctor was sent for, he came with all speed,
In a gown of black velvet from heel to the head;
The doctor was sent for and to her he came:
'Dear lady, fair lady, your labour's in vain.'

5. 'Dear doctor, dear doctor, will you do this for me?
O open my right side, and save my baby[.]'
Then out spake King Henry, 'That never can be,
I'd rather lose the branches than the top of the tree.'

6. The doctor gave a caudle, the death-sleep slept she,
Then her right side was opened and the babe was set free;
The babe it was christened, and put out and nursd,
But the royal Queen Jane lay cold in the dust.

2. "The Death of Queen Jane"

Hammond, *JFSS*, III, No. 11 (1907), p. 67. Sung by Mrs. Russell, Upwey, Dorset, January 1907.

p M

It is hard to believe that this variant was Mixolydian and not major like the others. Was there some error in transcription?

1. Queen Jane lay in labour full nine days or more,
Till the women were so tired, They could stay no longer there,
Till the women were so tired, They could stay no longer there.

2. "Good women, good women, good women as ye be,
Do open my right side and find my baby."

3. "Oh! no," said the women, "That never may be,
We will send for King Henry, and hear what he say."

4. King Henry was sent for, King Henry came:
"What do ail you, my fair lady, you look so [fair and wan]"?

5. "King Henry, King Henry, will you do one thing for me?
That's to open my right side and find my baby."

6. "Oh! no," says King Henry, "that's a thing I'll never do.
If I lose the flower of England, I shall lose the branch too."

7. Then they gave her some cordial which put her in a swound,
And her right side was opened, and her baby was found.

3. "Queen Jane"

Sharp MSS., 959/1001. Also in Sharp, *JFSS*, V, No. 20 (1916), p. 257; Sharp, 1916, p. 68; and Sharp, Selected Ed. [1920], II, p. 30. Sung by Mrs. Sweet (61), Somerton, Somerset, August 2, 1906.

a I

1. Queen Jane was in labour
For six days or more
Till the women got tired
And wished it all o'er.

2. Good women, good women
Good women if you be
Will you send for King Henry
King Henry I must see.

3. King Henry was a sent for,
King Henry did come home
For to meet with Queen Jane my love[1]
Your eyes look so dim.

4. King Henry King Henry
King Henry if you be
Will you have my right side cut open[2]
You will find my dear baby.

5. Queen Jane my love, Queen Jane my love
Such things were never known
If you open your right side
You will lose your dear baby.

6. King Henry, King Henry
King Henry if you be
Will you build your love a castle
And lie down so deep
For to bury my body
And to christen my dear baby.

7. King Henry went mourning
And so did his men
And so did his dear baby
For Queen Jane did die in.[3]

8. And how deep was the mourning
How wide was the bands
How yellow was the flower my boys
She carried in her hands.

9. How she hold[4] it, how she rumpled it,
How she hold it in her hand
Saying the flower of old England
Shall never detain[5] me long.

10. There was fiddling there was dancing
The day the babe was born
To see that Queen Jane my love
Lying so cold as a stone.

[1] *JFSS*: beloved
[2] *JFSS*: opened
[3] *JFSS*: die-en
[4] *JFSS*: rolled
[5] *JFSS*: retain

4. "The Death of Queen Jane"

Sharp MSS., 3988/2868. Also in Sharp and Karpeles, 1932, I, p. 230(A). Sung by Mrs. Kate Thomas, St. Helen's, Lee County, Ky., September 6, 1917.

m I/M

1. Queen Jane was in labour
   Six weeks and some more;
   The women grew wearied
   And the midwife gave o'er.

2. O women, kind women,
   I take you to be,
   Just pierce my right side open
   And save my baby.

3. O no, said the women,
   That never could be,
   I'll send for King Henry
   In the time of your need.

4. King Henry was sent for
   On horse-back and speed;
   King Henry he reached her
   In the hour of her need.

5. King Henry he come
   And he bent o'er the bed:
   What's the matter with my flower
   Makes her eyes look so red?

6. O Henry, kind Henry,
   Pray listen to me,
   And pierce my right side open
   And save my baby.

7. O no, said King Henry,
   That never could be,
   I would lose my sweet flower
   To save my baby.

8. Queen Jane she turned over
   And fell in a swound,
   And her side was pierced open
   And the baby was found.

9. The baby were christened
   All on the next day;
   But it's [*sic*] mother's poor body
   Lay cold as the clay.

10. So black was the mourning,
    So yellow was the bed,
    So costly was the white robe
    Queen Jane was wrapped in.

11. Six men wore their robes,
    Four carrying her along;
    King Henry followed after
    With his black mourning on.

12. King Henry he wept
    Till his hands was wrung sore.
    The flower of England
    Will flourish no more.

13. And the baby were christened
    All on the next day,
    And it's mother's poor body
    Lying mouldering away.

5. "Queen Jane"

Sharp MSS., 4152/2994. Also in Sharp and Karpeles, 1932, I, p. 231(B). Sung by Mrs. Margaret Dunagan, St. Helen's, Lee County, Ky., October 12, 1917.

m M (–VI; inflected VII)

1. King Henry was sent for
   All in the time of her need;
   King Henry he came
   In the time of her need.

2. King Henry he stooped
   And kissed her on the lips.
   What's the matter with my flower,
   Makes her eyes look so red.

3. King Henry, King Henry,
   Will you take me to be,
   To pierce my side open
   And save my baby.

4. O no, Queen Jane,
   Such thing never shall be;
   To lose my sweet flower
   For to save my baby.

5. Queen Jane she turned over
   And fell in a swound;
   Her side were pierced
   And her baby was found.

6. How bright was the mourning,
   How yellow were the bed,
   How costly was the shroud
   Queen Jane were wrapped in.

7. There's six followed after
And six carried her along;
King Henry he followed
With his black mourning on.

8. King Henry he wept
And wrung his hands till they're sore.
The flower of England
Shall never be no more.

6. "The Death of Queen Jane"

Archive, School of Scottish Studies. Sung by "Peasie." Collected by Hamish Henderson for the School of Scottish Studies. Transcribed by Francis M. Collinson.

a I/M, ending on II

O sister dear sister
Can you do this for me?
Will you send for my mother
To come and see me?

For the mother was sent for
And immediantly (*sic*)
Came settin' doon by her bedside
What ails you Queen Jane?

7. "Death of Queen Jane"

Sung by Bascom Lamar Lunsford, Swannanoah, N.C., 1946. LC/AAFS, Album 21, rec. No. 104(B6). Also in LC/AAFS, rec. No. 9476(A2); on Argonaut pressing, private dubbing, 1947; and in Scarborough, 1937, p. 422; text, p. 254. Recorded by Artus M. Moser.

a π^4

Well, Jane was in labor for three days or more,
She grieved and she grieved and she grieved her heart sore,
She sent for her mother, her mother came o'er,
Said, "The Red Rose of England shall flourish no more."

Well, Jane was in labor for three days or four,
She grieved and she grieved and she grieved her heart sore,
She sent for her father, her father came o'er,
Said, "The Red Rose of England shall flourish no more."

Well, Jane was in labor for four days or more,
She grieved and she grieved and she grieved her heart sore,
She sent for Prince Henry, Prince Henry came o'er,
Said, "The Red Rose of England shall flourish no more."

APPENDIX A

8. "Queen Jean"

Gilchrist, *JFSS*, II, No. 9 (1906), p. 221. Sung by Mrs. Alex Muir; learned from her uncle, Archibald Prentice, originally of Lanarkshire, c. 1845.

a I/M, ending on II

Queen Jean, she was sick and they thocht she wad dee,
And they sent for the doctor to come and see she;

The doctor was sent for and immenjently came
And he sat at the bedside along with Queen Jean.
"O doctor, dear doctor, if doctor ye be,
Oh, send for my mither to come and see me!"

Her mither was sent for and immenjently came,
And she sat at the bedside along with Queen Jean;
"Oh, mither, dear mither, if mither ye be,
Oh, send for my father to come and see me!"

"The list of relatives sent for—'brither,' 'sister,' etc.—is prolonged *ad lib.* . . ." [*Gilchrist's note.*]

9. "Jane was a neighbor"

Barry, *BFSSNE*, No. 2 (1931), p. 7. Transmitted by R. W. Gordon, as recollected from the singing of Miss Nellie Galt, Louisville, Ky., who learned it c. 1880 from an Irish servant girl, Katie Powers.

a D/Æ

1. Oh, Jane was a neighbor for six months or more,
Till the neighbors grew weary and left her alone.

2. "Oh neighbor, oh neighbor, oh neighbor," said she,
"Won't you send for my father to come and see me?"

3. Her father was sent for, and *immejitly* came;
Settin' down by the bedside,—"What's the matter of Jane?"

4. Then she cried and she murmured till she wept her heart sore,
Saying: "The red rose of England shall flourish no more!"

5. "Oh father, oh father, oh father," said she,
"Won't you send for my mother to come and see me?"

6. Her mother was sent for, and *immejitly* came;
Settin' down by the bedside, "What's the matter of Jane?"

7. Then she cried and she murmured till she wept her heart sore,
Saying: "The red rose of England shall flourish no more!"

8. "Oh mother, oh mother, oh mother," said she,
"Won't you send for King Henry to come and see me?"

9. King Henry was sent for and *immejitly* came;
Settin' down by the bedside,—"What's the matter of Jane?"

10. Then she cried and she murmured till she wept her heart sore,
Saying: "The red rose of England shall flourish no more!"

GROUP B

10. "Queen Jeanie"

Kinloch, 1827, App'x. to p. 116; text, p. 118.

a D (inflected IV, VII)

1. Queen Jeanie, queen Jeanie, travel'd six weeks and more,
Till women and midwives had quite gi'en her o'er:
"O if ye were women, as women should be,
Ye would send for a doctor, a doctor to me."

2. The doctor was called for, and set by her bedside:—
"What aileth thee, my ladie, thine eyes seem so red?"
"O doctor, O doctor, will ye do this for me?
To rip up my two sides, and save my babie."

3. "Queen Jeanie, queen Jeanie, that's the thing I'll ne'er do,
To rip up your two sides to save your babie."
Queen Jeanie, queen Jeanie, travel'd six weeks and more,
Till midwives and doctors had quite gi'en her o'er.

4. "O if ye were doctors, as doctors should be,
Ye would send for king Henry, king Henry to me."
King Henry was called for, and sat by her bedside;—
"What aileth thee, queen Jeanie, what aileth my bride?"

5. "King Henry, king Henry, will ye do this for me?
To rip up my two sides, and save my babie."
"Queen Jeanie, queen Jeanie, that's what I'll never do,
To rip up your two sides to save your babie."

6. But with sighing and sobbing she's fallen in a swoon,
Her side it was rip't up, and her babie was found.
At this bonnie babie's christ'ning there was meikle joy and mirth;
But bonnie queen Jeanie lies cold in the earth.

7. Six and six coaches, and six and six more,
And royal king Henry went mourning before:
O two and two gentlemen carried her away;
But royal king Henry went weeping away.

8. O black were their stockings, and black were their bands,
And black were the weapons they held in their hands.
O black were their mufflers, and black were their shoes,
And black were the cheverons they drew on their luves.

9. They mourned in the kitchen, and they mourn'd in the ha',
But royal king Henry mourn'd langest of a'.
Farewell to fair England, farewell for evermore,
For the fair flower of England will never shine more.

APPENDIX B

11. "Six Lords went a-hunting"

Sharp, *JFSS*, V, No. 18 (1914), p. 79. Also in Sharp, 1916, p. 50; and Sharp, Selected Ed. [1920], II, p. 10. Sung by William Atkinson (80), Marylebone Workhouse, October 9, 1908.

a Æ

1. Six Lords went a-hunting
Down by the seaside,
And they spied a dead body
Washed away by the tide.

2. They took him to Portsmouth
The place he was known,
And straight away to London
To the place he was born.

3. They opened his bowels,
And stretched out his feet,
And garnished him all over
With lilies so sweet.

4. 'Twas the noble duke of Bedford
The sea had upthrown,
'Twas the noble duke of Bedford
The sea had upthrown.

5. But some folk disputed
The huntsmen's bare word,
Until a grand lady
Cried: 'Tis my dear Lord.

6. She kneeled down beside him
And kissed his cold cheek
And sadly did murmur:
My poor heart will break.

7. For him I did worship,
Who no more will speak
To kindred and vassals
Who gazed on the form,

8. Of the noble duke of Bedford
In his coffin of stone,
Of the noble duke of Bedford
In his coffin of stone.

9. The courts of his father
No longer will ring
With the clink of his gold spurs
And the twang of bow string.

10. In chase and the tournament
A valiant knight,
Who kept his escutcheon
With honour most bright.

11. Within Woburn Abbey
His body was laid,
Amongst his ancestors
Whose deeds are not dead.

12. And a weird rush of waters
Is heard in the day,
A noble duke of Bedford
Is passing away.

12. "Two Dukes"

Flanders and Brown, 1931, p. 219. Also in Flanders, III, 1963, p. 160. Sung by Mrs. Ralph Harrington, Bennington, Vt., September 13, 1930; learned from her mother. From *Vermont Folk-Songs & Ballads*, edited by Helen Hartness Flanders and George Brown; copyright 1931 by Arthur Wallace Peach.

a I

1. Two dukes were a-walking down by the seaside.
They found a dead body washed away by the tide.

2. Great illustrations and thus they did say,
"It's the great Duke of Cotton has now cast away."

3. They took out his bowels and stretched forth his feet
And embalm-ed his body with spices so sweet.

4. Six dukes went before him, six bore him to the ground;
Six maidens followed after in their black velvet gowns.

5. Black was their mourning and white was their bands,
And yellow were their pinbows which they carried in their hands.

6. In Westminster Abbey he lies in cold clay
And the royal Queen Mary goes weeping away.

Mary Hamilton

CHILD NO. 173

This poignant ballad, whenever it arose, has been greatly favored in the last century and a half, particularly, of course, among the Scots and singers with Scottish connections.

There are about a dozen and a half apparently independent records of a tune, of which perhaps half form a single close group (D), late in the records, the others appearing to be distinct and usually separate. It is a little odd that whereas all the verbal texts are in CM, three of the oldest musical records are in LM. Two of these unfortunately lack words; but the third shows that the second and fourth lines were lengthened by the simple addition of "O" at the end of the line. Probably the same means was employed in the other two copies also. All the other tunes are CM four-phrase tunes. The homogeneous group is confined to the Major galaxy. A triple rhythm is the rule, usually in a 6/8 form, slowed sometimes to 3/4 in singing. Other tune-records, which I have not seen, are said to be in the Bunyan MS., 1877, pp. 27, 114; and N. Gow, 1810, p. 177. (Cf. Gray-Muir MS., NL Scotland MS. 2254.)

There is very considerable divergence among the texts, and this variety is matched by the outlying tunes:—a fact which has been noted earlier as characteristic of another ballad that may have arisen late, "Sir Patrick Spens" (No. 58). It is more usual for a ballad with firm roots in tradition to present a homogeneity in the musical records. Whether the present variation makes for the theory of a late origin, one cannot confidently say. I incline to that belief, but would not lean on it very heavily. Professor Davis joins A. H. Tolman in believing in a sixteenth-century origin. Cf. his recent discussion in *More Traditional Ballads of Virginia*, 1960, pp. 247-249.

Child has noted echoes of six other ballads in this one; to which I believe is certainly to be added "Geordie" (No. 209), reinforced by a tune-relation; and possibly "The Cruel Mother" (No. 20), to which Sharpe's tune of the present ballad also points. Such abundant indebtedness once again suggests a late but popular birth.

To attack the well-known essay of Andrew Lang, which reconverted Child (who wanted only to be persuaded) to the older date for the ballad, and which has held the field undisputed since 1895, would be presumptuous unless it were done exhaustively, or with the citation of new and positive evidence. Here it is improper to attempt the former, and it remains impossible to do the latter. It may be allowable, however, to remark that the weight of his argument rests on two piers, neither of which is entitled to the confidence he gives it. One is that ballads were no longer being composed in the old manner in eighteenth-century Scotland, and that that style was "utterly obsolete and unimitated," "entirely superseded by new kinds of popular poetry" (*Blackwood's Magazine*, CLVII [1895], pp. 388, 385). To this it can be replied that the line between creation and re-creation in this area is not easily to be drawn, and that nothing is more abundantly supported by evidence of the last two centuries, in the volumes of Child, Greig, and others, than the following: the style of the old balladry was so far from being obsolete in Scotland that it is mainly eighteenth-century Scottish forms of the ballads which give us English-speaking folk our clearest sense of ballad-style. Moreover, when he talks about "new" styles, he is simply comparing the work of the professional ballad-monger, or broadside poetaster, or sophisticated or semi-sophisticated versifier, with a sort of poetry the difference of which from the other no one knew better than himself—a difference which is, of course, undisputed. But if it is easy to show that the mass of poets which produced the broadsides was turning such things out by the score as early as the sixteenth century, it is equally easy to prove that the Mrs. Browns of eighteenth-century Scotland did not merely repeat what they had memorized from other singers, but actually recreated the song in other words (and musical notes) drawn from a reservoir of conventional language, theme, and phrase to which the community had equal rights—just as the community at large had rights of pasturage and cultivation in the eighteenth century to the Common Land of the district. Lang forgets that on one side of his opposition he has nothing to pose, only because the evidence was inevitably unwritten at the time: there was no *corpus delicti* to produce. One side of the evidence was written, the other was oral, until such time as the romantic revival instigated a *recording* of the other side as well.

The other main support to his argument is the great variety in the recorded texts. "We have," he says, "been invited to suppose that, about 1719, a Scot wrote a ballad . . . ; that his poem underwent, in seventy years, even more vicissitudes than most other ballads encounter in three or perhaps even five centuries" (p. 389). To this it is fair to reply that the demonstration by numbers in the field of popular poetry *proves* nothing, and serves at best as a straw in the wind. That, moreover, the rate of variational activity may depend on the vitality of the tradition; and, granted the vitality which can be demonstrated in eighteenth-century Scotland, more evidence of textual variation might easily be produced of a living ballad in seventy years than could be shown in a moribund or dead ballad, by written record, in three or five hundred years.

It will probably continue to be impossible to prove conclusively either an early or a late date for the present ballad. The object of the foregoing remarks is simply to suggest that nothing yet has been said on either side which need commit us to a decision.

LIST OF VARIANTS

GROUP A

1. "The Three Maries." Blaikie MS., National Library of Scotland MS. 1578, No. 51, p. 18.
2. "The Three Maries." Blaikie MS., NL Scotland MS. 1578, No. 51a, p. 18.
3. "Mary Hamilton." Lady John Scott's Sharpe MS., National Library of Scotland MS. 843, fol. 13.

GROUP B

4. "The Three Maries." Blaikie MS., NL Scotland MS. 1578, No. 111, p. 35.

GROUP C

5. "Marie Hamilton." Harris MS., No. 9, and fol. 10 b, Harvard College Library. Also in Francis James Child,

The English and Scottish Popular Ballads, 1882-98, V, p. 421, and III, p. 394(J).

GROUP D

6. "Mary Mild." Gavin Greig and Alexander Keith, *Last Leaves of Traditional Ballads and Ballad Airs*, 1925, p. 109(2) and (B). Also in Ralph Vaughan Williams MSS., III, p. 357; Arthur Kyle Davis, Jr., *Traditional Ballads of Virginia*, 1929, pp. 590 and 422(B); and sung by Jeannie Robertson, Caedmon recording No. TC 1146(A7). (Walker)
7. "Mary Hamilton." Phillips Barry, Fannie H. Eckstorm, and Mary W. Smyth, *British Ballads from Maine*, 1929, p. 258. Also in Helen Hartness Flanders and Marguerite Olney, *Ballads Migrant in New England*, 1953, p. 80; and Helen Hartness Flanders, *Ancient Ballads Traditionally Sung in New England*, III, 1963, p. 166(B).
8. "Mary Hamilton." Arthur Kyle Davis, Jr., *More Traditional Ballads of Virginia*, 1960, p. 250(AA). Also sung by Texas Gladden, LC Archive of American Folk Song, Album 7, record No. 32(B); and LC/AAFS, record No. L7(A4).
   a. "The Four Maries." Clarence H. (no last name given), LC Archive of American Folk Song, recording No. 10,884(A16).
9. "The Four Marys." William A. Owens, *Texas Folk Songs*, 1950, p. 64.

GROUP E

10. "Mary Hamilton." Anne G. Gilchrist, *JEFDSS*, III, No. 1 (1936), p. 59.

GROUP F

11. "Mary Mild." Greig and Keith, *Last Leaves*, 1925, pp. 109(1) and 108(A). (Wallace)

GROUP G

12. "Mary Hamilton." Phillips Barry, *BFSSNE*, No. 3 (1931), p. 8.

TUNES WITH TEXTS

GROUP A

1. "The Three Maries"

Blaikie MS., NL Scotland MS. 1578, No. 51, p. 18.

p I/M

2. "The Three Maries"

Blaikie MS., NL Scotland MS. 1578, No. 51a, p. 18.

p I/M

3. "Mary Hamilton"

Lady John Scott's Sharpe MS., NL Scotland MS. 843, fol. 13.

p I

1. There lived a knight into the North,
   And he had daughters three, O;
   The ane o' them was a barber's wife,
   The other a gay ladie, O.

2. The youngest o' them to Scotland is gane
   The Queen's Mary to be, O;
   And for a' that they could say or do
   Forbidden she wouldna be, O.

. . . .

3. "Busk ye, busk ye, Mary Hamilton,
   O busk ye to be a bride, O;
   For I am gaen to Edinbro' town
   Your gay wedding to bide, O.

4. "You must not put on your robes of black
   Nor yet your robes of brown, O;
   But you must put on your yellow gold stuffs,
   To shine thro' Edinbro' town, O."

5. "I will not put on my robes of black,
   Nor yet my robes of brown; O, [*sic*]
   But I will put on my yellow gold stuffs,
   To shine thro' Edinbro' town, O.["]

6. As she went up the Parliament Close,
   A riding on her horse, O;
   There she saw many a Burgess' lady
   Sit greeting at the cross, O.

7. "O what means a' this greeting here?
   I'm sure its nae for me, O;
   For I'm come this day to Edinbro' town
   Weel wedded for to be, O."

8. When she gaed up the Parliament stair,
   She gied loud lauchters three, O;
   But ere that she had come down again,
   She was condemn'd to die[, O].

9. "O little did my mother think,
That day she cradled me, O;
That I wad gae sae far frae hame
A shamefu' death to dee, O.

10. "O little did my mother think
The day she prinn'd my gown, O;
That I was to come sae far frae home
To be hang'd in Edinbro' town, O.

. . . .

11. "Yestreen the Queen had four Maries,
This night she'll hae but three, O;
There was Mary Beaton, and Mary Seaton,
And Mary Carmichael, and me, O."

This looks like a bowdlerized version of Child's D (from Motherwell's MS. not then printed).

GROUP B

4. "The Three Maries"

Blaikie MS., NL Scotland MS. 1578, No. 111, p. 35.

p Æ, ending on the octave

GROUP C

5. "Marie Hamilton"

Harris MS., No. 9; text, fol. 10 b. Also in Child, 1882-98, V, p. 421; text, III, p. 394(J). From Mrs. Amelia Harris; learned from an old nurse during childhood in Perthshire, late eighteenth century. Noted by her daughter.

m D/Æ

1. My mother was a proud, proud woman,
A proud, proud woman and a bold;
She sent me to Queen Marie's bour,
When scarcely eleven years old.

2. Queen Marie's bread it was sae sweet,
An her wine it was sae fine,
That I hae lien in a young man's arms,
An I rued it aye synsyne.

3. Queen Marie she cam doon the stair,
Wi the goud kamis in her hair:
"Oh whare, oh whare is the wee wee babe
I heard greetin sae sair?"

4. "It's no a babe, a babie fair,
Nor ever intends to be;
But I mysel, wi a sair colic,
Was seek an like to dee."

5. They socht the bed baith up an doon,
Frae the pillow to the straw,
An there they got the wee wee babe,
But its life was far awa.

6. "Come doon, come doon, Marie Hamilton,
Come doon an speak to me;
. . . .
. . . .

7. "You'll no put on your dowie black,
Nor yet your dowie broun;
But you'll put on your ried, ried silk,
To shine through Edinborough toun."

. . . .

8. "Yestreen the queen had four Maries,
The nicht she'll hae but three;
There was Marie Bethune, an Marie Seaton,
An Marie Carmichael, an me.

9. "Ah, little did my mother ken,
The day she cradled me,
The lands that I sud travel in,
An the death that I suld dee."

10. Yestreen the queen had four Maries,
The nicht she has but three;
For the bonniest Marie amang them a'
Was hanged upon a tree.

The text here printed is from Child. In the MS., the first stanza reads:

My mother was a proud woman;
A proud woman and a bold.
She sent me to Queen Marie's bour,
When scarce eleven years old.

GROUP D

6. [Mary Mild]

Greig and Keith, 1925, p. 109(2); text, (B). Also, from different singers, in Vaughan Williams MSS., III, p. 357; Davis, 1929, p. 590; text, p. 422(B); and on Caedmon rec. No. TC 1146(A7). From Mrs. Walker, Rayne; learned in the Huntly district.

a I

1. Last nicht there were four Maries,
The nicht they'll be but three;
There was Mary Seaton, an' Mary Beaton,
An' Mary Carmichael, an' me.

The variants appear in the copy in Colin Brown, *The Thistle*, 1884, according to Miss Gilchrist (*JEFDSS*, III, No. 1 [1936], p. 60). She quotes Brown, whom I have not seen, as saying that this tune had "always" been associated with the ballad in the highlands of Perthshire. There seems to be no earlier record of the tune.

2. O little did my mother think,
 When first she cradled me,
That I wad be sae far fae hame
 An' hang on a gallows tree.

3. They tied a napkin roon my e'en,
 To nae lat me see to dee;
They neither tell't my father or mother
 That I was awa ower the sea.

4. But I mysel am Mary Mill [*sic*],
 The flower o a' the three;
But I hae kill't my bonnie wee son,
 An' weel deserved to dee.

5. But ye'll bury me in the aul kirkyard
 Beneath the aul yew tree,
Where we pull'd the gowans an' ringed the rowans,
 My sisters an' brother an' me.

6. O what care I for a nameless grave
 If I've hope for eternity?
For it was for the blood of the dyin lamb,
 That's granted through grace unto me.

7. "Mary Hamilton"

Barry, Eckstorm, and Smyth, 1929, p. 258. Also, from a different singer, in Flanders and Olney, 1953, p. 80; and Flanders, III, 1963, p. 166(B). Sung by Mrs. James McGill, Chamcook, Charlotte County, New Brunswick, N.S., 1928. Tune recorded by George Herzog.

a I

1. Yestre'en the queen had four Maries,
 This nicht she'll hae but three;
There was Mary Beaton, an' Mary Seaton,
 An' Mary Carmichael an' me.

2. Last nicht I dressed Queen Mary,
 An' pit on her braw silken goon,
An' a' the thanks I've gat this nicht
 Is tae be hanged in Edinboro toon.

3. O little did my mither ken,
 The day she cradled me,
The land I was tae travel in,
 The death I was tae dee.

4. O happy, happy is the maid,
 That's born o' beauty free;
O it was my rosy dimplin' cheeks,
 That's been the deil tae me!

5. They-ve tied a hanky roon ma een,
 An' they'll no let me see tae dee:
An' they've pit on a robe o' black
 Tae hang on the gallows tree.

6. Yestre'en the queen had four Maries,
 This nicht she'll hae but three;
There was Mary Beaton, an' Mary Seaton,
 An' Mary Carmichael an' me.

8. "Mary Hamilton"

Davis, 1960, p. 250(AA). Also, sung by Texas Gladden, LC/AAFS, Album 7, rec. No. 32(B); and LC/AAFS, rec. No. L7(A4). Sung by Alfreda M. Peel, Salem, Va., August 9, 1932; originally heard from her grandmother, Mrs. Marion Chandler, from Bristol, England, who learned it from her father. Prior to the singing of this version, Miss Peel's memory of the ballad was refreshed by her uncle's singing. Tune noted by E. C. Mead.

a I

1. Word has come from the kitchen,
 And word has come to me,
That Mary Hamilton's slain her babe
 And thrown him in the sea.

2. Down came the old queen,
 Gold tassels in her hair.
 "O Mary Hamilton, where's your babe?
 I heard it greet so sair.

3. "Mary put on your robes of black,
 Or yet your robes of brown,
That you can go with me today
 To see fair Edinburgh town."

4. She put on her robe of black,
 Nor yet her robe of brown,
But she put on her robe so white
 To see fair Edinburgh town.

5. When she went up the Canno' gate,
The Canno' gate so free,
Many a lady looked o'er her casement
And wept for this ladye.

6. When she went up the Parliament stair
A loud, loud laugh laughed she.
But when she came down the Parliament stair,
A tear was in her ee.

7. "O, bring to me the red, red wine,
The best you bring to me,
That I may drink to the jolly bold sailors
That brought me o'er the sea.

8. "Little did my mother think,
When first she cradled me,
That I should die so far from home,
So far o'er the salt, salt sea.

9. "Last night there were four Maries,
Tonight there'll be but three;
There was Mary Seaton and Mary Beaton
And Mary Carmichael and me.

10. "Last night I washed the old queen's feet,
And carried her to her bed;
Today she gave me my reward,
The gallows hard to tread.

11. "They'll tie a napkin 'round my eyes
And ne'er let me see to dee;
They'll ne'er let on to my father and mother
That I'm far away o'er the sea.

12. "Last night there were four Maries,
Tonight there'll be but three;
There was Mary Beaton and Mary Seaton
And Mary Carmichael and me."

Chorus:

Last night there were four Marys,
Tonight there'll be but three;
There was Mary Seton and Mary Deaton
And Mary Carmichael and me.

They'll tie a napkin round my eyes,
They'll not let me see the deed,
And they'll never let on to my father and mother
But what I have gone o'er the sea.

GROUP E

10. "Mary Hamilton"

Gilchrist, *JEFDSS*, III, No. 1 (1936), p. 59. From the "Edinburgh MS.," "a sheet of manuscript airs . . . found amongst the papers of the late Frank Kidson."

a π^1, ending on VI

Yestreen the Queen had four Maries,
Tonight she'll hae but three.
There was Mary Beaton and Mary Seaton
And Mary Carmichael and me.

9. "The Four Marys"

Owens, 1950, p. 64. From the Bohler family, on the Neches river, near Silsbee, Texas.

a I

Oh, little did my mother think
When first she cradled me
That I should die so far from home
Or hang from a gallows tree.

GROUP F

11. "Mary Mild"

Greig and Keith, 1925, p. 109(1); text, p. 108(A). Sung by William Wallace, Leochel-Cushnie; learned from his mother about 70 years before (c. 1830).

m I/M

Compare the second half with the carol, "The Holly and the Ivy."

1. Word went up, an' word went doon,
An' word went through the ha',
That Mary Mild was great wi' child
To the highest Steward o a'.

. . . .

2. They've sought it up, an' so did they doon,
An' in below the bed;
There they found the little babe
Lyin wallowin in its blood.

. . . .

3. "Ye'll sit low doon by me, Mary Mild,
Ye'll sit low doon by me;
An' there's nae a favour that ye will ask
But I will grant it thee."

. . . .

4. "It's seyven lang years I had made the Queen's bed,
An' as lang dressed her hair.
But this is the reward that I'm to get,
The gallows tow to wear.

5. "There is Mary Beaton, an' Mary Seaton,
An' there's Mary Carmichael an' me;
This nicht there is four Maries o's,
But the morn there'll be but three."

6. "Will ye put on the black, the black,
Or will ye put on the broon?
Or will ye put on the sky-blue silk,
It would shine a' the toon?"

7. "I winna put on the black, the black,
Nor will I put on the broon,
But I'll put on the sky-blue silk,
To shine ower Edinburgh toon."

. . . .

GROUP G

12. "Mary Hamilton"

Barry, *BFSSNE*, No. 3 (1931), p. 8. From Miss Mary C. E. Jackson, who learned it in the 1880's from Mrs. Seville Martin Treat, Lynn, Mass.

a I/M (–VI) (compass of a fifth)

Last night there were four Maries,
This night there'll be but three;
There was Mary Beaton and Mary Seaton
And Mary Carmichael and me.

Captain Car, or, Edom o Gordon

CHILD NO. 178

Of this fine ballad, three tunes, all of the second half of the last century, have been recorded from tradition. There is, however, an older claimant for the place of honor: the Elizabethan tune supposed to be referred to in *Much Ado* as the "sick tune" (III. iv. 42). A ballad called "Sick, sick, &c." was licensed to be printed on March 24, 1578; another ballad on an incident of 1578, to the tune of "Sicke and sicke," is, as Chappell notes (*Popular Music* [1855-59], I, p. 226), in the *Harleian Miscellany*, X, p. 272. The latter is in eight-line CM stanzas rhyming alternately, with a four-line burden in the same metre as that of the A-text of "Captain Car." The present ballad is itself in CM quatrains followed in each case by the burden; but if the burden is to be sung to the same notes as the stanza, four lines will suit the tune as well as eight or twelve. The tune in question Chappell has found in Anthony Holborne's *Cittharn Schoole*, 1597, and in one of the Cambridge University lute MSS. (Dd. iv. 23). He prints a transcript, without saying which copy he follows (*loc.cit.*). The result is unsatisfactory in any case; and not much more can be said for other versions, of which one, for lute, has been lately transcribed and appears below.*

It is possible, if unlikely, that a ballad on a local incident in Scotland could be carried into England, and be Anglicized, and gain such currency that seven years after the actual event its burden would have become the accepted name of its tune. Since, however, burdens of this detachable kind are very rare in English balladry; since this one is not found in any other copy; and since, finally, it is not in the least appropriate to the ballad, which concerns matters very different from illness: it is easier to suppose that the burden got attached to this copy of the ballad when someone decided to sing the ballad to the tune of a pre-existent song with this burden—a song which itself has not survived, perhaps a song of the plague, something earlier and less artistic than Thomas Nashe's "Adieu, farewell earth's bliss," which yet has a very similar refrain. It is interesting that in the same work in which Nashe published his beautiful poem, he inserted a parody of the burden in question. (Cf. the extract published in Chappell, *loc.cit.*)

I take it, therefore, that the association of this tune and burden with our ballad is likely fortuitous and transient. The nineteenth-century tunes, on the contrary, though interestingly variant, are clearly related. They are forms of a tune in common use, however: the "Boyne Water" family. The earliest to be printed for this ballad is that in the second (1869) edition of Ritson's *Scotish Songs*. Its immediate provenience is not stated. Close variants are found with "Sir James the Rose" (Child No. 213). Greig and Keith, *Last Leaves*, give five examples; and it occurs with "Hardyknute," "Gil Morice" (Child No. 83), "Macdonald of the Isles" (No. 228), and no doubt elsewhere. The next copy to appear was Christie's, from an old Banffshire woman, who died in 1866 at the age of eighty and whose memory might therefore carry the tradition back to the beginning of the century and probably beyond. Christie has as usual given the tune a second strain: if there was one in the singer's version, it is yet unlikely that the whole tune had a compass of an octave and a sixth. This form of the tune probably belongs to the π^3 (–III, VI) type. A fourth, late record from New England appears to be a sport. Its tune is also found in the Florida copy of "Sir Hugh" (*ante*, No. 155, variant 11); the text is a literary *rifacimento* of Herd's version of the ballad, *Scottish Songs*, 1776, I, pp. 8-13 (reprinted 1869).

* See further, Claude M. Simpson, *The British Broadside Ballad and Its Music*, New Brunswick, 1966, pp. 660-61.

LIST OF VARIANTS

1. "The Sick Tune." David Lumsden, *An Anthology of English Lute Music* [1953], No. 37, p. 60.
2. "Sick, sick, and very sick." W. Chappell, *Popular Music of the Olden Time* [1855-59], I, p. 226.
3. " 'Adam' of Gordon." Joseph Ritson, *Scotish Songs*, ed. of 1869, II, p. 362.
4. "Edom o' Gordon." W. Christie, *Traditional Ballad Airs*, I, 1876, p. 56.
5. "Edom o' Gordon." Greig MSS., IV, p. 6, and Bk. 753, XLIII, p. 21a, King's College Library, Aberdeen. Also in Greig-Duncan MS. 785 (transcription of W. Walker), p. 89, King's College Library, Aberdeen; and Gavin Greig and Alexander Keith, *Last Leaves of Traditional Ballads and Ballad Airs*, 1925, p. 113. (Coutts)

APPENDIX

6. "Adam Gorman." Helen Hartness Flanders and Marguerite Olney, *Ballads Migrant in New England*, 1953, p. 134; and Helen Hartness Flanders, *Ancient Ballads Traditionally Sung in New England*, III, 1963, p. 174.

TUNES WITH TEXTS

1. [The Sick Tune]

Lumsden [1953], No. 37, p. 60. From Cambridge University MS., Dd. v. 78. 3, fol. 39 (first piece). Again, in MS. Dd. ix. 33, fol. 73-72v.

2. "Sick, sick, and very sick"

Chappell [1855-59], p. 226. From ?Anthony Holborne, *The Cittharn Schoole*, 1597.

m I, ending on *VI*

It befell at Martinmas,
When weather waxed cold,
Captain Car said to his men,
We must go take a hold.
Sick, sick, and very sick,
And sick and like to die;
The sickest night that I abode,
Good Lord, have mercy on me.

3. " 'Adam' of Gordon"

Ritson, ed. of 1869, II, p. 362.

p D/Æ

It fell about the Martinmas,
Quhen the wind blew schrile and cauld,
Said 'Adam' o' Gordon to his men,
We maun draw to a hauld.
[*Etc.*]

Ritson prints the Foulis text of 1755 (Child's D).

4. "Edom o' Gordon"

Christie, I, 1876, p. 56. From an old woman in Buckie, Banffshire (d. 1866, aged 80).

m π^3

It fell about the Martinmas,
When winds blew shrill and cauld,
Said Edom o' Gordon to his men,
"We maun draw to a hauld.
And whatna hauld shall we draw to,
My merrie men and me?
We will gae to the house o' Rodes,
To see that fair ladye."
[*Etc.*]

Christie "epitomizes" his text from Percy's *Reliques* (cf. Wheatley ed., 1910, I, p. 143) and Ritson's *Scottish Songs* (cf. ed. of 1869. II, p. 362).

5. "Edom o' Gordon"

Greig MSS., IV, p. 6; text, Bk. 753, XLIII, p. 21a. Also in Greig-Duncan MS. 785 (Walker transcript), p. 89; and Greig and Keith, 1925, p. 113. From Mrs. Coutts, Ellon.

p π^1

1. It fell aboot a Martmas time,
When the win' blew shrill & caul',
Says Edom o' Gordon to his men,
We maun draw to some ha'.

2. What ha', what ha', my merry men,
What ha', what ha' quoth he;
I think we'll gang to Towie's Hoose,
And see the fair ladie.

3. She thocht it was her ain dear lord
That she saw ridin' hame,
But 'twas that traitor Edom o' Gordon
That recked nae sin or shame.

4. Gie o'er your hoose, Lady Campbell, he cries,
Gie o'er your hoose to me;
Or I will burn you this nicht,
And a' your bairnies three.

5. I winna gie o'er my hoose, she says,
To laird nor yet to loon,
Nor yet to ony rank robber
That comes fae Auchindoun.

6. The lady fae the battlements
She leet twa bullets flee,
But it missed its mark wi' Gordon,
For it only grazed his knee.

7. . . . .
To bring the faggots near.

8. Haud yer (your) tongue—
I've paid ye lang yer fee;
And canna ye sit here the nicht,
And bear the reek wi' me.

9. Haud (your) yer tongue—
I've paid ye lang yer hire;
And canna ye sit here the nicht,
And bear wi' me the fire?

10. Up & spak' her young son there,
Sat on the nurse's knee,—
Open the door & lat me oot,
For the reek it's chokin' me.

11. I would gie a' my gowd, my child,
My silver & my fee,
For ae blast o' the western wind
To blaw the reek fae me (thee).

12. Then up it spak' her daughter dear,
. . . .
To row her in a pair o' sheets
And throw her o'er the wa.

13. They rowed her in a pair o' sheets,
And threw her o'er the wa',
But on the point o' Gordon's sword,
She got a deadly fa'.

14. Then Gordon turned her o'er & o'er again,
And oh, her face was white,—
I micht hae spared that bonnie face
To been some man's delight.

15. He turned her o'er & o'er again
And oh, her face was wan,
. . . .

16. And syne he turned till his men,
. . . .
For Towie's Hoose is in a flame,
Nae langer need we stay.

Because of the placement of ellipses, the division between the last stanzas is confusing in the MS. The arrangement here follows that in Greig and Keith, 1925, p. 111.

APPENDIX

6. "Adam Gorman"

Flanders and Olney, 1953, p. 134. Also in Flanders, III, 1963, p. 174. Sung by Mrs. Lily Delorme, Cadyville, N.Y., November 1943. From *Ballads Migrant in New England,* edited by Helen Hartness Flanders and Marguerite Olney; copyright 1953 by Helen Hartness Flanders.

a I

'Twas 'round about the Martin-mass,
When north winds froze the lake,
Said Adam Gorman to his men,
"We must some castle take!"
[*Etc.*]

See the headnote, final sentence.

The Bonny Earl of Murray

CHILD NO. 181

It is odd that Child did not note that this ballad appeared in the second edition of Thomson's *Orpheus Caledonius*, 1733, II, p. 8, an earlier date by seventeen years than that of the text he prints. It is the same text, except for variant spellings, and the readings *ha'e* for *have* in lines 2 and 3, and *ye* for *you* in line 2. Since Child says the song was not in the ninth edition of Ramsay's *Tea-Table Miscellany*, 1733, it would appear that Thomson is to be credited with its first printing, both text and tune. He was followed, according to Glen (*Early Scottish Melodies*, 1900, p. 119), by Barsanti, *A Collection of Old Scots Tunes*, 1742. The tune is also said to be in Oswald's *Caledonian Pocket Companion*, V [c. 1753], p. 14.* It was reprinted also in Neil Stewart's *Collection of Scots Songs* (1772, according to Glen); in Johnson's *Museum*; Ritson's *Scotish Songs*; R. A. Smith's *Scotish Minstrel*; Rimbault's *Musical Illustrations*; and Eyre-Todd's *Ancient Scots Ballads*. A late copy, collected from tradition in the 1920's in North Carolina, shows a curious, if distant, kinship, with this earliest of the ballad's musical records.

Christie gives a fresh tune which he traces back to his great-grandmother, c. 1760, in Buchan. Christie says his paternal grandmother sang this tune to "Young Grigor's Ghost" (Buchan, *Gleanings*, 1825, p. 26); and notes that it appears with "Frennet Hall" ("Fire of Frendraught," Child No. 196) in Johnson's *Museum*, III [1790], p. 286.

Two versions of another tune have appeared in our own century, one from tradition in Rye, New York, but going back to Scotland (variant 4); the other from a source unknown in Diack's *New Scottish Orpheus*, 1923-24 (variant 5). This has a mournful beauty, but seems not very folklike, or at any rate balladlike. Among the revivalists, however, it is the tune most likely to be known.

* Date according to J. C. Dick, ed., *The Songs of Robert Burns*, 1903, p. xli.

LIST OF VARIANTS

GROUP A

1. "The Bonny Earl of Murray." W. Thomson, *Orpheus Caledonius*, 1733, II, p. 8. Also in James Johnson, *The Scots Musical Museum*, II [1788], No. 177, p. 185 (repr. 1853); Joseph Ritson, *Scotish Songs*, 1794, II, p. 29; Robert Archibald Smith, *The Scotish Minstrel* [1820-24], IV, p. 101; Edward F. Rimbault, *Musical Illustrations of Bishop Percy's Reliques*, 1850, p. 68; and George Eyre-Todd, *Ancient Scots Ballads* [1894], p. 128.
2. "The Earl of Moray." Frank C. Brown MSS., 16 a 9, Library of Congress, photostat. Also in *The Frank C. Brown Collection of North Carolina Folklore*, IV (*The Music of the Ballads*, ed. Jan P. Schinhan), 1957, p. 83. Text, *Brown Collection*, II (*Folk Ballads from North Carolina*, ed. Henry M. Belden and Arthur Palmer Hudson), 1952, p. 160.

GROUP B

3. "The Bonny Earl of Murray." W. Christie, *Traditional Ballad Airs*, I, 1876, p. 202.

GROUP C

4. "Highlands and Lowlands." Elsie C. Parsons and Helen H. Roberts, *JAF*, XLIV (1931), p. 297.
5. "The bonnie Earl o' Murray." J. Michael Diack, *The New Scottish Orpheus*, II, 1923-24, p. 28. Also in John Goss, *Ballads of Britain*, 1937, p. 80(B).
6. "The Bonny Earl of Moray." Fred Williams, collected by Dorothea Jean Kirkhuff and Phyllis Klein; transcribed and sent to Editor by Edward Cray.

TUNES WITH TEXTS

GROUP A

1. "The Bonny Earl of Murray"

Thomson, 1733, II, p. 8. Also in Johnson, II [1788], No. 177, p. 185 (repr. 1853); Ritson, 1794, II, p. 29; Smith [1820-24], IV, p. 101; Rimbault, 1850, p. 68; and Eyre-Todd [1894], p. 128.

m M (–IV)

1. Ye *Highlands* and ye *Lawlands*,
Oh! where ha'e ye been:
They ha'e slain the Earl of *Murray*,
And they laid him on the Green.

2. Now wae be to thee *Huntly*,
And wherefore did ye sae;
I bad you bring him wi' you,
But forbad you him to slae.

3. He was a braw Gallant,
And he rid at the Ring;
And the bonny Earl of *Murray*,
Oh! he might have been a King.

4. He was a braw Gallant,
And he play'd at the Ba',
And the bonny Earl of *Murray*,
Was the Flower amang them a'.

5. He was a braw Gallant,
And he play'd at the Glove,
And the bonny Earl of *Murray*,
Oh! he was the Queen's Love.

6. Oh! lang will his Lady,
Look o'er the Castle-*Down*,
E'er she see the Earl of *Murray*,
Come sounding through the Town.

2. "The Earl of Moray"

Brown MSS., 16 a 9. Also in Schinhan, *Music, Brown Collection*, IV, 1957, p. 83. Text, Belden and Hudson, *Folk Ballads, Brown Collection*, II, 1952, p. 160. Sung by "Aunt Becky" Gordon, Stateline Hill, Henderson County, N.C., October 8, 1927. Collected by Mrs. Maude M. Sutton.

p π^1 (compass of a sixth)

The first two phrases suggest Thomson's first; the third of this suggests Thomson's third when lowered an octave; the closing phrases of both are not unlike. The range of the Thomson tune is so extreme that tradition would naturally find easier equivalents for the upper octave, and sheer coincidence seldom goes beyond a phrase. The change of metre is a common phenomenon.

1. Ye Highlands and ye Lowlands, it's where have ye been?
Oh, they've slain the Earl of Mo-ray and laid him on the ground.

2. Oh, he was a handsome feller, and wore a leather glove.
Oh, the bonny Earl of Mo-ray he was the Queen's love.

3. He was a noble rider, a-ridin' through the town,
And all the pretty ladies they watched him up and down.

4. He was a gallant player, a-playin' at the ball;
Oh, the bonny Earl of Mo-ray was the flower of them all.

5. He was a handsome feller and wore a golden ring.
Oh, the bonny Earl of Mo-ray he ort to a been king.

GROUP B

3. "The Bonny Earl of Murray"

Christie, I, 1876, p. 202. Passed down in the family from Christie's maternal great-grandmother, of Buchan, and dated back to 1760.

a M/D

Ye Highlands, and ye Lawlands,
O where have you been?
They have slain the Earl of Murray,
And they laid him on the green.
"Now wae be to thee, Huntly!
And wherefore did you sae?
I bade you bring him wi' you,
But forbade you him to slay."
[*Etc.*]

Christie's text is from *The Tea-Table Miscellany* (cf. ed. 1871, II, p. 158).

GROUP C

4. "Highlands and Lowlands"

Parsons and Roberts, *JAF*, XLIV (1931), p. 297. Sung by Mrs. May F. Hoisington of Rye, N.Y. Learned in 1906 from a Scot who had heard it from a kinsman of the Murray family.

p I/Ly

Ye highlands and ye lowlands,
Oh where ha' ye been?
They have slain the earl of Moray
And have laid him on the green.
He was a bra' gallant
And he playèd at the glove
And the bonny Earl of Moray
He was the queeny's love.

Ye highlands and ye lowlands,
Oh where ha' ye been?
They have slain the Earl of Moray
And have laid him on the green.
He was a bra' gallant
And he playèd at the ring
And the bonny Earl of Moray
He might ha' been the king.

Oh wae's me for ye, Huntley,
And wherefore did ye sae?
I bade ye him to capture
And forbade ye him to slay.
He was a bra' gallant
And he playèd at the ring
And the bonny Earl of Moray
He might ha' been the king.

Oh lang may his lady
Look fra' the castle doon
Ere the bonny Earl of Moray
Comes sounding through the toon.

5. "The bonnie Earl o' Murray"

Diack, II, 1923-24, p. 28. Also in Goss, 1937, p. 80(B).

p I/Ly

Ye Hielands and ye Lowlands,
O where ha'e ye been?
They hae slain the Earl o' Murray,
And laid him on the green;
He was a braw gallant,
And he rade at the ring;
And the bonnie Earl o' Murray,
He micht ha'e been a king!
O lang will his leddy
Look owre frae castle Doune,
Ere she see the Earl o' Murray
Come soundin' thro' the toon!

Noo wae be to thee, Huntly,
And wherefore did ye sae?
I bade ye bring him wi' ye,
But forbade ye him to slay:
He was a braw gallant,
And he play'd at the ba';
And the bonnie Earl o' Murray
Was the flow'r amang them a'.
O lang will his leddy
Look owre frae castle Doune,
Ere she see the Earl o' Murray
Come soundin' thro' the toon!

6. "The Bonny Earl of Moray"

Sung by Fred Williams of upper New York state; learned from an old Scotchman in Buffalo. Collected in Long Beach, Calif., in 1959, by Dorothea Jean Kirkhuff and Phyllis Klein. Transcribed for the Editor by Edward Cray.

p I/Ly

The timing seems doubtful but I have not ventured to adjust it.

Ye heelands and ye lowlands,
Oh where hae ye been.
They hae slain the Earl of Moray
An' laid him on the green.

He was a braw gallant
An' he played at the glove (*sic*)
And the Bonny Earl of Moray,
He was the Queen's love.

Oh, lang will his lady,
Look frae the castle doon,
Ere she see the Earl of Moray
Come stumblin' frae the toon.

Away ye Huntley
And wherefore be dead
I bade ye bring him wi' ye,
An' forbade ye him to slay.

He was a braw gallant
An' he rayed (*sic*) the ring.
And the bonny Earl of Moray,
He must have been a king.

Oh, lang will his Lady
Look frae the castle doon,
Ere she see the Earl of Moray
Come stumblin' frae the toon.

The Laird o Logie

CHILD NO. 182

THE three tunes on record that I have seen for this ballad appear to have no kinship, nor can one do much for them in the way of illustration. They are of approximately the same era. Two are in duple rhythm, the other in triple. Mrs. Harris's is a four-phrase, Motherwell's a six-phrase, and Christie's, as usual in his handling, an eight-phrase, or two-strain, tune. All three are hexatonic, but of different modes.

Mrs. Harris's tune is transparently a variant of the "Hind Horn" family. But it is odd in its revelation of kinship to the old "Duke of Norfolk" tune (cf. Playford, *The English Dancing Master*, 1651 and subsequently). Now, since Scott had a version of the present ballad which was sung to "Logan Water," the weight of tradition is thrown to Mrs. Harris for the tune. For "Logan Water" is the "Hind Horn" tune. Under the first name, it was well known in the seventeenth and eighteenth centuries. The tune appears in Ramsay's *Musick*, c. 1726, as noted by J. C. Dick, ed., *Songs of Robert Burns*, 1903, p. 458, q.v. also for a number of other references. Cf. also Glen, *Early Scottish Melodies*, 1900, pp. 49-50.

The Motherwell tune has an ambiguous tonal feeling. If we abandon the tune's final as tonic, we are at once adrift on a sea of possibilities. If the final is tonic, we have a hexatonic M/D (–III) tune; if the tonic be A, then the tune is D/Æ (–VI); if a stronger major feeling be sensed in the tune, then on C we get I/Ly (–IV), and on G, I/M (–VII). I find myself perplexed to decide.

Christie had so liberal an idea of the legitimate powers of an editor that it is puzzling to know what ought to be done in the way of reconstruction. The second strain is pretty certainly due to him; but the final itself, in both strains, seems so much less in keeping than E for this tune that one doubts whether E be not the true tonic. If so, the tune would be brought into the D/Æ field.

There is said to be a tune in the Bunyan MS., 1877, p. 115. (Cf. Gray-Muir MS., NL Scotland MS. 2254.)

LIST OF VARIANTS

GROUP A

1. "Young Logie." Harris MS., No. 17, and fol. 16, Harvard College Library. Also in Francis James Child, *The English and Scottish Popular Ballads*, 1882-98, V, p. 421, and III, p. 455(D).

GROUP B

2. "May Margaret." William Motherwell, *Minstrelsy: Ancient and Modern*, 1827, App'x., No. 25 and p. xxii.

GROUP C

3. "The Laird of Ochiltrie." W. Christie, *Traditional Ballad Airs*, II, 1881, p. 170.

TUNES WITH TEXTS

GROUP A

1. "Young Logie"

Harris MS., No. 17; text, fol. 16. Also in Child, 1882-98, V, p. 421; text, III, p. 455(D). From Mrs. Amelia Harris; learned from an old nurse during childhood in Perthshire, late eighteenth century. Noted by her daughter.

p D/Æ

1. Pretty is the story I hae to tell,
   Pretty is the praisin o itsel,
   An pretty is the prisner oor king's tane,
   The rantin young laird o Logie.

2. Has he brunt? or has he slain?
   Or has he done any injurie?
   Oh, no, no, he's done nothing at all,
   But stown a kiss frae the queen's marie.

3. Ladie Margaret cam doon the stair,
   Wringin her hands an tearin her hair;
   Cryin, Oh, that ever I to Scotland cam,
   Aye to see Young Logie dee!

4. "Had your tongue noo, Lady Margaret,
   An a' your weepin lat a bee!
   For I'll gae to the king my sell,
   An plead for life to Young Logie."

5. "First whan I to Scotland cam,
You promised to gie me askens three;
The first then o these askens is
Life for the young laird o Logie."

6. "If you had asked house or lands,
They suld hae been at your command;
But the morn, ere I taste meat or drink,
High hanged sall Young Logie be."

7. Lady Margaret cam doon the stair,
Wringin her hands an tearin her hair;
Cryin, Oh, that ever I to Scotland cam,
A' to see Young Logie dee!

8. "Haud your tongue noo, Lady Margaret,
An a' your weepin lat a bee!
For I'll counterfiet the king's hand-write,
An steal frae him his richt hand gloe,
An send them to Pitcairn's wa's,
A' to lat Young Logie free."

9. She counterfieted the king's hand-write,
An stole frae him his richt hand gloe,
An sent them to Pitcairn's wa's,
A' to let Young Logie free.

10. The king luikit owre his castle-wa,
Was luikin to see what he cald see:
"My life to wad an my land to pawn,
Yonder comes the young laird o Logie!"

11. "Pardon, oh pardon! my lord the king,
Aye I pray you pardon me;
For I counterfieted your hand-write,
An stole frae you your richt hand gloe,
An sent them to Pitcairn's wa's,
A' to set Young Logie free."

12. "If this had been done by laird or lord,
Or by baron of high degree,
I'se mak it sure, upon my word,
His life suld hae gane for Young Logie.

13. "But since it is my gracious queen,
A hearty pardon we will gie,
An for her sake we'll free the loon,
The rantin young laird o Logie."

The text here given is from Child. In the MS. the first stanza reads:

Prettie is the storie I hae to tell,
An prettie is the praisin o' itsel;
Prettie is the prisoner oo'r King's ta'en,
The rantin' young Laird o' Logie.

GROUP B

2. "May Margaret"

Motherwell, 1827, App'x., No. 25; text, App'x., p. xxii. Tune from Andrew Blaikie, Paisley.

a M/D (or if A, p D/Æ; if C tonic, a I/Ly; if G tonic, p I/M)

The last two lines of each quatrain must have been repeated to the tune.

Lament, lament na, May Margaret,
And of your weeping let me be,
For ye maun to the king himsell
To seek the life o' young Logie.

GROUP C

3. "The Laird of Ochiltrie"

Christie, II, 1881, p. 170. Tune from Jenny Meesic, c. 1850.

a I/M

O listen gude people to my tale,
Listen to what I tell to thee,
The king has taken a poor prisoner,
The wanton laird of Ochiltrie.
When news came to our guidly queen,
She sicht and said richt mournfullie,—
"O what will come of lady Margaret,
Wha bears sic love to Ochiltrie?"
[*Etc.*]

Christie's text follows that in David Herd, *Ancient and Modern Scottish Songs*, 1776, I, p. 21.

Willie Macintosh

CHILD NO. 183

The two texts printed by Child are perpetuated in the two copies since collected from oral sources. Child's A was printed in Alexander Laing's *The Thistle of Scotland*, Aberdeen, 1823, collated with Alexander Whitelaw's *The Book of Scottish Ballads* [1845], the latter said to be taken from an Aberdeen newspaper of about 1815. The slight verbal differences in Whitelaw are obviously only for metrical smoothness, but there is also a new stanza supplanting Laing's last two. The B text is prior in date: it was "recollected by a lady and communicated by Walter Scott" to John Finlay, who published it in his *Scottish Historical and Romantic Ballads*, 1808. Barry, Eckstorm, and Smyth in 1929 published a text learned in Scotland by Mrs. James McGill, of Chamcook, New Brunswick (*British Ballads from Maine*, 1929, p. 264). It was learned not as a song but as verses, and is obviously derived from Whitelaw. Mrs. McGill had never heard it sung. Latterly, Ewan MacColl has recorded the ballad with a tune learned from his father and a text from Child's B, or Finlay. In spite of Barry's sense that it was not made for singing, it goes with stirring effect as a song.

LIST OF VARIANTS

"The Burning o' Auchendoun." Ewan MacColl, Riverside recording No. RLP 12-628(A1), *The English and Scottish Popular Ballads*, IV, ed. Kenneth S. Goldstein.

TUNE WITH TEXT

"The Burning o' Auchendoun"

Sung by Ewan MacColl, Riverside rec. No. RLP 12-628(A1), ed. K. S. Goldstein.

m D

1. As I cam' in by Fiddich Side,
 On a May mornin',
I spied Willie Mackintosh
 An hour before the dawnin'.

2. Turn again, turn again,
 Turn again I bid ye.
If ye burn Auchendoun,
 Huntley he will heid ye.

3. Heid me or hang me,
 That shall never fear me;
I'll burn Auchendoun
 Though the life leave me.

4. As I cam' in by Fiddich Side
 On a May mornin',
Auchendoun was in a blaze,
 An hour before the dawnin'.

5. Crawin', crawin',
 For a' your crouse crawin',
Ye brunt your crop and tint your wings
 An hour before the dawnin'.

Dick o the Cow

CHILD NO. 185

As Child notes, Ritson called attention to an allusion in Nashe's *Have with you to Saffren Walden*, 1596, which would indicate that this ballad, or something like it, was known at that date: "Dick of the Cow, that mad demi-lance northren borderer, who plaied his prizes with the lord Jockey so bravely." A reference in 1613 and another in 1688 make up the sum of surviving seventeenth-century allusion to Dick. No other occurs till the copy of the ballad sent to Percy in 1775, from which Child prints his copy a. A second copy, Child's b, was printed by Caw in *The Poetical Museum*, 1784, the first ever to be published. Scott followed this in his *Minstrelsy*, 1802, and in the 1833 edition conflated it with a third, which had been taken down from singing in 1816 and printed, with its proper tune, in *Albyn's Anthology*, II [1818], p. 31. The tune, slightly modified, also appeared in the revised *Minstrelsy*. There is a very imperfect copy of the same tune in Lady John Scott's MS., NL Scotland MS. 840, with fifty-two stanzas of text. So far as I have discovered, no other tune has been sung or printed. The copy of 1818 is here given as the most painstaking and accurate. The others have no difference worthy of record. It ought perhaps to be noted that the refrain varies somewhat in the three basic texts; but as printed in a, it may probably only be intended as a short indication of kind and position—this would accord with the accurate transcript of c. The refrain in Caw's version is entirely omitted by Scott; but if it is accurately reported, as coming after the first and fourth line in an identical form, another tune would seem to be implied—or at least a considerable variation of the one we have: to be more specific, such a tune as that of "Jock o the Side" (No. 187), in Campbell's version, which came from the same family as his "Dick o the Cow" (the Shortreeds, father and son[s]).

LIST OF VARIANTS

"Dick o' the Cow." Alexander Campbell, *Albyn's Anthology*, II [1818], p. 30. Also in Lady John Scott's MS., National Library of Scotland MS. 840; and Sir Walter Scott, *The Poetical Works of Sir Walter Scott*, 1833-34, II, opp. p. 62.

TUNE WITH TEXT

"Dick o' the Cow"

Campbell, II [1818], p. 30. Also in Lady John Scott's MS., NL Scotland MS. 840; and Scott, 1833-34, II, opp. p. 62. Sung by Robert Shortreed, Liddesdale, 1816.

m I

The variant is as in the *Minstrelsy*, cited above.

1. Now Liddesdale has layen lang in,
Lal de ral, lal de ral, lal de ral, la lal de:
There is nae riding there at a';
Lal de ral, lal de ral, lal de ral, la dal de:
The horses are grown sae lither fat,
They downa stur out o' the sta'.
Lal lal de ridle la di, fal lal de ridle la di,
Fal lal di lal la, fal lal di ridle la.

2. Fair Johnie Armstrang to Willie did say—
"Billie, a-riding we will gae;
England and us have been lang at feid,
Ablins we'll light on some bootie."—

3. Then they are come on to Hutton Ha';
They rade that proper place about;
But the Laird he was the wiser man,
For he had left nae gear without.

4. For he had left nae gear to steal,
Except sax sheep upon a lee:
Quo' Johnie—"I'd rather in England die,
Ere thir sax sheep gae to Liddesdale wi' me."—

5. —"But how ca' they the man we last met,
Billie, as we cam' o'er the know?"—
"That same he is an innocent fule,
And men they call him Dick o' the Cow."—

6. "That fule has three as gude ky of his ain,
As there are in a' Cumberland, billie," quo' he:—
"Betide me life, betide me death,
These ky shall go to Liddesdale wi' me."—

7. Then they have come on to the poor fule's house,
And they hae broken his wa's sae wide;
They have loosed out Dick o' the Cow's three ky,
And ta'en three co'erlets frae his wife's bed.

8. Then on the morn when the day was light,
The shouts and cries rase loud and hie;
—"O had thy tongue, my wife," he says,
"And o' thy crying let me be!

9. "O had thy tongue, my wife," he says,
"And o' thy crying let me be;
And aye where thou hast lost ae cow,
In gude suith I shall bring thee three."

10. Now Dickie's gane to the gude Lord Scroop,
And I wat a dreirie fule was he;
—"Now had thy tongue, my fule," he says,
"For I may not stand to jest wi' thee."—

11. "Shame fa' your jesting, my Lord!" quo' Dickie,
"For nae sic jesting grees wi' me;
Liddesdale's been in my house last night
And they hae awa my three ky frae me.

12. "But I may nae langer in Cumberland dwell,
To be your puir fule and your leal,
Unless you gi' me leave, my Lord,
To gae to Liddesdale and steal."—

13. "I gi'e thee leave! my fule," he says—
"Thou speakest against my honour and me;
Unless thou gi' me thy trowth and thy hand,
Thou'lt steal frae nane but whae sta' frae thee."—

14. —"There is my trowth and my right hand,
My head shall hang on Hairibee;
I'll ne'er cross Carlisle sands again,
If I steal frae a man but whae sta' frae me."—

15. Dickie's ta'en leave o' lord and master,
I wat a merry fule was he!
He's bought a bridle and a pair of new spurs,
And pack'd them up in his breek thie.

16. Then Dickie's come on to Pudding-burn house,
E'en as fast as he might drie;
Then Dickie's come on to Pudding-burn,
Where there were thirty Armstrangs and three.

[*2 stanzas here in Scott*]

17. "I'm come to plain o' your man, fair Johnie Armstrang,
And syne o' his billie Willie," quo' he;
"How they've been in my house last night,
And they hae ta'en my three ky frae me."—

18. —"Ha!" quo fair Johnie Armstrang, "we will him hang."—
—"Na," quo' Willie, "we'll him slae."—
Than up and spak another young Armstrang,
"We'll gie him his batts and let him gae."—

19. But up and spak the gude Laird's Jock,
The best falla in a' the cumpanie;
—"Sit down thy ways a little while, Dickie,
And a piece o' thy ain cow's hough I'll gie ye."—

20. But Dickie's heart it grew sae grit,
That the ne'er a bit o't he dought to eat—
Then was he aware of an auld peat house,
Where a' the night he thought for to sleep.

21. Then Dickie was ware of an auld peat house,
Where a' the night he thought for to lye—
And a' the prayers the pure fule prayed
Were, "I wish I had amends for my gude three ky!"—

[*1 stanza here in Scott*]

22. The lads that hungry and weary were,
Abune the door-head they threw the key;
Dickie he took good notice o' that,
Says—"There will be a bootie for me."—

23. Then Dickie has into the stable gane,
Where there stood thirty horses and three;
He has tied them a' wi' St. Mary's knot,
A' these horses but barely three.

24. He has tied them a' wi' St Mary's knot,
A' these horses but barely three;
He's loupen on ane, ta'en another in hand,
And away as fast as he can hie.

25. But on the morn, when the day grew light,
The shouts and cries raise loud and hie—
—"Ah! whae has done this?" quo' the gude Laird's Jock,
"Tell me the truth and the verity."—

26. "Whae has done this deed?" quo' the gude Laird's Jock;
—"See that to me ye dinna lie!"
—"Dickie has been in the stable last night,
And has ta'en my brother's horse and mine frae me."—

27. —"Ye wad ne'er be tald," quo' the gude Laird's Jock;
"Have ye not found my tales fu' leil?
Ye ne'er wad out o' England bide,
Till crooked, and blind, and a' would steal."—

28. —"But lend me thy bay," Fair Johnie can say,
"There's nae horse loose in the stable save he;
And I'll either fetch Dick o' the Cow again,
Or the day is come that he shall die."—

[*1 stanza here in Scott*]

29. He has ta'en the Laird's jack on his back,
A twa-handed sword to hang by his thie;
He has ta'en a steil-cap on his head,
And galloped on to follow Dickie.

30. Dickie was na a mile frae aff the town,
I wat a mile but barely three,
When he was o'erta'en by Fair Johnie Armstrang,
Hand for hand on Cannobie lee.

[*4 stanzas here in Scott*]

31. Then Johnie let a speir fu' laigh by his thie,
Thought weil to hae slain the innocent, I trow;
But the powers above were mair than he,
For he ran but the puir fule's jerkin through.

32. Together they ran, or ever they blan;
This was Dickie the fule and he—
Dickie could na win at him wi' the blade o' the sword,
But feld him wi' the plummet under the e'e.

33. Thus Dickie has feld Fair Johnie Armstrang,
The prettiest man in the south country—
—"Gramercy!" then can Dickie say,
"I had but twa horse, thou hast made me thrie!"—

34. He's ta'en the steil-jack aff Johnie's back,
The twa-handed sword that hang low by his thie;
He's ta'en the steil-cap aff his head—
—"Johnie, I'll tell my master I met wi' thee."—

35. When Johnie wakened out o' his dream,
I wat a dreirie man was he:
—"And is thou gane? Now, Dickie, than
The shame and dule is left wi' me.

36. "And is thou gane? Now, Dickie, than
The deil gae in thy cumpanie!
For if I should live these hundred years,
I ne'er shall fight wi' a fule after thee."—

37. Then Dickie's come hame to the good Lord Scroop,
E'en as fast as he might hie—
—"Now, Dickie, I'll neither eat nor drink,
Till hie hanged thou shalt be."—

38. —"The shame speed the liars, my Lord!" quo' Dickie;
"This was na the promise ye made to me!
For I'd ne'er gane to Liddesdale to steal,
Had I not got my leave frae thee."—

39. —"But what garr'd thee steal the Laird's Jock's horse?
And, limmer, what garr'd ye steal him?" quo' he;
"For lang thou mightst in Cumberland dwelt,
Ere the Laird's Jock had stown frae thee."—

40. —"Indeed I wat ye lied, my Lord!
And e'en sae loud as I hear ye lie!
I wan the horse frae Fair Johnie Armstrang,
Hand to hand on Cannobie Lee."

41. "There is the jack was on his back,
This twa-handed sword hang laigh by his thie,
And there's the steil-cap was on his head;
I brought a' these tokens to let thee see."—

42. —"If that be true thou to me tells,
(And I think thou dares na tell a lie,)
I'll gie thee fifteen punds for the horse,
Well tald on thy cloak-lap shall be."

[2 *stanzas here in Scott*]

43. He's gien him twenty punds for the gude horse,
A' in goud and gude monie;
He's gien him ane o' his best milk ky,
To maintain his wife and children thrie.

44. Then Dickie's come down thro' Carlisle toun,
E'en as fast as he could drie;
The first o' men that he met wi'
Was my Lord's brother, Bailiff Glozenburrie.

45. —"Well be ye met, my gude Ralph Scroop!"—
"Welcome, my brother's fule!" quo' he;
"Where didst thou get Fair Johnie Armstrang's horse?"
—"Where did I get him? but steal him," quo' he.—

[3 *stanzas here in Scott*]

46. He's gi'en him twenty punds for the gude horse,
Baith in goud and gude monie;
He's gi'en him ane o' his best milk ky,
To maintain his wife and children thrie.

47. Then Dickie lap a loup fu' hie,
And I wat a loud laugh laughed he—
—"I wish the neck o' the third horse were broken,
If ony of the twa were better than he."

48. Then Dickie's come hame to his wife again,
Judge ye how the poor fule had sped:
He has gi'en her twa score English pund,
For the thrie auld coverlets taen aff her bed.

49. —"And tak thee these twa as gude ky,
I trow as a' thy thrie might be;
And yet here is a white-footed nagie,
I trow he'll carry baith thee and me.

50. "But I may nae langer in Cumberland bide,
The Armstrangs they would hang me hie."—
So Dickie's ta'en leave at lord and master,
And at Burgh under Stanmuir there dwells he.

"This celebrated Border (or rather Liddesdale) Ballad, is here given, as taken down by the present Editor, from the singing and recitation of a Liddesdale-man, namely, Robert Shortreed, Esq. Sheriff-substitute of Roxburghshire, in the autumn of 1816. In consequence of which the public are now in full possession of what partly appeared in the *Hawick Museum* 1784 [i.e., Caw's *Poetical Museum*], and afterwards a more perfect edition in the Minstrelsy of the Scottish Border, 1802. This popular Ballad is thus completed, by its melody being united to it; which seems to the present Editor to have a strong English *gout*, rather than a true Scottish flavour; but in this point he may be wrong; however it is certainly a spirited air, and highly worthy of musical record." [*Campbell's note.*]

Kinmont Willie

CHILD NO. 186

The authenticity of this piece of balladry has been debated variously and at length. One perusal is enough to convince the habitual ballad-reader that a very large part of its peculiar merit is owing to the Wizard who is its sole voucher. If Scott were its actual creator, however, instead of its mere agent of transfiguration, one would hardly have expected to find it appearing in a collection like *Albyn's Anthology* less than a decade and a half after its first publication. It need not disturb us that the text of this copy is Scott's own text; for the purpose of practically all the earlier musical editors was not to produce the texts actually sung to their tune, but, primarily, the tune *plus* an attractive text.

Nevertheless, there are disquieting considerations in this case. Campbell prints the ballad "to its own original melody." He gives us no hint as to where he found this melody, a suspicious circumstance when set against his full information in regard to other songs in the collection. Again, while some such phrase as "to its own tune" is not infrequently found on earlier broadsides, here it may be read as an ambiguous avowal that the editor or another has invented the tune, but with the certain intention of avoiding explicit confession of that fact. Had Campbell actually discovered the song in traditional currency—which is to say, a fresh text and a tune hitherto unrecovered—it seems unlikely that he would have rested content with so modest a statement of his achievement, and without a note on the state of the text and his reason for suppressing it in favor of Scott's. Although he may have been the dupe of deception, he is himself open to the suspicion of an independent effort to deceive. At any rate, we can be fairly certain that Scott is not implicated in this musical part of the deception, if deception there was: first, because Campbell would have been happy to acknowledge his obligation in so distinguished a quarter; and secondly, because Scott himself is the last person who would have been likely to have concocted anything of the kind. Support for the latter assertion lies in a note in Scott's transcript (in his own hand) of Mrs. Brown's ballads with their tunes: "The Music is copied as exactly as possible but as I do not know the value of a single note I [am] no judge of its merit" (Abbotsford MS. N 3 (1795), fol. 11; cf. Child, 1882-98, IV, p. 387, and Harvard College Library MS. 25241.23).

What evidence can be gathered from the tune itself is again negative. To be sure, the tune is in two strains and thus carries a double stanza. This fact certainly adds doubt of its being given just as it was sung in tradition; but there *are* two-strain ballad-tunes, and editors felt free to extend the tunes—Christie nearly always did so—so that the basic authenticity of the tune itself is not thereby necessarily impugned. The first strain, to which the tune reverts at the end, is of the most rudimentary sort, and certainly demanded no inspired powers to invent. It oscillates monotonously within a fifth from tonic to dominant, and repeats its two phrases with hardly more change than the words induce. A further circumstance which might deepen one's suspicion is that it calls up no associations, but seems to occupy a solitary position. At least, tunes imbedded in tradition generally have relatives; but this one, while not wearing any obvious marks of alien provenance, is not vouched by family resemblances. It might possibly be thought a debased variant of "Bonnie Doon" but, since the latter tune was familiarly current in tradition, the concealed resemblance here would be an argument for conscious invention.

On the whole, then, one gains no confidence from the tune in the genuineness of the ballad as a traditional song. Nor is it found in later tradition, so far as I can discover.

LIST OF VARIANTS

"Kinmont Willie." Alexander Campbell, *Albyn's Anthology*, I [1816], p. 78.

TUNE WITH TEXT

"Kinmont Willie"

Campbell, I [1816], p. 78, "to its own original melody."

a D/Æ

1. O have ye na heard o' the fause Sakelde?
   O have ye na heard o' the keen Lord Scroope?
   How they hae ta'en bauld Kinmont Willie,
   On Haribee to hang him up?

2. Had Willie had but twenty men,
   But twenty men as stout as he,
   Fause Sakelde had never the Kinmont ta'en,
   Wi' eight score in his cumpanie.

3. They band his legs beneath the steed,
   They tied his hands behind his back;
   They guarded him, fivesome on each side,
   And they brought him ower the Liddel-rack.

4. They led him thro' the Liddel-rack,
   And also thro' the Carlisle sands;
   They brought him to Carlisle castell,
   To be at my Lord Scroope's commands.

5. "My hands are tied, but my tongue is free,
And whae will dare this deed avow?
Or answer by the Border law?
Or answer to the bauld Buccleuch?"—

6. "Now haud thy tongue, thou rank reiver!
There's never a Scot shall set thee free:
Before ye cross my castle yate,
I trow ye shall take farewell o' me."

7. "Fear na ye that, my lord," quo' Willie:
"By the faith o' my body, Lord Scroope," he said,
"I never yet lodged in a hostelrie,
But I paid my lawing before I gaed."—

8. Now word is gane to the bauld Keeper,
In Branksome Ha', where that he lay,
That Lord Scroope has ta'en the Kinmont Willie,
Between the hours of night and day.

9. He has ta'en the table wi' his hand,
He garr'd the red wine spring on hie—
"Now Christ's curse on my head," he said,
"But avenged of Lord Scroope I'll be!

10. "O is my basnet a widow's curch?
Or my lance a wand of the willow-tree?
Or my arm a ladye's lilye hand,
That an English lord should lightly me!

11. "And have they ta'en him, Kinmont Willie,
Against the truce of Border tide?
And forgotten that the bauld Buccleuch
Is Keeper here on the Scottish side?

12. "And have they e'en ta'en him, Kinmont Willie,
Withouten either dread or fear?
And forgotten that the bauld Buccleuch
Can back a steed, or shake a spear?

13. "O were there war between the lands,
As well I wot that there is none,
I would slight Carlisle castell high,
Though it were builded of marble stone.

14. "I would set that castell in a low,
And sloken it with English blood!
There's never a man in Cumberland,
Should ken where Carlisle castell stood.

15. "But since nae war's between the lands,
And there is peace, and peace should be;
I'll neither harm English lad or lass,
And yet the Kinmont freed shall be!"

16. He has call'd him forty Marchmen bauld,
I trow they were of his ain name,
Except Sir Gilbert Elliot, call'd
The Laird of Stobs, I mean the same.

17. He has call'd him forty Marchmen bauld,
Were kinsmen to the bauld Buccleuch;
With spur on heel, and splent on spauld,
And gleuves of green, and feathers blue.

18. There were five and five before them a',
Wi' hunting-horns and bugles bright:
And five and five came wi' Buccleuch,
Like warden's men, array'd for fight.

19. And five and five, like a mason gang,
That carried the ladders lang and hie;
And five and five, like broken men;
And so they reach'd the Woodhouselee.

20. And as we cross'd the Bateable Land,
When to the English side we held,
The first o' men that we met wi',
Whae sould it be but fause Sakelde?

21. "Where be ye gaun, ye hunters keen?"
Quo' fause Sakelde; "come tell to me!"—
"We go to hunt an English stag,
Has trespass'd on the Scots countrie."

22. "Where be ye gaun, ye marshal men?"
Quo' fause Sakelde; "come tell me true!"—
"We go to catch a rank reiver,
Has broken faith wi' the bauld Buccleuch."

23. "Where are ye gaun, ye mason lads,
Wi' a' your ladders, lang and hie?"—
"We gang to herry a corbie's nest,
That wons not far frae Woodhouselee."—

24. "Where be ye gaun, ye broken men?"
Quo' fause Sakelde; "come tell to me!"—
Now Dickie of Dryhope led that band,
And the nevir a word of lear had he.

25. "Why trespass ye on the English side?
Row-footed outlaws, stand!" quo' he;
The nevir a word had Dickie to say,
Sae he thrust the lance through his fause bodie.

26. Then on we held for Carlisle toun,
And at Staneshaw-bank the Eden we cross'd;
The water was great and meikle of spait,
But the nevir a horse nor man we lost.

27. And when we reach'd the Staneshaw-bank,
The wind was rising loud and hie;
And there the Laird garr'd leave our steeds,
For fear that they should stamp and nie.

28. And when we left the Staneshaw-bank,
The wind began full loud to blaw;
But 'twas wind and weet, and fire and sleet,
When we came beneath the castle wa'.

29. We crept on knees, and held our breath,
Till we placed the ladders against the wa';
And sae ready was Buccleuch himsell
To mount the first before us a'.

30. He has ta'en the watchman by the throat,
He flung him down upon the lead—
"Had there not been peace between our lands,
Upon the other side thou hadst gaed!—

31. "Now sound out, trumpets!" quo' Buccleuch;
"Let's waken Lord Scroope right merrilie!"—
Then loud the warden's trumpet blew—
O wha dare meddle wi' me? (sic)

32. Then speedilie to wark we gaed,
And raised the slogan ane and a',
And cut a hole through a sheet of lead,
And so we wan to the castle ha'.

33. They thought King James and a' his men
Had won the house wi' bow and spear;
It was but twenty Scots and ten,
That put a thousand in sic a stear!

34. Wi' coulters, and wi' forehammers,
We garr'd the bars bang merrilie,
Until we came to the inner prison,
Where Willie o' Kinmont he did lie.

35. And when we cam to the lower prison,
Where Willie o' Kinmont he did lie—
"O sleep ye, wake ye, Kinmont Willie,
Upon the morn that thou's to die?"—

36. "O I sleep saft, and I wake aft;
It's lang since sleeping was fley'd frae me!
Gie my service back to my wife and bairns,
And a' gude fellows that spier for me."—

37. Then Red Rowan has hente him up,
The starkest man in Teviotdale—
"Abide, abide now, Red Rowan,
Till of my Lord Scroope I take farewell.

38. "Farewell, farewell, my gude Lord Scroope!
My gude Lord Scroope, farewell!" he cried—
"I'll pay you for my lodging maill,
When first we meet on the Border side."—

39. Then shoulder high, with shout and cry,
We bore him down the ladder lang;
At every stride Red Rowan made,
I wot the Kinmont's airns play'd clang!

40. "O mony a time," quo' Kinmont Willie,
"I have ridden horse baith wild and wood;
But a rougher beast than Red Rowan
I ween my legs have ne'er bestrode.

41. "And mony a time," quo' Kinmont Willie,
"I've prick'd a horse out oure the furs;
But since the day I back'd a steed,
I never wore sic cumbrous spurs!"—

42. We scarce had won the Staneshaw-bank,
When a' the Carlisle bells were rung,
And a thousand men on horse and foot,
Cam wi' the keen Lord Scroope along.

43. Buccleuch has turn'd to Eden Water,
Even where it flow'd frae bank to brim,
And he has plunged in wi' a' his band,
And safely swam them through the stream.

44. He turn'd him on the other side,
And at Lord Scroope his glove flung he—
"If ye like na my visit in merry England,
In fair Scotland come visit me!"

45. All sore astonish'd stood Lord Scroope,
He stood as still as rock of stane;
He scarcely dared to trew his eyes,
When through the water they had gane.

46. "He is either himsell a devil frae hell,
Or else his mother a witch maun be;
I wadna have ridden that wan water
For a' the gowd in Christentie."

Campbell's text follows that in Scott's *Minstrelsy*, which is here given (cf. Scott, *Poetical Works*, 1833-34, II, p. 51).

Jock o the Side

CHILD NO. 187

THAT there was a song on this subject known familiarly before the end of the sixteenth century is proved, as has been noted by Hyder Rollins, by a ballad in Bodleian Rawlinson MS. Poet. 185, fols. 9-10, the date of which is not later than 1592. It is to be sung to the tune of "Hobbinole and Iohn A Side." For the sake of the stanzaic pattern, the first stanza is here given. Cf., for the rest, Rollins, *Old English Ballads*, 1920, pp. 325ff.

Assist me now, you dolefull dames,
sing hevely now my ioyes do weare,
Sound forth your rewfull morning plantes,
lament my sorofull, wayling cheare;
Lament with me, for I am he
Who lives (alas!) and faine would die,
Oh paine, sorofull paine, paine that nipes me sore.

The ballad "Iohn a Side" may probably have been that which has survived in the Percy Folio (Child's A), where it appears, as usual for that MS., without any refrain. Nothing is clearer than the fact that whoever compiled the Percy Folio had no interest in *singing* his songs.

The next text, and the earliest extant in print, is that in Caw's *Poetical Museum*, 1784, which is said to be given "from an old manuscript copy." It is four stanzas shorter than the decapitated Folio copy, and differs considerably in names, narrative, and language, and has a fifth-line refrain (Child Ba). Nine years earlier (1775), Percy had received a very defective copy (C) taken down as imperfectly remembered by an "old person." Most of the stanzas are badly disordered, but the first one shows the same pattern as the Caw copy, and almost the identical refrain. It is, in fact, clearly to be made out that Ba and C were derived from copies differing in no essential respect. There is enough difference in phraseology, however, to show that this form had a certain currency, about the mid-eighteenth century.

The copy in Campbell's *Albyn's Anthology* was, as we are explicitly told, transcribed, both "the melody and particularly the words . . . from the singing and recitation of Mr. Thomas Shortreed, who learnt it from his father." Child has little hesitation in declaring it to have been derived from Caw, in spite of numerous verbal differences. I take it that both could equally well derive from a common original at one or two removes, as is probably the case with C, though the C copy is too mutilated for certainty. But Campbell's copy differs in the refrain pattern, introducing a refrain-line after the first, as well as after the fourth, regular line of the stanza. This alteration, of course, markedly affects the tune. I believe that Campbell himself may have been responsible for the change: his words seem to me to imply that he was conscious of having taken more liberties with the melody than with the words, as they were sung. But not, we are to understand, such liberties as to destroy the basic authenticity of the record.

Campbell's tune is of that very rare kind, of which we have other examples in Nos. 110 and 144, where an interpolated phrase after the first throws the balance off, so that the main cadence, the "turn" of the tune, comes on an odd phrase. The phenomenon is so unusual that the examples of it in Anglo-American folksong can probably be counted on one hand. The outstanding example of it is the "Arthur a Bland" tune (cf. No. 126), where, however, the tune is of only five phrases. The present tune belies the look of its text, and has really eight phrases, because the refrain-lines divide each into two full-length musical phrases. The shape of the tune fails to correspond with the stanzaic pattern, inasmuch as the latter breaks at the end of the fourth musical phrase ("Staid at hame"), whilst the tune has its natural emphases at the ends of the third and the fifth phrases.

At first glance, it might be guessed that the pattern of the sixteenth-century "Iohn a Side" (as exemplified by the stanza quoted above) conformed to such a tune, the refrain after line one, and the long final refrain-line which doubtless occupied two full musical phrases, seeming to lend itself to the present scheme. But it can hardly have been so: there appears to be one line too many in the second half of the stanza, and the first refrain-line would need to be extended by partial verbal repetition. I have not found the tune of "Hobbinole" (for Hobby Noble?); but it must have agreed with the scheme of "Greensleeves," to which "Assist me now, you doleful dames" could easily be sung.

Scott appears to have got his text of the present ballad from Campbell and to have published it sixteen years earlier than did Campbell, at the same time inserting three stanzas from Caw which had been omitted by Shortreed. (Cf. Child, 1882-98, III, p. 475.) But it is noteworthy that Scott, no singer, quite discards all trace of refrain from his copy. This is, in fact, his regular habit—another illustration of how undependable are printed texts without their tunes.

In 1844, Robert Chambers published an easier, simplified variant of the Shortreed tune, which may well be closer to the traditional form. The refrains close up to a single musical phrase apiece, while the rest of the tune is virtually unchanged. The highest note is eliminated and the rhythm is relaxed. Chambers, however, gives no source, and may himself merely have edited Campbell's tune into the new guise. He has, at least, presented something more orthodox from the point of view of traditional song.

In 1882, Bruce and Stokoe took strong exception to Campbell's tune—"which, in our opinion, was written for any purpose except that of having these ballads sung to it" (*Northumbrian Minstrelsy*, p. 41). *These* refers to "Dick o the Cow" (No. 185), "Hobbie Noble" (189), and the present ballad, all of which the editors mistakenly accuse Scott of assigning to this single tune. Bruce and Stokoe themselves print a tune (from Telfer's MS. of the mid-nineteenth century) which has very little about it to suggest the earlier tune, yet which may have some distant relation. The supposition would appear the more likely in that their tune is pretty distinctly related to one collected by Kidson, which in its turn ends with a phrase very close to the Shortreed tune. Both the Northumbrian and Kidson tunes are lacking the "fal lal diddle" etc. refrains of the earlier copies, and make their refrain by repeating the last line to a new musical phrase. One suspects that a chief reason why the Northumbrian editors took such violent exception to the earlier tune was the lack of dignity they felt in "fa ding diddle" syllabifying. Association is much in these matters; and if the song were sung at a moderate pace, with a refrain like that of "The Three Ravens" substituted—"with a down, down derry; heigh down down derry"—repugnance might be abated. For, in its way, Shortreed's is a capital tune, even in Campbell's handling. Given towardly circumstances—a long evening in a bothy, an excellent memory, a flexible voice, plenty of support in the choral refrains—the song would go far to make one forget cold, damp, and aching bones. To be sure, so performed it would be interminable. But who would not regard that as a great merit?

LIST OF VARIANTS

GROUP A

1. "Jock o' the Side." Alexander Campbell, *Albyn's Anthology*, II [1818], p. 28. Also in Lady John Scott's MS., National Library of Scotland MS. 840.
2. "Jock o' the Syde." Robert Chambers, *Twelve Romantic Scottish Ballads*, 1844, p. 22.

GROUP B

3. "Jock o' the Syde." James Telfer MS. ('Mr. Telfer's tunes'), No. 41, p. 20; in MS. C 30, Society of Antiquaries Library, Newcastle-upon-Tyne. Also in John Collingwood Bruce and John Stokoe, *Northumbrian Minstrelsy*, 1882, p. 37.
4. "Jock o' the Side." Anne G. Gilchrist, *JEFDSS*, III, No. 1 (1936), p. 53.

TUNES WITH TEXTS

GROUP A

1. "Jock o' the Side"

Campbell, II [1818], p. 28. Also, inaccurately, in Lady John Scott's MS., NL Scotland MS. 840. From the singing and recitation of Thomas Shortreed, Liddesdale; learned from his father.

m D

1. Now Liddesdale has ridden a raid,
Wi' my fa ding diddle, lal low dow diddle:
But I wat they had better hae staid at hame;
For Michael o' Winfield he is dead,
And JOCK O' THE SIDE is prisoner ta'en.
Wi' my fa ding diddle, lal low dow diddle.

2. For Mangerton house Lady Downie has gane,
Her coats she has kilted up to her knee;
And down the water wi' speed she rins,
While tears in spaits fa' fast frae her e'e.

3. Then up and spoke our gude auld Lord—
—"What news? what news, sister Downie, to me?"
—"Bad news, bad news, my Lord Mangerton;
Michael is killed, and they hae ta'en my son Johnie."

4. "Ne'er fear, sister Downie," quo' Mangerton;
—"I have yokes of ousen, eighty and three;
My barns, my byres, and my faulds a' weil fill'd,
And I'll part wi' them a' ere Johnie shall die.

5. "Three men I'll send to set him free,
A' harneist wi' the best o' steil;
The English louns may hear, and drie
The weight o' their braid swords to feel."

6. Lord Mangerton then orders gave,
—"Your horses the wrang maun be shod;
Like gentlemen ye mauna seim,
But look like corn caugers ga'en the road.

7. "Your armour gude you mauna shaw,
Nor yet appear like men o'weir;
As country lads be a' array'd,
Wi' branks and brecham on each mare."—

8. Sae now their horses are the wrang way shod,
And Hobbie has mounted his grey sae fine;
Jock's on his lively bay, Wat's on his white horse, behind,
And on they rode for the water of Tyne.

9. At the Cholerford they all light down,
And there, wi' the help of the light o' the moon,
A tree they cut, wi' fifteen nogs on each side,
To climb up the wa' of Newcastle toun.

10. But when they cam to Newcastle toun,
And were alighted at the wa',
They fand their tree three ells ower laigh,
They fand their stick baith short and sma'.

11. Then up and spak the Laird's ain Jock,
—"There's naithing for't; the gates we maun force."—
But when they cam the gate untill,
A proud porter withstood baith men and horse.

12. His neck in twa the Armstrangs wrang,
Wi' fute or hand he ne'er play'd pa!
His life and his keys at anes they hae ta'en,
And cast the body ahind the wa'.

13. Now sune they reach Newcastle jail,
And to the prisoner thus they call—
—"Sleeps thou, wakes thou, Jock o' the Side,
Or art thou weary of thy thrall?"—

14. Jock answers thus, wi' dulefu' tone,
—"Aft, aft, I wake—I seldom sleep;
But whae's this kens my name sae weil,
And thus to mese my waes does seik?"—

15. Then out and spak the gude Laird's Jock,
—"Now fear ye na, my billie," quo' he;
"For here are the Laird's Jock, the Laird's Wat,
And Hobbie Noble, come to set thee free."—

16. —"Now haud thy tongue, my gude Laird's Jock,
For ever, alas! this canna be;
For if a' Liddesdale was here the night,
The morn's the day that I maun die.

17. "Full fifteen stane o' Spanish iron,
They hae laid a' right sair on me;
Wi' locks and keys I am fast bound
Into this dungeon dark and dreirie."—

18. —"Fear ye na' that," quo' the Laird's Jock;
"A faint heart ne'er wan a fair ladie;
Work thou within, we'll work without,
And I'll be sworn we'll set thee free."—

19. The first strong door that they cam at,
They loosed it without a key;
The next chain'd door that they cam at,
They garr'd it a' to flinders flee.

20. The prisoner now upon his back,
The Laird's Jock has gotten up fu' hie;
And down the stair, him, irons and a',
Wi' nae sma' speid and joy, brings he.

21. Sae out at the gates they a' are gane,
The prisoner's set on horseback hie;
And now wi' speid they've ta'en the gate,
While ilk ane jokes fu' wantonlie:

22. —"O Jock! sae winsomely's ye ride,
Wi' baith your feet upon ae side;
Sae well ye're harniest, and sae trigg,
In troth ye sit like ony bride!"—

23. The night, tho' wat, they did na mind,
But hied them on fu' merrilie,
Until they cam to Cholerford brae,
Where the water ran like mountains hie.

24. But when they cam to Cholerford,
There they met with an auld man;
Says—"Honest man, will the water ride?
Tell us in haste, if that ye can."—

25. —"I wat weel no," quo' the gude auld man;
"I hae lived here threty years and thrie,
And I ne'er yet saw the Tyne sae big,
Nor running anes sae like a sea."—

26. Then out and spak the Laird's saft Wat,
The greatest coward in the cumpanie—
"Now halt, now halt, we needna try't;
The day is come we a' maun die!"—

27. "Puir faint-hearted thief!" cried the Laird's ain Jock,
"There'll nae man die but him that's fie;
I'll guide thee a' right safely thro';
Lift ye the pris'ner on ahint me."—

28. Wi' that the water they hae ta'en,
By ane's and twa's they a' swam thro';
—"Here are we a' safe," quo' the Laird's Jock,
"And puir faint Wat, what think ye now?"—

29. They scarce the other brae had won,
When twenty men they saw pursue;
Frae Newcastle toun they had been sent,
A' English lads baith stout and true.

30. But when the Land-serjeant the water saw,
—"It winna ride, my lads," says he;
Then cried aloud—"The prisoner take,
But leave the fetters, I pray, to me."—

31. —"I wat weil no," quo' the Laird's Jock;
"I'll keep them a'; shoon to my mare they'll be:
My gude bay mare—for I am sure
She has bought them a' right dear frae thee."—

32. Sae now they are on to Liddesdale,
E'en as fast as they could them hie;
The prisoner is brought to's ain fire-side,
And there o's airns they mak him free.

33. —"Now Jock, my billie," quo' a' the three,
"The day is com'd thou was to die;
But thou's as weil at thy ain ingle side
Now sitting, I think, 'twixt thee and me!"

2. "Jock o' the Syde"

Chambers, 1844, p. 22.

m D

Now Liddesdale has ridden a raid,
Fal la diddle dee dee dee diddle;
I wat they had better hae staid at hame,
For Michael o' Wingfield he is dead,
And Jock o' the Syde is pris'ner taen,
Fa la diddle dee dee dee diddle.
[*Etc.*]

Chambers' text is abridged from Scott's *Minstrelsy*.

GROUP B

3. "Jock o' the Syde"

Telfer MS., No. 41, p. 20. Also in Bruce and Stokoe, 1882, p. 37.

p D/Æ

In Bruce and Stokoe, the cadence-note of phrase 3 is C instead of B.

The text is taken from Caw's *Poetical Museum*, 1784, of which the only material differences from that in *Albyn's Anthology* (variant 1 above) are the two stanzas that follow Campbell's fifth, as follows:

"The Laird's Jock ane, the Laird's Wat twa;
O! Hobbie Noble, thou ane maun be!
Thy coat is blue, thou hast been true
Since England banish'd thee to me."

Now, Hobbie was an English man,
In Bewcastle-dale was bred and born;
But his misdeeds they were sae great
They banish'd him ne'er to return.

a stanza following Campbell's 20, thus:

"Now, Jock, my man," quo' Hobbie Noble,
"Some o' his weight ye may lay on me";
"I wat weel no," quo' the Laird's ain Jock,
"I count him lighter than a flee."

and the final stanza, as follows:

They hae garred fill up ae punch bowl,
And after it they maun hae anither;
And thus the night they a' hae spent,
Just as they'd been brither and brither.

4. "Jock o' the Side"

Gilchrist, *JEFDSS*, III, No. 1 (1936), p. 53. From the "Edinburgh MS.," "a sheet of manuscript airs . . . found amongst the papers of the late Frank Kidson."

p π^3

[Now Liddesdale has ridden a raid,
But I wat better had stayed at hame,
For Michael o' Winfield he is dead,
And Jock o' the Side is prisoner ta'en,
And Jock o' the Side is prisoner ta'en.]

No fresh text supplied.

Archie o Cawfield

CHILD NO. 188

The first tune to be published for this ballad, which is perhaps a *rifacimento*, or secondary form, of "Jock o the Side," is Christie's, which he got from his grandfather. It has resemblances to other Scottish songs, most notably, perhaps, to "The Beggar Laddie" (Child 280). Cf., e.g., Greig and Keith, *Last Leaves*, 1925, pp. 228-29, especially 1f and 2; Christie, I, 1876, p. 100.

The Maine editors, in a very interesting note, show that the ballad must have been brought over to this country as early as the beginning of the eighteenth century, and that it was remodelled to suit the affair of John Webster, who appears to have been rescued from jail in a fashion sufficiently similar to suggest the adaptation. Cf. Barry, Eckstorm, and Smyth, *British Ballads from Maine*, 1929, p. 395. Bryant discovered a Pitts broadside of the early nineteenth century, called "The Bold Prisoner," which gives the older ballad in greatly weakened and abbreviated form (Bryant, *History of English Balladry*, 1919, pp. 436-37; Barry, Eckstorm, and Smyth, 1929, p. 399). Greig recovered one version, of the Peter Buchan variety (Child C), from his redoubtable Bell Robertson, which is at least better than the Pitts broadside. It is interesting that no fewer than eight more or less fragmentary versions of the ballad and its cognates have been collected in this country in the present century, one as far West as Michigan, the rest in New England.

Miss Frye's *JAF* tune and Mrs. Linscott's are from the same source, and go to Child's text F. There are only two notes that differ, but one of these is the final. The copies were secured about forty years apart. The tune appears to be a good swinging major, having much in common with "King Henry V's Conquest of France" (No. 164). There was an indicated repeat of the last two lines of each quatrain which does not show up in the musical records.

The three tunes that come from Maine are perhaps members of the same family, but there are very considerable differences between them, and the first I have chosen to group with the English in B. I believe they are all plagal majors: the first has a fallen close; the second lacks its third, fourth, and seventh; the third lacks its sixth. All are basically in duple time, and the first might more properly be written in 6/8.

This ballad, speaking now more particularly of the words, is a good instance of a kind of variation of which more account will have to be taken. It is not gradual nor unconscious, but a deliberate making over to suit the changing times. The adaptation, if successful, goes on its own traditional way, and may be again remade at a later date. These are the sharp corners in oral tradition. It is probable that many of our most esteemed ballads have once, and more than once, been subjected to such treatment; and, no doubt, "in the fatness of these pursy times," the process will recur with increasing frequency, if anything at all is left of recognizable tradition. Though it be a kind of vandalism, leading to what in more recent decades has proved disintegrative in effect, there is little question that formerly it has given a new lease of life to many a song which would otherwise have perished.

Special attention may be called to the fragment in Sharp's MSS., "The Burglar," which has not hitherto been identified as relating to Child 188.

LIST OF VARIANTS

GROUP A

1. "The Three Brothers." W. Christie, *Traditional Ballad Airs*, I, 1876, p. 98.

GROUP B

2. "The Burglar." Sharp MSS., 748/821, Clare College Library, Cambridge. (Glover)
3. "Bold Archer." F. M. Collinson and F. Dillon, *Songs from the Countryside*, I, 1946, p. 20.
4. "Bold Dickie." Mary P. Frye, *JAF*, VIII (1895), p. 256. Also in Eloise Hubbard Linscott, *Folk Songs of Old New England*, 1939, p. 172.
5. "Archie o' Cawfield." Phillips Barry, *BFSSNE*, No. 6 (1933), p. 7.

GROUP C

6. "Billy and Johnny." Phillips Barry, Fanny H. Eckstorm, and Mary W. Smyth, *British Ballads from Maine*, 1929, p. 394. (Thornton and Young)
7. "Billy and Johnny." Barry, Eckstorm, and Smyth, 1929, p. 393. (Barker)

188. ARCHIE O CAWFIELD

TUNES WITH TEXTS

GROUP A

1. "The Three Brothers"

Christie, I, 1876, p. 98. Tune sung by Christie's maternal grandfather and arranged by his father.

m M

As I walked on a pleasant green,
    'Twas on the first morning of May,
I heard twa brothers make their mane,
    And hearken'd well what they did say.
The first he gave a grievous sigh,
    And said, "Alas! and wae's me!
We ha'e a brother condemned to death,
    And the very morn must hangèd be."
[*Etc.*]

Christie's text is abridged from Buchan, 1828, I, p. 111.

GROUP B

2. "The Burglar"

Sharp MSS. 748/821. Sung by Mrs. Glover at Huish Episcopi, January 5, 1906.

a M (inflected VII)

I'm just like an owl that flies by night
I fly tree to tree
Good iron will do to shoe our horses
And blacksmiths to ride in our company.

Dicky broke locks & Dicky broke keys
And why shan't your ten be much better than my eleven
This night we will set the bold prisoner free.

So boldly she took it her pistol in hand
She asked for his mind & his mind she soon filled,
And I'll have you stand back or you are a dead man.

3. "Bold Archer"

Collinson and Dillon, I, 1946, p. 20.

a I

1. It was all in the month of June,
    Just as the flowers were in full bloom,
A castle was built upon Kensal Green,
    All for to put bold Archer in.

2. O, now our brother in prison do lay,
    Condemned to die is he
If I had eleven such brothers as he,
    It's soon the poor prisoner I'd set free.

3. Eleven, says Richard, is little enough,
    Full forty there must be,
The chain and the bars will have to be broke,
    Before bold Archer you can set free.

4. Now ten for to stand by our horses' reins,
    And ten for to guard us round about,
And ten for to stand by the castle door,
    And ten for to bring bold Archer out.

5. Now Dickie broke locks and Dickie broke bars,
    Dickie broke everything he could see,
He took bold Archer under his arm,
    And carried him off most manfully.

6. They mounted their horses, away they did ride,
    Archer, he mounted his horse likewise.
They rode till they came to their family,
    And there they dismounted bold and free.

7. And there they ordered the music to play,
    It played so sweet and joyfully,
And the very first dancer among them all
    Was bold Archer, whom they set free.

Stanzas 2 and 3 are sung with the slight differences noted in the melodic variants above.

4. "Bold Dickie"

Frye, *JAF*, VIII (1895), p. 256. Also in Linscott, 1939, p. 172. Learned by Miss Frye as a child from J. M. Watson of Clark's Island, Mass.

a I, sometimes ending on III

The variants (a) and (b) are in Mrs. Linscott's copy.

1. As I walked out one morning in May,
Just before the break of day,
I heard two brothers making their moan,
And I listened a while to what they did say.

Chorus: repeat last two lines.

2. "We have a brother in prison," said they;
"Oh! in prison lieth he.
If we had ten men just like ourselves,
The prisoner we should soon set free."

3. "Oh, no! no!" bold Dickie said he;
"Oh, no! no! that never could be;
For forty men is full little enough,
And I for to ride in their companie."

4. "Ten to hold the horses in,
Ten to guard the city about,
And ten for to stand at the prison door,
And ten to fetch poor Archer out."

5. They mounted their horses, and so rode they,—
Who but they so merrilie.
They rode till they came to a broad river-side,
And there they alighted so manfullie.

6. They mounted their horses, and so swam they,—
Who but they so manfullie.
They swam till they came to the other side,
And there they alighted so drippinglie.

7. They mounted their horses, and so rode they,—
Who but they so gallantlie.
They rode till they came to that prison door,
And there they alighted so manfullie.

8. "Poor Archer! poor Archer!" bold Dickie says he;
"Oh! look you not so mournfullie;
For I've forty men in my companie,
And I have come to set you free."

9. "Oh, no! no! no!" poor Archer says he;
"Oh, no! no! no! that never can be;
For I have forty weight of good Spanish iron
Betwixt my ankle and my knee."

10. Bold Dickie broke lock, bold Dickie broke key;
Bold Dickie broke everything he could see:
He took poor Archer under one arm,
And he carried him out so manfullie.

11. They mounted their horses, and so rode they,—
Who but they so merrilie.
They rode till they came to that broad river,
And there they alighted so manfullie.

12. "Bold Dickie! bold Dickie!" poor Archer says he;
"Take my love home to my wife and children three;
For my horse grows lame, he cannot swim,
And here I see that I must dee!"

13. They shifted their horses, and so swam they,—
Who but they so daringlie.
They swam till they came to the other side,
And there they alighted so shiveringlie.

14. "Bold Dickie! bold Dickie!" poor Archer says he;
"Look you yonder there and see;
For the High Sheriff he is a-coming,
With an hundred men in his companie."

15. "Bold Dickie! bold Dickie!" High Sheriff says he,—
"You are the worst rascal that ever I see;
Go bring me back the iron you stole,
And I will set the prisoner free!"

16. "Oh, no! no! no!" bold Dickie says he;
"Oh, no! no! no! that never can be;
For the iron will do to shoe the horses,—
The blacksmith rides in our companie."

17. "Bold Dickie! bold Dickie!" High Sheriff says he,—
"You are the worst scoundrel that I ever see."
"I thank you for nothing," bold Dickie says he,—
"And you are a big fool for following me!"

5. [Archie o' Cawfield]

Barry, *BFSSNE*, No. 6 (1933), p. 7. From Mrs. Annie V. Marston, West Newton, Mass. (formerly of West Gouldsboro, Me.), February 1933.

p I, ending on *V*; or a M

"Bold Dickie, Bold Dickie, Bold Dickie," said he,
You're the damnedest rascal I ever did see!
If you'll return the locks and keys,
It's little Tom Archer whom we'll set free."

"Oh no, oh no," Bold Dickie, said he,
"Oh no, oh no, that never can be;
For the iron will do our horses to shoe,
And a blacksmith rides in our company."

GROUP C

6. "Billy and Johnny"

Barry, Eckstorm, and Smyth, 1929, p. 394. Text contributed by Mrs. Seth S. Thornton, Southwest Harbor, Me., in October 1926. Tune recorded by George Herzog in 1928 from the singing of Mrs. Thornton and her sister, Mrs. Alice Young.

p π^1—π^2 (–III, IV, VII)

1. There were nine to hold the British ranks,
And five to guard the town about,
And two to stand at either hand,
And one to let Old Tenor out.

2. And Billy broke locks and Billy broke bolts,
And Billy broke all that he came nigh,
Until he came to the dungeon door,
And that he broke right manfullye.

3. There was eighty weight of good Spanish iron
Between his neck-bone and his knee;
But Billy took Johnny up under his arm
And lugged him away right manfullee.

4. They mounted their horses and away they rode,
[And who but they rode gallantly,
Until they came to the riverbank,
And there they were most . . . . .]

5. And when they came to the river bank,
They swam its waters deep and wide,
. . . .
And safely reached the other side.

6. And then they called for a room to dance,
And who but they danced merrilee;
And the best dancer among them all
Was old John Webb, who was just set free.

The lines added to stanza 4 are from Mrs. Fred P. Barker (see *post*), who had the song from the same family tradition as Mrs. Thornton.

7. "Billy and Johnny"

Barry, Eckstorm, and Smyth, 1929, p. 393. From Mrs. Fred P. Barker, Brewer, Me. Tune noted by Mrs. C. Carter.

p I (–VI)

There was eighty weight of good Spanish iron,
Between his neck-bone and his knee.
But Billy took Johnny up under his arm,
And carried him away, most manfully

Billy broke locks and Billy broke bars,
And Billy broke all that he came nigh,
And Billy took Johnny up under his arm,
And carried him away most manfully.

Hughie Grame

CHILD NO. 191

CHILD says this ballad "is not so old as the middle of the sixteenth century" (1882-98, IV, p. 9). The earliest broadsides, which are the first surviving records of it, belong to the last quarter of the seventeenth century, and are English, though with one or two traces of Scots about them (Child A, 9^4: thou'st ner gang doun). Some of them are directed to go "to a pleasant new northern tune." In 1720, D'Urfey published the broadside copy (*Pills*, 1719-20, VI, p. 289), directing it to be sung to "Chevy Chase," but without giving the tune. The Chevy Chase tunes of his day, however, are CM, not LM tunes, and one assumes that the indication is mistaken.

Burns sent a traditional copy to Johnson for the fourth volume of the *Scots Musical Museum* (No. 303); but without the tune, which he said he had forgotten. Johnson printed this text with presumably an arbitrary tune which he seems to have taken from Oswald's *Caledonian Pocket Companion*, there called "Drimon Duff" (VIII, [c. 1756],* p. 12, according to J. C. Dick, ed., *The Songs of Robert Burns*, 1903, p. 362). This tune was later reprinted with the ballad by R. A. Smith, [1820-24]; Chambers, 1844; Maver, 1866; Eyre-Todd [1894]. As Alexander Keith has remarked, there is no evidence that this tune has ever been mated in tradition with "Hughie Grame." In any case, it should be compared with "Lumps of Pudding," the last tune of *The Beggar's Opera*, with which it is very interestingly connected.

Another tune circulated by the same name of "Druimion(n) Dubh," meaning "The Black Cow"; as J. C. Dick informs us, it appeared in Corri's *Scots Songs*, 1783, II, p. 29, and in McDonald's *Highland Airs*, c. 1784, No. 89. This last is reprinted by Dick, No. 32; it had also been given as No. 179 of Johnson's *Museum*, with the tune named as above, but put to Burns's original words, "Musing on the roaring ocean." So far as I can discern, the two tunes have nothing in common.

Thus far, we have nothing properly avouched as a traditional tune for this ballad. In the Blaikie MS., however, is a tune called "Good Lord Scroope alias Hughie Graham." There are no words, and the tune has an end-refrain of two phrases. Among Child's texts, only D, a late Roxburghe copy (second half of the eighteenth century), and I, from early nineteenth century, have any refrain. There it is also an end-refrain, but in D, of one line, "He derry derry down." It is possible that this is only an indication of the kind of syllabication employed, not an accurate rendering. The I version has a two-line end-refrain, "Fall all the day, fall all the dandy,/ Fall all the day, fall the dandy O." Fifty years later, Christie gives a tune from Banffshire tradition which appears to me distinctly related to the Blaikie tune. The thrice-repeated first phrase is a noticeable feature of both. As usual, Christie has filled up a second strain of four phrases, accommodating a second quatrain instead of a refrain. But he has not followed his usual practice of returning in the last two phrases to the phrases of the first strain. Instead, the pattern of the second strain here is two phrases repeating in alternation. These phrases are made out of the last phrase of the first strain, and I believe were (before Christie extended them) two phrases of probably syllabifying refrain. Confirming this surmise we have Greig's tune, an obvious relative from the same region, and with a two-phrase syllabified end-refrain of similar character. Here, then, is the central melodic tradition of this ballad.

We have still to take account of a tune from Liddesdale, of the middle or second half of the nineteenth century. This tune, given by Bruce and Stokoe, 1882, doubtless from James Telfer's MS., is farther from the center. It is in 3/4 instead of duple time, and it has no refrain. It is plagal; the rest are authentic (though Christie's is mixed). But it, too, leans to π^3 skeletally, and its plagalism is pretty well forgotten after the first bar or two. If we push the rhythm into a duple one by making quarter-notes of the first two eighths in each bar, the tune looks more like the others; and there would be no incongruity in adding the refrain-phrases of either Blaikie's or Greig's. The tune, we conclude, may well be a cousin of those. But it is also a variant of the one in C. K. Sharpe's MS. to "Otterburn" (No. 161) printed in Child, 1882-98, V, p. 419. It has lately been sung and recorded with the present ballad by Ewan MacColl.

It should also be mentioned that the Christie tune suggests "The Keeper" (e.g., Sharp's *One Hundred English Folksongs*, 1916, p. 178), and the Greig tune, Mrs. Harris's "Sir Colin" (*ante*, II, No. 61, variant 1). The Gray-Muir MS., NL Scotland MS. 2254, mentions a tune in the Bunyan MS., 1877, p. 32, which I have not seen.

* Date according to Dick.

LIST OF VARIANTS

GROUP A

1. "Hughie Graham." James Johnson, *The Scots Musical Museum*, IV [1792], No. 303, p. 312 (repr. 1853). Also in Robert Archibald Smith, *The Scotish Minstrel* [1820-24], IV, p. 22; Robert Chambers, *Twelve Romantic Scottish Ballads*, 1844, p. 24; Robert Maver, *Genuine Scottish Melodies*, 1866, No. 360, p. 180; and George Eyre-Todd, *Ancient Scots Ballads* [1894], p. 208.

GROUP Ba

2. "Good Lord Scroope alias Hughie Graham." Blaikie MS., National Library of Scotland MS. 1578, No. 102, p. 32.

GROUP Bb

3. "Hughie Graham." W. Christie, *Traditional Ballad Airs*, II, 1881, p. 82.

GROUP BC

4. "Hughie Grame." Gavin Greig and Alexander Keith, *Last Leaves of Traditional Ballads and Ballad Airs*, 1925, p. 118. From Duncan MS., No. 446. (Lyall)

GROUP Bd

5. "Oh! the Grahams and hey! the Grahams." James Telfer

MS. ('Mr. Telfer's tunes'), No. 6, p. 3; in MS. C 30, Society of Antiquaries Library, Newcastle-upon-Tyne. Also in John Collingwood Bruce and John Stokoe, *Northumbrian Minstrelsy*, 1882, p. 34; and John Stokoe and Samuel Reay, *Songs and Ballads of Northern England*, n.d. [1893?], p. 98.

6. "Hughie the Graeme." Ewan MacColl, Riverside recording No. RLP 12-626(B4), *The English and Scottish Popular Ballads*, III, ed. Kenneth S. Goldstein.

APPENDIX

7. "Druimionn Dubh." James C. Dick, ed., *The Songs of Robert Burns*, 1903, No. 32, p. 31.

TUNES WITH TEXTS

GROUP A

1. "Hughie Graham"

Johnson, IV, [1792], No. 303, p. 312 (repr. 1853). Also in Smith [1820-24], IV, p. 22; Chambers, 1844, p. 24; Maver, 1866, No. 360, p. 180; and Eyre-Todd [1894], p. 208. From James Oswald, *The Caledonian Pocket Companion*, VIII, [c. 1756], p. 12.

m D/Æ

1. Our lords are to the mountains gane,
A hunting o' the fallow deer,
And they hae gripet Hughie Graham
For stealing o' the Bishop's mare.

2. And they hae tied him hand and foot,
And led him up thro' Stirling town;
The lads and lasses met him there,
Cried, Hughie Graham thou art a loun.

3. O lowse my right hand free, he says,
And put my braid sword in the same;
He's no in Stirling town this day,
Daur tell the tale to Hughie Graham.

4. Up then bespake the brave Whitefoord,
As he sat by the bishop's knee,
Five hundred white stots I'll gie you,
If ye'll let Hughie Graham gae free.

5. O haud your tongue, the bishop says,
And wi' your pleading let me be;
For tho' ten Grahams were in his coat,
Hughie Graham this day shall die.

6. Up then bespake the fair Whitefoord,
As she sat by the bishop's knee;
Five hundred white pence I'll gee you,
If ye'll gie Hughie Graham to me.

7. O haud your tongue now lady fair,
And wi' your pleading let it be,
Altho' ten Grahams were in his coat,
Its for my honor he maun die.

8. They've taen him to the gallows knowe,
He looked to the gallows tree,
Yet never colour left his cheek,
Nor ever did he blin' his e'e.

9. At length he looked round about,
To see whatever he could spy;
And there he saw his auld father,
And he was weeping bitterly.

10. O haud your tongue, my father dear,
And wi' your weeping let it be;
Thy weeping's fairer on my heart,
Than a' that they can do to me.

11. And ye may gie my brother John,
My sword that's bent in the middle clear,
And let him come at twelve o'clock,
And see me pay the bishop's mare.

12. And ye may gie my brother James
My sword that's bent in the middle brown
And bid him come at four o'clock,
And see his brother Hugh cut down.

13. Remember me to Maggy my wife,
The niest time ye gang o'er the moor,
Tell her, she staw the bishop's mare,
Tell her, she was the bishop's whore.

14. And ye may tell my kith and kin,
I never did disgrace their blood;
And when they meet the bishop's cloak,
To mak it shorter by the hood.

This text = Child's B.

GROUP Ba

2. "Good Lord Scroope alias Hughie Graham"

Blaikie MS., NL Scotland MS. 1578, No. 102, p. 32.

a Anomalous (–III; inflected VI)

GROUP Bb

3. "Hughie Graham"

Christie, II, 1881, p. 82. From Banffshire tradition.

m I

Our lords are to the mountains gane,
A-hunting o' the fallow deer,
And they ha'e grippit Hughie Graham
For stealing o' the bishop's mare.
And they ha'e tied him hand and foot,
And led him up through Stirling town;
The lads and lasses met him there,
Cried, "Hughie Graham thou art a loun."

[*Etc.*]

Christie follows the text in Johnson's *Museum*, IV, [1792], No. 303, p. 312 (cf. variant 1 above).

GROUP BC

4. "Hughie Grame"

Greig and Keith, 1925, p. 118; from Duncan MS., No. 446. From Mrs. Lyall, Skene, as learned from a schoolgirl, c. 1870.

a M/D

He lookèd east, he lookèd west,
He lookèd far across the sea;
And there he spied his agèd father,
Standing weeping bitterly.
Tey ammarey, O Londonderry,
Tey ammarey, O London dee.

GROUP Bd

5. "Oh! the Grahams and hey! the Grahams"

Telfer MS., No. 6, p. 3. Also in Bruce and Stokoe, 1882, p. 34; and Stokoe and Reay, n.d. [1893?], p. 98. From Liddesdale tradition.

m D

Gude Lord Scroope's to the hunting gane,
He has ridden o'er moss and muir,
And he has grippit Hughie the Græme,
For stealing o' the Bishop's mear.

[*Etc.*]

The text is Child's C, from Scott's *Minstrelsy*, 1803, III, p. 85. For Scott's traditional versions, see Child's C, H, and I in his fourth volume, pp. 518-20.

6. "Hughie the Graeme"

Sung by Ewan MacColl, Riverside rec. No. RLP 12-626(B4), ed. K. S. Goldstein. Tune learned from Thomas Armstrong of Newcastle.

m Æ

Gude Lord Scroope's to the hunting gane,
He has ridden o'er moss an' muir;
And he has grippit Hughie the Graeme,
For stealing of the Bishop's mare.

[*Etc.*]

MacColl's text is Child's C, from Scott's *Minstrelsy*.

APPENDIX

7. "Druimionn Dubh"

Dick, ed., 1903, No. 32, p. 31. From Patrick McDonald, *A Collection of Highland Vocal Airs*, n.d. [1784].

a Æ (but –III)

The Lochmaben Harper

CHILD NO. 192

THIS ballad, except for gradual dilapidation as the nineteenth century wore on, shows a marked degree of consistency, both text and music. The extant tradition extends from the end of the eighteenth to the end of the nineteenth century, but we lack a late tune because of the fact that Bell Robertson, though she learned her vast store of ballads from singers, could not or would not "unlock her silent throat" in song even when death approached.

The Glenriddell and *Museum* copies are very close—almost identical as these things go. The Blaikie copy, which has not been published heretofore, shows some small variation, but nothing worthy of remark. All the variants are D/Æ, in 6/8 (or 12/8) time.

Child notes that the Stationers' Register for 1564-65-66 has entries of ballads about a blind harper or harpers. Whether these had anything to do with ours is not known. But as possible evidence that the present ballad has travelled some way from its source, we might note the neglect of the harper's blindness as a factor in the story. Beyond calling him blind, only one version, I believe (Child B), even mentions the possibility of a blind man's having difficulty in identifying one horse from another in a strange stable, let alone knowing whether every man of his audience had his eyes closed in slumber. We may suppose that originally more was done with this element of the story than has come down to us.

LIST OF VARIANTS

1. "The Blind Harper of Lochmaben." Glenriddell MSS. 1791, National Museum of Antiquaries of Scotland, XI, p. 45, Harvard College Library transcript HCL 25241.49, p. 66.
2. "Oh heard ye e'er of a silly blind Harper." James Johnson, *The Scots Musical Museum*, VI [1803], No. 579, p. 598 (repr. 1853).
3. "The Lochmaben Harper." Blaikie MS., National Library of Scotland MS. 1578, No. 69, p. 22.

TUNES WITH TEXTS

1. "The Blind Harper of Lochmaben"

Glenriddell MSS., 1791, XI, p. 45, HCL transcript, 25241.49, p. 66.

a D/Æ, ending on the octave

The MS. gives 12/8 as the time-signature.

Heard ye e'er of the silly Blind Harper
That long lived in Lochmaben Town
How he wad gang to fair England
To steal King Henry's wanton Brown?
Sing faden dilly and faden dilly
Sing faden dilly and deedle Dan.

2. "Oh heard ye e'er of a silly blind Harper"

Johnson, VI [1803], No. 579, p. 598 (repr. 1853). Contributed by Robert Burns.

a D/Æ, ending on the octave

1. O heard ye of a silly Harper,
Liv'd long in Lochmaben town,
How he did gang to fair England,
To steal King Henry's wanton brown?
How he did gang to fair England
To steal King Henry's wanton brown.

2. But first he gaed to his gude wife
Wi' a' the speed that he cou'd thole:
This wark, quo' he, will never work,
Without a mare that has a foal.
This wark, &c.

3. Quo' she, thou has a gude grey mare,
That'll rin o'er hills baith low & hie;
Gae tak' the grey mare in thy hand,
And leave the foal at hame wi' me.
Gae tak', &c.

4. And tak' a halter in thy hose,
And o' thy purpose dinna fail;
But wap it o'er the wanton's nose;
And tie her to the grey mare's tail:
But wap, &c.

5. Syne ca' her out at yon back yeate,
O'er moss and muir and ilka dale,
For she'll ne'er let the wanton bite,
Till she come hame to her ain foal.
For she'll, &c.

6. So he is up to England gane,
Even as fast as he can hie,
Till he came to King Henry's yeate;
And wha' was there but King Henry?
Till he, &c.

7. Come in, quo' he, thou silly blind Harper;
And of thy harping let me hear.
O! by my sooth, quo' the silly blind Harper,
I'd rather hae stabling for my mare.
O! by my, &c.

8. The King looks o'er his left shoulder,
And says unto his stable groom,
Gae tak the silly poor Harper's mare,
And tie her 'side my wanton brown.
Gae tak, &c.

9. And ay he harped, and ay he carpit,
Till a' the Lords gaed through the floor,
They thought the music was sae sweet,
That they forgat the stable door.
They thought, &c.

10. And ay he harpit, and ay he carpit,
Till a' the nobles were sound asleep,
Than quietly he took aff his shoon,
And saftly down the stair did creep.
Than quietly, &c.

11. Syne to the stable door he hies,
Wi' tread as light as light cou'd be,
And whan he open'd and gaed in,
There he fand thirty good steeds & three.
And whan, &c.

12. He took the halter frae his hose,
And of his purpose did na' fail;
He slipt it o'er the Wanton's nose,
And tied it to his grey mare's tail.
He slipt, &c.

13. He ca'd her out at yon back yeate,
O'er moss and muir & ilka dale,
And she loot ne'er the wanton bite,
But held her still gaun at her tail.
And she, &c.

14. The grey mare was right swift o' fit,
And did na fail to find the way,
For she was at Lochmaben yeate,
Fu' lang three hours ere it was day.
For she, &c.

15. When she came to the Harper's door,
There she gae mony a nicher and snear,
Rise, quo' the wife, thou lazy lass,
Let in thy master and his mare.
Rise, quo', &c.

16. Then up she raise, pat on her claes,
And lookit out through the lock-hole,
O! by my sooth then quoth the lass,
Our mare has gotten a braw big foal.
O! by my, &c.

17. Come haud thy peace, then foolish lass,
The moon's but glancing in thy ee,
I'll wad my haill fee 'gainst a groat,
It's bigger than e'er our foal will be.
I'll wad, &c.

18. The neighbours too that heard the noise,
Cried to the wife to put her in,
By my sooth, then quoth the wife,
She's better than ever he rade on.
By my, &c.

19. But on the morn at fair day light,
When they had ended a' their chear,
King Henry's wanton brown was stawn,
And eke the poor old Harper's mare.
King Henry's, &c.

20. Alace! alace! says the silly blind Harper,
Alace! alace! that I came here,
In Scotland I've tint a braw cowte foal,
In England they've stawn my guid grey mare.
In Scotland, &c.

21. Come had thy tongue, thou silly blind harper
And of thy alacing let me be,
For thou shall get a better mare,
And weel paid shall thy cowte foal be.
For thou shall get a better mare,
And weel paid shall thy cowte foal be.

3. "The Lochmaben Harper"

Blaikie MS., NL Scotland MS. 1578, No. 69, p. 22.

p D/Æ

The Death of Parcy Reed

CHILD NO. 193

James Telfer sent Sir Walter Scott a copy of this ballad "exactly as it is sung by an old woman of the name of Cathrine Hall, living at Fairloans, in the remotest corner of Oxnam parish": this was said in 1824. Telfer further remarked that the ballad had its own tune, "a very mournful air" (Child, 1882-98, IV, pp. 520-21), but obviously did not enclose it with the text, or there would have been no need to describe it. Kitty Hall's text was nowhere printed at the time, and when in 1844 a text was published by Richardson at Newcastle, as a twelve-page pamphlet, with an introduction by Robert White, although the title page read "an old ballad taken down by James Telfer from recitation," the text was actually remade and nearly doubled in length. This "improved" text of Telfer's was reprinted in 1846 in Richardson's *Borderer's Table Book*, and again by J. H. Dixon in the same year. The editors of *Northumbrian Minstrelsy* reprinted it with a tune in 1882; and in 1890 Child reprinted it once again as his B text (IV, pp. 26-28). By 1892 Child had recovered Kitty Hall's untouched version in the Abbotsford correspondence, and now for the first time printed it in the Additions and Correction of Vol. IV, pp. 520-21. No other copy, I believe, has been recovered except Child's A, which Robert White, who wrote the notes for the 1846 copy, himself collected (but did not publish) from a different source in 1829. In view of these facts, the procedure of the 1882 editors of *Northumbrian Minstrelsy* is a little blameworthy. As the only custodians of a tune for the ballad, they say nothing about its source. If they had recovered the tune from tradition, they would probably have had a different text from any yet printed. But in the Child MSS. at Harvard (XXVII, No. 2032) is a newspaper article contributed by John Stokoe to the *Newcastle Courant* in 1880, and containing the information that the tune is called "Lord Trowend" in old MSS. The tune appears in the article as it later was printed in *Northumbrian Minstrelsy* (1882, p. 42). One wishes for more light on these old MSS., on their nature, age, number, authority, and whereabouts. But in a separate MS. of tunes, 'Mr. Telfer's Tunes,' now in the library of the Society of Antiquaries, Newcastle-upon-Tyne, is one called "Hey sae green as the rashes grow," which proves to be the tune in question. A title, "Lord Trowend," has been faintly pencilled above. Presumably, Stokoe took his copy from this MS., which differs only in one note.

It may be observed that the tune belongs to the family of which "Loch Lomond" is a member. Cf. *post*, No. 199 ("Bonnie House o' Airlie").

LIST OF VARIANTS

"Hey sae green as the rashes grow" ["Lord Trowend"]. James Telfer MS. ('Mr. Telfer's tunes'), No. 5, p. 3; in MS. C 30, Society of Antiquaries Library, Newcastle-upon-Tyne. Text, Francis James Child, *The English and Scottish Popular Ballads*, 1882-98, IV, p. 520. Also in John Collingwood Bruce and John Stokoe, *Northumbrian Minstrelsy*, 1882, p. 42.

TUNE WITH TEXT

"Hey sae green as the rashes grow" ["Lord Trowend"]

Telfer MS., No. 5, p. 3; text, Child, 1882-98, IV, p. 520. Also in Bruce and Stokoe, 1882, p. 42. Tune taken down by James Telfer, perhaps from the singing of Kitty Hall (originally from Northumberland), Fairloans, Roxburghshire, from whom he obtained the text.

m I/M

1. O Parcy Reed has Crozer taen,
   And has deliverd him to the law;
But Crozer says he'll do warse than that,
   For he'll gar the tower of the Troughend fa.

2. And Crozer says he will do warse,
   He will do warse, if warse can be;
For he'll make the bairns a' fatherless,
   And then the land it may lie lea.

3. O Parcy Reed has ridden a raid,
   But he had better have staid at hame;
For the three fause Ha's of Girsenfield
   Alang with him he has them taen.

4. He's hunted up, and he's hunted down,
   He's hunted a' the water of Reed,
Till wearydness has on him taen,
   I the Baitinghope he's faen asleep.

5. . . . .
   . . . .
And the fause, fause Ha's o Girsenfield,
   They'll never be trowed nor trusted again.

6. They've taen frae him his powther-bag,
   And they've put water i his lang gun;
They've put the sword into the sheathe
   That out again it'll never come.

7. 'Awaken ye, awaken ye, Parcy Reed,
For I do fear ye've slept owre lang;
For yonder are the five Crozers,
A coming owre by the hinging-stane.'

8. 'If they be five and we be four,
If that ye will stand true to me,
If every man ye will take one,
Ye surely will leave two to me.

9. 'O turn, O turn, O Johny Ha,
O turn now, man, and fight wi me;
If ever ye come to Troughend again,
A good black nag I will gie to thee;
He cost me twenty pounds o gowd
Atween my brother John and me.'

10. 'I winna turn, I canna turn;
I darena turn and fight wi thee;
For they will find out Parcy Reed,
And then they'll kill baith thee and me.'

11. 'O turn, O turn now, Willie Ha,
O turn, O man, and fight wi me,
And if ever ye come to the Troughend again
A yoke of owsen I will gie thee.'

12. 'I winna turn, I canna turn;
I darena turn and fight wi thee;
For they will find out Parcy Reed,
And they will kill baith thee and me.'

13. 'O turn, O turn, O Thommy Ha,
O turn now, man, and fight wi me;
If ever ye come to the Troughend again,
My daughter Jean I'll gie to thee.'

14. 'I winna turn, I darena turn;
I winna turn and fight with thee;
For they will find out Parcy Reed,
And then they'll kill baith thee and me.'

15. 'O woe be to ye, traitors a'!
I wish England ye may never win;
Ye've left me in the field to stand,
And in my hand an uncharged gun.

16. 'Ye've taen frae me my powther-bag,
And ye've put water i my lang gun;
Ye've put the sword into the sheath
That out again it'll never come.

17. 'O far ye weel, my married wife!
And fare ye weel, my brother John!
That sits into the Troughend ha
With heart as black as any stone.

18. 'O fare ye weel, my married wife!
And fare ye weel now, my sons five!
For had ye been wi me this day
I surely had been man alive.

19. 'O fare ye weel, my married wife!
And fare ye weel now, my sons five!
And fare ye weel, my daughter Jean!
I loved ye best ye were born alive.

20. 'O some do ca me Parcy Reed,
And some do ca me Laird Troughend,
But it's nae matter what they ca me,
My faes have made me ill to ken.

21. 'The laird o Clennel wears my bow,
The laird o Brandon wears my brand;
Whae ever rides i the Border side
Will mind the laird o the Troughend.'

Lord Maxwell's Last Goodnight

CHILD NO. 195

THREE variants of the same tune, all of about the same date, complete the tale of musical records for this ballad. Two of them are hitherto unprinted; and of these the most interesting feature is that they imply an LM, instead of a CM, stanza which the printed texts employ. But it is to be observed that the same is true likewise of Scott's own tune in 1833, and that in suiting his text to it, an "O" is added to every second line. It should not be forgotten that Scott almost habitually eliminated the refrains in his *Minstrelsy*.

Blaikie's form of the tune, in both variants, is closely related to a tune in his manuscript entitled "Argyle's Courtship." It is interesting to compare the tune of "Kempy Kay" (No. 33), to see how readily the same melodic stuff lends itself to the sprightly or the melancholy.

Whether Blaikie's title for this tune may hint of now lost variants of Child 19 ("King Orfeo"), with an interlaced refrain of "The roses they smell sweetly," I do not know. Fairy *kings* are as geason as black swans.

It will not escape attention that the form of this piece is rather too elaborate and too lyrical to be safe in traditional circulation. Child observes that "the order of the stanzas, not being governed by an explicit story, might be expected to vary with every reciter." It seems, indeed, highly unlikely that the song could have survived in such good condition, even from the time which it celebrates (c. 1608), merely by oral delivery. If it has done so, the eight-line stanza, closed by a refrain line (or two lines), and interlocking by means of the rhyme at lines four and five, would have been a powerful assistant to hold it steady.

LIST OF VARIANTS

1. "The King of Fairies," or "The Roses they smell sweetly." Blaikie MS., National Library of Scotland MS. 1578, No. 55, p. 20.
2. "The King of Fairies," or "The Roses they smell sweetly." Blaikie MS., NL Scotland MS. 1578, No. 55a, p. 20.
3. "The Lord Maxwell's Good Night." Sir Walter Scott, *The Poetical Works of Sir Walter Scott*, 1833-34, II, opp. p. 140, and p. 141.

APPENDIX

4. "Argyle's Courtship." Blaikie MS., NL Scotland MS. 1578, No. 79, p. 25.

TUNES WITH TEXTS

1. "The King of Fairies," or "The Roses they smell sweetly"

Blaikie MS., NL Scotland MS. 1578, No. 55, p. 20.

p I

The MS. has a pencilled title, "Lord Maxwell's Goodnight."

2. "The King of Fairies," or "The Roses they smell sweetly"

Blaikie MS., NL Scotland MS. 1578, No. 55a, p. 20.

m I

3. "The Lord Maxwell's Good Night"

Scott, 1833-34, II, opp. p. 140; text, p. 141.

p I/M

1. "Adieu, madame, my mother dear,
   But and my sisters three!
   Adieu, fair Robert of Orchardstane!
   My heart is wae for thee.
   Adieu, the lily and the rose,
   The primrose fair to see;
   Adieu, my ladye, and only joy!
   For I may not stay with thee.

2. "Though I hae slain the Lord Johnstone,
   What care I for their feid?
   My noble mind their wrath disdains,—
   He was my father's deid.

Both night and day I labour'd oft
Of him avenged to be;
But now I've got what lang I sought,
And I may not stay with thee.

3. "Adieu! Drumlanrig, false wert aye,
And Closeburn in a band!
The Laird of Lag, frae my father that fled,
When the Johnston struck aff his hand.
They were three brethren in a band—
Joy may they never see!
Their treacherous art, and cowardly heart,
Has twined my love and me.

4. "Adieu! Dumfries, my proper place,
But and Carlaverock fair!
Adieu! my castle of the Thrieve,
Wi' a' my buildings there:
Adieu! Lochmaben's gate sae fair,
The Langholm-holm, where birks there be;
Adieu! my ladye, and only joy,
For, trust me, I may not stay wi' thee.

5. "Adieu! fair Eskdale up and down,
Where my puir friends do dwell;
The bangisters will ding them down,
And will them sair compell.
But I'll avenge their feid mysell,
When I come o'er the sea;
Adieu! my ladye, and only joy,
For I may not stay wi' thee."—

6. "Lord of the land!"—that ladye said,
"O wad ye go wi' me,
Unto my brother's stately tower,
Where safest ye may be!
There Hamiltons, and Douglas baith,
Shall rise to succour thee."—
"Thanks for thy kindness, fair my dame,
But I may not stay wi' thee."—

7. Then he tuik aff a gay gold ring,
Thereat hang signets three;
"Hae, tak thee that, mine ain dear thing,
And still hae mind o' me:
But if thou take another lord,
Ere I come ower the sea—
His life is but a three days' lease,
Though I may not stay wi' thee."—

8. The wind was fair, the ship was clear,
That good lord went away;
And most part of his friends were there,
To give him a fair convey.
They drank the wine, they didna spair,
Even in that gude lord's sight—
Sae now he's o'er the floods sae gray,
And Lord Maxwell has ta'en his Goodnight.

APPENDIX

4. "Argyle's Courtship"

Blaikie MS., NL Scotland MS. 1578, No. 79, p. 25.

m I/M

The Fire of Frendraught

CHILD NO. 196

THE incident which gave rise to this ballad occurred in 1630. In the Skene MS., which has been dated in the preceding decade, there is a tune called "Ladie Rothemayis Lilt." Dauney supposes that this was the tune to which the ballad would have been sung, on the principle that tunes already associated with a family would be used by minstrels when celebrating that family's history. Such a rule would be hard to prove, but nothing forbids its happening now and again. In the present case, one may admit that it would be easy to fit two quatrains (CM) to the tune. More telling would be a relation between this and later versions found in tradition. But the melodic material found here and in the nineteenth century tunes of this ballad is too common to support any confident assertions. The second strain of the Skene tune appears to be allied with the familiar "Boyne Water" family, and so does the late Greig tune from Mrs. Coutts, which, as Keith rightly observes, has further connections with "Sir James the Rose" (No. 213), "Sweet William and Fair Annie" (73-74), and, we may add, the same singer's "Edom o' Gordon" (178). The Greig tune and Christie's are also more distantly related. But, indeed, affiliations are far too frequent in this tribe to serve for evidence. The Skene tune is very much the sort of thing we find in Playford's *English Dancing Master* (cf., e.g., "All in a Garden Green," Margaret Dean-Smith edition, 1957, p. 60).

The tune printed by Johnson (*Museum*, No. 286) with the words of the eighteenth-century *rifacimento*, "Frennet Hall," has probably little claim to consideration as the proper traditional air of our ballad. This is rather a pity, because, stripped of its accidentals and reduced to a pure and simple Æolian form, it makes a fine and appropriate vehicle for a tragic ballad. As Miss Gilchrist has noted in *JEFDSS*, III, No. 3 (1938), p. 187, it is a variant of the tune printed in Johnson to "Good morrow, fair mistress, the beginner of strife" (*Museum*, No. 487). Of this, Miss Gilchrist contributes an Orkney variant (with other words) from the Balfour collection. It is also, as was noted earlier, a form of the tune Christie's family used for "The Bonny Earl of Murray" (No. 181), q.v.

Christie gives a tune from Banffshire tradition. Its second strain we may safely disregard as very much his own. This tune is a π^3 plagal, and should be closely compared with Greig's tune, which is a π^4 plagal and bears a different time-signature. Christie's predilection for a 3/4 signature is a noteworthy feature of his volumes. If we reduce both tunes to the same time, it is not difficult to see that Greig's tune is a dominant counterpart of Christie's.

LIST OF VARIANTS

1. "The Fire of Frendraught." W. Christie, *Traditional Ballad Airs*, I, 1876, p. 58.
2. "Frendraught." Greig MSS., IV, p. 6, and Bk. 753, XLIII, p. 25, King's College Library, Aberdeen. Also in Gavin Greig and Alexander Keith, *Last Leaves of Traditional Ballads and Ballad Airs*, 1925, p. 122.

APPENDIX

3. "Ladie Rothemayis Lilt." Skene MS., National Library of Scotland Adv. MS. 5.2.15; transcribed in William Dauney, *Ancient Scotish Melodies*, 1838, No. 4, p. 218.
4. "Frennett Hall." James Johnson, *The Scots Musical Museum*, III [1790], No. 286, p. 296 (repr. 1853). Also in Robert Maver, *Genuine Scottish Melodies*, 1866, No. 294, p. 147.

TUNES WITH TEXTS

1. "The Fire of Frendraught"

Christie, I, 1876, p. 58. From Banffshire tradition.

p π^3

The eighteenth of October,
A dismal tale to hear,
How good Lord John and Rothiemay
Were both burnt in the fire.

When steeds were saddled and well bridled,
And ready for to ride,
Then out came she and fause Frendraught,
Inviting them to bide.

[*Etc.*]

Christie says his text is "epitomized" and refers the reader to Motherwell's *Minstrelsy*, 1827, p. 161, and Chambers' *Scottish Ballads*, 1829, p. 85.

2. [Frendraught]

Greig MSS., IV, p. 6; text, Bk. 753, XLIII, p. 25. Also in Greig and Keith, 1925, p. 122. From Mrs. Coutts of Ellon.

p π^4

1. On the twenty-third October,
   A dismal tale to hear,
How good Lord John & Rothiemay
   Were burned in the fire.
      (doon by)

2. Lady Frendrat she sent messengers
   To call the Gordons a',
That the ancient feud might be forgot,
   And in peace they'd reap & saw.

3. The horses were from the stable brocht,
   And a' were bound to ride,
When out came Lady Frendrat gay,
   Cries, Abide, Lord John, abide.

4. Ye'll stay & sup wi' us to-night,
   And tomorrow we shall dine;
'Twill be a token o' richt goodwill,
   Atween your hoose & mine.

5. The horses were ta'en to the stable again,
   Which made them for to stay;
The horses were to the stable sent,
   And got both corn & hay.

6. When bells were rung & mass was sung,
   And a' man bound to bed,
Good Lord John & Rothiemay
   In a high chamber were laid.

7. They hidna been lang to their beds,
   And scarcely fa'en asleep,
When smoke & flames aboot them came,
   Which made them for to weep.

8. . . . .
   . . . .
The door is lockit & the window barred,
   And together we baith maun dee.

9. . . . .
And there they saw false Lady Frendrat
   A-walkin' on the green.
. . . .
   And unconcerned was she.

10. (Lord John cried) open the door Lady F.—
   And let us oot, cried he;
For the door is lockit & the window barred,
   And dead men soon we'll be.

11. . . . .
For the keys wis doon in the deep draw-wall,
   And widna be found till day.

12. Johnnie Chalmers was a bonnie boy,
   Jist new come fae the King,
And on the first alarm o' fire
(And when he saw the fire begun)
   He lightly leapt the wa'.

13. Come doon, come doon, my master dear,
   Come o'er the wa' to me;
And I'll kep you in my airms twa,
   One fit I winna flee.
. . . .

14. He drew the ring fae his finger,
   Which wis baith lang & sma',
And give it to my lady gay,
   But let not my mother ken.

15. And tell her now to mak' her bed
   Aye langer to the breid;
For the day will never dawn again
   That I'll lie by her side.

16. And bid her train her young son up,
   That when a man he'd be,
Upon this hoose for this cruel deed
   Avenged he will be.
. . . .

17. As for you, my good Lord John,
   My heart is very sore
But as for you, Rothiemay,
   I wish 'twere ten times more.

18. Woe be to you, false Lady F.—
   A murderess are ye;
For ye brought us

19. Woe be to you, false Lady F.—
   And ill death may ye dee;
For ye . . . .
   . . . .

20. And when that ye for pardon seek,
. . . .

21. Oh, gin I were a little bird,
   Wi' feathered wings & gray,
I'd fly aboot Lady F's gates,
   Crying vengeance till I die.

APPENDIX

3. "Ladie Rothemayis Lilt"

Skene MS., NL Scotland Adv. MS. 5.2.15; transcribed in Dauney, 1838, No. 4, p. 218.

a I/Ly, ending on III

4. "Frennett Hall"

Johnson, III [1790], No. 286, p. 296 (repr. 1853). Also in Maver, 1866, No. 294, p. 147.

m Minor (inflected VI, VII)

When Frennett castle's ivied wa's
Thro' yallow leaves were seen;
When birds forsook the sapless boughs,
And bees the faded green;
Then Lady Frennet, vengeful dame,
Did wander frae the ha',
To the wild forest's dewie gloom,
Among the leaves that fa'.

[*Etc.*]

The Bonnie House o Airlie

CHILD NO. 199

A TUNE for this ballad appeared in print almost as early as printed records of the text. The differences between later copies, whether printed or traditional, and this earliest recorded version are so slight as to indicate that oral tradition has never escaped control by one or other publication. The mode is I/M and authentic, usually with a plagal initial upbeat on the lower fifth. In two copies, the seventh slips in unobtrusively, and Christie has varied his second strain with a flattened seventh—editorially, we may assume.

Latterly, however, the earlier form has tended to be supplanted by a plagal tune, melodically akin, and universally familiar today with the more modern text of "The bonny banks of Loch Lomond." This is sung in Major, π^1, and I/M variants.

Eyre-Todd (variant 13) has substituted, without vouching authority, the tune belonging especially to "The Gypsy Laddie" (No. 200), q.v. This has an opening phrase identical throughout the first bar with the earlier form of the other tune.

Kinloch (variant 12), in 1827, mated this ballad with the "Cowdenknowes" tune (No. 218). If there was traditional authority, no other evidence of it has appeared.

The Gray-Muir MS. (NL Scotland MS. 2254) refers to tunes in the Bunyan MS., 1877, p. 52 and in Finlay Dun, 1840, p. 145. I have seen neither of them, but presume they do not differ from the original early form.

LIST OF VARIANTS

GROUP A

1. "The Bonny House o' Airlie." Robert Archibald Smith, *The Scotish Minstrel* [1820-24], II, p. 2. Also in George Thomson, *The Select Melodies of Scotland* [1822-23], I, p. 34; G. F. Graham, *The Songs of Scotland*, 1848-49, II, p. 130; and Robert Maver, *Genuine Scottish Melodies*, 1866, No. 102, p. 51.
2. "Bonnie House of Airlie." Sharp MSS., 4161/3001, Clare College Library, Cambridge. (Clapp)
3. "Bonnie House o' Airlie." Robert Chambers, *The Songs of Scotland Prior to Burns*, ed. of 1880, p. 444.
4. "The Bonnie Hoose o' Airlie." Gavin Greig and Alexander Keith, *Last Leaves of Traditional Ballads and Ballad Airs*, 1925, p. 125(1a). From Duncan MS., No. 23. (Gillespie)
5. "The Bonnie Hoose o' Airlie." Greig MSS., I, p. 189, King's College Library, Aberdeen. Also in Greig and Keith, 1925, p. 125(1b). (Riddell)
6. "The Bonny House o' Airlie." W. Christie, *Traditional Ballad Airs*, II, 1881, p. 276.
7. "The Bonnie Hoose o' Airlie." Ewan MacColl, Riverside recording No. RLP 12-622(B3), *The English and Scottish Popular Ballads*, I, ed. Kenneth S. Goldstein.

GROUP B

8. "Prince Charlie." Emelyn Elizabeth Gardner and Geraldine Jencks Chickering, *Ballads and Songs of Southern Michigan*, 1939, p. 209.
9. "The Bonnie Hoose o' Airlie." Greig MSS., IV, p. 6, and Bk. 753, XLIII, p. 31. Also in Greig and Keith, *Last Leaves*, 1925, p. 125(2a). (Coutts)
10. "The Bonnie Hoose o' Airlie." Greig and Keith, 1925, p. 125(2b). From Duncan MS., No. 125. (Gillespie)
11. "The Bonnie House o' Earlie." Phillips Barry, Fannie H. Eckstorm, and Mary W. Smyth, *British Ballads from Maine*, 1929, p. 266. (McGill)

GROUP C

12. "Bonny House of Airly." George R. Kinloch, *Ancient Scottish Ballads*, 1827, App'x. to p. 100, and p. 104.

GROUP D

13. "The Bonnie House o' Airlie." George Eyre-Todd, *Ancient Scots Ballads* [1894], p. 198.
14. "The Bonnie House of Airlie." Isabel Sutherland, Selection Records Ltd., 1960.
15. "The Bonny House of Aertie [Airlie]." Ralph Vaughan Williams MSS.

GROUP E

16. "The Bonny House o' Airlie." Helen Creighton and Doreen H. Senior, *Traditional Songs from Nova Scotia*, 1950, p. 70.

TUNES WITH TEXTS

GROUP A

1. "The Bonny House o' Airlie"

Smith [1820-24], II, p. 2. Also in G. Thomson [1822-23], I, p. 34; Graham, 1848-49, II, p. 130; and Maver, 1866, No. 102, p. 51.

p I/M

1. It fell on a day, a bonny simmer day,
   When the leaves were green and yellow,
That there fell out a great dispute
   Between Argyle and Airlie,
That there fell out a great dispute
   Between Argyle and Airlie.

2. Argyle he has taen a hundred o' his men,
   A hundred men and fifty,
And he's awa, on yon green shaw,
   To plunder the bonny house o' Airlie.

3. The lady looked owre the hie castle wa';
   And oh! but she sighed sairly,
When she saw Argyle and a' his men,
   Come to plunder the bonny house o' Airlie.

4. "Come down to me," said proud Argyle;
   "Come down to me lady Airlie,
Or I swear by the sword I haud in my hand,
   I winna leave a stanin stane in Airlie."

5. 'I'll no come down, ye proud Argyle,
   Until that ye speak mair fairly,
Tho' ye swear by the sword that ye haud in your hand,
   That ye winna leave a stanin stane in Airlie.

6. 'Had my ain lord been at his hame,
   But he's awa wi' Charlie,
There's no a Campbell in a' Argyle,
   Dare hae trod on the bonny green o' Airlie.

7. 'But since we can haud out nae mair,
   My hand I offer fairly;
Oh! lead me down to yonder glen,
   That I may nae see the burnin o' Airlie.'

8. He's taen her by the trembling hand,
   But he's no taen her fairly,
For he led her up to a hie hill tap,
   Where she saw the burnin o' Airlie.

9. Clouds o' smoke, and flames sae hie,
   Soon left the wa's but barely;
And she laid her down on that hill to die,
   Whan she saw the burnin o' Airlie.

2. "Bonnie House of Airlie"

Sharp MSS., 4161/3001. Sung by Mrs. Margaret Clapp, New York, December 23, 1917.

p I/M

1. It fell on a day, a bonny summer['s] [d]ay,
When the leaves were green and yellow,
That there fell oot a great dispute
Between Argyle and Airlie.

2. Argyle he has ta'en a hunder o' his men,
A hunder men and fifty,
And he's awa' on yon green strand
To plunder the bonny house o' Airlie.

3. The lady looked over the high castle wa',
And O she sighes sairly
When she saw Argyle and a' his men
Come to plunder the bonny house o' Airlie.

4. Come doon to me, said proud Argyle,
Come doon to me, Lady Airlie,
Or I swear by the swerd I haud in my hand
I winna' leave a standin' stane in Airlie.

5. I'll no come doon, ye proud Argyle,
Until that ye speak mair fairly,
Though ye swear by the swerd that ye haud in ye're hand
That ye winna leave a standin' stane in Airlie.

6. Had my ain lord been at his hame
As he's awa' wi' Charlie,
There's no a Campbell in a' Argyle
Daured hae trod on the bonny green o' Airlie.

7. But since we can haud oot nae mair,
My hand I offer fairly,
O lead me doon to yonder glen
That I may na' see the burnin' o' Airlie.

8. He's ta'en her by the trembling hand,
But he's no ta'en her fairly,
For he's led her up to a high hill tap
Where she saw the burnin' o' Airlie.

9. Clouds o' smoke and flames sae high
Soon left the wa's but barely,
And she laid doon on that hill to die
When she saw the burnin' o' Airlie.

3. [Bonnie House o' Airlie]

Chambers, ed. of 1880, p. 444 ("False Love, and Ha'e You Played Me This?").

a I/M

4. "The Bonnie Hoose o' Airlie"

Greig and Keith, 1925, p. 125(1a); from Duncan MS., No. 23. Sung by Mrs. Gillespie.

p I/M

It fell on a day, on a bonnie summer day,
When the corn bloomed fresh an' fairly,
That there fell oot a great dispute
Atween Argyle an' Airlie.

5. "The Bonnie Hoose o' Airlie"

Greig MSS., I, p. 189. Also in Greig and Keith, 1925, p. 125(1b). From George Riddell, Rosehearty, 1903.

m I

["]Come doon, come doon Lady Ogilvie" he said
"Come doon and kiss one fairlie,
Or I swear by the sword that I hold in my hand
That I winna leave a stanin stane in Airlie.["]

6. "The Bonny House o' Airlie"

Christie, II, 1881, p. 276. From a relative of Christie, who learned it from one of the family of Airlie.

m I (inflected VII)

It fell on a day, on a bonny simmer day,
When the corn was growing rarely,
That there fell out a great dispute
Atween Argyll and Airlie.
Argyll has ta'en a hundred men,
A hundred men and mairly,
And he's gane down by the back o' Dunkel',
To plunder the bonny house o' Airlie.

The Lady look'd over her high castle wa',
And vow but her heart beat sairly,
When she saw Argyll and 's chosen men
Come to plunder the bonny house o' Airlie.
"Come down, come down, Lady Ogilvie," he said,
"Come down and kiss me fairly;
For I swear by the sword I hold in my hand,
I winna leave a standin' stane in Airlie."

"I wadna kiss thee, fause Argyll,
I wadna kiss thee fairly;
Though you swore by the sword you hold in your hand,
You wadna leave a living soul in Airlie.
But ye'll tak' me by the milk white hand,
And ye'll tak' me by it fairly,
And ye'll lead me down to yon deep, deep den,
That I mayna see the burning o' Airlie."

He's ta'en her by the milk white hand,
But he hasna ta'en it fairly;
For he led her up to yon high hill tap,
Bade her look at the burning o' Airlie.
"Ye'll bring to me a cup o' wine,
Ye'll bring me it frae Airlie,
And I'll drink to Charlie the chief o' our clan,
And syne to my ain Lord Airlie."

7. "The Bonnie Hoose o' Airlie"

Sung by Ewan MacColl, Riverside rec. No. RLP 12-622 (B3), ed. K. S. Goldstein. Learned from Boston Dunn, an iron moulder, Falkirk, Stirlingshire.

p I/M

1. It fell on a day, on a bonnie summer's day
When the sun shone bright and clearly,
That there fell oot a great dispute
Atween Argylle and Airlie.

2. Argylle he has mustered a thousand o' his men
He has marched them oot richt early;
He has marched them in by the back o' Dunkeld
To plunder the bonnie hoose o' Airlie.

3. Lady Ogilvie has looked frae her window so high,
And O, but she grat sairly,
To see Argylle and a' his men
Come to plunder the bonnie hoose o' Airlie.

4. "Come doon, come doon, Lady Ogilvie," he cried,
"Come doon and kiss me fairly,
Or I swear by tye hilt o' my gweed braidsword
That I winna leave a stan'in' stane in Airlie."

5. "I winna come doon, ye cruel Argylle,
I winna kiss ye fairly;
I wadna kiss ye, fause Argylle,
Though ye sudna leave a stan'in' stane in Airlie."

6. "Come, tell me whaur your dowry is hid,
Come doon and tell me fairly."
"I winna tell ye whaur my dowry is hid,
Though ye sudna leave a stan'in' stane in Airlie."

7. They socht it up and they socht it down,
I wat, they socht it early,
And it was below yon bowling green
They found the dowrie o' Airlie.

8. "Eleven bairns I ha'e born
And the twelfth ne'er saw his daddie,
But though I had gotten as mony again,
They suld a' gang to fecht for Charlie.

9. "Gin my gweed lord had been at home,
As he's awa' for Charlie,
There dursna a Campbell o' a' Argylle
Set a fit on the bonnie hoose o' Airlie."

10. He's ta'en her by the milk-white hand,
But he did not lead her fairly;
He led her up to the top o' the hill,
Whaur she saw the burnin' o' Airlie.

11. The smoke and flame they rose so high,
The walls were blackened fairly;
And the lady laid her doon on the green to dee,
When she saw the burnin' o' Airlie.

GROUP B

8. "Prince Charlie"

Gardner and Chickering, 1939, p. 209. Sung by Mrs. Frank Gamsby, Saranac, Mich., 1935; learned in childhood from her sister, who heard it from a Scottish boy.

p I

1. "What loo is that," quoth the brave Lor' Heel,
"That rises this morning sae airlie?
By the God of me kin, 'tis the brave Ogilvie
And me ain bonnie hame o' Airlie.

2. "Draw your swords, draw your swords," quoth the brave Lor' Heel.
"And sheath your swords," cried Charlie,
"And we'll kendle sic a loo aroond the fause Argyle,
And we'll licht it wi' a spark oot o' Airlie."

He comes to Lady Ogilvie's door.

3. "Coom doon stairs, Lady Ogilvie," he cried,
"Coom doon and kiss me fairly,
Or I'll swear by the hilt of my broad sword
That I'll leave nae a standing stane on Airlie."

4. "I will nae coom doon for thee, fause Argyle,
And ne'er will I kiss thee fairly.
I will nae coom doon for thee, fause Argyle,
Though you leave nae a standing stane on Airlie.

5. "There's seven bonnie sons are there born unto me;
And the eighth will ne'er see his daddy.
And kent that I had as many, many more,
I'd gie them all to fight for Prince Charlie."

9. "The Bonnie Hoose o' Airlie"

Greig MSS., IV, p. 6; text, Bk. 753, XLIII, p. 31. Also in Greig and Keith, 1925, p. 125(2a). From Mrs. Coutts, Ellon.

m π^1

1. It fell on a day, a bonnie summer day,
When the clans wis a' wi' Charlie,
That there fell oot a great dispute
Between Argyle & Airlie.

2. Argyle he has chosen a hundred o' his men,
To come in the mornin' early,
And they're awa' doon by the back o' Dunkeld,
To plunder the bonnie Hoose o' Airlie.

3. The lady she lookt frae her window sae high, (high castle wa')
And oh, but she sighed sairly,
When she saw the great Argyle & his men
Come to plunder the bonnie Hoose o' Airlie.

4. Come doon, come doon, Lady Ogilvie, he cried,
Come doon & kiss me fairly,
Or ere the mornin's clear daylicht
I winna leave a stan'in' stane in Airlie.

5. I winna come doon, ye fause Argyle,
   And I widna kiss ye fairly;
I widna come doon, ye fause Argyle,
   Tho' ye shouldna leave a stan'in' stane in Airlie.

6. I hae borne seven bonnie sons,
   The last ne'er saw his daddie;
But tho' I hid as mony mair,
   They'll aye be followers o' Charlie.

7. They searched up & they searched doon,
   And they searched late & early,
Till they found it on the bonnie palm tree
   That grows in the plantins o' Airlie.

8. . . . .
   . . . .
And in spite o' the tears that the lady loot fa'
   He brunt doon the bonnie Hoose o' Airlie.

9. Gin my ain guid lord had been at hame,
   But noo he's awa wi' Charlie,
The great Argyle nor a' his men
   Durstna enter the bonnie Hoose o' Airlie.

10. "The Bonnie Hoose o' Airlie"

Greig and Keith, 1925, p. 125(2b); from Duncan MS., No. 125. Sung by Mrs. Gillespie and others.

p I/M

2. The Duke o' Montrose he's written tae Argyll
   Tae com' in the mornin' early
An' lead in his men by the back o' Dunkeld
   Tae plunder the bonnie hoose o' Earlie.

3. The Ladye looked ower her winda sae high
   An' O but she looked weary,
For there she espied the great Argyll
   Com' tae plunder the bonnie hoose o' Earlie.

4. "Com' doon, com' doon, Lady Margaret," he says,
   "Com' doon an' kiss me fairly,
For afore the morn is clear daylicht
   Ah'll no leave a stanin' stane in Earlie."

5. "I wadna kiss thee, great Argyll,
   I wadna kiss thee fairly,
Tho before the morn was clear daylicht
   Gin ye suldna leave a stanin' stane in Earlie."

6. He's taen her by the waist sae sma',
   Sayin' "Ladye, where is your dowie?"
"O, it's up, it's doon the bonnie burn side
   That rins thro the plantin's o' Earlie."

7. They socht it up, and they socht it doon,
   They socht it late an' early,
They foun' it in the bonnie balm tree
   That stan's in the bowlin' green o' Earlie.

8. He's taen her by the left shoulder,
   An' O, but she grat sairly,
An' he's led her doon tae yon green bank
   Till they plundered the bonnie hoose o' Earlie.

9. "O, it's a hae seven braw sons," she said,
   "An' the youngest ne'er saw his daddie,
An' gin I had as mony mair
   I'd gae them a' tae Prince Charlie.

10. "O, gin my lord had bin at hame,
   As this nicht he's wi' Charlie,
There dauna a Campbell in a' the west
   Hae plundered the bonnie hoose o' Earlie."

11. "The Bonnie House o' Earlie"

Barry, Eckstorm, and Smyth, 1929, p. 266. From Mrs. James McGill of Chamcook, New Brunswick, November 1927.

m I/M

1. It fell on a day, a bonnie simmer's day,
   When the corn grew ripe an' yellow,
There fell oot a great dispute
   Between Argyll an' Earlie.

GROUP C

12. "Bonny House of Airly"

Kinloch, 1827, App'x. to p. 100; text, p. 104.

a I/Ly

1. O gley'd Argyll has written to Montrose,
   To see gin the fields they war fairly;
And to see whether he shou'd stay at hame,
   Or come to plunder bonnie Airly.

2. The great Montrose has written to Argyll,
And that the fields they were fairly,
And no to keep his men at hame,
But come and plunder bonnie Airly.

3. The lady was looking oure the castle wa',
She was carrying her courage sae rarely,
And there she spied him, gley'd Argyll,
Coming for to plunder bonnie Airly.

4. "Wae be to ye, gley'd Argyll,
And are ye there sae rarely?
Ye micht hae kept your men at hame,
And no come to plunder bonnie Airly."

5. "And wae be to ye, Lady Ogilvie,
And are ye there sae rarely?
Gin ye had bow'd whan first I bade,
I never wad hae plunder'd bonnie Airly."

6. "O gin my gude Lord had been at hame,
As he is wi' prince Charlie,
There durst na a rebel on a' Scottish grund
Set a foot on the bonnie green o' Airly.

7. "But ye'll tak me by the milk-white hand,
And ye'll lift me up sae rarely;
And ye'll throw me out oure my ain castle wa',
Lat me never see the burning o' Airly."

8. He has tane her by the milk-white hand,
And he has lifted her up sae rarely,
He has thrown her out oure her ain castle wa',
And she never saw the plundering o' Airly.

9. Now gley'd Argyll he has gane hame,
Awa frae the plundering o' Airly,
And there he has met wi' Captain Ogilvie,
Coming over the mountains sae rarely.

10. "O wae be to ye, gley'd Argyll,
And are ye there sae rarely,
Ye micht hae kept your men at hame,
And na gane to plunder bonnie Airly."

11. "O wae be to ye, Captain Ogilvie,
And are ye there sae rarely?
Gin ye had bow'd whan first I bade,
I never wad hae plunder'd bonnie Airly."

12. "But gin I had my lady gay,
Bot and my sister Mary,
Ae fig I wadna gie for ye a',
Nor yet for the plundering o' Airly."

GROUP D

13. "The Bonnie House o' Airlie"

Eyre-Todd [1894], p. 198.

a I/M

It fell on a day, and a bonnie summer day,
When the corn grew green and yellow,
That there fell out a great dispute
Between Argyle and Airlie.

The Duke o' Montrose has written to Argyle
To come in the morning early,
And lead in his men by the back o' Dunkeld,
To plunder the bonnie house o' Airlie.
[*Etc.*]

Eyre-Todd took his text from John Finlay's *Scottish Historical and Romantic Ballads*, 1808, II, p. 25 (Child Ab).

14. "The Bonnie House of Airlie"

Sung by Isabel Sutherland, Selection Records Ltd., 1960. Learned from Belle Stewart, Blairgowrie, in the summer of 1955.

a I/M

1. It fell on a day, on a bonnie summer's day,
When the corn was ripe and yellow,
That there fell out a great dispute
Between Argyll and Airlie.

2. Lady Margaret looked from her high castle wa',
And O but she sighed sairly
To see Argyll and a hundred o' his men
Come to plunder the bonnie House o' Airlie.

3. "Come doun, come doun, Lady Marg'ret," he cried,
"Come doun and kiss me fairly,
Or in the morning's clear daylight
I winna leave a stan'in' stane in Airlie."

4. "I'll no come doun," Lady Margaret she cried,
"Nor wad I kiss ye fairly.
I wadna kiss the fause Argyll
Though ye wadna leave a stan'in' stane in Airlie.

5. "For I have born my seven bonnie sons
And the eighth has never seen his daddie,
But gin I had as many o'er again
They would a' be men for Chairlie."

6. Now Argyll in his rage he kindled sic a lowe
It rose tae the lift red and clearly,
And poor Lady Margaret and a' her bairns,
They were smothered in the dark reek o' Airlie.

15. "The Bonny House of Aertie [Airlie]"

Vaughan Williams MSS.

a D/Æ

GROUP E

16. "The Bonny House o' Airlie"

Creighton and Senior, 1950, p. 70. Sung by William Gilkie, Sambro, N.S.

a D

1. It was a solemn day as ever you did see
And the sun it shone most clearly
When she saw the great Argyle and all his Highland men
Come to plunder the Bonnie House o' Airlie.

2. Lady Ogilvie looked over the castle wall
And she vowed and she sighed right fairly
When she saw the great Argyle and all his Highland men
Coming to plunder the bonny house so early.

3. "Come downstairs, come downstairs Lady Ogilvie," he cries,
"Come downstairs and kiss me fairly,
And I'll swear by the heath of my broadsword
That I shan't leave a stone in St. Airlie."

4. "I won't come down to you Argyle,
I won't come down to you fairly,
I won't come down to you great Argyle
If you shouldn't leave a stone in St. Airlie.

5. "If my good laddie were aye here to-day,
He's away fighting for Prince Charlie,
It would not be you or all your royal men
That would plunder the bonny house o' Airlie.

6. "It's seven sons unto him I've born
And the eighth ne'er seen his daddy O,
And gif I had as many many more
I'd give them all to fight for Prince Charlie."

7. Then the men they went to work worse than heathen Jews or Turk
And they plundered the mansion so fairly,
And it was a solemn day as ever you did see
When they burned down the bonny house o' Airlie.

The Gypsy Laddie

CHILD NO. 200

THIS great favorite is one of those ballads which, if we had the re-ordering of Child's canon, might well be moved forward into the first hundred. Its connection with history is even more precarious than that of "Sir Patrick Spens" (No. 58), and only less so than that of "King John and the Bishop" (No. 45). For the tradition which associates the ballad with the Earl of Cassilis has, as Child shows, not a shred of historical fact behind it. At any rate, the romantic theme of "All for Love, or the World well lost" is one to the perennial appeal of which, so long as there are social distinctions, human nature will continue to respond.

Well over a hundred musical records of the last three centuries, most of them from tradition in our own, attest this popularity. It is fair to divide these into three main classes. The first class has one of the longest traditional sequences observable in all British balladry. Its earliest appearance is in the Skene MS., *ante* 1630; its latest is current today. The name which it bears in the Skene MS. is "Lady Cassiles Lilt," and Child as well as later students, failed, I believe, to note the full implications of this fact. Child says that we have no evidence that the ballad was associated in tradition with the Cassilis family until the end of the eighteenth century. But this tune yields such evidence. For it is indisputably the same tune as the one found with our ballad in Johnson's *Museum* and in a number of recent traditional versions. The Skene tune was never translated from tablature until Dauney published it in 1838, and anyhow it is obvious that later variants have developed traditionally, not by derivation from that or any other authoritative record. The most reasonable explanation of such a phenomenon is that the ballad was associated with the family which gave its name to the tune much earlier than explicit statements survive to show, and earlier indeed—supposing the ballad in anything like its later form to have been circulating around 1630—by nearly a hundred years than the first extant record of the text.

The Skene tune is of the highest interest in other ways as well. It is a two-strain tune, and both its strains, but especially the second, have had sufficient vitality to engender independent tunes which are very widespread in tradition. For the second strain is none other than the earliest recorded appearance of that ubiquitous melodic formula—the thrice-repeated sequence (IV) V VI I I VI V (IV)—which we had first occasion to notice in connection with "Lady Isabel and the Elf-Knight" (No. 4), and have seldom since lost sight of. It is today in America one of the two or three most generally employed formulae in folk song. Where this formula is found, another, (IV) V ♭VII I (2) ♭VII V (IV), which has been called "Boyne Water," is never far away, for the latter is but the dominant counterpart of the former—a continuation (a fifth higher, a fourth lower) of the pentatonic scale. It is therefore not surprising to find another group of the ballad's variants in some form of this latter scheme, which does not arise immediately from the original tune. The combinations and permutations of these two patterns are very suggestive for the student of folk-tune variation. By means of them, the different variants of this whole group oscillate in an arc stretching from π^1 to D/Æ. Scottish, English, and American traditions find these forms congenial.

The second large group belongs again to a familiar type of English folk-tune, of which there are two generally distinguishable branches among our variants. One branch falls into the Ionian-Mixolydian area, the other into the Dorian-Æolian. Most of these open with a familiar descending sequence twice repeated: a formula widely known and met not infrequently with other ballads; for example, in its major style, "The Bailiff's Daughter of Islington" (No. 105), and, in its minor, perhaps actually most familiar in Cecil Sharp's very favorite setting of a Somerset variant of the present ballad.

In the first of these two branches, the tunes are more or less evenly divided between major and Mixolydian varieties, and all are authentic. In the second branch, about a third are plagal Dorian tunes, the rest authentic Æolian. This class as a whole probably has a right to be considered the main line of English tradition for this ballad; but some Scottish, one or two Irish, and a fairly large number of American variants are included in it.

The third class is melodically the least consistent of the three, but it is loosely held together by the opening of the first phrase, rising emphatically on the major triad, by the lively character of the tunes, and by the major or Mixolydian tonality. In this class, also, there is generally an end-refrain, more or less elaborate, with nonsense syllables. Frequently this burden is as long as the stanza itself. There is an almost equal division of variants between authentic and plagal tunes. A few of the latter have fallen closes on the lower dominant. Probably, this whole class has a distant relation to the second class, but the recollection seems very dim, and a new and stronger influence has intervened. All or most of the members of this newer tradition, it should be added, are American.

LIST OF VARIANTS

GROUP A

1. "Lady Cassilles Lilt." Skene MS., National Library of Scotland Adv. MS. 5.2.15, No. 30; transcribed in William Dauney, *Ancient Scotish Melodies*, 1838, No. 30, p. 228. Also in John Goss, *Ballads of Britain*, 1937, p. 95(E).
2. "Johnny Faa, or the Gypsy Laddie." James Johnson, *The Scots Musical Museum*, II [1788], No. 181, p. 189 (repr. 1853). Also in Joseph Ritson, *Scotish Songs*, 1794, II, p. 176; Robert Archibald Smith, *The Scotish Minstrel* [1820-24], III, p. 90; James Hogg, *Jacobite Relics*, Second Series, 1821, p. 192; George Thomson, *The Select Melodies of Scotland* [1822-23], IV, p. 35; Robert Maver, *Genuine Scottish Melodies*, 1866, No. 61, p. 31; and George Eyre-Todd, *Ancient Scots Ballads* [1894], p. 14.

GROUP Aa

3. "The Three Gypsy Laddies." Gavin Greig and Alexander Keith, *Last Leaves of Traditional Ballads and Ballad Airs*, 1925, p. 129(2). (Davidson)
4. "Black Jack Davy." Bascom Lamar Lunsford, LC Archive

of American Folk Song, recording No. 9474(A1). Also in Bascom Lamar Lunsford and Lamar Stringfield, *30 and 1 Folk Songs from the Southern Mountains*, 1929, p. 4.
5. "The Gypsy Davie." Frank C. Brown MSS., 16 a 4 J, Library of Congress, photostat. Also in Brown MSS., 16 a 4 H; and *The Frank C. Brown Collection of North Carolina Folklore*, IV (*The Music of the Ballads*, ed. Jan P. Schinhan), 1957, p. 88(F).

GROUP Ab

6. "The Gypsy Laddie." Arthur Kyle Davis, Jr., *Traditional Ballads of Virginia*, 1929, pp. 590(A) and 424.
7. "I'm Seventeen Come Sunday," or "The Gypsy Laddie." Sharp MSS., 4615/3224, Clare College Library, Cambridge. (Callaway)
8. "The Davy." Mrs. Carrie Grover, LC Archive of American Folk Song, recording No. 4454(B1). Also in Carrie B. Grover, *A Heritage of Songs*, ed. Ann L. Griggs, privately printed by Gould Academy, Bethel, Me., n.d., p. 116.
9. "Gypsy Davy." John Harrington Cox, *Traditional Ballads Mainly from West Virginia*, 1939, p. 31; and 1964 (ed. George Boswell), p. 40. Also in Dorothy Scarborough, *A Song Catcher in Southern Mountains*, 1937, pp. 414(G) and 224.
10. "The Gypsy Laddie." Helen Creighton and Doreen H. Senior, *Traditional Songs from Nova Scotia*, 1950, p. 72.
a. "The Egyptian Davy O," or "Gypsy Daisy." Schinhan, *Music, Brown Collection*, IV, 1957, p. 85(C).
11. "Gypsy Davy." Lester A. Hubbard, *Ballads and Songs from Utah*, 1961, p. 26.
12. "Gypsy Davy." Alton C. Morris, *Folksongs of Florida*, 1950, p. 306.
13. "It Was Late in the Night When Johnny Came Home." Morris, 1950, p. 304.
14. "Gypsy Davy." Ruth A. Musick, *JAF*, LXX (1957), pp. 352 and 339.
15. "Gypsy Davy." Harold W. Thompson, *New York Folklore Quarterly*, X (1954), p. 52.
16. "The Gypsy Laddie." Sharp MSS., 4609/3222. (Ayres)
17. "The Gypsy Laddie." Sharp MSS., 3462/2549. Also in Cecil J. Sharp and Maud Karpeles, *English Folk Songs from the Southern Appalachians*, 1932, I, p. 234(C). (House)
b. "The Gypsy Davy." Woody Guthrie, LC Archive of American Folk Song, Album 1, record No. 2(A1). Also in LC/AAFS, recording No. L1(A3).
c. "How Old Are You, My Pretty Little Miss?" Schinhan, *Music, Brown Collection*, IV, 1957, p. 89(G).

GROUP AC

18. "The Gypsy Laddie." Sharp MSS., 4722/3288. (Mitchell)
19. "The Gypsy Laddie." Maud Karpeles, *JEFDSS*, VI, No. 3 (1951), p. 79.
20. "Gipsey Laddie." Sharp MSS., 3400/. Also in Sharp and Karpeles, *Appalachians*, 1932, I, p. 236(E). (Gwynne)
21. "The Gipsy Laddie." Sharp MSS., 3375/2468. Also in Sharp and Karpeles, 1932, I, p. 234(B). (Norton)
22. "The Gypsy Laddie." Winston Wilkinson MSS., 1935-36, p. 80(A), University of Virginia.
23. "The Gipsy Laddie." Sharp MSS., 4186/. (Fitzgerald)
24. "The Gypsy Laddie." Wilkinson MSS., 1936-37, p. 22(A).
25. "Black Eyed Davy." Brown MSS., 16 a 4 J.
26. "The Gypsy Laddie." James W. Raine, *The Land of Saddle-bags*, 1924, p. 119. Also in Sharp MSS., 3448/2540; and Sharp and Karpeles, *Appalachians*, 1932, I, p. 235(D). (Gentry)
27. "Gypsy Laddie." Mrs. Mary Bird McAllister, LC Archive of American Folk Song, recording No. 11,866(A1).
28. "Black Jack Gypsy." Myrtle Downing, LC Archive of American Folk Song, recording No. 11,715(B30).
29. (Untitled.) Mrs. Texas Gladden, LC Archive of American Folk Song, recording No. 5233(A1).
30. "The Gypsy Laddie." Wilkinson MSS., 1935-36, p. 83(C).

GROUP Ad

31. "The Gypsy Laddie." Wilkinson MSS., 1935-36, p. 82(B).
32. "The Lady's Disgrace." Scarborough, *A Song Catcher in Southern Mountains*, 1937, pp. 413(F) and 223.
33. "The Gypsy Laddie." Sharp MSS., 3548/2622. Also in Davis, *Traditional Ballads of Virginia*, 1929, pp. 591(H) and 431; and Sharp and Karpeles, *Appalachians*, 1932, I, p. 237(G). (Chisholm)
34. "The Gipsy Laddie." Sharp MSS., 4761/. Also in Sharp and Karpeles, 1932, I, p. 239(J). (Hughes)
35. "The Gypsy Laddie." Sharp MSS., 3368/2465. Also in Sharp and Karpeles, 1932, I, p. 233(A). (Coates)
36. "The Gypsy Laddie." Sharp MSS., 4183/3017. Also in Sharp and Karpeles, 1932, I, p. 238(I). (Gibson)

APPENDIX A

37. "The Gipsy Laddie." Sharp MSS., 4652/. (Webb)
38. "Gypsy Laddie." Jean Ritchie, Folkways LP recording No. FA 2301(A1), ed. Kenneth S. Goldstein.
39. "The Gipsy Laddy." Sharp MSS., 3637/2696. (Sloan)
40. "The Gypsy Lover." Vance Randolph, *Ozark Folksongs*, I, 1946, p. 160(H).

GROUP B

41. "The Wraggle Taggle Gipsies." Sharp MSS., 738/. (Gordge)
42. "Gipsies-O." F. M. Collinson, *JEFDSS*, V, No. 1 (1946), p. 14. Also in F. M. Collinson and F. Dillon, *Folk Songs from "Country Magazine,"* 1952, p. 43.
43. "The Gipsy Laddie." Greig MSS., I, p. 113, King's College Library, Aberdeen. Also in Greig and Keith, *Last Leaves*, 1925, p. 129(1c). (Ritchie)
44. "The Three Gipsies." Greig MSS., II, p. 143. Also in Greig and Keith, 1925, p. 128(1a). (Fowlie)
45. "The Gipsy Laddie." Greig MSS., I, p. 154, and Bk. 714, IV, p. 77. Also in Greig and Keith, 1925, p. 128(1b). (Spence)
46. "Wraggle Taggle Gipsies." Sharp MSS., 943/999. (Vincent)
47. "Gipsy Laddie." Greig-Duncan MS. 785 (transcription of of W. Walker), p. 96, King's College Library, Aberdeen. From Duncan MS., No. 14. (Gillespie)
48. "The Gipsy Laddie." Greig MSS., IV, p. 155. (Morice)
49. "The Gypsy Laddie." Ewan MacColl, Riverside recording No. RLP 12-637(A5), ed. Kenneth S. Goldstein.
d. "Three Gypsies came to the door." Alice E. Gillington, *Songs of the Open Road*, 1911, p. 12.
e. "There were seven Gypsies." Gillington, 1911, p. 16.
50. "The Dark-Clothed Gypsy." Elisabeth B. Greenleaf and Grace Y. Mansfield, *Ballads and Sea Songs of Newfoundland*, 1933, p. 38.

51. "Wraggle Taggle Gipsies." Sharp MSS., 1034/. (Brooks)
52. "The Gypsy Laddie." Maud Karpeles MSS., No. 5296 and p. 4843.
53. "Wraggle Taggle Gipsies O." Sharp MSS., 69/123. (Spearman)
54. "The Gipsy Countess." Sabine Baring-Gould MSS., L(4) and (C), Plymouth Public Library. Also in Sabine Baring-Gould and H. Fleetwood Sheppard, *Songs and Ballads of the West*, 1895, p. 108; and Goss, *Ballads of Britain*, 1937, p. 94(B).
55. "Draggletail Gipsies." Sharp MSS., 301/407. (Pond)
56. "Gipsies of Agee (Egypt) Oh!" H. E. D. Hammond MSS., No. 226 and D.V., p. 65, Cecil Sharp House, London.
57. "The Ragtail Gipsies, Oh!" Hammond MSS., No. 363 and V, pp. 64v and 65v.
58. "The Gipsy Laddie Oh!" Hammond MSS., No. 421.
59. "The Draggletail Gipsy O." Sharp MSS., 360/482. (King)
60. "The Gypsie Laddie." John Ord, *The Bothy Songs and Ballads*, 1930, p. 411.
61. "The Wraggle Taggle Gipsies." Sharp MSS., 478/. (Nott)
62. "The Gipsy Laddie." Karpeles MSS., No. 5172 and p. 4708. Also in Maud Karpeles, *Folk Songs from Newfoundland*, 1934, I, p. 14.
63. "The Gipsy Laddie." Karpeles MSS., No. 5258.
64. "The Gipsy Laddie." Karpeles MSS., No. 5277.
65. "Wraggle Taggle Gipsies O." Sharp MSS., 1423/. (Parish)
66. "Wraggle Taggle Gipsies." Sharp MSS., 1447/. (Geen)
67. "Wraggle Taggle Gipsies." Sharp MSS., 837/909. (Cridland)
68. "Wraggle Taggle Gipsies O." Sharp MSS., 1580/. (Coles)
69. "Wraggle Taggle Gipsies." Sharp MSS., 1389/. (Bodley)
70. "Wraggle Taggle Gipsies O." Sharp MSS., 1880/. (Gullyford)
71. "Wraggle Taggle Gipsies." Sharp MSS., 2308/2103. (Haden)
72. "The Gipsy Countess." Baring-Gould MSS., L(2). Also in Sabine Baring-Gould and H. Fleetwood Sheppard, *A Garland of Country Song*, 1895, p. 68; and Goss, *Ballads of Britain*, 1937, p. 94(C).
73. "The Draggletail Gipsies." Sharp MSS., 264/373. Also in Cecil J. Sharp and Charles L. Marson, *Folk Songs from Somerset*, 1904, p. 18; Sharp, *One Hundred English Folksongs*, 1916, p. 13; and Sharp, *English Folk Songs*, Selected Ed., Novello and Co. [1920], I, p. 13. (Overd)
74. "The Raggle Taggle Gypsies, O." Cox, *Traditional Ballads Mainly from West Virginia*, 1939, p. 33; and 1964 (ed. Boswell), p. 42.
75. "The Three Gypsies." Scarborough, *A Song Catcher in Southern Mountains*, 1937, pp. 411(A) and 216.
76. "Wraggle Taggle Gipsies O." Sharp MSS., 772/. (Slade)
77. "The Gypsy Laddie." Mary O. Eddy, *Ballads and Songs from Ohio*, 1939, p. 67.
78. "The Gipsy Laddie." Charlotte S. Burne, *Shropshire Folk-Lore* [1886], pp. 652 and 551.
79. "The Gypsie Laddie." Josephine McGill, *Folk-Songs of the Kentucky Mountains*, 1917, p. 15.
80. "The Gypsy Laddie." Wilkinson MSS., 1936-37, p. 23(B).
81. "The Gypsy Laddie." Florence Shiflett, LC Archive of American Folk Song, recording No. 12,006(B24).
82. "Gypsy Laddie." David Morris, LC Archive of American Folk Song, recording No. 12,007(A7).
83. "Gypsy Laddie." Robert Shiflett, LC Archive of American Folk Song, recording No. 12,004(A2).
84. "The Gipsies came to Lord M——'s Gate." Patrick Weston Joyce, *Old Irish Folk Music and Songs*, 1909, No. 334, p. 154.
85. "The Dark-Eyed Gipsy O!" C. Milligan Fox, *Journal of the Irish Folk Song Society*, I (1904), p. 42.
86. "Wraggle Taggle Gipsies O!" Sharp MSS., 2610/. (Unnamed)

APPENDIX B

87. "The Gypsy Countess." Baring-Gould MSS., L(1) and (A). Also in Baring-Gould and Sheppard, *Songs and Ballads of the West*, 1895, p. 106.
88. "The Gipsy Laddie." Greig MSS., I, p. 43. (J. B. Duncan)
89. "The Gypsy Lady." Phillips Barry MSS., II, No. 200H, Harvard College Library.
90. "Wraggle Taggle Gipsies O." Sharp MSS., 2079/1931. (Sister Emma)
91. "The Gypsy Laddie." Davis, *Traditional Ballads of Virginia*, 1929, pp. 591(D) and 427.
f. "The Gipsy Countess." Baring-Gould MSS., L(3) and (B).
g. "The Gypsy Davy." Phillips Barry, *JAF*, XXII (1909), p. 80. Also in Helen Hartness Flanders, *Ancient Ballads Traditionally Sung in New England*, III, 1963, p. 219(P).

GROUP C

92. "The Gipsy Laddie." Sharp MSS., 4227/. (Coffey)
h. "Gypsy Laddie." Schinhan, *Music, Brown Collection*, IV, 1957, p. 89(G1).
93. "The Gypsy Davy." George Lyman Kittredge, *JAF*, XXX (1917), p. 324.
94. "The Gypsy Davy." John Harrington Cox, *Folk-Songs of the South*, 1925, pp. 524 and 130.
95. "Gypsy Davie." Phillips Barry, *JAF*, XVIII (1905), p. 194(E).
96. "Gypsy Laddie." Arthur Keefe, LC Archive of American Folk Song, recording No. 10,501(A16).
i. "Gypsy Daisy." Eloise Hubbard Linscott, *Folk Songs of Old New England*, 1939, p. 208.
97. "The Gipsy Laddy." Sharp MSS., 3507/. Also in Sharp and Karpeles, *Appalachians*, 1932, I, p. 237(F). (Buckner)
98. "Gypsy Davy." Eddy, *Ballads and Songs from Ohio*, 1939, p. 68(B).
99. "Gypsy Davy." Tolman MS., Harvard College Library. Also in Carl Sandburg, *The American Songbag*, 1927, p. 311.
100. "The Gypsy Davy." Randolph, *Ozark Folksongs*, I, 1946, p. 152(A).
101. "Black Jack Davy." Mrs. T. M. Davis, LC Archive of American Folk Song, recording No. 11,894(B18).
102. "Gipsy Draly." Mrs. Oleava Houser, LC Archive of American Folk Song, recording No. 11,908(B34).
103. "The Gypsy Davy." Randolph, *Ozark Folksongs*, I, 1946, p. 155(E).
104. "Gipsy Laddie." Sharp MSS., 3674/. Also in Sharp and Karpeles, *Appalachians*, 1932, I, p. 237(H). (Franklin)
105. "Gypsum Davy." Mrs. Donald (Emma) Shelton, LC Archive of American Folk Song, recording No. 10,008 (A9).
106. "Gypsy Davy." Scarborough, *A Song Catcher in Southern Mountains*, 1937, pp. 412(E) and 221.

107. "Gipsy Daisy." Helen Hartness Flanders, *A Garland of Green Mountain Song*, 1934, p. 78. Also in Flanders, *Ancient Ballads*, III, 1963, p. 216(N).
108. "Gypsy Davy." Barry, *JAF*, XVIII (1905), p. 195(G).
109. "Gypsy Davy." Phillips Barry, Fannie H. Eckstorm, and Mary W. Smyth, *British Ballads from Maine*, 1929, p. 272. (Young)
110. "Gipsy Davy." Barry, Eckstorm, and Smyth, 1929, p. 276. (Patch)
111. "Gyps of David." Frank Proffitt, Folk-Legacy LP recording FSA-1.
j. "Black Cat Davy." Arthur Kyle Davis, Jr., *More Traditional Ballads of Virginia*, 1960, p. 258(BB).
112. "Black Jack Davy." Maurice Matteson and Mellinger Edward Henry, *Beech Mountain Folk-Songs and Ballads*, 1936, p. 6.
113. "David." Mrs. Wayne (Claudia) Roberts, LC Archive of American Folk Songs, recording No. 10,007(A16).
114. "Black Jack Davy." Herbert Shellans, *North Carolina Folklore*, VI (1958), p. 18.
115. "Black Jack David." Arthur Palmer Hudson and George Herzog, *Folk Tunes from Mississippi*, 1937, No. 26.
116. "Black Jack Davy." Buck Buttery, LC Archive of American Folk Song, recording No. 11,909(B24).
117. "Black Jack David." John Pennington, LC Archive of American Folk Song, recording No. 11,894(B7).
k. "Black Jack David." Schinhan, *Music, Brown Collection*, IV, 1957, p. 85(B1).
l. "Black Jack Davy." Davis, *More Traditional Ballads of Virginia*, 1960, p. 256(AA).
m. "Black Jack David." Schinhan, *Music, Brown Collection*, IV, 1957, p. 84(B).
n. "Black Jack David." Schinhan, *Music, Brown Collection*, IV, 1957, p. 84(A).
118. "Black Jack Davy." Henry Wacaster Perry, "A Sampling of Folklore from Carter County, Tennessee" (George Peabody College for Teachers, M.A. thesis), 1938, p. 298.
119. "Black Eyed Davy." Brown MSS., 16 a 4 J. Also in Schinhan, *Music, Brown Collection*, IV, 1957, p. 87(D1).
120. "Black Jack David." Brown MSS., 16 a 4 J (*bis*). Also in Schinhan, *Music, Brown Collection*, IV, 1957, p. 88(E1). Text, *The Frank C. Brown Collection of North Carolina Folklore*, II (*Folk Ballads from North Carolina*, ed. Henry M. Belden and Arthur Palmer Hudson), 1952, p. 165(E).
o. "Black Jack David." Schinhan, *Music, Brown Collection*, IV, 1957, p. 87(E).
121. "Gypsy Davy." Barry, *JAF*, XVIII (1905), p. 192(C).
122. "Black Jack Davie." David Seneff McIntosh, "Some Representative Southern Illinois Folk Songs" (Iowa State University M.A. thesis in music), 1935, p. 18. Also in McIntosh, *JAF*, XLVIII (1935), p. 385.
123. "Gypsy Davy." Mrs. May Kennedy McCord, LC Archive of American Folk Song, recording No. 5303(A1). Also in Randolph, *Ozark Folksongs*, I, 1946, p. 158(G).
124. "Gypsy Davy." William A. Owens, *Texas Folk Songs*, 1950, p. 48.
p. "Black Jack David." Schinhan, *Music, Brown Collection*, IV, 1957, p. 90(I).
125. "Gypsy Davy." Mellinger Edward Henry, *Folk-Songs from the Southern Highlands* [1938], p. 110.
q. "Black Jack David." Schinhan, *Music, Brown Collection*, IV, 1957, p. 90(H).
126. "Black Jack Davy." Scarborough, *A Song Catcher in Southern Mountains*, 1937, pp. 412(B) and 218.

APPENDIX C

127. "Gypsy Davy." Barry MSS., IV, No. 189. (Longee)
128. "Harrison Brady." George Korson, *Pennsylvania Songs and Legends*, 1949, p. 52.

TUNES WITH TEXTS

GROUP A

1. "Lady Cassilles Lilt"

Skene MS., NL Scotland Adv. MS. 5.2.15, No. 30; transcribed in Dauney, 1838, No. 30, p. 228. Also in Goss, 1937, p. 95(E).

a π^2

Or thus, at the level of singing:

2. "Johnny Faa, or the Gypsy Laddie"

Johnson, II [1788], No. 181, p. 189 (repr. 1853). Also in Ritson, 1794, II, p. 176; Smith [1820-24], III, p. 90; Hogg, Second Series, 1821, p. 192 ("Wae's Me for Prince Charlie"); G. Thomson [1822-23], IV, p. 35; Maver, 1866, No. 61, p. 31; and Eyre-Todd [1894], p. 14.

a M

1. The gypsies came to our Lord's yett,
   And vow but they sang sweetly;
   They sang sae sweet, and sae compleat,
   That down came the fair lady.
   When she came tripping down the stair,
   And a' her maids before her;
   As soon as they saw her weel fair'd face,
   They coost the glamer o'er her.

2. Gae tak frae me this gay mantile,
   And bring to me a plaidie;
   For if kith and kin and a' had sworn,
   I'll follow the gypsie laddie.
   Yestreen I lay in a weel-made bed,
   And my good lord beside me;
   This night I'll ly in a tenant's barn,
   Whatever shall betide me.

3. Oh! come to your bed says Johny Faa,
   Oh! come to your bed, my deary;
   For I vow and swear by the hilt of my sword,
   That your lord shall nae mair come near ye.
   I'll go to bed to my Johny Faa,
   And I'll go to bed to my deary;
   For I vow and swear by what past yestreen,
   That my lord shall nae mair come near me.

4. I'll make a hap to my Johny Faa,
   And I'll make a hap to my deary;
   And he's get a' the coat gaes round,
   And my lord shall nae mair come near me.
   And when our lord came hame at e'en,
   And speir'd for his fair lady,
   The tane she cry'd, and the other reply'd,
   She's awa wi' the gypsie laddie.

5. Gae saddle to me the black, black steed,
   Gae saddle and mak him ready;
   Before that I either eat or sleep,
   I'll gae seek my fair lady.
   And we were fifteen well made men,
   Altho' we were nae bonny;
   And we are a' put down for ane,
   The earl of Cassilis' lady.

GROUP Aa

3. "The Three Gypsy Laddies"

Greig and Keith, 1925, p. 129(2). Sung by John Davidson, Glenbuchat.

a I/M

Three gypsies cam to oor lord's yett,
  An' O but they sang bonnie;
They sang sae sweet an' sae complete,
  They charmed the hert o' the lady.

4. "Black Jack Davy"

Sung by Bascom Lamar Lunsford of Turkey Creek, N.C., March 1949, in the Library of Congress, Washington, D.C. LC/AAFS, rec. No. 9474(A1). Also in Lunsford and Stringfield, 1929, p. 4. Learned from Selma Clubb, Buncombe County, c. 1925. Collected by Mrs. Rae Korson and Duncan Emrich.

a π^2

1. Black Jack Davy come a-riding through the woods
   He sang so loud and merrily,
   His voice rang out on the green grass lea
   And he charmed the heart of a lady,
   He charmed the heart of a lady.

2. How old are you, my pretty little Miss,
   How old are you, my honey?
   Well, she smiled so sweet with a te-he-hee,
   I'll be sixteen next Sunday,
   I'll be sixteen next Sunday.

3. O will you come and go with me,
   Come go with me, my honey?
   We'll go away to the deep blue sea,
   You'll never want for money,
   You'll never want for money.

4. As she put on her Sunday shoes
 All made of Spanish leather
And he put on his old cork boots
 And they both rode off together,
 And they both rode off together.

5. The landlord come a-riding in
 Inquiring for his lady.
O one of his maids then said to him,
 She is gone with Black Jack Davy,
 She is gone with Black Jack Davy.

6. Then bridle and saddle my old gray mare
 And hand me down my derby
And I'll ride east and I'll ride west
 And overtake my lady,
 And overtake my lady.

7. Well, he rode east and he rode west
 He rode to the deep blue sea
And there he found with tears in his eyes
 O there he found his lady,
 O there he found his lady.

8. Will you forsake your house and home
 Your husband and your baby?
Will you forsake all else on earth
 And go with Black Jack Davy,
 And go with Black Jack Davy?

9. Last night I slept on the cold cold ground
 Beside the Black Jack Davy,
I'll sleep tonight in a warm feather bed
 Between my husband and baby,
 Between my husband and baby.

5. "The Gypsy Davie"

Brown MSS., 16 a 4 J. Also in Brown MSS., 16 a 4 H; and Schinhan, *Music, Brown Collection*, IV, 1957, p. 88(F). Sung by Mrs. J. J. Miller, King's Creek, Caldwell County, N.C.

a I/M

Cf. also variant 25.

One stanza, supplied by Mrs. Maude M. Sutton with Mrs. Miller's tune, is written under the notes, as follows:

So late in the night when the landlord came
Inquiring for his lady—
The answer was quickly replied:
'She has gone with the Gypsy Davy.'

The conclusion of Mrs. Miller's version is given thus in *Folk Ballads, Brown Collection*, II, 1952, p. 167(F):

'Last night I lay on a warm feather bed,
My arms were around my baby;
Tonight I shall lie on some cold river bank
In the arms of a Gypsy Davie.'

'Pull off, pull off those fine kid gloves,
They're made of Spanish leather,
And give to me your lily-white hand
And we'll shake hands together.'

'I can pull off those fine kid gloves,
They're made of Spanish leather,
And give to you my lily-white hand—
Bid you farewell forever.'

GROUP Ab

6. [The Gypsy Laddie]

Davis, 1929, p. 590(A); text, p. 424. Contributed by Alfreda M. Peel, August 28, 1923, from the singing of Miss Myrtle Harmon, Bland, Va.

m π^1

1. Young Davie he came whistling by,
 He whistled so loud and gaily,
He whistled till he made the green buds ring
 And charmed the heart of a lady.

Chorus

Oh, rum, diddle dum, diddle dum, diddle dum,
 Oh, rum, diddle dum, diddle do di,
Oh, rum, diddle dum, diddle doo, diddle dum,
 Oh, rum, diddle dum, diddle do di.

2. The lady she came stepping down stairs,
 With her waiting maid behind her,
A glass of wine in her hand,
 To drink a health to Davie.

3. The new Ingram lord came home that night,
 Inquiring for his lady;
The waiting maid she vowed and said,
 "She's gone with a Gypsy Laddie."

4. "Go saddle me my brightest bay,
My roan is not so speedy;
I'll ride all night and I'll ride all day
Till I overtake my lady."

5. He rode till he came to the broad waters
That run so deep and muddy,
And there the tears ran down his cheeks,
"And it's where will I find my lady?"

6. He overtook her at Gravel Hill,
Where the grass grows green and swarthy:
"Have you forsaken your house and home?
Have you forsaken your baby?
Have you forsaken your new Ingram lord
To go with Gypsy Davie?"

7. "Yes, I have forsaken my house and home,
Yes, I have forsaken my baby,
Yes, I have forsaken my new Ingram lord
To go with Gypsy Laddie."

8. "Last night you lay on a fine feather bed,
Your own true husband beside you;
Tonight you lie on the cold damp ground,
With Gypsy Davie beside you.

9. "Oh now pull off those high-heeled shoes,
That are made of Spanish leather,
And reach to me your little white hand,
And I'll bid farewell forever."

7. "I'm Seventeen Come Sunday," or "The Gypsy Laddie"

Sharp MSS., 4615/3224. Sung by Mrs. Margaret Callaway, Burnsville, N.C., September 16, 1918.

a π^2

Will you court me, my pretty little Miss?
Will you court me, my honey?
She answered me with a smile on her face:
I'll court just any body.

I'll sling my shot-pouch to my back,
My musket on my shoulder,
I'll march away to the foreign land,
And there I'll make a soldier.

I'll go catch up my little bay horse,
My bay it is so speedy;
I'll ride all day and I'll ride all night,
I'll overtake my daisy.

I rid all day and I rid all night,
And I overtook my daisy.
I found her lying on a cold river bank
In the arms of a gypsen baby.

8. "The Davy"

Sung by Mrs. Carrie Grover, Gorham, Me., 1941. LC/AAFS, rec. No. 4454(B1). Collected by Alan Lomax. Also in Grover, n.d., p. 116.

a π^2

1. The Squire came home late at night
Inquiring for his lady,
The servant made him this reply,
"She's gone with the Gypsy Davy."

Refrain

Too-riddle ink tom toor de lie (?Toor de linktum)
Too riddle ink tom tido
The servant made him this reply,
"She's gone with the Gypsy Davy."

2. "Go harness up my milk-white steed,
The gray is not so speedy.
I'll ride all night and I'll ride all day,
Till I overtake my lady."

[*Refrain as before, changing line three*]

3. He rode till he came to the river's side
It looked so dark and dreary
There he espied his lady fair
Along with the Gypsy Davy.

[*Refrain as before, lines three and four changing*]

4. "Would you forsake your house and home
Would you forsake your baby?
Would you forsake your own wed lord,
And go 'long with the Gypsy Davy?"

[*Refrain as before*]

5. "Yes, I'd forsake my house and home,
Yes, I'd forsake my baby,
Yes, I'd forsake my own wed lord,
And go 'long with the Gypsy Davy."

[*Refrain as before*]

6. "Last night I lay on a bed of down
My baby lay beside me
Tonight I'll lay on the cold cold ground
Along with Gypsy Davy."
Toor de linktum toor de lie
Toor de linktum tido
Tonight I'll lay on the cold cold ground,
Along with the Gypsy Davy.

9. "Gypsy Davy"

Cox, 1939, p. 31; and 1964 (ed. Boswell), p. 40. Also in Scarborough, 1937, p. 414(G); text, p. 224. Contributed in 1925 by Mrs. Margaret Widdemer Schauffler of New York City; obtained from Miss Lucia Sanderson, Cleveland, Ohio, who learned it from an Englishwoman. Tune noted (from Mrs. Schauffler's singing?) by Frances Sanders, Morgantown, W.Va.

a M/D

In the Scarborough copy cited above, there are slight differences, both in text and tune, and Mrs. Schauffler is quoted as having learned the song from Mrs. Margaret Leamy, who learned it in Ireland as a child.

1. Gypsy Davy came over the hill,
Down through the valley shady,
He whistled and sang till the wild woods rang,
And he won the heart of a lady.

Refrain

Ah dee doo, ah dee doo, doo day,
Ah dee doo, doo doo, day dee.
He whistled and sang till the wild woods rang,
And he won the heart of a lady.

2. My lord returning home that night,
Asking for his lady;
The servants made him this reply,
"She's gone with the Gypsy Davy."

3. "O saddle to me my jet black steed,
The brown is not so speedy,
O saddle to me my jet black steed,
Till I seek and find my lady."

4. He sought her up, he sought her down,
Through woods and valleys shady;
He sought her down by the muddy water side,
And there he found his lady.

5. "What made you leave your home and lands,
What made you leave your baby?
What made you leave your own wedded lord
To go with the Gypsy Davy?"

6. "I never loved you in my life,
I never loved my baby,
I never loved my own wedded lord,
As I love the Gypsy Davy."

10. [The Gypsy Laddie]

Creighton and Senior, 1950, p. 72. Sung by Mrs. Edward Gallagher, Chebucto Head, N.S. Tune collected by Nina Bartley Finn.

a M/D

"Would you forsake your house and home,
Would you forsake your baby,
Would you forsake your new married man
And go with the Gypsy Davy."

Chorus

To iddle inktum tie iddle ay,
To iddle inktum tidy,
To iddle inktum tie iddle ay,
And go with the Gypsy Davy.

"Yes I'd forsake my house and home,
Yes, I'd forsake my baby O
Yes, I'd forsake my new married man
And go with the Gypsy Davy."

Chorus.

"Last night I slept in a feather bed,
Last night I slept with my baby O,
To-night I'll sleep on the cold damp ground
In the arms of the Gypsy Davy."

Chorus.

11. "Gypsy Davy"

Hubbard, 1961, p. 26. Sung by Mrs. Salley A. Hubbard, Salt Lake City, Utah, and her sister, Mrs. Lottie Marsh Heed of Ogden; learned before 1885 from their mother.

a I

1. There was a gypsy come over the hill,
. . . .
He sank so loud, he sang so shrill
That he charmed the heart of the lady.

Rum diddle um diddle um,
Rum diddle um dum tu riddle aye,
Rum dum do dum di do.

2. "Come go with me, my pretty fair maid,
Come go with me, my honey,
I swear by the sword that hangs by my side
You never shall want for money."

3. "I'll take off my high-heeled shoes,
They're made of Spanish leather,
I'll put on my low-heeled shoes
And we will ride together."

4. "Will you forsake your house and land?
Will you forsake your baby?
Will you forsake your own married lord
And follow the Gypsy Davy?"

5. "Yes, I'll forsake my house and land,
And I'll forsake my baby,
And I'll forsake my own married lord
To follow the Gypsy Davy."

6. Next day her husband came to the farm
Inquiring for his lady.
The servant girls all cried out,
"She's gone with the Gypsy Davy."

7. "Go saddle up my old gray horse,
The brown is not so speedy.
I've rode all day and I'll ride all night
Till I overtake my lady."

8. He rode till he came to the river side,
Where the water was deep and muddy;
Then the tears came to his eyes,
There he saw his lady.

9. "Last night I slept on a feather bed,
With a blanket all around me;
Tonight I'll lie on the cold, cold ground,
With the wolves howling round me."

12. "Gypsy Davy"

Morris, 1950, p. 306. Sung by P. F. Skofield, Gainesville, Fla.; learned from his mother in Maine.

a I/M

1. The Gypsy Davy came over the hills,
Came over the eastern valley;
He sang till he made the wild woods ring,
And charmed the heart of a lady.

Chorus

Twaddle la de dinktum, dinktum, dinktum,
Twaddle la de dinktum Davy;
He sang till he made the wild woods ring,
And charmed the heart of a lady.

2. The lord, returning home at night,
Inquired for his lady
The servant made him this reply:
"She's gone with the Gypsy Davy."

3. "Go harness me my coal black steed:
The grey is not so speedy;
I'll ride all day, and I'll ride all night
Till I overtake my lady."

4. He rode till he came to the water's side—
It looked so dark and dreary—
Till there he spied his bonny bride
By the side of the Gypsy Davy.

5. "Would you forsake your home and friends?
Would you forsake your baby?
Would you forsake your wedded lord
And go with the Gypsy Davy?"

6. "Yes, I'll forsake my home and friends.
Yes, I'll forsake my baby.
Yes, I'll forsake my wedded love
And go with the Gypsy Davy.

7. "I never loved you in my life;
I never loved my baby;
I never loved my home and friends,
But I love my Gypsy Davy.

8. "Last night I slept on a warm, soft bed,
And in my arms my baby;
Tonight I'll sleep on the cold, cold ground,
Beside my Gypsy Davy."

13. "It was Late in the Night When Johnny Came Home"

Morris, 1950, p. 304. Sung by Mrs. G. A. Griffin, Newberry, Fla.

a I/M

1. It was late in the night when Johnny came home
Inquiring for his lady O.
But this reply was made to him,
"She's gone with the Gypsy David."

Chorus

Raddle up a dinktum, a dinktum, a dinktum,
Raddle up a dink kye aisy,
Raddle up a dinktum, whoopee little dinktum,
My, ain't I aisy?

2. "Saddle up, saddle up, my little black horse;
My roan is not so speedy.
I've rode him all night, and I'll ride him all day,
Or I'll overtake my lady.

3. "I rode and I rode to the sea seaside,
And there it was black and muddy;
Come back, come back, my own true love,
Come back, come back, my honey.

4. "I swear by my side and hang by my side
That you'll never lack for money."
. . . .
. . . .

5. "I won't come back, and I shan't come back
For you or your land and money;
I wouldn't give a kiss from the Gypsy's lips
For you and your land and money."

6. "O what will you do with your house and land?
O what will you do with your money?
O what will you do with your two little babes,
To go with the Gypsy David?"

7. "With you I'll leave my house and land;
With you I'll leave my money;
With you I'll leave my two little babes,
To go with the Gypsy David."

8. "Pray when you get to the Gypsy's land,
Please write me back a letter;
And if they don't treat you well,
Perhaps I'll come after you."

9. She hadn't been there but a very short time,
And she wrote him back a letter,
"Perhaps if you'll come after me,
Perhaps I'll treat you better.

10. "Once I had a nice feather bed,
And once I had a honey,
But now I'm a-lying all over the hay
With the gypsies marching round me."

14. "Gypsy Davy"

Musick, *JAF*, LXX (1957), p. 352; text, p. 339. Contributed by John Rittenhouse, Mannington, W.Va.

m I

Gypsy Davy crossed the plains
He sang so loud and sweetly
Sang till he made the greenwoods ring,
And charmed the heart of a lady;
Charmed the heart of a lady.

Chorus

Raddle, daddle, ding, ding, ding, ding, ding;
Raddle, daddle, ding, oh daisy;
Get up, get up, my pretty little miss,
Come along with the Gypsy Davy.

"Harness up the milk-white steed,
For the brown is not so steady,
Ride and I'll ride and I'll ride all night
Till I overtake my lady,
Overtake my lady."

He rode, he rode, he rode all night,
He rode where the crick was shady;
There he found his own true-love
In the arms of Gypsy Davy,
The arms of Gypsy Davy.

["Now he was wanting to take her back, you know, and she said":]

"Last night I slept in the mud and the rain
In the arms of Gypsy Davy,
But tonight I'll sleep in a feather bed,
With my arms around my baby,
My arms around my baby."

15. "Gypsy Davy"

Thompson, *NYFQ*, X (1954), p. 52. Contributed by Ruth C. Wright, January 1935; learned from her mother of Schenectady, N.Y.

a I/M

Chorus: Rally cum a ringum, ringum ray,
Rally cum a ringum randy.
Rally cum a ringum, ringum ray,
She's off with the Gypsy Davy.

"Would you leave your house and home?
Would you leave your baby?
Would you leave your own true love
To roam with the Gypsies, Daisy?"

Chorus, with last line: "I think you must be crazy."

"Yes, I'd leave my house and home,
Yes, I'd leave my baby,
Yes, I'd leave my own true love
To roam with Gypsy Davy."

Chorus, with last line: "I'm sure I must be crazy."

"Last night I slept on a fine feather bed,
In my arms my baby,
Tonight I sleep on the damp, cold ground,
In the arms of Gypsy Davy."

Chorus, same as after second stanza.

16. [The Gypsy Laddie]

Sharp MSS., 4609/3222. Sung by Mrs. Rosie Ayres, Burnsville, N.C., September 14, 1918.

a I/M

1. The landlord came home so late in the night
Enquiring for his lady.
The servant made him this reply:
She's gone with the gipsum Davy.
To my rattle tum a gipsum, gipsum,
To my rattle tum a gipsum Davy.

2. Go saddle up the milk-white steed,
I'll ride so fast and speedy,
I'll ride by day and I'll ride by night
Till I overtake my lady.

3. He rode away to the eastern shore.
And there he spied his lady.
Can you for[s]ake your house and home?
Can you forsake your baby?
Can you forsake your old landlord
To go with the Gipsum Davy?

4. I can forsake my house and home,
I can forsake my baby,
I can forsake my old landlord
To go with the gipsum Davy.

5. Pull of[f] them high-heeled pumps
Made from Spanish leather,
And give to me your lily-white hand
And bid farewell for ever.

6. It's on last night and the night before,
I lay on the cold, damp ground;
To-night I lie on a fine feather bed
With the old landlord all in my arms.

17. [The Gypsy Laddie]

Sharp MSS., 3462/2549. Also in Sharp and Karpeles, 1932, I, p. 234(C). Sung by Mrs. Hester House, Hot Springs, N.C., September 15, 1916.

a M (inflected VII)

Sharp's MS. note on the C♮ in bar 3 and C♯ in bar 4: "I think both ways, but it was difficult always to hear."

1. Go catch up my old grey horse,
My blanket is so speedy O.
I'll ride all night and I'll ride all day,
Or I'll overtake my lady O.

2. It's he caught up his old grey horse,
His blanket being so speedy O.
He rode all night and he rode all day,
And he overtaken of his lady O.

3. It's come go back, my dearest dear,
Come go back, my honey O.
Come go back, my dearest dear,
And you never shall lack for money O.

4. I won't go back, my dearest dear,
No I won't go back, my honey O.
For I wouldn't give a kiss from the gipsy's lips
For the sake of you and your money, O.

5. It's go pull off those snow-white gloves
That's made of Spanish leather O,
And give to me your lily-white hand,
And bid me farewell for ever O.

6. It's she pulled off them snow-white gloves
That's made of Spanish leather O,
And give to him her lily-white hand,
And bid him farewell for ever O.

7. I once could have had as many fine things,
Fine feather-beds and money O.
But now my bed is made of hay
And the gipsies a-dancing (all) around me O.

8. She soon went through with many fine things,
Fine rockum (morocco) shoes and stockings O.
She soon went through with her finger rings
And the breast pin off her bosom O.

2. Go bridle up my milk-white steed,
And saddle him so gaily.
I'll ride by day, I'll ride by night
Till I overtake my lady.

3. I rode up to the riverside,
It was wet and muddy.
Looked away on the other side,
And there I spied my lady.

4. Come back, come back, my pretty little Miss,
Come back, come back, my honey.
I'd rather give a kiss from gipsum's lips
Than all your gold and money.

5. How can you leave your house and home?
How can you leave your baby?
How can you leave your fine feather-bed
For to go with the gipsum Davy.

6. I can leave my house and home,
I can leave my baby,
I can leave my fine feather-bed
For to go with the gipsum Davy.

7. Where did you lay last Friday night,
With the gipsum Davy boy?
Yes, sir, I lay on the frozen ground
With the gipsum Davy by me.

8. Pull off them high-heeled shoes,
That's made of morocco leather,
And give to me your lily-white hand,
And we'll bid farewell for ever.

GROUP AC

18. [The Gypsy Laddie]

Sharp MSS., 4722/3288. Sung by Mrs. Becky Mitchell, Burnsville, N.C., September 29, 1918.

a D/M

1. The squire he come home at night
Enquiring for his lady.
She answered him and quick replied:
She's gone with the gypsum Davy.
Rattle tum a gipsum, gipsum,
Rattle tum a gipsum davy.

19. [The Gypsy Laddie]

Karpeles, *JEFDSS*, VI, No. 3 (1951), p. 72. Sung by Mrs. Donald Shelton (née Emma Hensley), N.C., in the autumn of 1950.

a π^2

1. It was late last night when the squire came home
Enquiring for his lady.
The answer that they gave to him:
She's gone with the gipsy Davy.
Rattle tum a gipsum, gipsum,
Rattle tum a gipsum Davy O.

2. Go catch up my old grey mare,
The black he ain't so speedy,
I'll ride all night and I'll ride all day
Till I overtake my lady.

3. He rode and he rode till he came to the town,
And he rode till he came to Barley.
The tears came rolling down his cheeks
And there he spied his lady.

4. O come back, my own true love
O come back, my honey.
I'll lock you up in the chamber so high
Where the gypsums can't come round you.

5. I won't come back, your own true love,
Nor I won't come back, your honey.
I wouldn't give a kiss from the gypsen's lips
For all your land and money.

6. She soon ran through her gay clothing
Her velvet shoes and stockings;
Her gold ring off her finger was gone
And the gold plate from her bosom.

7. O once I had a house and land,
Feather-bed and money,
But now I've come to an old straw pad
With gypsums all around me.

20. [Gipsey Laddie]

Sharp MSS., 3400/. Also in Sharp and Karpeles, 1932, I, p. 236(E). Sung by Mrs. Kitty Gwynne (28), Flag Pond, Tenn., September 5, 1916.

a D/M

I once had houses riches and lands
I once had money plenty
But now I've come to an old straw pad
And the gipsies all around me
Rattle tum a gipsey gipsey
Rattle tum a gipsey Davie

21. [The Gypsy Laddie]

Sharp MSS., 3375/2468. Also in Sharp and Karpeles, 1932, I, p. 234(B). Sung by Mrs. Mary Norton (37), Rocky Fork, Tenn., September 2, 1916.

a D/M

1. The squire he came home at night
Enquiring for his lady.
The answer that came back to him:
She's gone with the gypsy Davy.
[She's gone with the gypsy Davy.][1]

2. Go saddle up my milk-white horse,
And go saddle up my pony,
And I will ride both night and day
Till I overtake my lady.

3. How can you leave your house and land
And how can you leave your baby,
And how can you leave your kind husband
To go with the gypsy Davy?

4. It's I can leave my house and land,
And I can leave my baby,
And I can leave my kind husband
To go with the gypsy Davy.

5. Go pull off them high-heeled pumps
That's made of Spanish leather,
And give me your lily-white hand,
We'll bid farewell for ever.

[1] 1932 reading; not in MS.

22. "The Gypsy Laddie"

Wilkinson MSS., 1935-36, p. 80(A). Sung by Mrs. Jane Morris, Harriston, Va., October 16, 1935.

a M/D

1. Is there any Gypsies in the North
That's bound unto Sweet Borzey-O?
They'll sing to you such a beautiful song,
It'll charm the heart of a lady-O!

2. It was late in the night when the Captain came home,
Inquiring for his honey-O!
The servant Miss replied to him:
She's gone with the Gypsie laddie-O!

3. Saddle up, saddle up, my milk-white steed,
Saddle up, saddle up, in a hurry-O!
I'll ride all night till the broad day-light
And overtake my honey-O!

4. He rode to the east and he rode to the west,
He rode unto Sweet Borzey-O!
And there he spied his own true love
A-going with the Gypsie laddie-O!

5. Come back, come back, my own true love,
Come back, come back, my honey-O!
I'll lock you up in a chamber so high
Where the Gypsies can't come nigh you-O!

6. I won't come back, and I shan't come back,
I won't come back my husband-O!
For I'd rather have a kiss from the Gypsie's lips
Than all your land and money-O!

7. How can you leave your house and lands?
How can you leave your husband-O?
How can you leave your sweet little babe?
To go with the Gypsie laddie-O?

8. I can leave my house and land
And I can leave my husband-O!
And I can leave my sweet little babe,
To go with the Gypsie laddie-O!

9. She hadn't been traveling but a very short time,
Before she spent all her money-O!
She spent the gold rings off her fingers,
And the breast pins off her bosom-O!

10. It's once she was used to a new feather bed,
And a servant to her parlor-O!
It's now she's come to a bed of hay
With the Gypsies all around her.

23. [The Gipsy Laddie]

Sharp MSS., 4186/. Sung by Mrs. Florence Fitzgerald, Royal Orchard, Afton, Va., April 27, 1918.

a M/D (Refrain, a D)

He saddled up his old black horse,
The grey was not so speedy,
He rode all night and part tomorrow
To overtake his sweety.
De addle daddle ding, de addle daddle ding
De arl darl ding, my darling.

24. [The Gypsy Laddie]

Wilkinson MSS., 1936-37, p. 22(A). Sung by Mrs. Harrison Eagle, Monterey, Va., May 7, 1937.

a π^3

1. It'll never get too dark for me,
It'll never get too rainy;
I'll travel all night till broad daylight,
Till I overtake my Gypsy Daisy.
I'll travel all night till broad daylight,
Till I overtake my Gypsy Daisy.

2. Would you forsake your house and lot?
Would you forsake your baby?
Yes, I'd forsake my own wooden lord,
And go with the Gypsy Daisy.
Yes, I'd, &c.

3. It'll never get too dark for me,
It'll never get too rainy;
I'll travel all night till broad daylight,
Till I overtake my Gypsy Daisy.
I'll travel, &c.

4. Last night I lay in a warm feather bed,
Beside of my little baby;
Tonight I'm out in the cold mud and rain,
Along with the Gypsy Daisy.
Tonight I'm, &c.

5. It's if I ever get married again,
It'll be for love, not riches.
It beats the very old boy on earth,
For the women to wear the breeches.
It beats, &c.

25. "Black Eyed Davy"

Brown MSS., 16 a 4 J. Sung by Mrs. J. J. Miller, Lenoir, Caldwell County, N.C.

a D/Æ, ending on III

A different variant, ostensibly from the same singer, is *ante*, variant 5.

26. [The Gypsy Laddie]

Raine, 1924, p. 119. Also in Sharp MSS., 3448/2540; and Sharp and Karpeles, 1932, I, p. 235(D). Sung by Mrs. Jane Gentry, Hot Springs, N.C., 1916.

a D/Æ

The variant (a) is Sharp's reading of the same singer, as given in 1932. But the MS. 3448/2540 is in 4/4 and 2/4 barring.

1. Oh, when Lord Thomas he came home,
Enquiring for his lady,
The answer that they made to him,
She's gone with the gypsy Davy.
All a lipto tally doney,
Hair, hair,
All a lipto lady.

2. It's he caught up his old grey horse,
And he caught up his pony;
He rode all night and he rode all day
Till he overtook his doney.

3. It's come go back, my dearest dear,
It's come go back, my honey,
It's come go back, my dearest dear,
And you never shall lack for money.

4. I won't go back, my dearest dear,
Nor I won't go back, my honey;
I wouldn't give a kiss from my gypsy's lips
For you and all your money.

5. It's go pull off those snow-white gloves
A-made of Spanish leather,
And give to me your lily-white hand
And bid me farewell forever.

6. It's she pulled off those snow-white gloves
A-made of Spanish leather,
And gave to him her lily-white hand
And bade him farewell forever.

7. I once did have so many fine things,
Fine feather-beds and money;
But now my bed is made of hay
And the gypsies a-dancing around me.

Sharp's text, taken the same year as Raine's, is quite different after the first stanza:

It's will you forsake your house and land?
And will you forsake your baby?
And will you forsake your own wedded lord
And go with gypsy Davy?

I'll forsake my house and land,
And I'll forsake my baby;
And I'll forsake my own wedded lord
And go with the gypsy Davy.

The night before last I lay on a feather bed,
Lord Thomas he lay with me.
Last night I lay on a cold straw bed
And with the calves a-bawling all around me.

27. "Gypsy Laddie"

Sung by Mrs. Mary Bird McAllister, Brown's Cove, Va., June 17, 1958. LC/AAFS, rec. No. 11,866(A1). Recorded by Paul C. Worthington.

a π^3

1. Twas late in the night when the Captain came home,
Inquiring for his honey O.
[The servant miss] replied to him,
She's gone with the gipsies' laddie O.

2. Saddle up, saddle up my milk-white steed,
Saddle up, saddle up in a hurry O.
I'll ride all night till the broad daylight,
Till I overtake my honey O.

3. He rode to the East and he rode to the West,
And he rode unto sweet Bosly O,
And there he spied his own true love
A-going with the gipsies' laddie O.

4. Come back, come back, my own true love,
Come back, come back, my honey O,
I'll lock you up in the chamber (chanler?) so high,
The gipsies can't come anigh you.

5. I won't come back nor I shan't come back,
And I won't come back, my husband O.
I'd rather have a kiss from the gipsy's lips
Than all of your land and your money O.

6. O how can you leave your house and land
And how can you leave your husband O?
And how can you leave your sweet little babes
To go with the gipsies' laddie O?

7. O I can leave my house and land
 And I can leave my husband O
And I can leave my sweet little babes
 To go with the gipsies' laddie O.

8. She hadn't been a trav'ling but a very short while
 Before she spent all of her money O,
She spent the gold rings off of her fingers
 The breast pins off of her bosom O.

9. It was once she was used to a good feather bed
 And also had her parlors O
But now she's come to a bed of hay,
 The gipsies they all around her.

28. "Black Jack Gypsy"

Sung by Myrtle Downing, Somerton, Ariz., December 10, 1948. LC/AAFS, rec. No. 11,715(B30). Recorded by Sam Eskin.

a D/M

Last night I slept on a warm feather bed,
 My true love he lay by me,
But tonight I'll sleep at the roots of a tree
 And the Yankee's arms around me.

29. [Untitled]

Sung by Mrs. Texas Gladden, Salem, Va., 1941. LC/AAFS, rec. No. 5233(A1). Recorded by Alan Lomax.

a π^3 (M/D)

1. One night after dark the landlord came
 A-looking for his lady.
One of the servants then spoke up,
 She's gone with the Gypsy Davy.

2. Go saddle to me my fine brown steed
 And bring to me my money.
I've rode all day and I'll ride all night
 Or overtake my honey.

3. Come go with me, my fair young Miss,
 Come go with me, my honey.
I swear by the gold that hangs by my side
 You never shall want for money.

4. If you'll forsake your house and land,
 If you'll forsake your baby,
If you'll forsake your own true love
 And go with the Gypsy Davy.

5. I could forsake my house and land,
 I could forsake my baby,
I could forsake my own true love
 And go with the Gypsy Davy.

6. Last night you lay in a warm feather bed,
 Your arms around your baby,
Tonight you'll lay on the cold river-side,
 In the arms of the Gypsy Davy.

"Arrangement copyrighted by Texas Gladden."

30. [The Gypsy Laddie]

Wilkinson MSS., 1935-36, p. 83(C). Sung by R. E. Carter, Schuyler, Va., June 11, 1936.

a π^3

1. It was late one night, landlord rode out
Enquiring for his honey.
She merrily replied to him:
She's gone with the Gypsy Dardy.

Refrain:

Tu ma yaddle daddle dink, tu ma yaddle daddle dink,
Tu ma ya da dink tum dardy.
Tu ma yaddle daddle dink, tu ma yaddle daddle dink,
Tu ma ya da dink tum dardy.

2. He saddled up his milk-white steed;
He rode away quite speedy.
He rode all night till broad daylight,
Till he overtook his sweety.

3. So he rode East, and he rode West,
He rode just to Morty.
There he spied his own true love,
Going with the Gypsy Dardy.

4. Won't you come back with me, my love?
Won't you come back, my honey?
I'll swear by the sword that's buckled by my side
That you'll never lack for money.

5. I won't come back with you, my love;
I won't come back, my honey.
I'd rather have one kiss from the Gypsy's lips
Than all your land and money.

6. She pulled off her little white glove,
'Twas made of Spanish leather,
And she handed down her lily-white hand,
And she bid farewell forever.

7. She wrote me a word that her bed was straw,
And nothing else hardly.
She wrote me a word that her bed was straw,
And not a Gypsy in the county.

8. He wrote her that his bed was feathers;
And for to stay where she was.
He wrote her that his bed was feathers,
And his place was full of Gypsies.

GROUP Ad

31. [The Gypsy Laddie]

Wilkinson MSS., 1935-36, p. 82(B). Sung by T. Henry Lam, Elkton, Va., November 6, 1935.

m I/M

The Gipsum Davy came a-tripping on the plain,
And he sung so loud and boldly;
He sung so loud that he made the woods ring,
And charmed the hearts of the lady.

Refrain

Fol di rum, fol di rum, fol di ru-di,
Fol di rum, fol di rum, fol di riddle diddle dum,
Fol di riddle diddle dum, dum doo di.

The land lord he came riding by
Inquiring for his lady.
And the lady of the house made her reply:
She's gone with the Gipsum Davy.

Refrain.

32. "The Lady's Disgrace"

Scarborough, 1937, p. 413(F); text, p. 223. Sung by Mrs. Genevieve Ingersoll, Scarsdale, N.Y., c. 1932. Learned from her grandmother's cousin, of Pike County, Ill.; traditional in her family.

a I/M (inflected IV)

One would gladly banish the sharp in bar 6.

1. The Lord came home so late at night,
Inquiring for his Lady,
The chambermaid gave him this reply,
"She's gone with a drunken Davey."

Chorus

Ra diddle ding, diddle ding, ding, dey,
Ra diddle ding, ding, dadey
Ra diddle ding, diddle ding, ding, dey,
Ra diddle ding, ding, dadey.

2. "Have you forsaken your house and home?
Have you forsaken your baby?
Have you forsaken you[r] new landlord
To go with a drunken Davey?"

Chorus

Ra diddle ding, diddle ding, ding, dey . . .

3. "So saddle me up my little gray mare,
For the brown one ain't so speedy.
I've rode all day and I'll ride all night
Till I overtake my lady.

Chorus

Ra diddle ding, diddle ding, ding, dey . . .

4. He rode away on his little gray mare
To overtake his lady,
Who heard the horse on the turnpike road
In search of her drunken Davey.

Chorus

Ra diddle ding, diddle ding, ding, dey . . .

5. They lashed the mare, and the woods were near,
My Lord's horse wasn't so speedy.
They plunged in the stre[a]m and the mare fell down,
Alas for the drunken Davey.

Chorus

Ra diddle ding, diddle ding, ding, dey . . .

6. Now all ye wives who hear this tale
Be content to be a lady,
And never let your hearts be set
On a careless drunken Davey.

Ra diddle ding, diddle ding, ding, dey,
Ra diddle ding, ding, dadey.
And never let your hearts be set
On a careless drunken Davey.

33. [The Gypsy Laddie]

Sharp MSS., 3548/2622. Also in Davis, 1929, p. 591(H); text, p. 431; and Sharp and Karpeles, 1932, I, p. 237(G). Sung by N. B. Chisholm, Woodridge, Va., September 27, 1916.

a M

The printed copies, 1929 and 1932, change the MS. signature to 2/2.

O Davy I'm so glad to meet you,
I've got something to tell you will fret you.
Way down there at the old barn door
I saw your wife just a week ago.
Ta de ra etc.

Then he went unto the house
Enquiring for his baby;
The answer that she made to him:
She's gone with the black boy Davy.

The first stanza is proper to another song: "Will the Weaver."

34. [The Gipsy Laddie]

Sharp MSS., 4761/. Also in Sharp and Karpeles, 1932, I, p. 239(J). Sung by Mrs. Delie Hughes, Cane River, Burnsville, N.C., October 5, 1918.

a M

The Squire came home late in the night,
Enquiring for his lady.
She answered him with a quick reply:
She's gone with the gipsy Davy.
Rattle tattle ding tattle ding tattle ding, ding.
Rattle tattle ding die aisy,
Rattle tattle ding, sing liddle ding a ding
Sing liddle diddle ding die aisy.

35. [The Gypsy Laddie]

Sharp MSS., 3368/2465. Also in Sharp and Karpeles, 1932, I, p. 233(A). Sung by Mrs. J. Gabriel Coates, Flag Pond, Tenn., September 1, 1916.

a M

Originally Sharp wrote this throughout in 4/4 bars.

1. It was late in the night when the squire came home
Enquiring for his lady;
His servant made a sure reply:
She's gone with the gypsum Davy.
Rattle tum a-gypsum, gypsum,
Rattle tum a-gypsum Davy.

2. O go catch up my milk-white steed,
He's black and then he's speedy.
I'll ride all night till broad daylight,
Or overtake my lady.

3. He rode and he rode till he came to the town,
And he rode till he came to Barley.
The tears came rolling down his cheeks
And there he spied his lady.

4. O come, go back, my own true love,
O come, go back, my honey.
I'll lock you up in the chamber so high
Where the gypsums can't come round you.

5. I won't come back, your own true love,
Nor I won't come back, your honey.
I wouldn't give a kiss from gypsum's lips
For all your land and money.

6. She soon run through her gay clothing,
Her velvet shoes and stockings;
Her gold ring off her finger was gone
And the gold plate off her bosom.

7. O once I had a house and land,
Feather-bed and money,
But now I've come to an old straw pad
With the gypsums all around me.

36. [The Gypsy Laddie]

Sharp MSS., 4183/3017. Also in Sharp and Karpeles, 1932, I, p. 238(I). Sung by Mrs. Lizzie Gibson, Crozet, Va., April 26, 1918.

a M

1. The good lord he come trav'ling home,
   Enquiring for his lady,
   And the housewoman that she did tell him,
   She was gone with the gipsum Davy.
      To my hoo dar dan,
      To my hoo dar dan,
      To my hoo dar dan,
      To my dar dee O.

2. It's go and get it's my grey nag
   And draw them saddles all around her.
   I'll ride all night till the broad daylight,
   Or overtake my lady.

3. As he was riding up the road,
   The rain poured down so muddy,
   The first thing he spied up the road,
   O there he spied his lady.

4. Come go back with me, my pretty Miss,
   Come go back with me, my honey.
   I'll swear by the sword that hangs by my side
   You never shall want for money.

5. I won't go back with you, my love,
   I won't go back with you, my honey;
   For I'd rather have a kiss from gipsum's lips
   Than all your land and money.

6. Pull off, pull off your high-heel-ed shoes,
   What's made of Spanish leather,
   And hand you down your lily-white hand,
   We'll bid farewell for ever.

7. She pull-ed off her high-heeled shoes,
   Was made of Spanish leather,
   She handed him down her lily-white hand,
   And bid him farewell for ever.

8. Last night she lied on a soft feather bed
   With the good lord by the side of her;
   To-night she's a-lying on the damp, cold ground
   With the gypsies all around her.

APPENDIX A

37. [The Gipsy Laddie]

Sharp MSS., 4652/. Sung by Mrs. Ellen Webb, Cane River, Burnsville, N.C., September 21, 1918.

a M

The Squire came in, it was late at night,
Enquiring for his lady
The servant made a short reply,
She's gone with the Gipsum Davy
Rattle tum a gipsum, gipsum,
Rattle tum a gipsum Davy.

38. "Gypsy Laddie"

Sung by Jean Ritchie. Folkways LP rec. No. FA 2301(A1), ed. K. S. Goldstein.

p π^1

1. An English Lord came home one night
   Enquiring for his lady,
   The servants said on every hand,
   She's gone with the Gypsy Laddie.

2. Go saddle up my milk-white steed,
   Go saddle me up my brownie
   And I will ride both night and day
   Till I overtake my bonnie.

3. Oh he rode East and he rode West,
   And at last he found her,
   She was lying on the green, green grass
   And the Gypsy's arms around her.

4. Oh, how can you leave your house and land,
   How can you leave your money,
   How can you leave your rich young lord
   To be a gypsy's bonnie.

5. How can you leave your house and land,
   How can you leave your baby,
   How can you leave your rich young lord
   To be a gypsy's lady.

6. Oh come go home with me, my dear,
Come home and be my lover,
I'll furnish you with a room so neat,
With a silken bed and covers.

7. I won't go home with you, kind sir,
Nor will I be your lover,
I care not for your rooms so neat
Or your silken bed or your covers.

8. It's I can leave my house and land,
And I can leave my baby,
I'm a-goin' to roam this world around
And be a gypsy's lady.

9. Oh, soon this lady changed her mind,
Her clothes grew old and faded,
Her hose and shoes came off her feet
And left them bare and naked.

10. Just what befell this lady now,
I think it worth relating,
Her gypsy found another lass
And left her heart a-breaking.

39. [The Gipsy Laddy]

Sharp MSS., 3637/2696. Sung by Mrs. Alice Sloan, Barbourville, Ky., May 6, 1917.

m π^1

This variant is at home in the B group of "Barbara Allan" (No. 84).

1. I'll saddle up my white milk horse,
I'll saddle up my pony,
I'll ride and ride to the river-side
Till I overtake my darling,
Till I overtake my darling.

2. Go back, go back, my pretty little girl,
Go back, go back, my darling,
I'll lock you in a room so high
That a gipsy can't get around you.

3. Well, I won't go back, well, I can't go back,
Well, I won't go back, my darling,
I wouldn't give a kiss from a gipsie's lips
For you and all your money.

4. How old are you, my pretty little girl,
How old are you, my honey?
She spied with her little sweet mouth:
I'll be sixteen next Sunday.

5. Pull off, pull off, your white kid gloves
Made with Spanish leather;
Give to me your pretty white hand,
I'll bid you farewell for ever.

6. I'll pull off my white kid glove,
Made with Spanish leather,
I'll give to you my pretty white hand,
I'll bid you farewell for ever.

40. "The Gypsy Lover"

Randolph, I, 1946, p. 160(H). Sung by Mrs. Olga Trail, Farmington, Ark., February 12, 1942; learned from her father.

p π^1

Cf. the preceding variant.

1. Go fetch out my little black horse,
The speed it is of all,
I've rode all day and I'll ride all night,
Or I'll overtake my lady,
I'll overtake my lady.

2. I rode and I rode to the broad river's side,
And there I could ride no farther,
And there I spied my lily-white love
Talkin' to her Gypsy lover,
Talkin' to her Gypsy lover.

3. Oh give to me your lily-white hand
Encased in Spanish leather,
And give to me your lily-white hand
And leave your Gypsy lover,
And leave your Gypsy lover.

4. Pull off, pull off those dainty little shoes,
All made of Spanish leather,
And give to me your lily-white hand
And leave your Gypsy lover,
And leave your Gypsy lover.

5. Oh I'll pull off my dainty little shoes,
All made of Spanish leather,
And I'll give to you my lily-white hand,
But I'll stay with my Gypsy lover,
But I'll stay with my Gypsy lover.

GROUP B

41. "The Wraggle Taggle Gipsies"

Sharp MSS., 738/. Sung by Mr. Gordge, Bridgwater, January 2, 1906.

a I

O seven jolly gipsies all in a row
They was dressed and bonny bow
And a waiting maid made this reply
She's gone with the wraggle taggle gipsies O
The gipsies O the gipsies O
She's gone with the wraggle taggle gipsies O

42. "Gipsies-O"

Collinson, *JEFDSS*, V, No. 1 (1946), p. 14. Also (edited) in Collinson and Dillon, 1952, p. 43. Sung by Harry Cox, Catfield, Norfolk, 1946.

a I

1. Oh seven gipsies all in a gang,
They were brisk and bonny-o.
They went till they came to the Earl Castle's hall (*sic*)
And there they sang so sweetly-o.
Sweetly-o, sweetly-o;
They went till they came to the Earl Castle's hall,
And there they sang so sweetly-o.

2. They sang so sweet and so complete
Until downstairs came a lady-O,
And as soon as they saw her pretty, pretty face,
They cast their gazes over her.
Over her, over her, etc.

3. She gave to them a bottle of wine.
She gave to them some money-O.
She gave to them some far finer things
'Twas the gold rings on her fingers-O.
Fingers-O, fingers-O, etc.

4. She pulled off her high-heeled boots,
Put on her highland plaidie-O.
"Last night I slept with my own wedded lord,
And tonight with the gipsies' laddy-O."

5. When her dear lord came home that night
Inquiring for his lady-O,
The waiting maid made her reply,
"She is gone with the black-guarded gipsies-O."

6. "So come saddle me my best black horse,
Come saddle it quite swiftly-O,
So I may search for my own wedded wife,
Who is gone with the black-guarded gipsies-O."

7. He rode high and he rode low,
He rode brisk and bonny-O,
He rode till he came to a far water-side
And there he found his lady-O.

8. "What made you leave your house and land,
What made you leave your money-O,
What made you leave your own wedded lord,
To follow the black-guarded gipsies-O?"

9. "I know I've left my house and land,
I know I've left my money-O,
But here I am and here I remain,
So fare-you-well my honey-O."

10. Seven gipsies all in a gang
They were brisk and bonny-O.
To-night they are all condemned to die,
For stealing Earl Castle's lady-O.

43. "The Gipsy Laddie"

Greig MSS., I, p. 113. Also in Greig and Keith, 1925, p. 129(1c). Sung by Miss Annie Ritchie, Whitehill, April 1906.

a π^1

What made me leave my hooses & lan',
What made me leave my siller.
What made me leave my children three,
To follow the gipsy laddie.

Yestreen I was lyin' in a weel-made bed,
Wi' my ain lord beside me;
Noo I am lyin' in a cauld open barn,
And a' the gipsies round me.

44. [The Three Gipsies]

Greig MSS., II, p. 143. Also in Greig and Keith, 1925, p. 128(1a). Sung by Mrs. Fowlie, Bonnykelly, September 1907.

a I/M

There were three gipsies all in a row,
  And oh but they sang bonnie O,
They sang so sweet and so complete
  That they charmèd the heart of a lady O.

45. [The Gipsy Laddie]

Greig MSS., I, p. 154; text, Bk. 714, IV, p. 77. Also in Greig and Keith, 1925, p. 128(1b). Sung by J. W. Spence, Fyvie, April 1906.

a π[1]

1. Three gipsy laddies, all in a row
   And o' but they sang bonnie, oh,
   They sang so sweet and so complete
   Till they charmed the hea[rt][1] of a lady oh.

2. Lady Castle she came tripping down the stair
   And all the maids came behind her, oh!
   And in her hand was a bottle of Red Wine
   To treat all the gipsy laddies [oh!].[2]

3. She treated them all to a bottle of Red Wine
   Likewise to a bottle of brandy, oh,
   Till one of them, stepped to your (her) side
   Stole the gold ring from off her finger, oh.

4. Oh ye'll cast off, ye're bonnie silken gown
   Put on our Tartan Plaidie oh!
   And came awa' the lea lang day
   For to follow the Gipsy laddies oh!

5. Oh she's castin off, her bonnie silken gown
   Put on their tartan plaidie oh.
   And she's awa, the lee lang day
   For to follow the gipsy laddies oh!

6. Lord Castles he came home at night
   Inquiring for his lady oh
   The one denied but other replied
   She's away wi the Gipsy Laddies oh!

7. Make haste, make haste, my milk white steed
   Make haste, make haste, my ready oh!
   For I will neither, eat nor drink
   Till I bring back my lady oh.

8. He rode east and he rode west
   Till he came to yonder Bogie oh
   And the bonniest Lassie, that ever he saw
   She was following, the gipsy laddies oh!

9. ["]Oh, ye'll come back wi me" he said
   ["]I canna come back" cried she
   For I've made a vow, and I ma'n keep it true
   For to follow the Gipsy laddies oh

10. Last nicht, I lay in a fine feather bed
    And my good lord, lay beyond me oh!
    But this nicht, I maun lie in a caul open barn
    Wi' the gipsies all lying roon me oh!

11. Oh haven't ye got gold in store
    Oh, haven't ye got treasures three
    Oh haven't ye got all that ye want
    And a bonnie bonnie boy till amase ye wi.

12. Oh yes I have got gold in store
    Oh yes I have got treasures three
    Oh yes I have got all that I want
    And a bonnie bonnie boy till amase me wi'.

13. There is sixteen of you gipsy men
    Not one of you I can call bonnie oh!
    So this nicht ye all shall hanged be
    For the stealing of Lord Castle's lady oh.

[1] MS.: head
[2] MS.: we.

46. [Wraggle Taggle Gipsies]

Sharp MSS., 943/999. Sung by John Vincent (72). Priddy, April 25, 1906.

a I

1. It's of seven gipsies all of a row
   They were brisk & bonny O
   They ride on to the aller castle gate
   And there they sung most sweetly O.

2. The aller castle lady was coming downstairs
And her own waiting-maid along side o' her
These words she replied to her own waiting maid
Here's off along the road with the gipsies O.

3. O how can you leave your houses & lands
O how can you leave your money O
O how can you leave your own wedded one
To gang along the road with the gipsies O.

4. What cares I for houses & lands
What cares I for money O
What cares I for my own wedded one
Here's off along the road with the gipsies O.

5. Last night I slept on a soft down bed
And alongside of my lovyer O
But to night I'll lay in the green woods away
And gang along the road with the gipsies O.

6. O aint it wet & very very wet
O aint it wet & weary O
And I pray did you see any gay lady
A-ganging on the road with the gipsies O.

7. O yes, it's wet & very very wet
O yes, it's wet & weary O
And of all the gayest ladies that ever I did see
Was ganging on the road with the gipsies O.

47. [Gipsy Laddie]

Greig-Duncan MS. 785 (Walker transcript), p. 96; from Duncan MS., No. 14. Sung by Mrs. Gillespie; learned c. 1870.

a I

Three gipsy laddies stood a' in a row,
An' oh but they sang bonnie oh
They sang sae sweet and so complete
That they charmèd the heart o' a lady O.

48. "The Gipsy Laddie"

Greig MSS., IV, p. 155. Sung by K. Morice.

a π^1 (VII in variant)

49. "The Gypsy Laddie"

Sung by Ewan MacColl, Riverside rec. No. RLP 12-637(A5), ed. K. S. Goldstein. Tune learned from his father.

a I

1. There were three gypsies all in a row
And O but they sang bonnie O.
They sang sae sweet and sae complete
That they chairmed the hairt of the lady O.

2. The lady she cam doun the stair
And the twa maidéns cam wi' her O,
But as soon as they spied her weel-faur'd face
They cast their camprols oer her O.

3. They ha' gien tae her the nutmeg fine
And they gien tae her the ginger O,
But she's gien tae them a far better thing
The gold ring aff her finger O.

4. It's ye'll cast aff your silken goun
And put on this tartan plaidie O
And ye'll come awa this lee-lang nicht
And follow the gypsy laddie O.

5. Lord Cassells he cam hame at nicht
Inquirin for his lady O.
The hound is run and the hawk is flown
And the gypsy's awa wi' your lady O.

6. Come saddle tae me the black, the black,
Mak haste and soon be ready O,
For it's meat and drink I winna taste
Till I get back my lady O.

7. Then they've rode east and they've rode west
Till they cam tae yonder boggy O,
And there they spied the weel-faur'd may
With the gypsies a' standin round her O.

8. Will ye gang, my honey and my hairt,
Will ye gang wi' me, my lady O?
And I'll swear by the sword that hangs by my side
The black band shall never steal thee O.

9. I winna come wi' you, my honey and my hairt,
I winna come wi' you, my dearie O,
Till I drink the breest that I hae brewn
And that's in the water of Eerie O.

Conflated text, mainly from Greig's variant copies.

50. "The Dark-Clothed Gypsy"

Greenleaf and Mansfield, 1933, p. 38. Sung by Victoria White, Sandy Cove, Newfoundland, 1929.

a I

There's three young gypsies all in a row;
They sang so sweet, so very, very sweet,
They sang so sweet, so very, very sweet,
It would charm the heart of a lady fair.

"Are you going to forsake your houses and land,
Are you going to forsake your children, too?
Are you going to forsake your own true wedded love
And follow the dark-clothed gypsy, O?"

"Yes, I'm going to forsake my houses and land;
Yes, I'm going to forsake my children, too;
I'm going to forsake my own wedded love
And follow the dark-clothed gypsy, O."

"Last night you lay on a warm feather bed
With the sheets all white as snow,
And to-night you may lie on the damp, cold ground,
In the arms of a dark-clothed gypsy, O."

2. The lady was sitting in her window so high,
Enjoying of her children three,
Some jealousy thought came into her mind,
She would follow the dark-eyed gypsy O.

3. The old farmer came home in the middle of the night,
Enquiring for his lady O.
I'm afraid, I'm afraid, cried the gay gaging (*sic*) girl,
That she followed the dark-eyed gypsy O.

4. Hurry up, hurry up and get my tea (*sic*)
With a sword and pistol by my side,
With a sword and pistol by my side,
I will follow the dark-eyed gypsy O.

5. He rode East and he rode West,
Till he came up to an old farmer,
Saying: Farmer, tell me, tell me true,
Have you seen the dark-eyed gypsy O.

6. Ride on, ride on, the old farmer cried,
Till you come to yonder valley O,
The prettiest girl that ever I did see
In the arms of the dark-eyed gypsy O.

7. Last night you were lying on a soft down bed
With a sheet so white as the linen O,
To-night you are lying on the hard cold ground
In the arms of the dark-eyed gypsy O.

51. [Wraggle Taggle Gipsies]

Sharp MSS., 1034/. Sung by Mrs. Brooks, Bridgwater, August 16, 1906.

a I

52. "The Gypsy Laddie"

Karpeles MSS., No. 5296; text, p. 4843. Sung by Mrs. Wilson Northcott, Gaultois, Hermitage Bay, Newfoundland, July 22, 1930.

a I

1. Seven dark-eyed gypsies sitting in a row
They sang so sweet and so very low,
They sang so sweet and so very, very sweet,
They charmed the heart of the lady O.

53. [Wraggle Taggle Gipsies O]

Sharp MSS., 69/123. Sung by Mr. Spearman, miller, at Ile Brewers, January 6, 1904.

a I

1. Three jolly gipsies all in a row,
One sings high & the other sings low,
Which made this young lady come right-down stairs
For to follow the draggle tail gipsies oh

2. Oh when her Johnny he came home
Saying oh where, oh where is my true love gone
Saying she's gone with the draggle tail gipsies oh

3. Oh get my horse & saddle it quick
That I might go in search of my love
He rode through woods and valleys deep
Until he came to his own true love

4. (Saying what) makes you leave your houses and land
And what makes you leave your money oh
Oh what makes you leave your new & married love
For to follow the draggle tail gipsies oh

5. For what care I for my houses or land
Or what care I for my money oh
Or what care I for my new & married love
But to follow the draggle tail gipsies oh

6. Last night you slept on a soft & feathered bed
All along with your Johnny oh
But to-night you'll sleep on the cold cold clay
Along with the draggle tail gipsies oh

54. [The Gipsy Countess]

Baring-Gould MSS., L(4); text, (C). Also in Baring-Gould and Sheppard, 1895, p. 108; and Goss, 1937, p. 94(B). Sung by John Woodrich, blacksmith, Wollacot Moor, Thrushleton, 1888. Noted by F. W. Bussell.

a I

Three jolly gipsies all in a row
They sang high, & they sang low,
They sang so loud, so shrill, so fair
That it made the lady come down the stair
Then she put off her silken gown,
And the staircase she came down,
Determined to follow the gipsies O
To follow the raggle taggle gipsies O!
Past twelve o'clock her lord came home
    Inquiring for his lady O
The servants replied on every side
    She's gone away with the gipsies O.
Go saddle my horse, my serving man,
    Go saddle me my dapple O.
That I may ride & seek my bride,
    That's gone with the raggle taggle gipsies O!
Then he rode high & he rode low,
    He rode through hills & valleys too
Until he espied his own fair bride,
    Following the raggle taggle gipsies O.
What makes you leave your house & lands?
    What makes you leave your mammy?
What makes you leave your new married lord?
    To follow the raggle taggle gipsies O!
O what care I for house & lands
    What care I for my mammy?
Neither do I care for my new married lord
    I will follow the raggle taggle gipsies O!
Last night you slept in a feather bed,
    Rolled in the arms of your husband, O
But now you must lie, 'neath the cold, cold sky,
    If you follow the raggle taggle gipsies O.
Last night I slept in a feather bed
    Rolled in the arms of my husband O
But far rather I'd lie 'neath the cold, cold sky
    And follow the raggle taggle gipsies O

55. [Draggletail Gipsies]

Sharp MSS., 301/407. Sung by Mrs. Anna Pond, Shepton Beauchamp, August 16, 1904.

a I

1. Last night the gipsies came at my door
And they sing bonny bonny Biscay O
One sing Nay the other sing Low
And downstairs runs this a-lady O.
She pulled off her silk finished gown
She put on a hose of leather O
The ragged ragged rags about our door,
She's gone with the wriggle taggle gipsy O.

2. It was late last night when my lord he came home
Enquiring for his lady O
One cried Nay and the other cried Low
She's gone with the wriggle taggle gipsy O.
O saddle to me my milk white steed
Go and fetch to me my pony O
That I may go and ride and seek for my bride
Who is gone with the wriggle taggle gipsy Oh.

3. He ride high and he ride low
He ride through woods and copses too
Until he came to a wide open field
Where he espies his a-lady O.
What made you leave your houses & land?
What made you leave your money O?
What made you leave your own wedding pride
To go with a wriggle taggle gipsy O.

4. I don't mind my houses and land
Nor I don't mind my money O
Nor I don't mind my new wedding pride,
I'm going with the wriggle taggle gipsy O.
Last night you slept on a goose [good?] feather bed
Into the arms of your Johnny O
And now you're sleeping in a wide open field
Along with a wriggle taggle gipsy O.

5. I don't mind my new feather bed,
Nor I don't mind my money O,
Nor I don't mind my new wedding pride,
I'll go with a wriggle taggle gipsy O.

56. "Gipsies of Agee (Egypt) Oh!"

Hammond MSS., No. 226; text, D. V, p. 65. Sung by John Greening, Cuckold's Corner, Dorset, 1905-08.

a I

a

a (other stanzas)

etc.

1. It's two little gipsies come begging at my door
Oh! one sung high and the other sung low
They both sung brisk and bonny, bonny O!
And downstairs came a lady O!

2. Go saddle me my milkwhite steed
And bridle me my pony O!
That I may ride to the greenwood side
And along with the gipsies of Agie O!

3. When her master he came home at night
Enquiring for his lady O
The servant maid made this reply
She's agone with the ragtail gipsies O

4. Saddle me the milkwhite steed
And bridle you your pony O
That we may ride to the greenwoodside
For to find out the rag-tail gipsies O

5. One rode high and the other rode low
They both rode brisk and bonny O
They rode till they came to the greenwoodside
There they found out the rag-tail gipsies O

6. How can you leave your house and land
How can you leave your money too
How can you leave your new marriage lord
For to follow these rag-tail gipsies O

7. I don't care for [my house and land]*
Nor neither do I value [my money too]
Nor nor [*sic*] I don't care [for my new marriage lord]
But I'll follow the gipsies of Agie O

8. Last night you slept on a nice feather bed
With the sheet turned down and neatly spread
All this long night† in the cold open field
All along with these rag-tail gipsies O

9. Last night I slept [on a nice feather bed]
With [the sheet turned down and neatly spread]
[All this long night in the cold open field]
[All along with these rag-tail gipsies O]

* The bracketed phrases are indicated in the MS. by et cetera signs.
† Lacuna in MS.

57. "The Ragtail Gipsies, Oh!"

Hammond MSS., No. 363; text, V, pp. 64v and 65v. Sung by John Pauley, Westbury, Sherborne, Dorset, 1905-08.

a I

1. Now three gipsies once came begging at my door
Two of them sang high and the other sang low [*bis*]
Till downstair came a lady O!

2. Off she pulled her silken gown
And round her body a blanket flung
And she bade her servants all farewell
For to roam with the draggle tail gipsies O!

3. Late that same night Squire he came home
Enquiring for his lady O
The lady's maid etc.
She's gone etc.

4. Bring round to me my white milk mare
And put on her a bridle and saddle O
For I will neither eat nor drink
Until I've found my lady love O

. . . .

5. What care I for etc.
What care I for etc.
I'd rather lie with a man I love
So I'll stick to my draggle tailed gipsies O

. . . .

6. You used to sleep on a good feather bed
With sheets turned back so neatly O
But now you will lie in the cold open field
Cold and wet and dreary O!

58. "The Gipsy Laddie Oh!"

Hammond MSS., No. 421. Sung by Mrs. Baskett, Wareham, Dorset, c. 1905.

a I

etc.

59. [The Draggletail Gipsy O]

Sharp MSS., 360/482. Sung by Farmer King, East Harptree, August 25, 1904.

a I

Last night you slept on a goose feather bed
With the sheets turned down so bravely O
And to night you must sleep on the cold open field
Along with the gipsy laddie O

60. "The Gypsie Laddie"

Ord, 1930, p. 411. From the north of Scotland.

a I

1. There were three gipsies all in a row,
    And O but they sang bonnie, O;
  They sang so sweet and so complete
    That they charmed the hearts of our ladies, O.

2. Lord Cassils' lady came downstairs
    With all her maids behind her, O;
  With a bottle of red wine into her hand
    For to treat the gipsy laddies, O.

3. She's treated them all to a glass of red wine,
    Likewise a little ginger, O;
  And one of them steppèd her behind,
    Stole the gold ring from her finger, O:

4. Says, "Ye'll tak aff your bonnie silk dress,
    Put on a tartan plaidie, O,
  And ye'll travel on a' the lee lang day
    And follow the gipsy laddie, O."

5. "I'll tak aff my bonnie silk dress,
    Put on a tartan plaidie, O,
  And I'll travel on a' the lee lang day
    And follow my gipsy laddie, O."

6. "Surely you've got gold in store,
    And surely you've got treasures three,
  And surely you've got all that you want,
    And three bonnie boys to amuse you wi'?"

7. "O yes, I have got gold in store,
    O yes, I have got treasures three,
  O yes, I have got all that I want,
    And I've three bonnie boys to amuse me wi'.

8. "Last night I lay on a well-made bed,
    Wi' my guid lord beside me, O;
  This night I'll lie in a tenant's barn
    Wi' a' the gipsies around me, O."

9. Lord Cassils he came home at night,
    A-calling for his lady O;
  The ane denied, but the other replied,
    "She's awa wi' the gipsy laddies, O!"

10. "Gae saddle to me my bonnie black steed;
    Mak haste, mak haste, mak ready, O,
  For I will neither eat nor drink
    Till I bring back my lady, O."

11. He rode east and he rode west,
    Till he came to yonder bogie, O,
  And the bonniest lassie that ever he saw
    She was following the gipsy laddies, O.

12. There's sixteen o' ye, well-made men,
    Although ye are na bonnie, O,
  And ye will a' high hangèd be
    For stealing Lord Cassils' lady, O.

61. [The Wraggle Taggle Gipsies]

Sharp MSS., 478/. Sung by William Nott, Meshaw, January 5, 1905.

a M

O why will you leave your houses and land
And why will you leave your money O
O why will you leave your new wedded life
For to follow the draggle tailed gipsies O

62. "The Gipsy Laddie"

Karpeles MSS., No. 5172; text, p. 4708. Also in Karpeles, 1934, I, p. 14. Sung by Mrs. Margaret Quilter, Harbour Grace, Newfoundland, October 8, 1929.

a M

Two little gipsies live at the East
And they were smart and gaily O
And they sang so sweet and so very very sweet
They stole Lord Charlie's lady O.

So Lord Charlie he came home
Enquiring for his lady O.
Up speaks one of his old servant men,
Saying: She's follow on a gipsy laddie O.

Saying: Will you come home, my fair lady,
Will you come home, my honey,
And will you forsake your own native land
And follow on a gipsy laddie O?

I'll forsake my own native land,
Likewise my lord and Charlie O,
And I'll forsake my own native land
And follow on a gipsy laddie O.

63. [The Gipsy Laddie]

Karpeles MSS., No. 5258. Sung by Mrs. May Joseph Mitchell, Maryston, Placentia Bay, Newfoundland, July 10, 1930.

a M

O seven young gipsies come down here last night,
O sev'n young gipsies come down here last night,
They sang so sweetly through the air
They charmed the heart of the lady fair.

64. [The Gipsy Laddie]

Karpeles MSS., No. 5277. Sung by Mrs. Jacob Courage, Frenchman's Cove, Garnish, Newfoundland, July 15, 1930.

a M

Will you forsake your house and land,
Will you forsake your mother too,
Will you forsake your house and land
To follow the dark-eyed gipsy true?

65. [Wraggle Taggle Gipsies O]

Sharp MSS., 1423/. Sung by Robert Parish (86), Oxford, August 20, 1907.

a M

Last night I slept in silken sheets
Silken sheets and blankets too
But now I must lay in the cold & open field
And gang along with the diggle taggle gipsies O

66. [Wraggle Taggle Gipsies]

Sharp MSS., 1447/. Sung by Mr. Green, Rose Ash, August 26, 1907.

a M

English copies of "The Cruel Mother" (No. 20) are close to this form of the tune. Compare Sharp's version recorded five days later than the present song (*ante*, I, p. 287, variant 31).

67. [Wraggle Taggle Gipsies]

Sharp MSS., 837/909. Sung by Henry Cridland (81), Old Cleeve, April 5, 1906.

a M (inflected VII)

Under the first phrase of the tune is written one line:

There were three gipsies come to my door And

In the text MS. there is only this:

Variants noted.

O there were some gipsies.
O she pulled off her sandal pumps.
Wriggle Taggle.
Saddle him quite ready O.
To *gang* with the . . .
Sleepin' on the cold board floor.

But these feathers and a standard text should get it a fellowship in a cry of gypsies.

68. [Wraggle Taggle Gipsies O]

Sharp MSS., 1580/. Contributed by Miss ?Scoby, January 1908, as sung by Mrs. Grace Coles, Enmore.

a M

I value value not my newly married man
But I'll gang with the wraggle tail gipsies O

These lines are written under the second half of the tune.

69. [Wraggle Taggle Gipsies]

Sharp MSS., 1389/. Sung by Martha Bodley (52), North Petherton, August 8, 1907.

a M (inflected VII)

Three jolly gipsies all in a row
Some sing brace and bonny O
And some sing high and some sing low
And out of the window the lady O
And out of the window the lady O.

70. [Wraggle Taggle Gipsies O]

Sharp MSS., 1880/. Sung by Mrs. Gullyford, Combe Florey, September 10, 1908.

a M

Last night I slept on a nice feather bed
In the arms of my Johnny O
But to night I slept in the wide open field
Along in the draggle tailed gipsies O gipsies O
Along with the draggle tailed gipsies O

71. [Wraggle Taggle Gipsies]

Sharp MSS., 2308/2103. Sung by Shepherd Haden (83), Bampton in the Bush, August 21, 1909.

m D

1. There was three gipsies came to the door
And they sang brisk and bonny O
And they sang high and they sang low
And downstairs ran the lady O.

2. Then she pulled off her new silk gown
And round her shoulders a blanket thrown
And round her shoulders a blanket thrown
For to toddle with the draggle tail gipsies O.

3. When the old Lord he came home
Enquiring for his lady O
The housemaid made him this reply
She's gone with the draggle tail gipsies O.

4. Bridle me my milk white steed
And saddle him so bonny O
That I may ride and seek for my dear
Who is gone with the draggle tail gipsies O.

5. Then he rode all that night long
And part of the next morning O
And there he saw his own true love
A setting with the draggle tail gipsies O.

6. How could you leave your house & land?
How could you leave your money O?
How could you leave your new wedded lord
To toddle with the draggle tail gipsies O?

7. What care I for house or land?
What care I for money O
I don't care a fig for my new wedded lord.
I'll toddle with the draggle tail gipsies O.

8. Last night I lied on a warm feathered bed
And my new wedded lord by my side O.
And to night I'll lie in the cold open field
Along with the draggle tail gipsies O.

72. [The Gipsy Countess]

Baring-Gould MSS., L(2). Also in Baring-Gould and Sheppard, 1895, p. 68; and Goss, 1937, p. 94(C). Sung by Samuel Fone, March 1893; learned from an old woman in 1825. Noted by F. W. Bussell.

m D

73. "The Draggletail Gipsies"

Sharp MSS., 264/373. Also in Sharp and Marson, 1904, p. 18; Sharp, 1916, p. 13; and Sharp, Selected Ed. [1920], I, p. 13. Sung by Mrs. Overd, Langport, Somerset, August 4, 1904.

a Æ

1. There was three gipsies a come to my door
One sung high & the other sung low
The one sung high & the other sung low
And the other sung bonny bonny brisky O.

2. This lady come down in a silken gownd
Put on her spanish livery O
Says she this night I'll resign
To follow the draggletail gipsies O.

3. Twas late at night when her Lord came home
Inquiring for his lady O
The servants replied on every side
She's gone with the draggletail gipsies O.

4. Come saddle me my milk white steed,
Come bridle me my pony too
That I might ride & seek for my bride.
She's gone with the draggletail gipsies O.

5. Then he rode high and he rode low
He rode through woods and copses too
He rode till he came to the woodside
And there he found his lady O.

6. What makes you leave your house & land?
What makes you leave your money too
What makes you leave your new wedded Lord
To follow the draggletail gipsies O?

7. What care I for house or land
What care I for my money O?
What care I for my new wedded Lord
I'll follow the draggletail gipsies O.

8. Last night you could lie on a good feather bed
And into the arms of your Johnny too.
And now you must ride on the wide open land
Along with the draggletail gipsies O.

74. "The Raggle Taggle Gypsies, O"

Cox, 1939, p. 33; and 1964 (ed. Boswell), p. 42. Contributed by Dorothy Manassee, Hamlin, Lincoln County, W. Va., August 5, 1925; learned in New York City. Noted by Mrs. Byron W. Hess.

a Æ (almost P/Æ)

1. Last night three gypsies came to my door
      And down the stairs ran my Lady, O!
   And one sang high and one sang low
      And the other sang "Bonnie, Bonnie Bisca, O!"

2. Then she stripped off her silk-finished gown
      And put on hose of leather, O!
   And ragged ragged rags around the door,
      She's off with the raggle taggle gypsies, O!

3. It was late last night when my Lord came home
      Inquiring for his Lady, O!
   The servants said on every hand,
      "She's off with the raggle taggle gypsies, O!"

4. "Unsaddle for me my milk-white steed
      And fetch to me my pony, O!
   That I may ride and fetch my bride,
      Who's off with the raggle taggle gypsies, O!"

5. Then he rode high and he rode low,
      He rode through fields and copses, O!
   Until he came to a wide, open field
      And there he espied his Lady, O!

6. "What makes you leave your house and lands,
      What makes you leave your money, O?
   What makes you leave your new-wedded Lord
      To go with the raggle taggle gypsies, O?"

7. "What care I for my house and lands,
      What care I for my money, O?
   What care I for my new-wedded Lord?
      I'm off with the raggle taggle gypsies, O!"

8. "Last night you slept on a goose-feather bed,
      With the sheets turned down so bravely, O!
   To-night you sleep in a wide, open field,
      Along with the raggle taggle gypsies, O!"

9. "What care I for a goose-feathered bed,
      With the sheets turned down so bravely, O?
   To-night I sleep in a wide, open field,
      Along with the raggle taggle gypsies, O!"

75. "The Three Gypsies"

Scarborough, 1937, p. 411(A); text, p. 216. Sung by Clara Callahan, Saluda, N.C., c. 1932.

a Æ

1. There were three gypsies that came to my door,
      And down-stairs ran this lady-O.
   One sang high and the other sang low,
      And the other sang Bonny, Bonny Biscay-O.

2. Then she pulled off her silk finish gown,
      And she put on leather holstery, O.
   The ragged rag-rags about her door,
      And she's off with the raggle-taggle Gypsies, O.

3. It was late at night when the lord came home,
      Inquiring for his lady, O.
   The servants said on every hand,
      She's gone with the raggle-taggle Gypsies, O.

4. Go saddle to me my milk-white steed,
      The black one's not so speedy, O.
   That I may ride and seek my bride
      Who has gone with the raggle-taggle Gypsies, O.

5. Oh, he rode high and he rode low,
      He rode through the woods and the copses, O.
   Till he came to the cold open field
      And there he espied his lady, O.

6. What makes you leave your house and home?
      What makes you leave your money, O?
   What makes you leave your new wedded lord
      To be off with the raggle-taggle Gypsies, O?

7. What care I for my house and land?
      What care I for the money, O?
   What care I for my new-wedded lord?
      To be off with the raggle-taggle Gypsies, O.

8. Last night you slept on a goose-feather bed,
      With a sheet turned down so bravely, O.
   Tonight you'll sleep in a cold open field
      Along with the raggle-taggle Gypsies, O.

9. What care I for my goose-feather bed?
      A sheet turned down so bravely, O?
   For tonight I shall sleep in a cold open field
      Along with the raggle-taggle Gypsies, O.

76. [Wraggle Taggle Gipsies O]

Sharp MSS., 772/. Sung by Mrs. Slade, Minehead, January 15, 1906.

a Æ, ending on ? *VII*

"I think the last phrase is a reminiscence of the Bonny Bunch of Roses. Mrs. Slade tried to sing this latter song afterwards but could only recollect the characteristic phrase at the end." [*Sharp's MS. note.*]

77. [The Gypsy Laddie]

Eddy, 1939, p. 67. Sung by S. Daixel, Canton, Ohio; learned from Utah Mormons.

a Æ

1. There came three gypsies to my door,
   And downstairs 'round my lady, ho,
   One sang high, the other sang low,
   And the third sang bonnie, bonnie, bonnie, ho.

2. She pulled down her silken gown,
   And put on one of leather, ho,
   And the bell rang, rang about the door,
   She has gone with the raggle, taggle gypsies, ho.

3. It was late last night when my lord came home,
   Inquiring for his lady, ho;
   The servants stood at every end;
   "She has gone with the raggle, taggle gypsies' band."

4. He rode, rode high, and he rode, rode low,
   And he rode through the woods and copses low,
   Until he came to the wide open field,
   And there he discovered his lady, ho.

5. "What made you leave your horses and land,
   What made you leave your stable, ho?
   What made you leave your goose-feathered bed,
   And the sheets turned down so bravely, oh?"

6. "Oh, what care I for your horses and land,
   What care I for your stable, ho?
   I'd rather stay in the wide open field
   Alone with the raggle, taggle gypsies, ho."

78. "The Gipsy Laddie"

Burne [1886], p. 652; text, p. 551. Sung by some gypsy children named Wharton, travelling in North Shropshire and Staffordshire, May 23, 1885. Noted by James Smart.

a Æ

1. There came a gang o' gipsies by,
   And they was singing so merry O!
   Till they gained the heart o' my lady gay,
   [To follow the gipsy laddie, O!]

2. As soon as the lawyer [*read* lord he] did come in,
   Enquirèd for his lady, O!
   And some o' the sarvants did-a reply,
   'Her's away wi' the gipsy laddie, O!'

3. 'O saddle me the bay, and saddle me the grey,
   Till I go and sarch for my lady, O!'
   And some o' the sarvants did-a reply,
   'Her's away wi' the gipsy laddie, O!'

4. And he rode on, and he rode off,
   Till he come to the gipsies' tent-ie, O!
   And there he saw his lady gay
   By the side o' the gipsy laddie, O!

5. 'Didn't I leave you houses and land?
   And didn't I leave you money, O?
   Didn't I leave you three pretty babes
   As ever was in yonder green island, O?'

6. 'What care I for houses and land?
   And what care I for money, O?
   What do I care for three pretty babes
   [Compared to my gipsy laddie, O?']

7. 'The tother night you was on a feather bed,
   Now you're on a straw one, O!'
   . . . .
   . . . .

79. [The Gypsie Laddie]

McGill, 1917, p. 15.

a π^4

Cf. the I. G. Greer version of "Earl Brand" (No. 7), *ante*, I, p. 123, variant 34a.

1. There came two gypsies from the north,
   They were all wet and weary O;
   They sang so neat and so complete,
   It charmed the heart of the lady O.

2. The squire he came home one night
Inquiring for his lady O;
The news so quickly lit on him,—
"She's gone with the dark-eyed gypsie O."

3. "Go saddle up my milk-white steed,
Go saddle up my browny O;
And I will ride both night and day
To overtake my honey O."

4. He rode east and he rode west,
He rode north and southward too;
There he spied his sweet little miss
A-following the dark-eyed gypsie O.

5. She pulled off the garment that she wore,
And laid it down for a head-rest O;
She lay on the grass and drank of the dew;
And followed the dark-eyed gypsie O.

6. "Would you forsake your house and land,
Would you forsake your baby O;
Would you forsake your own true love,
And follow the gypsie laddie O?"

7. "What cares I for house and land,
What cares I for money O;
I'd rather have a kiss from the gypsie's lips
Than all your land and money O."

80. [The Gypsy Laddie]

Wilkinson MSS., 1936-37, p. 23(B). Sung by E. F. Comins, Washington, D.C., May 13, 1937.

a D/Æ

81. [The Gypsy Laddie]

Sung by Florence Shiflett, Wyatt's Mountain, near Dyke, Va., July 13, 1962. LC/AAFS, rec. No. 12,006(B24). Collected by George Foss.

a D

1. It was late in the night when the Captain came home,
Inquiring for his honey O,
The reply that was made unto him, my love,
She's gone with the gipsies and the laddies O.

2. Saddle up, saddle up my milk-white steed,
Saddle up, saddle up in a hurry O,
I will ride all night till the broad daylight,
Till I overtake my honey O.

3. He rode to the East and he rode to the West,
He rode till he came to ?Barreno.
And there he met with his pretty little Miss,
A-going with the gipsies and the laddies O.

4. . . . Come and go along with me,
You never be lacking for money O.
I'll lock you up in a chamber so high,
Where the gipsies and the laddie won't come anigh.

5. I won't go back nor I shan't go back,
Nor I won't go back, my husband O.
I wouldn't give a kiss from the gipsy boy's lips
For all your house and your money O.

6. Once you produced [= were used?] to a good feather bed,
But now you produced to another one,
Now you produced to an old torn bed,
With the gipsies and the laddies all around you.

82. [Gypsy Laddie]

Sung by David Morris (76), Wyatt's Mountain, near Dyke, Va., July 13, 1962. LC/AAFS, rec. No. 12,007 (A7). Collected by George Foss.

a D/Æ (VI in variant b)

1. It was late in the night when the Captain came home,
Inquiring for his honey O,
The reply that was made unto him, my dear,
She's gone with the gipsies and the laddie O.

2. Saddle up, saddle up my milk-white ?gray,
Saddle up, saddle up in a hurry O.
F'r I will ride all night until broad daylight,
Till I overtake my honey O.

3. He rode to the East, and he rode to the West,
From there he rode to Bontum O.
There I was led with my pretty little Miss,
She was going with the gipsies and the laddie O.

4. I won't go home but I shan't go back,
I haven't but a moment to tell you.
. . . .
. . . .

5. Once you were due to a nice feather bed,
Now you are due to another one,
Now you are due to an old torn tick,
With the gipsies and the laddies all around you.

83. "Gypsy Laddie"

Sung by Robert Shiflett, Brown's Cove, Va., July 15, 1961. LC/AAFS, rec. No. 12,004(A2). Collected by George Foss.

a D/Æ

The F's are frequently uncertain in this singer's intonation.

1. Young Gipsy Davy came merrily by
   Whistling loud and gaily,
   He whistled and sang till the green woods rang,
   Charmed the heart of a lady.

2. Merrily down the castle stair
   Came this fair young lady,
   In her hand so fine was a glass of wine
   To drink a health to Davy.

3. Her own ?grim ["engram"] lord came home that night
   Inquiring for his lady,
   The waiting-maid cried as she replied,
   She's gone with (the) Gipsy Davy.

4. O saddle with speed my milk-white steed,
   Quickly make him ready,
   I will ride this night till broad daylight,
   Till I overtake my lady.

5. He rode that night, he rode next day,
   Till he came to the banks of the river,
   On the other side his wife he spied
   Beside her gipsy lover.

6. Turn back, turn back, my own fair one,
   Turn back to your {lord? / home?} and baby,
   How can you roam from your (own) fair home
   To follow a gipsy laddie?

7. I won't turn back, I shan't turn back,
   For neither lord nor baby;
   I would give your home and the rest you own
   For one sweet kiss from Davy.

8. Last night on a bed of down you lay,
   Your baby lay by you.
   Tonight you will lay on the cold cold clay,
   With the gipsy lad beside you.

9. I won't turn back, I shan't turn back,
   For all your words of honey;
   I wouldn't give a kiss from the gipsy's lips
   For all your lands and money.

10. Take off, take off your costly glove
    That's made of Spanish leather,
    Your hand I will grasp in a farewell clasp,
    'Twill be farewell forever.

84. "The Gipsies came to Lord M——'s Gate"

Joyce, 1909, No. 334, p. 154. From the district around Newtownards.

a Æ

85. "The Dark-Eyed Gipsy O!"

Fox, *JIFSS*, I (1904), p. 42. Sung by Katherine Young, County Down, Ireland, in 1899. Complete text obtained in 1904 from Ann Carter (64), a native of County Galway, who had learned it in her youth. Collected by Mrs. C. Milligan Fox and Edith Wheeler.

a D (–II, inflected VI)

1. There was three gipsies in the East,
   They sang so sweet and bonny O!
   They sang so sweet, so very, very sweet,
   They charmed the heart of a Ladye O!

2. When Lord Charles came home at night,
   Inquiring for his Ladye O!
   "She's gone! she's gone!" said his old servin' man;
   "She's followed the dark-eyed gipsy O!"

3. "Saddle me my milk-white steed;
   The grey was ne'er so speedy O!
   And I'll travel all night, through the length of the night,
   Till I find out the dark-eyed gipsy O!"

4. He travelled East, he travelled West,
   He travelled North and Southward O!
   Until he met with an old beggar man,
   Who was both wet and weary O!

5. "Where have you been, my good old man?
Where have you been so early O?
And have you seen a fair Ladye
Following a dark-eyed gipsy O?"

6. "I have been in East, I've been in West,
I have been in North and Southward O!
The fairest Ladye that e'er my eyes beheld
Was following the dark-eyed gipsy O!"

7. He travelled East, he travelled West,
He travelled North and Southwards O,
Until he came to his fair Ladye,
A-following the dark-eyed gipsy O!

8. He drew out his lightning sword,
That showed most bright and bonny O!
"I'll swear by the handle of my broad sword
That no dark-eyed gipsy will come near you O!"

9. "Come back with me, my dear," he says;
"Come back with me, my honey O!
I'll swear by the handle of my broad sword,
No dark-eyed gipsy will come near you O!

10. "Why did you leave your houses and lands?
Why did you leave your children O?
Why did you leave your own wedded lord
To follow the dark-eyed gipsy O?"

11. "What do I care for my houses and lands?
And what do I care for my children O?
I will eat the grass and drink the dew,
And follow the dark-eyed gipsy O!"

12. He pulled out his lightning sword,
It shone so bright and bonny O!
He fought like a hero among them all,
Till he wounded the seven yellow gipsies O.

13. Then these three gipsies were put in jail,
Bound down in iron strongly O!
And next they were condemned for to die,
For stealing of this Ladye O!

86. [Wraggle Taggle Gipsies O!]

Sharp MSS., 2610/. Sung by an 85-year-old man, Retford Union, May 1, 1911.

a Æ

1. O Seven jolly gipsies all in a gang
They were brisk & bonny O
They sang till they came to the Abbey Castle Gate
And then they sang so sweetly O,

2. The lady coming down with the waiting maid aside of her
They gave to her a brown nutmeg
She gave to them a far better thing
A ring from her fair finger.

3. She pulled off her highland shoes
And put on her Spanish leather O
To follow the gipsy laddie O

4. When her own wedded Lord comes home
Enquiring for his lady O
The waiting maid made this reply
She's following the gipsy laddie O,

5. He travelled all that long Summer's night
And part of the very next morning O
And then he spied his own wedded lady
Both wet & weary O

6. What made thou (or thee) leave thy houses in the land
What made thee leave thy money
What made thee leave thy own wedded Lord
To follow the gipsy laddie O

7. What care I for house or land,
What care I for money O
What care I for my own wedded Lord,
I follow up the gipsy laddie O

8. Seven jolly gipsies hung in a row
For stealing of the Abbey Castle lady O

APPENDIX B

87. [The Gypsy Countess]

Baring-Gould MSS., L(1); text (A). Also in Baring-Gould and Sheppard, 1895, p. 106. Sung by James Parsons, December 1888. Noted by F. W. Bussell.

m Æ (but inflected VI and VII)

There came an Earl a riding by,
  A Gipsy maid espied he,
O nut brown maid, to her he said,
  I prithee come away with me.
I'll take you up, I'll carry you home,
  I'll put a safe-guard over you;
Your shoes shall be of the Spanish leather,
  And silken stockings all of blue.
"My brothers three no more I'll see,
  If that I went along with you.
I'd rather be torn by thistle & thorn,
  With my bare feet all in the dew."

I'll lock you up in a castle tall
    I'll bar you up in a room so high,
Thou gipsy maid, from greenwood glade,
    That ne'er a gipsy shall come by.
Thou shalt no more be set in stocks
    And trudge about from town to town,
But thou shalt ride in pomp & pride
    In velvet and a broidered gown.
"I'll pawn my hat, I'll pawn my gown,
    I'll pawn my silken stockings blue.
I'll pawn my petticoat next my shift
    To follow along with the gipsies O!"
All night you lie 'neath the starry sky
    In rain & snow you walk all day.
But now thy head shall have a feather bed
    And in the arms of a husband lay.
"I love to lie 'neath a starry sky,
    I do not heed the rain & snow,
And I will away, come night, come day,
    To follow along with the gipsies O!"
I will thee wed, sweet maid he said,
    I will thee wed with a golden ring,
Then thou shall dance, & merry, merry be,
    And I'll make thee a gay wedding.
"I will not wed, kind Sir," she said
    ["]I will not wed with a golden ring
For fickle as wind I fear I'll find
    The man that would make my wedding."

. . . .

Three gipsies stood at the castle gate
    They sang so high, they sang so low,
The lady sat in her chamber late,
    Her heart it melted away as snow.
They sang so sweet, they sang so shrill
    That fast her tears began to flow,
And she laid down her golden gown,
    Her golden rings & all her show.
O she put off her silken shoes
    That were of spanish leather, O
All forth for to go in the rain & snow,
    All forth in the stormy weather.

And down the stair came the lady fair
    To go away with the gipsies O!

At past midnight her lord came home
    And where his lady was would know,
The servants replied on every side,
    She's gone away with the gipsies O.
Come saddle my horse, come saddle my man (*sic*)
    And hang my sword to my saddle bow,
That I may ride for to seek my bride,
    That is gone away with the gipsies O!
They saddled his horse, they saddled his man (*sic*)
    And hung his sword to his saddle bow,
That he might ride for to seek his bride,
    That was gone away with the gipsies O.
Then he rode high & he rode low,
    He rode through hills & valleys O
He rode till he spied his own fair bride,
    Following along with the gipsies O!
What makes you leave both house & lands?
    What makes you leave your money O?
What takes you abroad from your wedded Lord,
    To follow along with the gipsies O?
"O I want none of your house & lands,
    And I want none of your money, O
Neither care I for my wedded lord,
    I will follow along with the gipsies, O."
Last night you slept in a feather bed
    Rolled in the arms of your husband, O
And now you must sleep on the cold, cold ground,
    And walk along in the rain & snow.
I care not to sleep in a feather bed,
    Rolled in the arms of a husband, O
For rather I'd sleep on the cold, cold ground,
    And walk along in the rain & snow.
Nay that shall not be, I swear said he
    He drew his sword from his saddle bow,
And once he smote on her lily-white throat,
    And then her red blood down did flow.

88. "The Gipsy Laddie"

Greig MSS., I, p. 43. From Rev. J. B. Duncan, 1905.

m D/Æ

89. "The Gypsy Lady"

Barry MSS., II, No. 200H. Transcribed by Phillips Barry from B. V. Osgood's transcript of the Whittier Perkins MS., 1790.

a Æ, ending on the octave

This, the oldest recorded American variant, if it really be one, sounds like an imperfect reminiscence of "The Blind Harper of Lochmaben" (No. 192).

90. [Wraggle Taggle Gipsies O]

Sharp MSS., 2079/1931. Sung by Sister Emma (71), Clewer, February 27, 1909.

p I

1. There were two gipsies come singing at the door
One sang high & the other sang low
They sang so brisk & so bonnie O.

2. My lady came down in a fine silken gown
All wrapped up in a blanket O
And away she went to the greenwood side
Along with the Driggle Driggle gipsies O.

3. At twelve o'clock the Squire came home
Enquiring for his lady O
The serving maid she thus replied
She's gone with the driggle driggle gipsies O.

4. O saddle me my milk white steed
And give to me the bridle O
And you shall ride all by my side
Till we find out the driggle driggle gipsies O.

5. One rides high the other rides low
They ride so brisk & so bonnie O
They rode till they came to the greenwood side
And there they spied his lady O.

6. Where have you been this cold winter's day
You look so wan & so dreary O
Last night you slept in a warm feather bed
With the sheets turned down so neatly O
Tonight you sleep in a cold open field
Along with the driggle driggle gipsies O.

7. O what care I for my nice feather bed?
With the sheets turned down so neatly O
And what care I for the cold open field
I'll follow the driggle driggle gipsies O.

8. How can you you [*sic*] leave your houses & land
And how can you leave your money O
And how can you leave your new-wedded Lord
To follow the driggle driggle gipsies O.

9. What care I for my houses & land
And what care I for my money O?
And what care I for my new wedded Lord
I'll follow the driggle driggle gipsies O.
(Last 2 lines repeated.)

91. [The Gypsy Laddie]

Davis, 1929, p. 591(D); text, p. 427. Contributed by John Stone, November 3, 1920, from the singing of Misses Fannie and Hattie Via, Stage Junction, Va.; they learned it from Mrs. Orilla Keeton in Albemarle County.

p I/Ly, ending on *V*

1. There are seven sweet gypsies in the North,
They are calling to sweet Baltimore,
They will sing a song that will charm your heart
And cause you to leave your husband.

2. It was eight o'clock the captain came,
He was calling for his honey O.
"O your honey and-er she is not here,
She is gone with the gypsies to Laddie O."

3. "Saddle up, saddle up my milk-white team,
Saddle up, saddle up in a hurry O;
I will ride all night till the broad daylight
Until I overtake my honey O."

4. He rode to the east, he rode to the west,
He rode on to sweet Baltimore.
When he got there he found his honey;
She had gone with the gypsies to Laddie O.

5. "Come back, come back, my pretty miss,
Come back, come back, my honey O;
It's how can you leave your three little babes
And go with the gypsies to Laddie O?"

6. "O yes, I can leave my three little babes,
O yes, I can leave my honey O;
For I'd rather have a kiss from the gypsy's lips
Than all of your land and money O."

7. She hadn't been gone but a very short while
Until she spent all of her money O;
She spent the gold rings off of her fingers
And the breastpins off of her bosom.

8. It's once she was used to a feather bed
And servants to her parlor;
But now she is used to the old hay bed
And the gypsies all around her.

GROUP C

92. [The Gipsy Laddie]

Sharp MSS., 4227/. Sung by Mrs. Fanny Coffey, White Rock, Va., May 8, 1918.

a M (–IV)

She used to sleep on a warm feather bed
With servants to wait on her,
But now she goes to a bed of straw
With the gipsies all around her.

93. "The Gypsy Davy"

Kittredge, *JAF*, XXX (1917), p. 324. From Mrs. William L. R. Gifford, 1914, as recalled from the singing of Mrs. Catharine B. Dexter, Rochester, Mass., c. 1872.

a I/Ly

1. My lord came home quite late one night,
   Inquiring for his lady.
The servant made him this reply:
   "She's gone with a Gypsy Davy."
Raddle daddle dingo day,
   Raddle daddle dingo davy.
The servant made him this reply:
   "She's gone with a Gypsy Davy."

2. "Go saddle for me the white," said he,
   "The brown is not so speedy.
I'll ride all night and I'll ride all day
   Till I find my charming lady."
Raddle daddle, etc.

3. My lord rode down by the water's side,
   The waters there flowed freely;
The tears were trickling down his cheeks,
   For there he spied his lady.
Raddle daddle, etc.

4. "Will you forsake your house and lands?
   Will you forsake your baby?
Will you forsake your own true love
   And go with a Gypsy Davy?"
Raddle daddle, etc.

5. "I care not for my house and lands,
   I care not for my baby,
I care not for my own true love,
   And I'll go with a Gypsy Davy."
Raddle daddle dingo day,
   Raddle daddle dingo davy.
"I care not for my own true love,
   And I'll go with a Gypsy Davy."

94. "The Gypsy Davy"

Cox, 1925, p. 524; text, p. 130. Learned by Cox from farm hands in Illinois, c. 1880.

m π^1

1. The Gypsy Davy crossed the plain,
   He sang so loud and sweetly;
He sang till he made the green woods ring,
   To charm the heart of a lady.

Tum-a-roe-eye ink-a-toodle ink-a-toodle-a
   Tum-a-roe-eye ink-a-toodle-a-dy

2. The lord of the house came home at night,
   Inquiring for his lady;
The servants all made quick reply,
   "She's gone with the Gypsy Davy."

3. "Go saddle me up my milk-white steed,
   The brown he ain't so speedy;
I've rode all day and I'll ride all night,
   Or overtake my lady."

4. They saddled him up his milk-white steed,
   His milk-white steed so speedy;
He rode all night and he rode all day,
   To overtake his lady.

5. He rode till he came to the river side,
   That runs so deep and shady;
The tears came trickling down his cheeks,
   For there he met his lady.

6. "Have you forsaken your house and lands,
   Have you forsaken your baby?
Have you forsaken your own true-love,
   And gone with the Gypsy Davy?"

7. "Yes, I've forsaken my house and lands,
   And I've forsaken my baby;
And I've forsaken my own true-love,
   And gone with the Gypsy Davy."

8. The lord of the house rode home that night,
   Rode home without his lady,
For she remained by the river side,
   In the arms of the Gypsy Davy.

95. "Gypsy Davie"

Barry, *JAF*, XVIII (1905), p. 194(E). Sung by Mrs. S. A. Flint, Providence, R.I., April 7, 1904.

a π^1

The rich man came from o'er the sea,
Inquiring for his Lady,
The servant gave him this reply,—
"She's gone with the Gypsy Davie."
Rattle dattle ding, O rattle dattle day,
Rattle dattle ding O daisy.

96. [Gypsy Laddie]

Sung by Arthur Keefe, June 28, 1949. LC/AAFS, 10,501 (A16). Collected by Sam Eskin.

a I/M

O, why did you leave your house and home?
Why did you leave your baby?
Why did you leave your own true love
And go with the gipsy ladie?

Raddle diddle dingdo dingdo day
Raddle diddle dingdo daisy
Raddle diddle dingdo dingdo day
And agone with the gipsy ladie.

Last night I slept on a feather-bed
Last night I slept with baby,
Tonight I'll sleep on the cold cold ground
Along with the gipsy ladie.

O Raddle diddle dingdo dingdo day
Raddle diddle dingdo daisy
Raddle diddle dingdo dingdo day
And agone with the gipsy ladie.

97. [The Gipsy Laddy]

Sharp MSS., 3507/. Also in Sharp and Karpeles, 1932, I, p. 237(F). Sung by Mrs. Sarah Buckner, Black Mountain, N.C., September 19, 1916.

a I

It's come go back my pretty little Miss
It's come go back my honey
It's come go back my pretty little Miss
You never shall lack for money

98. "Gypsy Davy"

Eddy, 1939, p. 68(B). From Miss Helen Hobart, Medina, Ohio; learned from Mrs. E. J. Schlabach, Canton, Ohio.

a I

He was a high born gentleman,
She was a high born lady,
They lived in a castle great and tall
Till she met with the Gypsy Davy.
Lala fala dilla dilla dale
Lala fala dilla daisy,
Come one and all, both great and small,
But beware of the Gypsy Davy.

Last night she slept in her warm feather bed,
And in her arms her baby;
But tonight she sleeps on the cold, cold ground
In the arms of the Gypsy Davy.

99. "Gypsy Davy"

Tolman MS. Also in Sandburg, 1927, p. 311. From the singing of Mrs. E. J. Schlabach, Canton, Ohio.

a I

I was a high-born gentleman,
She was a high-born lady.
We lived in a palace great and tall,
Till she met with Gypsy Davy.

Last night she slept in a goose-feather bed,
With her arms around her baby.
To-night she lies in the cold, cold ground
In the arms of her Gypsy Davy.

Sandburg gives no source, and omits the chorus; but the close correspondence of text and notes (though not identical) points to the Tolman copy.

Chorus

Rolla folla dilla dilla dale,
Rolla folla dilla daisy,
Come one come all, both great and small,
But beware of the Gypsy Davy.

100. "The Gypsy Davy"

Randolph, I, 1946, p. 152(A). Sung by Mrs. Emma L. Dusenbury, Mena, Ark., June 1, 1930.

m π^1

1. There was a young man, a very young man,
His name was Gypsy Davy,
He sung so loud he made the green woods ring,
An' charmed the heart of a lady,
An' charmed the heart of a lady.

2. Oh won't you forsake your house an' home,
An' won't you forsake your baby?
Oh won't you forsake your own dear one
An' go with the Gypsy Davy?
An' go with the Gypsy Davy?

3. Oh yes, I'll forsake my house an' home,
Oh yes, I'll forsake my baby,
Oh yes, I'll forsake my own dear one
An' go with the Gypsy Davy,
An' go with the Gypsy Davy.

4. An' when the old man come home that night,
Enquirin' for his lady,
The Injun took him up to the chamber room,
She's gone with the Gypsy Davy,
She's gone with the Gypsy Davy.

5. Go saddle me up my milk white steed,
The young-un is too gaily,
I'll ride all day, an' I'll ride all night,
Or I'll overtake my Mary,
Or I'll overtake my Mary.

6. He rode all day an' he rode all night
Until he come to the river,
The water mark was up very high,
An' it was very muddy,
An' it was very muddy.

7. How can you forsake your house an' home?
How can you forsake your baby?
How can you forsake your own dear one
An' go with the Gypsy Davy,
An' go with the Gypsy Davy?

8. Very well I can forsake my house an' home,
Very well I can forsake my baby,
Very well I can forsake my own dear one
An' go with the Gypsy Davy,
An' go with the Gypsy Davy.

9. Oh send to me your little white hand,
All wrapped in Spanish leather,
Oh send to me your little white hand,
We'll bid farewell forever,
We'll bid farewell forever.

10. Oh once I had a house an' home,
Oh once I had some money,
But now I lay on an old hay bed
An' the Gypsies dance around me,
An' the Gypsies dance around me.

101. "Black Jack Davy"

Sung by Mrs. T. M. Davis, Fayetteville, Ark., November 15, 1953. LC/AAFS, rec. No. 11,894(B18). Collected by Mary Celestia Parler.

a I/M

1. Black Jack Davy came a-riding o'er the plains
Singing his song so gaily O.
He sang so loud he made the echoes ring,
And charmed the heart of a lady O.

2. He says, little Miss, will you go with me?
   Will you be my baby O?
   I swear by the sword that hangs at my side,
   You never'll want for money O.

3. Will you forsake your house and home?
   Will you forsake your baby O?
   Will you forsake the one that loves you
   To go with Black Jack Davy O?

4. O yes, I'll forsake my house and home,
   Yes, I'll forsake my baby O,
   Yes, I'll forsake the one that loves me
   To go with Black Jack Davy O.

5. Then pull off that little black glove you wear
   Made out of Spanish leather O,
   Place your little white hand in mine,
   And here we'll part forever O.

6. She pulled off that little black glove she wore,
   Made out of Spanish leather O,
   Placed her little white hand in his,
   And there they parted forever O.

7. Well, they rode all night and they rode all day,
   Till the sun set in the evening O,
   There they came to a dark salt lake,
   And looked so dark and dreary O.

8. O once I had a home so fine,
   And jewels very costly O,
   Now I sit me down in rags
   By the side of the gipsy draily O.

9. Last night I slept on a new feather bed,
   By the side of my darling baby O,
   Tonight I sleep on an old straw bed
   With the gipsies piled all around me O.

During her childhood, Mrs. Davis learned two different versions of this ballad: one from her father, which is given above, and another from her mother, which Mrs. Davis in turn taught to her daughter, Mrs. Oleava Houser (see variant No. 102).

1. Black Jack Davy went a-riding o'er the plains,
   Singing his song so gaily O,
   Singing (?sang) so loud he made the echoes ring,
   And charmed the heart of a lady O.

2. Says, Go with me, my pretty little Miss,
   And will you be my baby O?
   I'll swear by the sword that hangs by my side
   You shall never want for money O.

3. O will you forsake your house and home,
   Will you forsake your baby O?
   Will you forsake the one who loves you,
   To go with Black Jack Davy O?

4. Yes, I'll forsake my house and home,
   Yes, I'll forsake my baby O,
   Yes, I'll forsake the one who loves me
   To go with Black Jack Davy O.

5. Then pull off that little black glove you wear
   Made out of that Spanish leather O,
   Place your lily-white hand in mine,
   And here we'll part forever O.

6. She pulled off that little black glove she wore,
   Made out of that Spanish leather O,
   Placed her lily-white hand in his,
   And there they parted forever O.

7. Well they rode all night and they rode that day
   Till the sun set in the evening O,
   And then they came to a broad salt lake
   That looked so dark and dreary O.

8. Last night I slept on a new feather bed,
   Beside my darling baby O,
   Tonight I'll sleep on the old hay-pile,
   With the gipsies piled all around me O.

9. O once I had a home so fine,
   And jewels very costly O,
   Now I sit me down in rags
   Beside the gipsy draily O.

102. "Gipsy Draly"

Sung by Mrs. Oleava Houser, Fayetteville, Ark., September 28, 1958. LC/AAFS, rec. No. 11,908(B34). Collected by Mary Celestia Parler.

a I/M

103. "The Gypsy Davy"

Randolph, I, 1946, p. 155(E). Sung by Miss Rose O'Neill, Day, Mo., May 14, 1938. Learned in the late 1890's from Conrad Cornelison, Reeds Spring, Mo.

a I/M

1. There was a young lady come a-trippin' along,
An' at each side a servant O,
An' in each hand a glass of wine
To drink with th' Gypsy Davy O,
An' in each hand a glass of wine
To drink with th' Gypsy Davy O.

2. Oh will you fancy me, my dear,
An' will you be my honey O?
I swear by the sword that's a-hangin' by my side
You never shall lack for money O,
I swear by the sword that's a-hangin' by my side
You never shall lack for money O.

3. Oh she's put on her high-heeled shoes,
All made of Spanish leather O,
An' she's put on her bonnie bonnie brown,
An' they've rode off together O,
An' she's put on her bonnie bonnie brown,
An' they've rode off together O.

4. Soon after that her lord come home
Inquirin' for his lady O,
When some of the servants made him this reply,
She's gone with the Gypsy Davy O,
When some of the servants made him this reply,
She's gone with the Gypsy Davy O.

5. Go saddle me my milk-white steed,
For the gray is not so speedy O,
An' I'll ride all night, an' I'll ride all day
Until I overtake my lady O,
An' I'll ride all night, an' I'll ride all day
Until I overtake my lady O.

6. He rode all night an' he rode all day,
Until he come to the water O,
Then he paused an' a tear come a-trinklin' down his cheek,
For there he spied his lady O,
Then he paused an' a tear come a-trinklin' down his cheek,
For there he spied his lady O.

7. Will you forsake your houses an' lands,
Will you forsake your baby O,
Will you forsake your own wedded lord
To foller a Gypsy Davy O?
Will you forsake your own wedded lord
To foller a Gypsy Davy O?

8. Yes, I'll forsake my houses an' lands,
Yes, I'll forsake my baby O,
For I am bewitched an' I know the reason why,
It's a-follerin' a Gypsy Davy O,
For I am bewitched an' I know the reason why,
It's a-follerin' a Gypsy Davy O.

9. Last night I lay on a velvet couch,
Beside my lord an' baby O,
Tonight I will lie on the cold cold ground,
In the arms of a Gypsy Davy O,
Tonight I will lie on the cold cold ground,
In the arms of a Gypsy Davy O.

104. [Gipsy Laddie]

Sharp MSS., 3674/. Also in Sharp and Karpeles, 1932, I, p. 237(H). Sung by Mrs. Franklin, Barbourville, Knox County, Ky., May 9, 1917.

a I

There was a gipsy came to this country,
He sang so loud and sweetly,
He sang till he made the whole dell ring
To win the heart of a lady
Rattle arter ding and a hoodle arter day
Rattle arter ding, ding Davey.

105. "Gypsum Davy"

Sung by Mrs. Donald Shelton (née Emma Hensley), Flagpond, Tenn. (or N.C.: on state line), September 29, 1950. LC/AAFS, rec. No. 10,008(A9). Collected by Maud Karpeles and Sidney Robertson Cowell.

a I/M

1. It was late last night when the Squire came home,
Inquiring for his lady.
The answer that they gave to him
[S]he's gone with the Gipsy Davy.
Rattle-tum-a-gipsum gipsum
Rattle-tum-a-gipsum Davy-O.

2. Go catch up my old gray mare,
F' th' black he ain't so speedy.
I'll ride all night and I'll ride all day
Till I overtake my lady.
Rattle-tum-a-gipsum gipsum
Rattle-tum-a-gipsum Davy-O.

3. He rode and he rode till he came to the town,
And he rode till he came to Barley,

The tears came rolling down his cheeks,
And there he spied his lady.
Rattle-tum-a-gipsum gipsum
Rattle-tum-a-gipsum Davy-O.

4. O come back, my own true love,
O come back, my honey,
I'll lock you up in the chamber high,
Where the gipsums can't come round you.
Rattle-tum-a-gipsum gipsum
Rattle-tum-a-gipsum Davy-O.

5. I won't come back your own true love,
Nor I won't come back your honey.
I wouldn't give a kiss from the gipsum's lips
For all your lands and money.
Rattle-tum-a-gipsum gipsum
Rattle-tum-a-gipsum Davy-O.

6. She soon run through her gay clothing,
Her velvet shoes and stockings,
The gold ring off her finger gone,
The gold plates from her bosom.
Rattle-tum-a-gipsum gipsum
Rattle-tum-a-gipsum Davy-O.

7. Once I had a house and land
Featherbed and money,
But now I've got that old straw pad
With the gipsums all around me.
Rattle-tum-a-gipsum gipsum
Rattle-tum-a-gipsum Davy-O.

The last two stanzas were sung from print (Sharp's A).

106. "Gypsy Davy"

Scarborough, 1937, p. 412(E); text, p. 221. Sung by Miss Harriet Foster, Charleston, S.C., c. 1932; learned from her mother.

a I

1. Gypsy Davy came over the hills
And out of the woodland shady—
He sang so sweet and he sang so fine,
That he won the heart of a Lady.

Oh, widdy um, widdy um, widdy ay,
Oh, widdy um, widdy ady.
He sang so sweet and he sang so fine
That he won the heart of a Lady.

2. Milord returning late at night,
Inquiring for his lady—
The maid she made him this reply,
"She's gone with the Gypsy Davy."

Oh, widdy um, widdy um, widdy ay,
Oh, widdy um, widdy ady.
The maid she made him this reply,
"She's gone with the Gypsy Davy."

3. "Then harness me my blackest steed,
My gray is not so speedy.
I'll ride all night and I'll ride all day
But I'll overtake my lady."

Oh, widdy um, widdy um, widdy ay,
Oh, widdy um, widdy ady.
"I'll ride all night and I'll ride all day
But I'll overtake my lady."

4. He rode all day and he rode all night,
And he rode till he came to a sad, muddy site
And he beheld his lady—
The tears came down his cheeks like rain
As he beheld his lady.

Oh, widdy um, widdy um, widdy ay,
Oh, widdy um, widdy ady.
The tears came down his cheeks like rain
As he beheld his lady.

5. "Do you forsake your house—your home,
Do you forsake your baby?
Do you forsake your own wedded lord
To go with the Gypsy Davy."

Oh, widdy um, widdy um, widdy ay,
Oh, widdy um, widdy ady.
"Do you forsake your own wedded lord
To go with the Gypsy Davy?"

6. "Yes, I forsake my house—my home,
Yes, I forsake my baby;
Yes, I forsake my own wedded lord
To go with the Gypsy Davy."

Oh, widdy um, widdy um, widdy ay,
Oh, widdy um, widdy ady.
"Yes, I forsake my own wedded lord
To go with the Gypsy Davy?"

7. "Do you not love your house—your home?
Do you not love your baby?
Do you not love your own wedded lord
As you love the Gypsy Davy?"

Oh, widdy um, widdy um, widdy ay,
Oh, widdy um, widdy ady.
"Do you not love your own wedded lord
As you love the Gypsy Davy?"

8. "I do not love my house my home,
I do not love my baby;
I do not love my own wedded lord
As I love the Gypsy Davy."

Oh, widdy um, widdy um, widdy ay,
Oh, widdy um, widdy ady.
"I do not love my own wedded lord
As I love the Gypsy Davy."

107. "Gipsy Daisy"

Flanders, 1934, p. 78. Also in Flanders, III, 1963, p. 216(N). Sung by Delmer Brigham, East Calais, Vt., July 29, 1933. From *A Garland of Green Mountain Song*, edited by Helen Hartness Flanders; copyright 1934 by Helen Hartness Flanders.

a I/M

Gipsy Daisy come over the hills,
Come over the hills and the valleys.
He sang so sweet that he made the valley ring
And charmed the heart of a lady.

Chorus:

Rattle dattle dum, dattle dum, dattle dum;
Rattle dattle dum, dinka daisy,
Rattle dattle dum, to my myrinka dinka dum
To the mo ry ro, myrinka dinka daisy.

The boss being late come home one night
Enquiring for his lady.
A waiter girl gave this reply,
"She's gone with a gipsy Daisy."

Chorus.

"Would you forsake your true wedded lord,
Would you forsake your baby,
Would you forsake your warm feather bed
And go with a gipsy Daisy?"

Chorus.

"Last night you slept on a warm feather bed
And in your arms your baby.
To-night you'll sleep on the cold, cold ground
Along with a gipsy Daisy."

Chorus.

108. "Gypsy Davy"

Barry, *JAF*, XVIII (1905), p. 195(G). From Miss E. E. Dana, Cambridge, Mass., 1904.

a I/M

Raddle, raddle dingo, dingo day,
Raddle, raddle dingo Davie,
Raddle, raddle, dingo dingo day,
She's gone with the Gypsy Davy.

109. "Gypsy Davy"

Barry, Eckstorm, and Smyth, 1929, p. 272. Sung by Mrs. Susie Carr Young, Brewer, Me. Tune recorded by George Herzog, 1928.

a M (inflected VII)

How could you leave your house and home?
How could you leave your baby?
How could you leave your love and lord
And elope with a Gypsy Davy?
Faddle-daddle-lingo-dingo-day,
Faddle-daddle-lingo-davy,
I married you against my will,
In sport for the Gypsy Davy.

110. "Gipsy Davy"

Barry, Eckstorm, and Smyth, 1929, p. 276. Contributed in 1928 by Dr. Edith M. Patch, University of Maine, Orono. Learned from her mother.

a I/M (–II)

1. [The gipsy came from o'er the hills
    They called (him) the] gipsy Davy,
  Sitting beneath a greenwood tree,
    And charming the heart of a lady.

Refrain

Twadle-la-de dinktum dinktum dinktum!
  Twadle-la-de dinktum Davy!
Sitting beneath a greenwood tree,
  And charming the heart of a lady.

2. "Will you forsake your hearth and hame,
    Will you forsake your baby,
  Will you forsake your ain true love,
    To roam with a gipsy Davy?"

3. "Yes, I'll forsake my hearth and hame,
    And I'll forsake my baby,
  And I'll forsake my ain true love,
    To roam with a gipsy Davy."

4. My laird came hame very late one night,
    Enquiring for his lady.
  "My lady's gone," the servant said,
    "To roam with a gipsy Davy."

5. "Then bring to me my old bay mare,
    The grey is not so speedy;
  I'll ride all night, and I'll ride all day,
    But I'll overtake my lady!"

111. "Gyps of David"

Sung by Frank Proffitt, Reese, N.C., January 1962. Folk-Legacy LP recording No. FSA-1. Collected by Sandy Paton.

p π^1

1. Who's that gallopin' on the King's highway,
    Singin' so gay and haily?
  It's that dark and handsome lad
    Known as the Gyps of David,
    Known as the Gyps of David.

2. Where may the good man be, said he,
    My own true fair lady?
  He's gone a-searchin' far and wide,
    Searchin' for the Gyps of David,
    Searchin' for the Gyps of David.

3. Will you come away with me
    And give up all you've saved,
  And give up all the ones you've loved
    To go with the Gyps of David,
    To go with the Gyps of David?

4. I'll leave the good man of the house,
    The baby in the cradle,
  And all the gold that's stored away
    To go with the Gyps of David,
    To go with the Gyps of David.

5. So away they rode for many a day
    Across the miry heather;
  They didn't stop for bran (?) nor briar
    Or any sort of weather,
    Or any sort of weather.

6. The good man when he returned
    Inquirin' for his lady,
  She sped away a while ago,
    In the arms of the Gyps of David,
    In the arms of the Gyps of David.

7. Go saddle me up my fleetest steed,
    And don't fool time a-dawdlin';
  I'll have his head on the end of my sword
    The head of the Gyps of David,
    The head of the Gyps of David.

8. He rode till he come to the waters wide
    And couldn't go no farther;
  On the other side he spied his bride
    In the arms of the Gyps of David,
    In the arms of the Gyps of David.

9. Will you return to the gold I have,
    Will you return to your baby?
  No never will I leave the arms,
    The arms of the Gyps of David,
    The arms of the Gyps of David.

10. He jumped into the waters wide,
    In madness he was ravin',
  And floated off down to the sea
    Because of the Gyps of David,
    Because of the Gyps of David.

112. "Black Jack Davy"

Matteson and Henry, 1936, p. 6. Sung by Mrs. J. E. Schell, Banner Elk, N.C., July 15, 1933.

m π^1

1. Black Jack Davy came a-riding through the woods,
  A-singing so loud and halely;

Many green trees all around him stood,
And he charmed the heart of a lady,
And he charmed the heart of a lady.

2. How old are you, my pretty little miss?
How old are you, my lady?
She answered him with a hee hee hay:
I'll be sixteen next Sunday,
I'll be sixteen next Sunday.

3. Can you go with me, my pretty little miss?
Can you go with me, my lady?
I'll carry you across the deep blue sea,
Where you never shall want for money,
Where you never shall want for money.

4. Will you forsake your home and lands?
Will you forsake your babies?
Will you forsake your husband dear
To go with Black Jack Davy,
To go with Black Jack Davy?

5. Yes, I'll forsake my home and lands;
Yes, I'll forsake my babies;
Yes, I'll forsake my husband dear
And go with Black Jack Davy,
And go with Black Jack Davy.

6. . . . .

7. That night the husband coming home
Inquired for his lady;
He soon found out from his two little babes
She'd gone with Black Jack Davy,
She'd gone with Black Jack Davy.

8. Go saddle me up my milk-white steed;
Go, saddle me up my derby;
I'll ride all day and I'll ride all night
Till I overtake my lady,
Till I overtake my lady.

9. He rode all day and he rode all night;
The sea was deep and muddy;
On the other side he spied his bride,
His bride and Black Jack Davy,
His bride and Black Jack Davy.

10. Have you forsaken your home and lands?
Have you forsaken your babies?
Have you forsaken your husband dear
To go with Black Jack Davy,
To go with Black Jack Davy?

11. Yes, I've forsaken my home and lands;
Yes, I've forsaken my babies;
Yes, I've forsaken my husband dear
To go with Black Jack Davy,
To go with Black Jack Davy.

12. Last night you slept in a warm feather bed
All with your husband and babies.
Tonight you sleep on the cold damp ground
With a roving Black Jack Davy,
With a roving Black Jack Davy.

13. Then you take off that long white glove,
All made of Spanish leather,
And reach me here your lily-white hand
And I'll bid you adieu forever,
And I'll bid you adieu forever.

113. "David"

Sung by Mrs. Wayne (Claudia) Roberts (56), Hot Springs, N.C., September 28, 1950. LC/AAFS, rec. No. 10,007 (A16). Collected by Maud Karpeles and Sidney Robertson Cowell.

p π^1

Jack Davy came riding through the woods,
Singing loud and merry,
"With green fields laying all around
I've charmed the heart of a lady,
I've charmed the heart of a lady.

"Will you forsake your house and home,
Will you forsake your baby?
Will you forsake your husband, too,
And go with Black Jack David,
And go with Black Jack David?"

"I will forsake my house and home,
And I will forsake my baby.
I will forsake my husband, too,
And go with Black Jack David,
And go with Black Jack David."

She then put off her low-heeled shoes,
All made of Spanish leather,
And then put on her high-heeled shoes
And they both rode off together,
And they both rode off together.

114. "Black Jack Davy"

Shellans, *North Carolina Folklore*, VI (1958), p. 18. Sung by Lattye Eunice Arnold, a music teacher; learned c. 1918 from a sharecropper's young son on her father's Wake County farm.

m π^1

1. Black Jack Davy came a-riding through the woods,
A-singing so loud and halely,
Many green trees all around him stood,
And he charmed the heart of a lady,
And he charmed the heart of a lady.

2. How old are you, my pretty little miss,
How old are you, my lady?
Think I heard my mother say,
I'll be sixteen next Sunday,
I'll be sixteen next Sunday.

3. Can you go with me, my pretty little miss,
Can you go with me, my lady?
I'll carry you across the deep blue sea,
Where you never shall want for money,
Where you never shall want for money.

4. Will you forsake your home and lands,
Will you forsake your babies,
Will you forsake your husband dear,
To go with Black Jack Davy,
To go with Black Jack Davy?

5. Yes, I'll forsake my home and lands,
Yes, I'll forsake my babies,
Yes, I'll forsake my husband dear,
And go with Black Jack Davy,
And go with Black Jack Davy.

6. That night the husband coming home
Enquired for his lady.
He soon found out from his two little babes,
She'd gone with Black Jack Davy,
She'd gone with Black Jack Davy.

7. Send for my fiddle and send for my bow,
Send for my black-eyed daisy.
She won't come and I can't go;
It almost runs me crazy,
It almost runs me crazy.

8. Go saddle me up my milk-white steed,
Go saddle me up my derby;
I'll ride all day and I'll ride all night,
'Til I overtake my lady,
'Til I overtake my lady.

9. He rode all day and he rode all night.
The sea was deep and muddy.
On the other side he spied his bride,
His bride and Black Jack Davy,
His bride and Black Jack Davy.

10. Have you forsaken your home and lands,
Have you forsaken your babies,
Have you forsaken your husband dear,
To go with Black Jack Davy,
To go with Black Jack Davy?

11. Yes, I've forsaken my home and lands,
Yes, I've forsaken my babies,
Yes, I've forsaken my husband dear,
To go with Black Jack Davy,
To go with Black Jack Davy.

12. Then take off that long white glove,
All made of Spanish leather,
And reach me here your lily-white hand,
And I'll bid you adieu forever,
And bid you adieu forever.

This and variant 112 can hardly be unrelated.

115. "Black Jack David"

Hudson and Herzog, 1937, No. 26. Sung by a Lafayette County tenant's daughter, and noted by Mrs. Buchanan, Blue Mountain, Miss. Text from Miss Annie Laurie Roberts.

p I/Ly

Black Jack David came ridin' around;
He sang so loud and merry;
He hung his bugle around his side
Till he charmed in the arms of a lady
Till he charmed in the arms of a lady.

116. "Black Jack Davy"

Sung by Buck Buttery, Lincoln, Ark., August 19, 1958. LC/AAFS, rec. No. 11,909(B24). Collected by Marvin Wallace.

p π^1 (VII in variant)

1. O Black Jack Davy ?crossed the field
Listning to my . . .
Pretty little girl leaning out the door,
With a glass of wine before her,
With a glass of wine before her.

2. Pretty little Black Jack Davy, she said,
We'll drink this wine together,
Speak a word or two of love
And ride the trail together,
And ride the trail together.

3. Well go pull off those high-topped shoes,
   Lined with Spanish leather,
 And go put on your low-heeled boots
   And away we'll go together,
   And away we'll go together.

4. So she pulled off her high-topped shoes
   That's lined with Spanish leather,
 And she put on her low-heeled boots
   And away they went together,
   And away they went together.

5. When her husband he came in that night
   Inquiring for his lady,
 Two little babies crying out loud,
   She's gone with the Black Jack Davy,
   She's gone with the Black Jack Davy.

6. Well, he caught (?called) out his ?iron-gray horse
   Was so young and gaily,
 Rode all day and he rode all night
   Till he overtook his lady,
   Till he overtook his lady.

7. Have you forgotten your house and home,
   Have you forgotten your husband?
 Have you forgotten those two little babes
   To go with the Black Jack Davy,
   To go with the Black Jack Davy?

8. I have forsaken my house and home,
   I have forsaken my loved one,
 (I) have forsaken those two little babes,
   (I'll) go with Black Jack Davy,
   I'll go with Black Jack Davy.

9. Last night you slept on a soft feather bed,
   The feather was white and downy,
 Tonight you'll sleep on the cold damp ground
   And the wolves'll howl all round you,
   And the wolves'll howl all round you.

10. Last night I slept on a soft feather bed,
   The feather was white and downy,
 Tonight I'll sleep on the cold damp ground,
   With the Davy's arms around me,
   With the Davy's arms around me.

11. He mounted on his iron-gray horse,
   That was so young and gaily,
 He rode back to rock his babes
   And dream of his lady,
   And dream of his lady.

117. "Black Jack David"

Sung by John Pennington, Fayetteville, Ark., July 20, 1954. LC/AAFS, rec. No. 11,894(B7). Collected by Mary Celestia Parler.

p π^1

1. Now the Black Jack David come riding through the plains,
   He sings so loud and merry,
 That he made the green woods around him ring,
   And he charmed the heart of a lady,
   And he charmed the heart of a lady.

2. How old are you, my pretty little Miss,
   How old are you, my honey?
 She answered him most modestly,
   I'll be seventeen next Monday,
   I'll be seventeen next Monday.

3. Come and go with me, my pretty little Miss,
   Come and go with me, my honey.
 I'll swear by the sword that hangs to my side
   That you never will need for money,
   That you never will need for money.

4. The old landlord came home that night
   Inquiring of his lady.
 He soon found out from the waiting-maid,
   She's gone with Black Jack David,
   She's gone with Black Jack David.

5. Go saddle up my milk-white horse,
   The one that runs so speedy.
 I'll ride all day and I'll ride all night,
   Or I'll overtake my lady,
   Or I'll overtake my lady.

6. He rode till he come till the ocean wide
   Where the waters look deep and muddy,
 He turned hisself in the valleys green
   And there he spied his lady,
   And there he spied his lady.

7. O how can you leave your house and land,
   And how can you leave your Mommy?
 And how can you leave your tender little babe,
   And go with Black Jack David,
   And go with Black Jack David?

8. I do not care for my house and land
   I do not care for my money,
 I do not care for my tender little babe,
   I'll go with Black Jack David,
   I'll go with Black Jack David.

9. O you pull off them high-heel'd shoes
   That is made out of Spanish leather,
 And reach to me your lily-white hand,
   And bid me farewell for ever,
   And bid me farewell for ever.

10. And she pulled off her high-heeled shoes
   That was made out of Spanish leather,
 And she reached to him her lily-white hand,
   And they both rode off together.

118. "Black Jack Davy"

Perry, 1938, p. 298. Sung by Fred and Hildra Stout, Buck Mountain, Bitter End, Tenn.

p π¹

Black Jack Davy came a-singing through the woods
 A-singing so loud and merry
That he made the green hills all around him ring
 For he charmed the heart of a lady
 He charmed the heart of a lady.

119. "Black Eyed Davy"

Brown MSS., 16 a 4 J. Also in Schinhan, *Music, Brown Collection*, IV, 1957, p. 87(D1). Sung by Mrs. N. T. Byers.

p I/M

How old are you my pretty Polly
How old are you my honey
She answered him most modestly
I'm between sixteen and twenty
I'm between sixteen and twenty.

120. "Black Jack David"

Brown MSS., 16 a 4 J. Also in Schinhan, *Music, Brown Collection*, IV, 1957, p. 88(E1). Sung by Dr. I. G. Greer. Collected by C. Alphonso Smith and Thomas Smith, n.d. Another copy, unidentified in Brown MSS., 16 a 4 J, nearly identical with this, probably also from Dr. Greer.

p I/M

Four stanzas not preserved with tune. The full text of this singer is given as follows in Belden and Hudson, *Folk Ballads, Brown Collection*, II, 1952, p. 165(E):

1. Black Jack David come ridin' through the woods,
 Singin' so loud and merry
 That the green hills all around him ring,
 And he charmed the heart of a lady,
 And he charmed the heart of a lady.

2. 'How old are you, my pretty little miss,
 How old are you, my lady?'
 She answered him with a 'tee, hee, hee,
 I'll be sixteen next summer.'

3. 'Come, go with me, my pretty little miss,
 Come, go with me, my lady;
 I'll take you across the deep blue sea
 Where you never shall want for money.

4. 'Won't you pull off those high heel shoes
 All made of Spanish leather;
 Won't you put on some low heel shoes?
 And we'll ride off together.'

5. She soon pulled off those high heeled shoes
 All made of Spanish leather;
 She put on those low heeled shoes
 And they rode off together.

6. 'Twas late at night when the land-lord come
 Inquirin' for his lady.
 He was posted by a fair young maid:
 'She's gone with Black Jack David.'

7. 'Go saddle me my noble steed,
 Go bridle me my derby;
 I'll ride to the east, I'll ride to the west,
 Or overtake my lady.'

8. He rode till he came to the deep below;
 The stream was deep and muddy.
 Tears came tricklin' down his cheeks,
 For there he spied his lady.

9. 'How can you leave your house and land,
 How can you leave your baby,
 How can you leave your husband dear
 To go with Black Jack David?'

10. 'Very well can I leave my house and land,
 Very well can I leave my baby,
 Much better can I leave my husband dear
 To go with Black Jack David.

11. 'I won't come back to you, my love,
 Nor I won't come back, my husband;
 I wouldn't give a kiss from David's lips
 For all your land and money.

12. 'Last night I lay on a feather bed
 Beside my husband and baby;
 Tonight I lay on the cold damp ground
 Beside the Black Jack David.'

13. She soon run through her gay clothing,
 Her velvet shoes and stockings;
 Her gold ring off her finger was gone,
 And the gold plate off her bosom.

14. 'Oh, once I had a house and land,
 A feather bed and money,
 But now I've come to an old straw pad,
 With nothing but Black Jack David.'

121. "Gypsy Davy"

Barry, *JAF*, XVIII (1905), p. 192(C). Sung by Miss Maria L. Johnson, Lynn, Mass., September 5, 1904. Learned in Swansea, Mass., 50 years before.

p π^1

The Gypsy came riding o'er the field,
The Gypsy he sang gaily,
He sang till he made the merry woods ring,
And he charmed the heart of the lady.
Ally ally ding, ally ding, ally da-day,
Ally ally ding, ally da-day.

So when the master he came home,
Inquiring for his lady,
The servants made him this reply,—
"She's gone with the Gypsy Davy."

"Now bring me here my good black horse,
The brown one he is lazy,
For I will neither eat nor drink (sleep)
Till I overtake my lady."

122. "Black Jack Davie"

McIntosh, 1935, p. 18. Also in McIntosh, *JAF*, XLVIII (1935), p. 385. Sung by Louise Southall, Johnston City, Ill., 1933.

p π^1

1. Black Jack Davie came ridin' through the plain.
He sang so loud and clearly
He made the green-wood around him sing,
To charm the heart of a lady,
To charm the heart of a lady.

2. "How old are you, my pretty little Miss?
How old are you, my honey?"
She made him an answer, with a hug and a kiss.
"I'll be sixteen next Sunday,
I'll be sixteen next Sunday."

3. "Will you go with me, my pretty little Miss?
Will you go with me, my honey?
I'll swear by the sword that hangs by my side
You never shall want for money,
You never shall want for money."

4. She took off her high-heeled shoes
All made of Spanish leather.
She put on her low-heeled shoes,
And they rode off together,
And they rode off together.

5. The landlord he came home at night
Inquiring for his lady.
The chamber maid made this reply,
"She's gone with Black Jack Davie,
She's gone with Black Jack Davie."

6. "Go bridle and saddle my little yellow mare;
The grey one's not so speedy.
I've rode all day, and I'll ride all night
So that I'll overtake my lady,
So that I'll overtake my lady."

7. He rode till he came to the dark blue sea;
It looked so dark and dreary,
And there he spied his own, dear bride
By the side of Black Jack Davie,
By the side of Black Jack Davie.

8. "Will you forsake your house and home?
Will you forsake your baby?
Will you forsake your own married love,
And go with Black Jack Davie?
And go with Black Jack Davie?"

9. She took off her sky blue gloves,
All made of Spanish leather.
She bade him farewell with her lily white hand,
She said farewell forever,
She said farewell forever.

123. "Gypsy Davy"

Sung by Mrs. May Kennedy McCord, Springfield, Mo., October 21, 1941. LC/AAFS, rec. No. 5303(A1). Also in Randolph, I, 1946, p. 158(G). Collected by Vance Randolph.

m I/Ly, sometimes ending on the octave

1. Gypsy̆ Davy come ridin' around,
He sang so loud and lovely,
He swung his bugle around his waist,
As he charmed the heart of a lady
As he charmed the heart of a lady.

2. Come, go with me, my pretty fine Miss,
   Come, go with me, my Honey,
Come, go with me, my pretty fine Miss,
   You shall never want for money,
   You shall never want for money.

3. She put on her high-heeled shoes
   All made of Spanish leather,
And he put on his old cork boots,
   And they both rode off together,
   And they both rode off together.

4. Her husband he come home that night
   Inquiring for his lady,
He was informed by a pretty fair miss,
   She's gone with the Gypsȳ Davy,
   She's gone with the Gypsȳ Davy.

5. Go saddle me up my blonde-ale horse
   And bring to me my flagons,
I'll ride to the East and I'll ride to the West
   Till I overtake my lady,
   Till I overtake my lady.

6. Oh he rode till he came to the banks of the sea,
   The sea was dark and muddy.
The tears came pouring down his cheeks
   For there he spied his honey,
   For there he spied his honey.

7. Will you forsake your babe, he cried,
   Will you forsake your baby?
Will you forsake your husband, too,
   To go with the Gypsȳ Davy,
   To go with the Gypsȳ Davy.

8. Yes, I'll forsake my home,
   And I'll forsake my baby,
And I'll forsake my husband, too,
   (For) I love the Gypsȳ Davy,
   (For) I love the Gypsȳ Davy.

9. Last night you slept on a fair white bed,
   Between me and your baby:
Tonight you'll be sleeping on the cold cold ground,
   Forever with the Gypsȳ Davy,
   Forever with the Gypsȳ Davy.

124. "Gypsy Davy"

Owens, 1950, p. 48.

p π^1

1. Gypsy Davy come a-riding around,
He sang so loud and lovely;
He hung his bugle around his waist
'Til he charmed the heart of a lady;
'Til he charmed the heart of a lady.

2. "Come go with me, my pretty fine miss,
Come go with me, my honey;
Come go with me, my pretty fine miss,
You shall never want for money;
You shall never want for money."

3. She put on her fine new Sunday shoes
All made of Spanish leather;
He put on his old cork boots,
And they both rode off together;
And they both rode off together.

4. Her husband he came home that night
Inquiring for his lady;
He was informed by a pretty fair maid,
"She's gone with the Gypsy Davy;
She's gone with the Gypsy Davy."

5. "Go saddle me up my blondale horse
And hand me down my flagon;
I'll ride to the east and I'll ride to the west
'Til I overtake my lady;
'Til I overtake my lady."

6. He rode till he came to the banks of the stream,
The sea was dark and muddy;
The tears came a-rolling down his cheeks,
For there he spied his honey.
For there he spied his honey.

7. "Will you forsake your home," he cried,
"Will you forsake your baby?
Will you forsake your husband, too,
To go with the Gypsy Davy;
To go with the Gypsy Davy?"

8. "Yes, I'll forsake my home," she cried,
"And I'll forsake my baby,
And I'll forsake my husband, too,
To go with the Gypsy Davy;
To go with the Gypsy Davy."

9. "Last night you slept on a fair white bed
Between me and your baby;
Tonight you're a-sleepin' on the cold, cold ground,
A-sleeping with the Gypsy Davy;
A-sleeping with the Gypsy Davy."

This and the preceding variant are suspiciously alike.

125. [Gypsy Davy]

Henry [1938], p. 110. Sung by Mrs. Samuel Harmon, Cade's Cove, Tenn., August 12, 1930.

p π^1 (–VI)

1. Black Jack Davy came a-singing through the woods
And he sang so loud and merry
Till he charmed the heart of a lady,
Till he charmed the heart of a lady.

2. "How old are you, my pretty little miss?
How old are you, my honey?"
She answered me quite modestly:
"I'll be sixteen next Sunday,
I'll be sixteen next Sunday."

3. "Oh, come, go with me, my pretty little miss,
Come, go with me, my honey;
Come, go with me, my pretty little miss,
And you never will lack for money,
And you never will lack for money.

4. "Well, you'd better leave your house and land,
You'd better leave your baby;
You'd better leave your own landlord
And go with Black Jack Davy,
And go with Black Jack Davy."

5. She put on her high-heel shoes
All made of Spanish leather
And then she kissed her sweet little babe
And then they parted forever,
And then they parted forever.

6. The landlord he came home
Late in the evening
Enquiring for his lady,
Enquiring for his lady.

7. The servant then
She answered him:
"She's gone with Black Jack Davy,
She's gone with Black Jack Davy."

8. "You go, saddle me the milk white speed [*sic*];
The old mare she's not able;
I'll ride till I come to the deep blue sea
Or I'll overtake my lady,
Or I'll overtake my lady.

9. "Have you forsaked your house and land?
Have you forsaked your baby?
Have you forsaked your own true love
And gone with Black Jack Davy,
And gone with Black Jack Davy?"

10. "Yes, I forsaked my house and land;
Yes, I forsaked my baby;
Yes, I forsaked my own landlord
And gone with Black Jack Davy,
And gone with Black Jack Davy."

11. "You pull off those fine, finger gloves
That's made of Spanish leather
And give to me your lily white hand
And we will part forever,
And we will part forever."

12. She pulled off her fine, finger gloves
All made of Spanish leather;
She gave to him her lily white hand
And they were parted forever,
And they were parted forever.

13. "Last night I lay in a fine feather bed
Besides my husband and baby;
But now I lay on the cold, cold ground
With nothing but Black Jack Davy,
With nothing but Black Jack Davy."

126. "Black Jack Davy"

Scarborough, 1937, p. 412(B); text, p. 218. Sung by Selma Clubb, South Turkey Creek, Leicester, N.C., c. 1932.

p π^1

See variant 4 above for a re-creation by oral transmission and traditional recollection of Selma Clubb's ballad.

1. Black Jack Davy came through the woods,
Singing loud and merry.
Till he made the green hills all round him ring,
He charmed the heart of a lady,
He charmed the heart of a lady.

2. How old are you, my pretty little miss?
How old are you, my honey?
She answered him with a tee-hee-hee,
I'll be sixteen next Sunday,
I'll be sixteen next Sunday.

3. Come ride with me, my pretty little miss,
Come ride with me, my honey.
I'll take you across the dark blue sea
And you shall never want for money,
And you shall never want for money.

4. She pulled on her high-heeled slippers,
Made of Spanish leather,
And he pulled on his old cork boots
And they both rode off together,
And they both rode off together.

5. Go bring me out my one-horned steer,
Go bring me out my derby;
I'll ride to the east, I'll ride to the west
Till I overtake my darling,
Till I overtake my darling.

6. He rode east and he rode west,
The way grew dark and weary,
And there he spied his own true love
Beside the Black Jack Davy,
Beside the Black Jack Davy.

7. Have you forsaken your house and home?
Have you forsaken your baby?
Have you forsaken your husband dear
And gone with a Black Jack Davy?
And gone with a Black Jack Davy?

8. Yes, I have forsaken my house and home,
   And I've forsaken my baby,
   And I have forsaken my husband dear
   And gone with a Black Jack Davy,
   And gone with a Black Jack Davy.

9. Last night I slept on a feather bed
   Beside my husband and baby,
   But tonight I sleep on the cold, cold ground
   Beside of the Black Jack Davy,
   Beside of the Black Jack Davy.

APPENDIX C

127. "Gypsy Davy"

Barry MSS., IV, No. 189. Sung by Mrs. Anna W. Longee, Thornton, N.H., October 25, 1908. Learned from her aunt 50 years before.

p I

This and the following variant illustrate the pitfalls that lie in wait for the folk memory.

The gypsy he came tripping o'er the plain
Sang so loud and sweetly
Sang so loud by the merry merry woods,
That he charmed the heart of the Lady.

Addy addy dum dum diddle iddy dum dum
Addy addy dum dum Davy
Addy addy dum dum diddle iddy dum dum
Addy addy dum dum Davy.

128. "Harrison Brady"

Korson, 1949, p. 52. Sung by Lily Bell Dietrick, Morgantown, W.Va., 1944. Recorded by Samuel P. Bayard.

p I

1. Go harness up my milk-white steed,
   My bonny brown is not so speedy;
   I'll ride all night and I'll ride all day
   Till I overtake my lady.

2. He rode as far as Pittsburgh, O,
   And there he spied his lady;
   With one arm around her baby, O,
   And the other around her Brady.

3. Oh, why did you leave your husband dear,
   Oh, why did you leave your baby,
   Oh, why did you leave your pretty little home
   To roam with Harrison Brady?

4. I never loved you in my life,
   I never loved your baby;
   I married you against my will,
   And I'll roam with Harrison Brady.

5. Last night I slept in my downy bed,
   And in my arms my baby;
   Tonight I'll sleep in the Pittsburgh jail
   In the arms of Harrison Brady!

Bessy Bell and Mary Gray

CHILD NO. 201

THE historico-legendary event that gave rise to this fragmentary song would appear to assign its earliest commencement to the year 1645 or '46. But, as Child failed to observe, or thought not worth noting, there was a song with the title "Bessy Bell" in existence as early as 1629, in which year, on June 22, Martin Parker's "Fourepence halfepenney Farthing," to be sung to that tune, was licensed to Francis Grove (Pepys Ballads, I, f. 274; reprinted Hyder Rollins, *A Pepysian Garland*, 1922, pp. 323ff.). An alternative tune named for Parker's ballad is "A Health to Betty," and it could be surmised that the two names referred to the same song. I believe that they did not: the currency of a new ballad could be increased by naming more than one familiar tune to which it would go. "A Health to Betty" is preserved as a country dance tune in Playford's *English Dancing Master* (1651 and subsequently) and was used over and over again with new sets of words, for more than a century (cf. Chappell, *Popular Music* [1855-59], I, pp. 366-67; D'Urfey, *Pills*, 1719-20, II, p. 110; etc.). It does not resemble the tune of "Bessy Bell," which also recurs throughout the eighteenth century, both with Allan Ramsay's words and, with new ones, in a number of ballad operas (*The Beggar's Opera*, 1728; *The Highland Fair*, 1731; *The Mock Doctor*, 2nd ed., 1732; *An Old Man Taught Wisdom*, 1735; *The Plot*, 1735). Presumptive evidence that the "Bessy Bell" named in 1629 was the same *tune* as that later sung under that title lies in the fact that Parker's words fit the tune so well. His internal rhyme in every other line brings out the rocking motion of the tune, of which the first and third phrases of the first strain fall into echoing halves; and his second and fourth lines have the feminine cadence which is so characteristic a feature of the tune. His stanzas are for a double-strain tune, as the refrain at every stanza's end makes clear, in spite of the print's breaking the third and seventh lines into two short rhyming lines. It should be observed that Parker's ballad goes only with effort to the alternative tune of "A Health to Betty." One may also call attention to "The London Gentleman," or "The Hemp-Dresser," in Playford's *English Dancing Master*, 1651 (ed. Dean-Smith, 1957, p. 50), as evidence that "Bessy Bell" is sib to English country dance tunes. The first extant appearance of the tune is thought to be in the Guthrie MS., c. 1675-80; the next in Henry Playford's *Original Scots Tunes*, 1700 ("Bess Bell"); subsequently in Ramsay's *Musick* for the *Tea-Table Miscellany*, c. 1726; Thomson's *Orpheus Caledonius* [1725] and 1733; Watt's *Musical Miscellany*, 1729, I, p. 158, and often thereafter.

The Guthrie version, as transcribed from tablature by Nellie Diem, is a plagal major, while most of the later versions that I have seen, from *Orpheus Caledonius* onward, are Mixolydian variants. (*The Beggar's Opera* copy is an exception.) There is very little difference among these later copies, except in degree of editorial ornamentation, and it would appear that no traditional variants were picked up in the record of the eighteenth or nineteenth century.

The tune which Greig collected at the opening of the present century is by bare possibility an ill-recollected variation of the old tune, but few readers will see any relation. It is a plagal tune, and may have been slightly influenced by "Green grow the rashes O"—which the mention of *rashes* in the text would have encouraged. The singer, Mrs. Gillespie, said that she had heard the song sung also to that tune. Her tune for "Bessy Bell" (variant 5 below) is less attractive by far than the earlier one, but much more characteristically traditional, and has the look of being worn down to a repetitive burden. It may be thought more in keeping with the melancholy text.

In the nineteenth century, if not before, the song came to rest—or the contrary?—in the nursery. Since the story had already disappeared in Ramsay's *rifacimento*, and since there was little chance that his added stanzas would appeal to the folk memory, it was not unnatural that something ludicrous should be tagged to the traditional first stanza by way of conclusion. Child has printed this nursery text from Halliwell (*Nursery Rhymes of England*, 1874, No. 484, p. 246). It seems to have had some circulation in print, both in Britain and in America. Two tunes have been preserved, one from Scottish tradition, the other from Maine, also probably Scottish. The first is plagal, I/Ly, and could more easily have grown out of the old tune than could Mrs. Gillespie's, through insensitive repetition. But it has pretty clearly been strongly influenced by "Comin' thro' the Rye."* The other is in common time, but with the held third beat which is so likely among folk singers to break over into 3/4 by a slight additional prolongation. It is a single-strain, major plagal tune, of little distinction (variant 7 below).

A word of comment may be ventured on the ancient text, in so far as it has survived. Its compressed and condensed state gives it the air—which it may very well have lacked in a fuller form—of a sardonic commentary, like the "Twa Corbies," upon the chances of worldly pride. Walter Scott, however, found it the repository, "to a Scottish ear, of much tenderness and simplicity" (*Poetical Works*, 1833-34, I, p. 45). One may wonder if he was not to some extent reading into the song feelings that were derived from the local tradition which he so tenderly relates. Child's cautious remarks deserve to be pondered before we let our tears flow uncontrolled. The lover, he says, "who ought to have had his place in the song, appears only in [prose] tradition, and his reality [i.e., assuming the ladies to have been historical] may be called in question. It is not rational that the young women should seclude themselves to avoid the pest and then take the risk of the visits of a person from the seat of the infection. To be sure it may be doubted, notwithstanding the tenor of the ballad, whether the retirement of these young ladies was voluntary, or at least whether they had not taken the plague before they removed to their bower. In that case the risk would have been for the lover, and would have been no more than he might naturally assume" (1882-98, IV, p. 76). Child quotes close historical analogies in support of the last, more ingratiating and pathetic, hypothesis; and we may readily grant that it would have improved the narrative element of the ballad. As it is, we may wonder at the incalculable chances of tradition, which have kept such a fragment alive for so long a time. It is another demonstration of the fact that the lifeblood of traditional balladry does not lie in the story alone.

* Copyright difficulties have forced the removal of this nursery version ("a" in the List of Variants).

201. BESSY BELL AND MARY GRAY

LIST OF VARIANTS

GROUP A

1. "Bessie Bell." Guthrie MS. [1675-80], fol. 4, Edinburgh University Library; transcribed in Nellie Diem, *Beitrage zur Geschichte der Schottischen Musik in XVII Jahrhundert,* 1919, p. 155.
2. "Bessie Bell." W. Thomson, *Orpheus Caledonius* [1725], fol. 2.
3. "Bessy Bell & Mary Grey." Allan Ramsay, *Musick for Allan Ramsay's Collection of Scots Songs*, c. 1726, Pt. 5, p. 106.
4. "Bessy Bell." W. Thomson, *Orpheus Caledonius*, 1733, I, opp. p. 3. Also in James Johnson, *The Scots Musical Museum*, II [1788], No. 128, p. 134 (repr. 1853); Robert Archibald Smith, *The Scotish Minstrel* [1820-24], IV, p. 21; G. F. Graham, *The Songs of Scotland*, 1848-49, II, p. 96; and Robert Maver, *Genuine Scottish Melodies*, 1866, No. 68, p. 34.

GROUP Ba

5. "Bessy Bell and Mary Gray." Gavin Greig and Alexander Keith, *Last Leaves of Traditional Ballads and Ballad Airs*, 1925, p. 130. From Duncan MS., No. 474. (Gillespie)
6. "Bessie Bell and Mary Gray." Ewan MacColl, Riverside recording No. RLP 12-628(A3), *The English and Scottish Popular Ballads*, IV, ed. Kenneth S. Goldstein.

GROUP Bb

a. "Bessie Bell and Mary Gray." Alfred Moffat, *Fifty Traditional Scottish Nursery Rhymes* [1933], p. 3.

GROUP C

7. "Bessie Bell and Mary Lee." Phillips Barry, Fannie H. Eckstorm, and Mary W. Smyth, *British Ballads from Maine*, 1929, p. 279(B). (Young)

TUNES WITH TEXTS

GROUP A

1. "Bessie Bell"

Guthrie MS. [1675-80], fol. 4; transcribed in Diem, 1919, p. 155.

a I, ending on 3

2. "Bessie Bell"

Thomson [1725], fol. 2.

a M, ending on 3

3. "Bessy Bell & Mary Grey"

Ramsay, c. 1726, pt. 5, p. 106. Text from Ramsay's *Tea-Table Miscellany*, ed. of 1871, II, p. 54.

a M

O Bessy Bell and Mary Gray,
They are twa bonny lassies,
They bigg'd a bow'r on yon burn-brae,
And theek'd it o'er wi' rashes.
Fair Bessy Bell I loo'd yestreen,
And thought I ne'er could alter;
But Mary Gray's twa pawky een,
They gar my fancy falter.

[*Etc.*]

4. "Bessy Bell"

Thomson, 1733, I, opp. p. 3. Also in Johnson, II [1788], No. 128, p. 134 (repr. 1853); Smith [1820-24], IV, p. 21; and Graham, 1848-49, II, p. 96; and Maver, 1866, No. 68, p. 34.

a M, ending on 3

O Bessy Bell and Mary Gray,
They are twa bonny Lasses,
They bigg'd a Bower on yon Burn-brae,
And theek'd it o'er wi' rashes.
[Fair Bessy Bell I loo'd yestreen,
And thought I ne'er cou'd alter;
But Mary Gray's twa pawky Een,
They gar my Fancy falter.

Now Bessy's Hair's like a Lint-tap;
She smiles like a May Morning,
When Phoebus starts frae Thetis' Lap,
The Hills with Rays adorning:
White is her Neck, saft is her Hand,
Her waste and Feet's fu' genty;
With ilka Grace she can command;
Her Lips, O wow! they're dainty.

And Mary's Locks are like the Craw,
Her Een like Diamonds glances;
She's ay sae clean, redd up and braw,
She kills whene'er she dances:
Blyth as a Kid, with Wit at will,
She blooming tight and tall is;
And guides her Airs sae gracefu' still,
O Jove! she's like thy Pallas.

Dear Bessy Bell and Mary Gray,
Ye unco sair oppress us;
Our Fancies jee between you twa
Ye are sic bonny Lasses;
Wae's me! for baith I canna get,
To ane by Law we're stented;
Then I'll draw Cuts, and take my Fate,
And be with ane contented.]

[Bracketed text by Allan Ramsay.]

GROUP Ba

5. "Bessy Bell and Mary Gray"

Greig and Keith, 1925, p. 130; from Duncan MS., No. 474. Sung by Mrs. Gillespie.

a π^4, ending on V

Bessie Bell an' Mary Gray
They were twa bonnie lasses,
They biggit their boo'r on yon burnside,
An' thickit it owre wi rashes.

6. "Bessie Bell and Mary Gray"

Sung by Ewan MacColl, Riverside rec. No. RLP 12-628 (A3), ed. K. S. Goldstein. Learned from Margaret Logan, Corsham, Wiltshire.

a D/Æ, ending on V

Bessie Bell and Mary Gray,
They were twa bonnie lasses,
They biggit their bower on yon burnside,
And thackit it ower wi' rushes.

GROUP C

7. "Bessie Bell and Mary Lee"

Barry, Eckstorm, and Smyth, 1929, p. 279(B). From Mrs. Susie Carr Young of Brewer, Me., October 30, 1928; learned from her mother.

p I

Bessie Bell and Mary Lee,
They were two bonnie lasses,
They built a house upon the lea,
And covered it with rushes.

Bessie lived at garden gate,
While Mary lived at pantry:
And Bessie always had to wait,
While Mary lived in plenty.

The Battle of Philiphaugh

CHILD NO. 202

This ballad has not been recovered by anyone, so far as I have learned, save Walter Scott, who got it from "tradition in Selkirkshire." I am therefore unable to explain the supposed existence in the Bunyan MS., 1877, p. 34, of a tune, since Scott was unable to read music and nowhere mentions having acquired a tune. The claim for the Bunyan MS. is made in the Gray-Muir MS., NL Scotland MS. 2254.

The Baron of Brackley

CHILD NO. 203

Of this excellent ballad, the records, verbal and musical, are very scanty. It seems not to have achieved more than a regional currency; but at least we are spared the spectacle of dilapidation that too often discomfits us in these walks.

The two tunes which are preserved have little in common, but perhaps enough, in metre and melodic contour, to relate them to a single family. (Miss Gordon's tune surely derives from Christie's.) Christie's tune dates, he says, from about 1816 in Buchan tradition, and was "arranged"—whatever that may mean—by his father. In this case, at least, it is unlikely that the second half of the tune was invented by the editor. It is, properly regarded, not a two-strain tune, but is composed, like other dactylic or anapaestic ballad-tunes, of four long phrases. There may be some distant kinship, most marked in the final cadence, between this and "Hay Tutti Taiti." There would be no doubt that the final is tonic, were it not that the Lady John Scott tune raises a query whether the second which ends the first phrase of Christie's tune might not have been the earlier tonic. Such a decision would throw both tunes into the same modal region, since the other has an Æolian cast. But Lady Scott's can be taken as pure major in its first three phrases: it is only the last phrase that is Æolian. So that, conversely, the π^2 character of Christie's tune as it stands may be thought closer to the modal norm than would be π^4, the other possibility. Lady Scott's tune may remind some readers of Sharp's Somerset tune, "O Sally, my dear" (Cecil J. Sharp and Charles L. Marson, *Folk Songs from Somerset*, 3rd series, 1906, p. 60; *ante*, I, p. 353). Where she got it has not been ascertained. Comparison may also be made with some of the tunes for "Queen Jane" (No. 170).

LIST OF VARIANTS

GROUP Aa

1. "The Baron of Brackley." W. Christie, *Traditional Ballad Airs*, I, 1876, p. 20.
2. "The Baron of Brackley." Miss M. Douglas Gordon (singer), Archive, School of Scottish Studies, University of Edinburgh.

GROUP Ab

3. "The Baron of Brackley." Lady John Scott's MS., National Library of Scotland MS. 840.

TUNES WITH TEXTS

GROUP Aa

1. "The Baron of Brackley"

Christie, I, 1876, p. 20. Obtained by Christie's father, c. 1816, from tradition in Buchan.

a π^2 (or π^4, ending on *VII*)

Down Dee side came Inverey, whistling and playing,
He's lighted at Brackley yates at the day dawing.
Says, "Baron o' Brackley, O are ye within?
There's sharp swords at the yate will gar your blood spin."
[*Etc.*]

Christie "epitomizes" his text from Jamieson's *Popular Ballads*, 1806, I, p. 102.

2. "The Baron of Brackley"

Archive, School of Scottish Studies. Sung by Miss M. Douglas Gordon, 1953. Collected by Francis M. Collinson for the School of Scottish Studies. Transcribed by the collector.

a π^2

1. Doon Deeside cam Inverey,
   A-whistlin and singin,
And lighted at Braikley's yetts
   When the day was dawin.
O braw Lord Braikley,
   O are ye within—
There's sharp swords at your yett
   Will gar your bluid spin.

2. Now rise up, my Baron,
   And turn back your kye,
For the lads o' Drumwharron
   Are driving them by.
O how can I rise up,
   And how can I gang,
For when I hae ae man
   I wat they hae ten.

3. Now rise up my lassies,
   Tak your rocks in your hands,
And turn back the kye—
   I hae you at command.
Gin I had a husband
   As it seems I hae nane,
He wadnae lie in bed
   And see his kye taen.

4. Now kiss me, my lady,
   Nor think I'm to blame;
I well may rin oot,
   But I'll never win hame.
When Braikley was buskit
   And leapt on his horse,
A bonnier Baron
   Ne'er rade o'er a close.

5. There came wi' Inverey
   Full thirty and three,
But wi' Braikley was nane
   But his brither and he.
Two gallanter Gordons
   Did never sword draw,
But against four and thirty
   Wae's me, what is twa?

6. Wi' sword and wi' dirk
   They did him surround,
And they pierced bonny Braikley
   Wi' mony a wound.
From the head o' the Dee
   To the banks o' the Spey,
The Gordons may mourn him
   And curse Inverey.

7. O cam ye by Braikley yetts,
   Or went ye in there—
And saw ye his lady
   A-rivin her hair?
O I cam by Braikley yetts
   And I went in there,
And I saw his lady
   A-making good cheer.

8. She leuch wi' them and drank wi' them
   And welcomed them ben;
She showed them the way
   Where they wouldna be taen.
O there's wae in the kitchen
   And mirth in the ha'
But the Baron o' Braikley
   Is dead and awa.

GROUP Ab

3. "The Baron of Brackley"

Lady John Scott MS., NL Scotland MS. 840.

a Æ

1. Inverey cam down Dee side whistling and playing
He lighted at Brackley yetts, ere the day-dawing
Cries Baron o Brackley are ye within?
There's sharp swords at your yett will gar yer blude spare.

2. His Ladye she rose to the window she went
She heard her Kye lowing over hill and over bent
She cried, rise up then Brackley and turn back yer Kye
For the Lads o' Dumwharran are driving them bye.

3. Theres sheep in the aitneuk [?Etnach] an' goats on the brae
An' a' will be harried by young Inverey
Rise up, Rise up Brackley an' be not afraid
They are but herd-wuddifas [?hir'd widdifus] wi' kilted plaids.—

4. How can I [?gae out] and turn them again
Where'er I hae ae man I wot they hae ten
Then rise up my maidens tak rokes in your hand
An turn back the kye I hae you at command.

5. Gin' I had ae husband as it seems I hae nane
He wadna bide in the bower an see his kye taen.
Then up raise the Baron and cried for his graith
Saying, Ladye I'll gang tho' to leave thee I'm laith.

6. Oh kiss me my ladye and gie me my spear
I aye was for peace tho I never feared war
Farewell then my ladye, nor think me to blame
I weel may gae out but I'll never come hame.

7. When Brackley was busket & strode thro' the close
A gallanter baron neer sprang on a horse
When Brackley was mounted an rode o'er the green
He was as bauld a baron as ever was seen.

8. Tho' there cam' wi fause Inverey thirty & three
There was nane wi Bonnie Brackley but his Brother & he
Twa gallanter Gordons did never sword draw
But against four & thirty wae's me—what are twa?

9. At the head of the aitneuk [?Etnach] the Battle began
At little Aquhulzie they killed the first man
First they killed ane and syne they killed twa
And they killed Bonnie Brackley the flower o' them a'—

10. Wi swords and wi daggers they did him surround
An' they've pierced Bonnie Brackley wi' mony a wound
Frae the head o' the dee to the banks of the Spey
The Gordons may mourn him and curse Inverey.

11. Oh! cam ye by Brackley yetts were ye in there
Saw ye his ladye dear reiving her hair
Oh I cam by Brackley yetts I was in there
An' I saw his ladie dear making good cheer

12. That ladye she feasted them carried them ben[?]
She laughed wi' the men that her Baron had slain
She kept them till evening she bade them be gane
An' shewed them the road that she [*sc.* they?] might na be ta'en

13. Through Birse and Aboyne she says hie ye [?attour]
Over the hills o' Glentanner ye'll ride in an hour
Theres grief in the kitchen theres mirth in the ha'
For the Baron o' Brackley is dead and awa'.

Jamie Douglas

CHILD NO. 204

Child has reprinted as an appendix a broadside of late seventeenth- or early eighteenth-century date, called "Arthur's Seat Shall Be My Bed, etc.," or "Love in Despair." This is obviously a piece cobbled for print out of scraps of traditional song and invented stanzas. The first two stanzas are untraditional and serve ill as a prologue. The third has still less to do with the narrative and shifts the rhyme-scheme to couplets. The fourth is the true commencement, and starts with the title line. The fifth departs again from the narrative and drops again into couplets. Its first two lines are favorites in folk-song and are still current (cf. the ubiquitous "Died for Love"). The rest of this stanza and the next belong to some song about a jilted girl (or boy) who is defiant under the blow (cf. "Early, Early" and "Werena my heart licht I wad die"). The seventh stanza is again in couplets; but it and the next are a restatement of matter found in the song now to be mentioned.

Allan Ramsay was the first to publish the beautiful lament of a forsaken girl, "Waly, Waly, Gin Love be Bony" (*Tea-Table Miscellany*, c. 1724). This appears to be genuinely traditional stuff and may very probably antedate the song described above. Its fifth stanza is identical in all important respects with the "Arthur's Seat" stanza of the other, and its sixth and tenth stanzas with the tenth and eleventh of the other. As mentioned above, also, the seventh and eighth stanzas of the other correspond in matter to two stanzas, the seventh and fourth, of "Waly, Waly." It appears indeed quite probable that the broadside, although earlier in point of record, was made out of imperfect recollections of "Waly, Waly." As Child notes, the third stanza of "Waly" closely corresponds with a proverbial stanza in a MS. of about 1620, which appears again in a medley in the 1666 edition of Forbes' *Songs & Fancies*.

When Thomson printed "Waly, Waly" in *Orpheus Caledonius* in 1725, he introduced a stanza about cockle-shells and "siller" bells. This latter reappears in all but one of the fuller texts of our present ballad, "Jamie Douglas." The ballad-texts also usually make use, variously, of seven out of ten of the other stanzas printed by Ramsay as "Waly, Waly." Most texts, however, use no more than one or two of these stanzas.

The earliest text of "Jamie Douglas" to see print was a five-stanza fragment given by David Herd in *Ancient and Modern Scottish Songs*, 1776, I, p. 144, entitled only "Tune, Wally, wally up the bank." Now Herd also gives "Waly, Waly" in Ramsay's text, in the same volume (I, p. 81). It is interesting that there is no connection, other than in the titles, between these two texts of the ballad and the song. Herd includes in the ballad the cockle-shells stanza, but this, it will be recalled, was not in the Ramsay text of "Waly" (nor indeed in the "Arthur's Seat" broadside). What we have here is excellent evidence that "Jamie Douglas," in the second half of the eighteenth century, was sung to the tune of the better known song. Similar testimony is offered fifty years later than Herd by Motherwell (1827, App'x., p. xvii), who says that the ballad is often so sung, although he himself gives another tune.

Child says that the ballad "must date from the last quarter of the seventeenth century" (1882-98, IV, p. 92, note ‡). He may not have meant that it would have had to be made immediately after the events it purports to celebrate, but that, at least, would be a natural assumption. He points out that stanza eight of "Waly Waly," "When we came in by Glasgow town," hardly suits the song, but is quite fitting in the ballad, and suggests: "it may have been taken up from this ballad . . . or from some other" (*loc.cit.*).

It appears to me an entirely unwarranted inference that the song "Waly Waly," as R. Chambers declared (*Songs of Scotland Prior to Burns*, ed. of 1880, p. 280), and as G. F. Graham agreed (*Songs of Scotland*, 1848-49, I, p. 101), forms, without room for doubt, part of the ballad of "Jamie Douglas." There is, on the contrary, every reason to suppose that the makers of "Jamie Douglas," like the cobbler of "Arthur's Seat," made free use of a popular song to fill out their ballad, and sang the latter to the same tune. As counterweight for the inappropriate —but traditionally conventional—stanza about Glasgow town in the song, we may set the still less appropriate borrowing in most of the ballad-texts of the lament for lost maidenhood, and other touches befitting a deserted damsel, and quite unsuited to the Marchioness' married state. Her eldest son, the Earl of Angus, was in fact a promising lad of ten or more by the date of separation: in this light, her remarks look oddly unmaternal.

> But gin I had wist or I had kist
> That young man's love was sae ill to win,
> I would hae lockt my heart wi a key o gowd,
> And pinnd it wi a sillar pin.
>
> (Child F 3)

There is little doubt, then, as to which way the borrowing went, and we may suppose that the ballad was made with the tune of "Waly Waly" in mind and regularly sung to it. How old the tune may be I have no skill to say; but it was in print so early and so constantly that it has suffered little change from traditional transmission.

But the statement just made needs to be qualified. While it is true that the standard song books go back and re-establish the melody from early print (e.g., A. Moffat, *Minstrelsy of Scotland*, 2nd ed. [1896], p. 175), there are at least three copies of tunes for this song that appear to be distantly related. One is in R. A. Smith's *Scotish Minstrel* [1820-24], VI, p. 98 (variant 4), where a different text is given to "Waly Waly, Old Set." This has the Mixolydian cast, like the other, and a final phrase clearly resembling the other. But the melodic contour as a whole is quite different. Again, Baring-Gould picked up on Dartmoor a tune (variant 6) not in the least like "Waly Waly," but slightly akin to R. A. Smith's: its first phrase, for instance, is close to Smith's second. It is a major plagal tune in 4/4 time. It is barely possible that these are both traditional variants. Furthermore, Dean Christie's mother sang a version (variant 3) which, if we may trust the record after Christie had done "arranging," was quite different, but yet more recognizably related to "Waly Waly" than either Smith's or Baring-Gould's. This again is major, and authentic.

There remain to be mentioned two other quite beautiful tunes. One is the M/D setting which Motherwell printed for the ballad "Jamie Douglas" in 1827 (App'x., No. 9). This has no discernible relation with any form of the "Waly Waly" tune. The last is the haunting and lyrically free tune that Sandburg has found in this country, a plagal major set to the two stanzas, "cockle shells" and "love is bonny" (1927, p. 16). This melody appears to be a "sport," with no affiliations in tradition.

It may be added, finally, of the Greig variant (7 below), that it appears to be a nonce-borrowing of the tune associated with "Hind Horn" and other familiar songs (e.g., "Logan Water," G. F. Graham, *Songs of Scotland*, 1848-49, I, p. 70).

LIST OF VARIANTS

GROUP A

1. "Waly, Waly." W. Thomson, *Orpheus Caledonius*, 1733, I, opp. p. 71.
2. "O Waly, Waly." James Johnson, *The Scots Musical Museum*, II [1788], No. 158, p. 166; and V [1796], No. 446, p. 458 (repr. 1853). Also in Joseph Ritson, *Scotish Songs*, 1794, I, p. 156; George Thomson, *A Select Collection of Original Scotish Airs* [1803], I, p. 19; G. F. Graham, *The Songs of Scotland*, 1848-49, I, p. 100; John Goss, *Ballads of Britain*, 1937, p. 98(A); and elsewhere.
3. "Marchioness of Douglas." W. Christie, *Traditional Ballad Airs*, II, 1881, p. 158.
4. "Waly, Waly, Old Set." Robert Archibald Smith, *The Scotish Minstrel* [1820-24], VI, p. 98, and II, p. 1.

GROUP B

5. "Jamie Douglas." William Motherwell, *Minstrelsy: Ancient and Modern*, 1827, App'x., No. 9 and p. xvii.

APPENDIX

6. "A Ship Came Sailing." Sabine Baring-Gould, H. Fleetwood Sheppard, and F. W. Bussell, *Songs of the West*, 1905, p. 176.
7. (Untitled.) Greig MSS., I, p. 116, King's College Library, Aberdeen. (A.R.)
8. "Waillie, Waillie!" Carl Sandburg, *The American Songbag*, 1927, p. 16. Also in Goss, *Ballads of Britain*, 1937, p. 99(D).

TUNES WITH TEXTS

GROUP A

1. "Waly, Waly"

Thomson, 1733, I, opp. p. 71; less simply in [1725].

a I (inflected VII)

1. O Waly, Waly, up yon Bank,
    And Waly, Waly, down yon Brea;
   And Waly by yon River's side,
    Where my Love and I was wont to gae.

2. Waly, Waly, gin Love be bonny,
    A little while when it is new;
   But when it's auld, it waxes cauld,
    And wears away, like Morning Dew.

3. I leant my Back unto an Aik,
    I thought it was a trusty Tree;
   But first it bow'd, and sine it brake,
    And sae did my fause Love to me.

4. When Cockle-shells turn siller Bells,
    And Muscles grow on ev'ry Tree;
   When Frost and Snaw shall warm us a',
    Then shall my Love prove true to me.

5. Now *Arthur-Seat* shall be my Bed,
    The Sheets shall ne'er be fyl'd by me;
   Saint *Anton*'s Well shall be my Drink,
    Since my true Love has forsaken me.

6. O *Martinmas* Wind, when wilt thou blaw,
    And shake the green Leaves off the Tree?
   O gentle Death, when wilt thou come?
    And take a Life that wearies me.

7. 'Tis not the Frost that freezes fell,
    Nor blawing Snaw's Inclemency;
   'Tis not sic Cauld that makes me cry,
    But my Love's Heart grown cauld to me.

8. When we came in by *Glasgow* Town,
    We were a comely Sight to see;
   My Love was cled in the black Velvet,
    And I my sell in Cramasie.

9. But had I wist before I kiss'd,
    That Love had been sae ill to win;
   I'd lock'd my Heart in a Case of Gold,
    And pin'd it with a silver Pin.

10. Oh, oh! if my young Babe were born,
    And set upon the Nurse's Knee,
   And I my sell were dead and gane,
    For a Maid again I'll never be.

2. "O Waly, Waly"

Johnson, II [1788], No. 158, p. 166; and V [1796], No. 446, p. 458 (repr. 1853). Also in Ritson, 1794, I, p. 156; G. Thomson [1803], I, p. 19; Graham, 1848-49, I, p. 100; Goss, 1937, p. 98; and elsewhere.

a I (inflected VII)

The *Museum* text is substantially identical with Thomson's (variant 1).

O waly, waly, up yon bank!
And waly, waly, down yon brae!
And waly by yon river side,
Where I and my love wont to gae!
O waly, waly! love is bonnie,
A little while when it is new;
But when 'tis auld, it waxes cauld,
And wears awa like morning dew.

O wherefore should I busk my head?
O wherefore should I kame my hair?
For my fause love has me forsook,
And says he'll never loe me mair.
Now Arthur's seat shall be my bed,
The grey mist will my covering be;
Saint Anton's well shall be my drink,
Since my fause love's forsaken me.

'Tis not the frost that freezes fell,
Nor blawing snaw's inclemencie;
'Tis not sic cauld that makes me cry,
But my love's heart grown cauld to me.
O Mart'mas wind, when wilt thou blaw,
And shake the green leaves aff the tree?
O gentle death, when wilt thou come,
And tak a life that wearies me?

3. "Marchioness of Douglas"

Christie, II, 1881, p. 158. "Arranged" by Christie from his mother's singing.

a I (inflected VII)

"O waly, waly, up yon bank,
And waly, waly, doun yon brae;
And waly, waly, by yon burn-side,
Where I and my love wont to gae!
My mother tauld me, when I was young,
That young man's love was ill to trow;
But untill her I would give nae ear,
And, alas, my ain wand dings me now!"
[*Etc.*]

Christie's text is apparently abridged from that in Robert Chambers, *The Scottish Ballads*, 1829, p. 150.

4. "Waly, Waly, Old Set"

Smith [1820-24], VI, p. 98 ("I'll Lay Me on the Wintry Lea"); text, II, p. 1.

a M (inflected VII)

GROUP B

5. "Jamie Douglas"

Motherwell, 1827, App'x., No. 9; text, App'x., p. xvii. From A. Blaikie, Paisley.

a M/D (or a I/Ly, ending on II)

O come down stairs Jamie Douglas
O come down stairs and speak to me,
And I'll set thee in a fine chair of gowd
And I'll kindly daut thee upon my knee.

APPENDIX

6. "A Ship Came Sailing"

Baring-Gould, Sheppard, and Bussell, 1905, p. 176. From a Dartmoor singer.

p I

1. A ship came sailing over the sea
As deeply laden as she could be;
My sorrows fill me to the brim,
I care not if I sink or swim.

*2. Ten thousand ladies in the room,
But my true love's the fairest bloom,
Of stars she is my brightest sun,
I said I would have her or none,

3. I leaned my back against an oak,
But first it bent and then it broke,
Untrusty as I found that tree,
So did my love prove false to me.

4. Down in a mead the other day,
As carelessly I went my way,
And plucked flowers red and blue,
I little thought what love could do.

5. I saw a Rose with ruddy blush,
And thrust my hand into the bush,
I pricked my fingers to the bone,
I would I'd left that rose alone!

6. I wish! I wish! but 'tis in vain,
I wish I had my heart again!
With silver chain and diamond locks,
I'd fasten it in a golden box.

* "May be omitted in singing." [*Baring-Gould's note.*]

7. [Untitled]

Greig MSS., I, p. 116. Sung by A. R., New Deer, Aberdeenshire, February 1906.

m D/Æ

I leaned my back against an oak,
I thocht it was a trusty tree,
First it bent and then it broke,
And sae has my love done to me.

8. "Waillie, Waillie!"

Sandburg, 1927, p. 16. Also in Goss, 1937, p. 99(D).

p I

When cockle shells turn silver bells,
Then will my love return to me.
When roses blow, in wintry snow,
Then will my love return to me.
Oh, waillie! waillie!
But love is bonnie
A little while when it is new!
But it grows old and waxeth cold,
And fades away like evening dew.

Bothwell Bridge

CHILD NO. 206

Of the four tunes extant for this ballad, two are authentic, π^1, and nearly alike. The other two are respectively π^3 and Æolian; but the last gives such slight notice to the sixth as to be virtually D/Æ. The second strain, also, of the Æolian tune looks trumped up and artificial: the simpler π^3 tune looks genuine. This second pair is also closely related.

It is harder to decide whether the two pairs themselves have any kinship. If we reduce them all to the same metre, we are tempted to imagine the plagal form as a counterpart to the other pair. But to suppose such a development is, I believe, to argue a late and sophisticated origin; and it may be that the relation is fanciful and hypnotically induced by rhythmical similarities only. Lacking a more abundant supply of variants, we can reach no security, nor even determine which of the types has the greater weight of tradition behind it. To be sure the Blaikie copy looks rudest and most primitive: I have not discovered whence it came.

This ballad appears not to have been found by Greig, nor is it (as yet) in the archive of the School of Scottish Studies. There is said to be a copy of a tune (probably R. A. Smith's?) in the *Scottish Garland* (Turnbull and Buchan), 1840, p. 107. The reference comes from the Gray-Muir MS., NL Scotland MS. 2254.

Variants of the Smith tune occur also with the bothy song, "The Barnyards of Delgaty," for which see, e.g., Greig MSS., I, pp. 38-39; John Ord, *The Bothy Songs and Ballads*, 1930, p. 214.

LIST OF VARIANTS

GROUP A

1. "The Battle of Bothwell Brig." Robert Archibald Smith, *The Scottish Minstrel* [1820-24], III, p. 62.
2. "Earlistoun." Robert Chambers, *Twelve Romantic Scottish Ballads*, 1844, p. 26.

GROUP B

3. "Bonny Billie." Blaikie MS., National Library of Scotland MS. 1578, No. 54, p. 20.
4. "The Battle of Bothwell Brigg." Sir Walter Scott, *The Poetical Works of Sir Walter Scott*, 1833-34, II, opp. p. [246], and p. 237.

TUNES WITH TEXTS

GROUP A

1. "The Battle of Bothwell Brig"

Smith [1820-24], III, p. 62.

a π^1

Oh, Billy, Billy, bonny Billy,
Will ye gang to the wood wi' me?
We'll ca' our horse hame masterless,
And gar them trow slain men are we.
Oh no! oh no! says Earlistoun,
For that's the thing that canna be,
For I am sworn to Bothwell-hill,
And I maun either gae or die.
[*Etc.*]

The text is clearly taken from the *Minstrelsy*, for which see variant 4 (and Child 1882-98, IV, pp. 109-110).

2. "Earlistoun"

Chambers, 1844, p. 26. Tune from John Shortrede of Jedburgh.

a π^1

O billy, billy, bonnie billy,
Will ye gae to the woods wi' me?
We'll ca' our horse hame masterless,
And gar them trow slain men are we.

"Oh no, oh no," says Earlistoun,
"For that's the thing that may not be;
For I am sworn to Bothwell hill,
Where I maun either gae or die."

[*Etc.*]

Chambers' version follows that in Scott's *Minstrelsy*: see variant 4.

GROUP B

3. "Bonny Billie"

Blaikie MS., NL Scotland MS. 1578, No. 54, p. 20.

p π[3]

4. "The Battle of Bothwell Brigg"

Scott, 1833-34, II, opp. p. [246]; text, p. 237.

m Æ

1. "O, billie, billie, bonny billie,
   Will ye go to the wood wi' me?
We'll ca' our horse hame masterless,
   An' gar them trow slain men are we."—

2. "O no, O no!" says Earlstoun,
   "For that's the thing that mauna be;
For I am sworn to Bothwell Hill,
   Where I maun either gae or die."—

3. So Earlstoun rose in the morning,
   An' mounted by the break o' day;
An' he has joined our Scottish lads,
   As they were marching out the way.

4. "Now, farewell, father, and farewell, mother,
   And fare ye weel, my sisters three;
An' fare ye weel, my Earlstoun,
   For thee again I'll never see!"—

5. So they're awa' to Bothwell Hill,
   An' waly they rode bonnily!
When the Duke o' Monmouth saw them comin',
   He went to view their company.

6. "Ye're welcome, lads," the Monmouth said,
   "Ye're welcome, brave Scots lads, to me;
And sae are you, brave Earlstoun,
   The foremost o' your company!

7. "But yield your weapons ane an a';
   O yield your weapons, lads, to me;
For gin ye'll yield your weapons up,
   Ye'se a' gae hame to your country."—

8. Out then spak a Lennox lad,
   And waly but he spoke bonnily!
"I winna yield my weapons up,
   To you nor nae man that I see."—

9. Then he set up the flag o' red.
   A' set about wi' bonny blue;
"Since ye'll no cease, and be at peace,
   See that ye stand by ither true."—

10. They stell'd their cannons on the height,
   And showr'd their shot down in the howe;
An' beat our Scots lads even down,
   Thick they lay slain on every knowe.

11. As e'er you saw the rain down fa',
   Or yet the arrow frae the bow,—
Sae our Scottish lads fell even down,
   An' they lay slain on every knowe.

12. "O hold your hand," then Monmouth cry'd,
   "Gie quarters to yon men for me!"—
But wicked Claver'se swore an oath,
   His Cornet's death revenged sud be.

13. "O hold your hand," then Monmouth cry'd,
   "If onything you'll do for me;
Hold up your hand, you cursed Græme,
   Else a rebel to our King ye'll be."—

14. Then wicked Claver'se turn'd about,
   I wot an angry man was he;
And he has lifted up his hat,
   And cry'd, "God bless his Majesty!"—

15. Than he's awa' to London town,
   Aye e'en as fast as he can dree;
Fause witnesses he has wi' him ta'en,
   And ta'en Monmouth's head frae his body.

16. Alang the brae, beyond the brig,
   Mony brave man lies cauld and still;
But lang we'll mind, and sair we'll rue,
   The bloody battle of Bothwell Hill.

Lord Derwentwater

CHILD NO. 208

One of the most interesting things about this ballad is its thoroughly popular tone, in view of its late date. It is made, of course, out of the stuff of earlier balladry, produced and recombined in the interests of a new hero, who was beheaded February 24, 1716. Tradition can be traced back to about the middle of the eighteenth century, or a very little earlier. Child's ten variants show that the ballad had a good purchase on life in the first half of the nineteenth century, in Scotland and the north of England. Lately it has been found in Florida.

Motherwell's tune is an excellent example of folk music. Its feeling is major, but it ends on the second, so as to make a graceful return to the beginning. Technically, therefore, it may be classed as Dorian. It has many relatives in tradition, one of the best known, possibly, being Cecil Sharp's "Outlandish Knight" (*One Hundred English Folksongs*, 1916, p. 29), Child No. 4, *ante*, Vol. I, p. 51.

Vaughan Williams' second tune, from Hampshire (variant 3), is also major in its first three phrases, but it has a dropped close, and might be regarded as Mixolydian. It has to my ear more major feeling than Mixolydian. The tune at any rate is soundly traditional, and is obviously related to Motherwell's. Less obviously, Vaughan Williams' other tune (variant 2) appears to be similarly affiliated. Vaughan Williams says, in a note in the *Journal*, that he has also a very fine Æolian tune from Cambridgeshire for this ballad. This has not been identified. Could it be the one here called Dorian? Cf. also Sharp's "Lady Maisry" (*ibid.*, p. 26), Child No. 65, *ante*, Vol. II, p. 54.

Mrs. Griffin's Florida tune is a plagal major, perhaps half-improvised.

LIST OF VARIANTS

GROUP A

1. "Lord Derwentwater." William Motherwell, *Minstrelsy: Ancient and Modern*, 1827, App'x., No. 4, and p. 350.
2. "Lord Ellenwater." Ralph Vaughan Williams MSS., I, p. 89.
3. "Lord Ellenwater." Charles Gamblin and Vaughan Williams, *JFSS*, III, No. 13 (1909), p. 270.

GROUP B

4a. "The King's Love Letter." Mrs. G. A. Griffin, LC Archive of American Folk Song, recording No. 9263(A2). Also in LC/AAFS, recording No. L58(A3).

4b. "The King's Love Letter." Alton C. Morris, *Folksongs of Florida*, 1950, p. 308. Also in Morris, *JAF*, XLVII (1934), p. 95.

TUNES WITH TEXTS

GROUP A

1. [Lord Derwentwater]

Motherwell, 1827, App'x., No. 4; text, p. 350. From A. Blaikie, Paisley.

a D

1. Our King has wrote a long letter,
   And sealed it ower with gold;
He sent it to my lord Dunwaters,
   To read it if he could.

2. He has not sent it with a boy,
   Nor with any Scots lord;
But he's sent it with the noblest knight,
   E'er Scotland could afford.

3. The very first line that my lord did read,
   He gave a smirkling smile;
Before he had the half of it read,
   The tears from his eyes did fall.

4. "Come saddle to me my horse," he said,
   "Come saddle to me with speed;
For I must away to fair London town,
   For to me there was ne'er more need."

5. Out and spoke his lady gay,
   In child bed where she lay;
"I would have you make your will, my lord Dunwaters,
   Before you go away."

6. "I leave to you, my eldest son,
   My houses and my land;
I leave to you, my youngest son,
   Ten thousand pounds in hand.

7. "I leave to you, my lady gay,
   You are my wedded wife;
I leave to you, the third of my estate,
   That'll keep you in a lady's life."

8. They had not rode a mile but one,
   Till his horse fell owre a stane;
"Its a warning good enough," my lord Dun-
   waters said,
   "Alive I'll ne'er come hame."

9. When they came to fair London town,
   Into the courtier's hall;
The lords and knights of fair London town,
   Did him a traitor call.

10. "A traitor, a traitor," says my lord,
   "A traitor how can that be?
An it be nae for the keeping five thousand
   men,
   To fight for King Jamie.

11. "O all you lords and knights in fair London
   town,
   Come out and see me die;
O all you lords and knights in fair London
   town,
   Be kind to my ladie.

12. "There's fifty pounds in my right pocket,
   Divide it to the poor;
There's other fifty in my left pocket,
   Divide it from door to door."

2. "Lord Ellenwater"

Vaughan Williams MSS., I, p. 89. Sung by "Happy" Flack at ?Foulmire, July 12, 1907.

a D

1. The king he wrote a letter
He sealed it up with gold
He sent it to Lord Ellenwater
To read it if he could.

2. The first few lines that he did read,
It caused him for to smile,
And the next few lines that he did read
Made the tears trinckle down from his eyes.

3. O saddle me my milk white steed
Get it ready with all speed
[For I must away to fair London Town
For ? me was ne'er more need.] [Motherwell]
And the ring from his finger did burst
And his nose had begun to bleed.

4. As he was agoing along the high road
His horse it stumbled at a stone,
"It's a token," says Lord Ellenwater,
"That I never shall return."

5. Now when he came to fair London
Among the high quality
There were Lords and dukes and all sorts of gentlemen
But a traitor they called him all.

6. "No traitor," cried my Lord Ellenwater,
"No traitor you never knew me
For I'm keeping of five thousand brave men
For to fight in my own countree."

7. Then up did step a brave old man
(With) a sword drawn in his hand,
"Make your will, make your will sir," (says?) Lord
   Ellenwater,
"Your life is at my command."

8. "If my life is at your command,
One thing I will freely give [thee?]
The green velvet coat that I've got on
You shall have it for your fee."

9. "And here's one thing more that I have to have
It is before I die
Why (?) O? the Lords and the dukes in fair London
   town
Shall be given to the[e] (my?) gay ladie."

The textual queries and conjectures are from the MS.

3. "Lord Ellenwater"

Gamblin and Vaughan Williams, *JFSS*, III, No. 13 (1909), p. 270. Sung by Mrs. Goodyear (74), Axford, Hampshire, August 1907.

a M (inflected VII)

1. The king he wrote a long letter,
And sealed it up with gold,
And sent it unto Lord Ellenwater,
For to read it if he could.

2. The first three lines Lord Ellenwater read,
It made his heart to revive;
And the next three lines Lord Ellenwater read,
The tears fell from his eyes.

3. He callèd for his stable groom,
To saddle his milk-white steed,
That up to London I might go,
For I am sure there never was more need.

4. He put one foot all in his stirrup,
Another across his steed,
Three drops of blood fell from his nose,
As he mounted his milk-white steed.

5. "That token's enough," Lord Ellenwater said,
"That I never no more shall return,
. . . .
. . . .

6. "Here to you, my gay lady,
Which is my wedded wife,
. . . . . an estate
To maintain you all the days of your life.

7. "Here is fifty thousand pounds in one pocket,
To be given away to the poor,
Fifty thousand in the other pocket,
Shall be strewed from door to door."

8. There stands the old grim man
With the shining axe all in his hand,
Saying, "Come, you, along here, Lord Ellenwater,
For your life is at my command."

9. The people all amazed stood
And well enough they may
For he jumped three times upon his legs
After they had cut off his head.

3. He called up his oldest one
To bridle and saddle my steed
For I've got to go to Lunnon Town
Although I have no need.

4. It's make your will, you Duke of Melanto(r?)
It's make your will all around
It's two and two to my two oldest sons
It's two, it's two all around
For all of my steeds and the rest of my property
We'll retain to her lady's side.

5. Before he rode up in the edge of town
He met a jolly old man
Your life, your life, you Duke of Melanto(r?)
Your life I will command.

6. He stooped over the window
There the flowers swelled so gay
Till his nose gushed out and bleed
Come all you lords, you pretty lords, ye,
Be kind to my baby
Come all your lords, you pretty lords, ye,
Be kind to my baby
For all my steeds and the rest of my property
We'll retain to her lady's side.

GROUP B

4a. "The King's Love Letter"

Sung by Mrs. G. A. Griffin, Newberry, Fla., 1937. LC/AAFS, rec. No. 9263(A2). Also in LC/AAFS, rec. No. L58(A3). Collected by John Lomax.

p I

1. The king he wrote a love letter
And he sealed it all with gold
And he sent it to the Duke of Melanto(r?)
To read it if he could.

2. The first few lines that he did read
It caused him for to smile
But the next few lines that he did read
The tears from his eyes did flow.

4b. "The King's Love Letter"

Morris, 1950, p. 308. Also in Morris, *JAF*, XLVII (1934), p. 95. Sung by Mrs. G. A. Griffin, Newberry, Fla., 1933; learned from her father in Dooly County, Ga.

p I

1. The king he wrote a love letter,
And he sealed it over with gold;
And he sent it to the Duke of Bellanter
To read it if he could.

2. The first few lines that he did read
Hit caused him for to smile,
But the next few lines that he did read,
The tears from his eyes did flow.

3. He called up his oldest one
To bridle and saddle his steed.
"I've got to go to London town
Although I have no need."

4. Before he rode up in the edge of town,
He met a jolly old man.
"Your life, your life, you Duke of Bellanter,
Your life I will command.

5. "Hit's make your will, you Duke of Bellanter,
Hit's make your will all around."
"Hit's two and two to my two oldest sons,
Hit's two and two all round.

6. "Hit's all my ox, steed, and the rest of my property
Will retain you to a Lady's side."
. . . .
. . . .

7. He stooped over the window;
The flowers smelt so gay
Till his nose gushed out and bleeding
. . . .

8. Just before his head busted quite open
He spoke one word or two:
"Come all you lords, you pretty lordies
And be kind to my baby."

Geordie

CHILD NO. 209

LIKE the textual tradition, the musical tradition for this ballad is confused and crossed between the Scottish and English forms. If we accept Burns's text (Child A) as approximating the old norm of Scottish tradition, we find that norm accompanied by a series of variant tunes all belonging to a very familiar family best identified as the "Gypsy Laddie" (No. 200). Child's headnote, in fact, makes passing reference to a casual and probably accidental connection between "Geordie" and the Earl of Cassilis, a leading figure in the "Gypsy Laddie" tradition. At any rate, the Scottish tunes seem not to establish any independent tradition for the present ballad. The group under discussion can be read as members of the Dorian-Mixolydian galaxy, all authentic: most of them M/D, that is, lacking the third; two variants, however, from North Carolina lacking the seventh also. Yet it might be argued that they are really I/M tunes, and all plagal, with finals on the lower fifth. Half are in 3/4, half in common time. All but the two North Carolina variants are Scottish.

The second, and largest, group is English, mainly from the Southwest, but with scattered examples eastward and as far north as Lincolnshire, with two or three from the Appalachians as well. This is definitely the strongest English tradition, and is clearly connected with the later ballad about George of Oxford, which itself goes back to the seventeenth century. None of these preserves the burden of the earliest broadsides. The tune is of a favorite English pattern, found in a great variety of permutations and associations with other song-texts, both religious and secular. "Walsingham" is perhaps the earliest of these ("How should I your true love know"), but Lucy Broadwood and Anne Gilchrist (in *JFSS*, III, p. 191) noted affiliations also with "The man that lives," "The Truth sent from above," "Dorcas," "The Sinner's Dream," "There is a fountain," "The Holy Well," "The Carnal and the Crane" (No. 56), and an old Scottish psalm-tune, "Coleshill." (Cf. *JFSS*, IV, pp. 16, 20.) Others might be added: "Bailiff's Daughter" (No. 105), "Searching for Lambs." All of these are plagal tunes swinging between the Æolian and Dorian modes. There are one or two arguable variants, including a characteristic Scottish one (Greig and Keith's 2) found with many other ballads and not at all typical here.

A third group belongs to the "Boyne Water" family (also frequent with "Barbara Allan," No. 84 [Group D]). Variants are found from Aberdeenshire to the Ozarks, from Yorkshire to North Carolina and Arkansas. The modal center is again Æolian and Dorian, with π^4 and π^3 variants in America. Most are authentic tunes. There is a Somerset variant which may be a freak plagal major in this group. Kinloch's tune appears to be a sport here: it is certainly related to Mrs. Brown's of Child No. 32, Campbell's of No. 86, and Christie's of No. 97; and not closely to the present group.

A fourth, not very homogeneous, group has, again, relationship with "Barbara Allan" in another tradition. Its spread is from Sussex to North Carolina, and possibly Hogg's (perhaps traditional) tune belongs to it. It is definitely in the major area (π^1, I/Ly, I/M), and always plagal.

The last group is quite small, three variants coming from Somerset, two from the Appalachians. It, too, is major and plagal; and not unusual in general pattern.

LIST OF VARIANTS

GROUP A

1. "Geordie." James Johnson, *The Scots Musical Museum*, IV [1792], No. 346, p. 356 (repr. 1853). Also in Robert Archibald Smith, *The Scotish Minstrel* [1820-24], II, p. 68; and Robert Maver, *Genuine Scottish Melodies*, 1866, No. 448, p. 224.
2. "Will ye go to the Hielans, Geordie?" W. Christie, *Traditional Ballad Airs*, II, 1881, p. 290.
3. "Bog o' Gight." Greig MSS., III, p. 7, and Bk. 722, XII, p. 82, King's College Library, Aberdeen. Also in Gavin Greig and Alexander Keith, *Last Leaves of Traditional Ballads and Ballad Airs*, 1925, p. 133(1a). (McAllan)
4. "Gight's Ladye." Greig MSS., II, p. 22. Also in John Ord, *The Bothy Songs and Ballads*, 1930, p. 408. (W. W[alker])
5. "Georgy O." Dorothy Scarborough, *A Song Catcher in Southern Mountains*, 1937, pp. 411 and 214.
6. "Georgie, O." Susannah Wetmore and Marshall Bartholomew, *Mountain Songs of North Carolina*, 1926, p. 13.
7. "Will ye go the Hielans, Geordie?" Christie, *Traditional Ballad Airs*, II, 1881, p. 44.

GROUP B

8. "Georgie." Percy Grainger MS., NYPL MS. *MO+(English), No. 137, New York Public Library. Also in Grainger, *JFSS*, III, No. 12 (1908), p. 191.
9. "Geordie." Sharp MSS., 317/430, Clare College Library, Cambridge. Also in Cecil J. Sharp, *JFSS*, II, No. 6 (1905), p. 27(2). (White)
10. "Geordie." Sharp MSS., 1874/. (Callow)
11. "Georgie." Ralph Vaughan Williams MSS., III, p. 394; also I, p. 436. Also in Sharp MSS., 980/; and Cecil J. Sharp, ed., *Folk Songs of England*, 1908-12, II (*Folk Songs from the Eastern Counties*, ed. R. Vaughan Williams), p. 47.
12. "Geordie." Sharp MSS., 980/. Also in Cecil J. Sharp, *JFSS*, IV, No. 17 (1913), p. 333(3). (Mantle)
13. "Georgie." Ada Jane Mehrten, LC Archive of American Folk Song, recording No. 11,335(A2).
14. "Georgie." Dorothy Mehrten, LC Archive of American Folk Song, recording No. 11,334(A2).
15. "Geordie." Mrs. Tiny Gaunt, LC Archive of American Folk Song, recording No. 9981(A11).
16. "Geordie." Sharp MSS., 1876/. (Fudge)
17. "Geordie." H.E.D. Hammond MSS., No. 238, and D. VI, p. 46, Cecil Sharp House, London.
18. "Geordie." Sharp MSS., 312/423. Also in Sharp, *JFSS*, II, No. 6 (1905), p. 27(1); Cecil J. Sharp and Charles L. Marson, *Folk Songs from Somerset*, 2nd series, 1905, p. 5; Sharp, *One Hundred English Folksongs*, 1916, p.24; and

Sharp, *English Folk Songs*, Selected Ed., Novello & Co. [1920], I, p. 24. (Overd)

a. "Geordie." Ruth A. Musick, *JAF*, LXX (1957), pp. 352 and 340.

b. "Georgie." Mrs. May Kennedy McCord, LC Archive of American Folk Songs, recording No. 11,866(B16).

19. "Georgie." Mrs. Kendall Sigmund, LC Archive of American Folk Song, recording No. 11,899(A12).

20. "Georgie." Mrs. Evelyn Skaggs, LC Archive of American Folk Song, recording No. 11,896(A13).

21. "Georgie." Hammond MSS., No. 466.

22. "Georgie." Hammond MSS., No. 213. Also in H.E.D. Hammond, *JFSS*, IV, No. 17 (1913), p. 333(1).

23. "Geordie." Helen Creighton and Doreen H. Senior, *Traditional Songs from Nova Scotia*, 1950, p. 73.

c. "The Warminster Song." Alice E. Gillington, *Songs of the Open Road*, 1911, p. 6.

24. "Georgie." Harry Cox, Caedmon LP recording No. TC 1146(A9).

25. "Georgie." Vaughan Williams MSS., I, p. 35. Also in Ralph Vaughan Williams, *JFSS*, IV, No. 15 (1910), p. 89.

26. "Georgie." Hammond MSS., No. 393. Also in Hammond, *JFSS*, IV, No. 17 (1913), p. 332(3).

27. "Geordie." Sharp MSS., 1840/. Also in Sharp, *JFSS*, IV, No. 17 (1913), p. 333(2). (Neville)

28. "Geordie." Vaughan Williams MSS., I, p. 124. Also in Vaughan Williams, *JFSS*, IV, No. 17 (1913), p. 332(2).

29. "As I walked over London Bridge." Vaughan Williams, *JFSS*, II, No. 8 (1906), p. 208.

30. "Geordie." Sharp MSS., 4336/3096. Also in Cecil J. Sharp and Maud Karpeles, *English Folk Songs from the Southern Appalachians*, 1932, I, p. 242(D); and Arthur Kyle Davis, Jr., *Traditional Ballads of Virginia*, 1929, pp. 592(B) and 437. (Donald)

31. "Geordie." Sharp MSS., 3451/2542. Also in Sharp and Karpeles, 1932, I, p. 241(B). (Gentry)

32. "Georgie." Vaughan Williams MSS., I, p. 359. Also in Ralph Vaughan Williams and George Butterworth, *JFSS*, IV, No. 17 (1913), p. 332(1).

d. "Geordie." John Jacob Niles, *Songs of the Hill-Folk*, 1934, p. 12.

e. "Geordie." Isla Cameron, Riverside recording No. RLP 12-656(B7), ed. Kenneth S. Goldstein.

33. "Charlie Condemned." Jean Thomas and Joseph A. Leeder, *The Singin' Gatherin'*, 1939, p. 42.

34. "The Lady o'Gight." Greig MSS., III, p. 102, and Bk. 751, XLI, p. 93. Also in Greig and Keith, *Last Leaves*, 1925, p. 133(2). (Corbet)

GROUP C

35. "The Lady o' Gight." Christie, *Traditional Ballad Airs*, I, 1876, p. 52.

36. "The Life of Georgie." Vance Randolph, *Ozark Folksongs*, I, 1946, p. 161(A). Also in Randolph, *Ozark Mountain Folks*, 1932, p. 224.

37. "Geordie." Greig and Keith, *Last Leaves*, 1925, p. 133(1b). From Duncan MS., No. 415. (Troup)

38. "Geordie." George R. Kinloch, *Ancient Scottish Ballads*, 1827, App'x. to p. 187, and p. 192.

39. "Geordie." Frank Kidson, *Traditional Tunes*, 1891, p. 25.

40. "Georgie." Mrs. Georgia Dunaway, LC Archive of American Folk Song, recording No. 10,821(A7). Also in Randolph, *Ozark Folksongs*, I, 1946, p. 164(D).

41. "Geordie." Sharp MSS., 4750/3309. Also in Sharp and Karpeles, *Appalachians*, 1932, I, p. 243(F). (Boone)

42. "As I Walked Over London's Bridge." S. F. Russell, LC Archive of American Folk Song, recording No. 3159(B1).

f. "London's Bridge." Arthur Kyle Davis, Jr., *More Traditional Ballads of Virginia*, 1960, p. 264(AA).

43. "Geordie." Sharp MSS., 447/563. (Glover)

GROUP D

44. "A Lamentable Ditty on the Death of Geordie." James Hogg, *The Jacobite Relics of Scotland*, 2nd series, 1821, p. 104.

45. "Georgie," or "Banstead Downs." Lucy E. Broadwood, *JFSS*, I, No. 4 (1902), p. 164. Also in Broadwood, *English Traditional Songs and Carols*, 1908, p. 32.

46. "Geordie." Vaughan Williams MSS., III, p. 305.

47. "Geordie." Winston Wilkinson MSS., 1935-36, p. 85, University of Virginia.

48. "Geordie." Vaughan Williams MSS., III, p. 112.

49. "Johnny Wedlock." Louis W. Chappell, *Folk-Songs of Roanoke and the Albemarle*, 1939, p. 37.

g. "Geordie." *The Frank C. Brown Collection of North Carolina Folklore*, IV (*The Music of the Ballads*, ed. Jan P. Schinhan), 1957, p. 94(3).

50. "Geordie." Sharp MSS., 3416/2507. Also in Sharp and Karpeles, *Appalachians*, 1932, I, p. 240(A). (Wells)

51. "Geordie." Sharp MSS., 3504/. Also in Sharp and Karpeles, 1932, I, p. 241(C). (Buckner)

GROUP E

52. "Geordie." Sharp MSS., 1011/. (Young)

53. "Geordie." Sharp MSS., 2119/2008. (Wixey)

54. "Geordie." Mrs. Mary Bird McAllister, LC Archive of American Folk Song, recording No. 11,868(A11).

55. "Geordie." Sharp MSS., 4384/. Also in Sharp and Karpeles, *Appalachians*, 1932, I, p. 242(E). (Bowyer)

56. "Geordie," or "As I strolled over London Bridge." Vaughan Williams MSS., I, p. 110.

57. "Geordie." Sharp MSS., 924/. (Bailey)

h. "Geordie." Schinhan, *Music*, *Brown Collection*, IV, 1957, p. 93(2).

58. "I'd fight for the life of Georgie." Frank C. Brown MSS., 16 b IV, Library of Congress, photostat. Also in Schinhan, *Music*, *Brown Collection*, IV, 1957, p. 94(4).

i. "Georgie." Schinhan, *Music*, *Brown Collection*, IV, 1957, p. 91.

j. "Geordie." Schinhan, *Music*, *Brown Collection*, IV, 1957, p. 92(1).

TUNES WITH TEXTS

GROUP A

1. "Geordie"

Johnson, IV [1792], No. 346, p. 356 (repr. 1853). Also in Smith [1820-24], II, p. 68; and Maver, 1866, No. 448, p. 224. From Robert Burns.

a M/D

1. There was a battle in the north,
   And nobles there was many,
   And they hae kill'd Sir Charlie Hay,
   And they laid the wyte on Geordie.

2. O he has written a lang letter,
   He sent it to his lady;
   Ye maun cum up to Enbrugh town
   To see what words o' Geordie.

3. When first she look'd the letter on,
   She was baith red and rosy;
   But she had na read a word but twa,
   Till she wallow't like a lily.

4. Gar get to me my gude grey steed,
   My menzie a' gae wi' me;
   For I shall neither eat nor drink,
   Till Enbrugh town shall see me.

5. And she has mountit her gude grey steed,
   Her menzie a' gaed wi' her;
   And she did neither eat nor drink
   Till Enbrugh town did see her.

6. And first appear'd the fatal block,
   And syne the aix to head him;
   And Geordie cumin down the stair,
   And bands o' airn upon him.

7. But tho' he was chain'd in fetters strang,
   O' airn and steel sae heavy,
   There was na ane in a' the court,
   Sae bra' a man as Geordie.

8. O she's down on her bended knee,
   I wat she's pale and weary,
   O pardon, pardon, noble king,
   And gie me back my Dearie!

9. I hae born seven sons to my Geordie dear,
   The seventh ne'er saw his daddie:
   O pardon, pardon, noble king,
   Pity a waefu' lady!

10. Gar bid the headin-man mak haste!
    Our king reply'd fu' lordly:
    O noble king, tak a' that's mine,
    But gie me back my Geordie.

11. The Gordons cam and the Gordons ran,
    And they were stark and steady;
    And ay the word amang them a'
    Was, Gordons keep you ready.

12. An aged lord at the king's right hand
    Says noble king, but hear me;
    Gar her tell down five thousand pound
    And gie her back her Dearie.

13. Some gae her marks some gae her crowns,
    Some gae her dollars many;
    And she's tell'd down five thousand pound,
    And she's gotten again her Dearie.

14. She blinkit blythe in her Geordie's face,
    Says, dear I've bought thee, Geordie.
    But there sud been bluidy bouks on the green,
    Or I had tint my laddie.

15. He claspit her by the middle sma',
    And he kist her lips sae rosy:
    The fairest flower o' woman-kind
    Is my sweet, bonie Lady!

2. "Will ye go to the Hielans, Geordie?"

Christie, II, 1881, p. 290.

a M/D

3. "Bog o' Gight"

Greig MSS., III, p. 7; text, Bk. 722, XII, p. 82. Also in Greig and Keith, 1925, p. 133(1a). Sung by John McAllan, Shevado, 1907.

a M/D

1. Will you (ye) go to the Highlands my bonnie love
   Will you (ye) go to the Highlands wi' Geordie
   It's you'll tak' the high road & I'll tak the low
   And I'll be in the Highlands afore you (ye).

2. I wad far rather stay on the bonny banks o' Spey
And see a' the fish boaties rowin
Before I wad go to your high Highland hills
And hear a' yer white kye lowin

3. He had not been in the high highland hills
Months but barely three (two) O
Before he was cast into prison strong
For hunting the deer & the roe O

4. Where will I find a bonny little boy
Who (that) will run an errand shortly
And who (that) will run on to the bonny Bog o' Gight
Wi' a letter to Gighty's lady o'

5. Here am I a bonny little boy
Who will run an errand shortly
And will run on to the bonny Bog o' Gight
Wi' a letter to Gighty's (ie's) lady.

6. When that you (ye) come where the grass grows long
(Ye'll) Slack your shoes & run o'
When that you come where the bridge is broke
(Ye'll) Bend your bow & swim o'

7. When that you come to Gighty's (ie's) gates
Stop neither to chap nor call o'
But bend your bow right clean to your breast
And jump right over the wall o'

8. When that he came where the grass grew long
He slacked his shoes & ran o'
And when he came where the bridge was broke
He bent his bow & swam o'.

9. When that he came to Gighty's (ie's) gates
He stopped neither to chap nor to call O
But he's bent his bow right close to his breast
And jumped right over the wall O

10. When (that) she looked the letter upon
A loud loud laugh laughed she o'
But ere she had the half o't read
The saut tear blinded her eé o'.

11. Go saddle to me the black horse she cried
The brown never rode so boldly
Until I ride to Edinburgh toon
To see & get life for my Geordie
(And borrow the life o' my Geordie)

12. When that she came to yon ford mou'
The boatman he wasna ready,
But she clasped her hands round her high horse neck
And she swam the ferry shortly.

13. When that she cam' to the pier o' Leith
The poor people they stood many (mony)
She parted the yellow gold them among
Bade them pray for the life o' her Geordie.

14. When that she cam' to Edinburgh toon
The nobles they stood mony
And every one had his hat on his heid,
But hat in hand stood her Geordie.

15. Oh has he killed or has he brunt
Oh, has he robbèd ony?
Or what has my love Geordie done
That he's going to be hanged shortly?

16. He hasna killed nor has he brunt
Nor has he robbèd ony
But he's been a-hunting the king's own deer
And he's going to be hanged shortly.

17. Will the yellow gold buy off my bonnie love
Will the yellow gold buy off my Geordie
It's five hundred crowns if ye wad pay doon
Ye'll get the hat on your Geordie.

18. She's taen the red mantle frae her neck
She's spread it oot fu' bonny
And she's taen the hat oot o' Geordie's hand
And she's beggèd round them shortly.

19. Some gae her crowns & some gae her pounds
And some gae her hundreds mony
And the king himsel' gien her one hundred more
To get the hat on her Geordie.

20. When she was on her high horse set
And in behind her Geordie
The bird ne'er sang sae sweetly on the bush
As she did behind her Geordie.

21. Oot an spak' an Irish Duke
An auld bow-leggit body
Says I wish that Gightie had lost his heid
Or I had gotten his lady.

22. She turned her high horse quickly about
And o' but she was saucy
Says Pokes be upon your Irish face
For ye never could compare wi my Geordie.

23. First I wis lady o' bonny Auchindown
And next I was lady o' Gartly
But noo I'm guidwife o' Bog o' Gight
And I beggèd the life o' my Geordie.

4. "Gight's Ladye"

Greig MSS., II, p. 22. Also in Ord, 1930, p. 408. From William Walker, May 3, 1907.

a D

It is odd that the copy in the *Bothy Songs*, though note for note the same, and with the same first stanza, as Greig's copy, is attributed to a different source. On the possibility that the two were alike throughout—for Greig's twenty-three stanzas are missing—the Ord text, with twenty-three stanzas, is given here. The source is said to be James B. Allan, Glasgow.

1. Will ye gang to the Hielands, my bonnie love?
Will ye gang to the Hielands, Geordie?
I'll tak' the high road gin ye tak' the low,
And I'll be in the Hielands afore ye.

2. I'd rather for to stay on the bonnie banks o' Spey
To see a' the fish boaties rowin',
Afore that I would gang to your high Hieland hill
To hear a' the black kye lowin'.

3. He had not been in the high Hieland hills
Months but barely twa, O,
When he was put in a prison strong
For hunting the deer and the roe, O.

4. Where will I get a little wee boy
That is both true and steady,
That will run on to the bonnie Bog o' Gight
Wi' a letter to my ladye?

5. Oh, here am I, a bonnie wee boy
That is baith true and steady,
And I'll run on to the bonnie Bog o' Gight
Wi' a letter to your ladye.

6. When you come where the grass grows green
You'll slacken your shoes and run, O;
And when you come where the bridge is broke
You'll bend your bow an' swim, O.

7. And when you come to the bonnie Bog o' Gight
You'll neither shout nor call, O,
But you'll bend your bow to your left breast
Then leap in over the wall, O.

8. When he came where the grass grew green
He slackened his shoes and ran, O,
And when he came where the bridge was broke
He bent his bow and swam, O.

9. And when he came to the gates of Gight
He did neither shout nor call, O,
But he bent his bow to his left breast
And he leaped in over the wall, O.

10. When that the ladye the letter looked on,
I wat little laugh got she, O;
Afore she had read it half-way down
A saut tear blinded her e'e, O.

11. Gae saddle to me the grey horse, she cried,
The broon never rode so smartly,
And I'll awa to Edinburgh town
And borrow the life o' my Geordie.

12. When she came to the pier o' Leith
The puir folk stood thick and mony.
She threw the red gowd right them among,
Bade them pray for the life o' her Geordie.

13. When that she came to Edinburgh town
The nobles there were mony,
Ilka ane wi' his hat on his head,
But hat in hand stood Geordie.

14. O has he killed, or has he robbed,
Or has he stolen ony?
Or what's the ill that my love has done
That he's going to be hanged shortly?

15. He has not killed, he has not robbed,
He has not stolen ony,
But he has hunted the King's young deer,
So he's going to be hanged shortly.

16. Will the red gowd buy aff my love, she said,
Will the red gowd buy aff Geordie?
Ten thousand crowns, if ye pay down,
Ye'll get on your hat on your Geordie.

17. Then out it speaks Lord Montague
(O woe be to his body),
This day we hanged young Charlie Hay,
The morn we'll hang your Geordie.

18. She's taen the silk mantle frae her neck,
And, O, but she spread it bonnie;
Wi' his hat in her hand she has begged all around,
Till she's begged the life o' her Geordie.

19. Some gave crowns and some gave pounds,
Some gave dollars mony;
The King himself gave five hundred crowns
To get on her hat on her Geordie.

20. Then out it speaks Lord Montague
(O wae be to his body),
I wish that Gight had lost his head,
I might enjoyed his ladye.

21. But out it speaks the ladye herself,
Ye need ne'er wish my body;
O ill befa' your wizened snout,
Would ye compare wi' my Geordie?

22. Now since she's on her high horse set,
And on behind her Geordie,
There was ne'er a bird so blythe in a bush
As she was behind her Geordie.

23. First I was lady at bonnie Auchindoun,
And next I was mistress at Kincraigie,
But now I'm guidwife at the bonnie Bog o' Gight,
And I've ventured my life for my Geordie.

5. "Georgy O"

Scarborough, 1937, p. 411; text, p. 214. Sung by Mrs. J. G. Stikeleather, Asheville, N.C., c. 1932. Learned from an old mountaineer.

a π^2

1. Come bridle me up my milk-white steed;
   The browny ain't so able, oh;
   While I ride down to Charlotte town
   To plead for the life of my Georgy-O.

2. When I got in sight of Charlotte town,
   The gentlemen were so plenty, oh.
   And the table was sot and the supper was got,
   And the gentlemen were so merry, oh.

3. Come bridle me up my milk-white steed;
   The browny ain't so able, oh.
   While I ride down to Gallows Hill
   To plead for the life of Georgy-O.

4. When I got in sight of Gallows Hill,
   The gentlemen were so plenty, oh.
   And the gallows all round my Georgy's neck,
   And the rings of gold were so yellow, oh.

5. Then spoke the noble girl,
   She spoke most brief and sorry, too.
   I lay you down ten thousand pounds
   To spare the life of my Georgy-O.

6. Then spoke the noble judge.
   He looked most grieved and sorry, oh.
   For to honor you both and for the money, oh.
   I'll spare the life of your Georgy-O.

6. "Georgie, O"

Wetmore and Bartholomew, 1926, p. 13. Sung by Mrs. J. G. Stikeleather, Asheville, N.C., September 1924.

a π^2

1. Come bridle me up my milk-white steed,
   The brownie ain't so able, O.
   While I ride down to Charlottetown
   To plead for the life of my Georgie, O.

2. When I got in sight of Charlottetown
   The gentlemen were so plenty, O,
   The table was sot and supper was got,
   And the gentlemen were so plenty, O!

3. When I got in sight of Gallows Hill,
   The gentlemen were so plenty, O!
   And the gallows all round my Georgie's neck,
   And the rings of gold were so yellow, O!

4. Then spoke the noble girl,
   She spoke most brief and sorry too,
   "I'll lay you down ten thousand pounds,
   If you'll spare the life of my Georgie, O!"

5. Then spoke the noble judge,
   He spoke most brief and sorry too,
   "For to honor you both—and for the money, O,
   I will spare the life of your Georgie, O!"

7. "Will ye go to the Hielans, Geordie?"

Christie, II, 1881, p. 44. From Aberdeen and Banffshire tradition.

a M/D

1. "Will ye go to the Hielans, my bonny lad,
   Will ye go to the Hielans, Geordie?
   Though ye tak' the high road, and I tak' the low,
   I will be in the Hielans afore ye."
   He hadna been in the high Hielans,
   A month but barely twa, O;
   Till he was laid in prison strong,
   For hunting the king's deer and rae, O.

2. "O where will I get a bonny, bonny boy,
   That will run my errand cannie;
   And gae quickly on to the bonny Bog o' Gight
   Wi' a letter to my lady."
   "O here am I a bonny, bonny boy,
   That will run your errand cannie;
   And will gae on to the bonny Bog o' Gight,
   Wi' a letter to your lady."

3. When she did get this broad letter,
   A licht, licht laugh gae she, O;
   But before she read it to an end
   The saut tear was in her e'e, O.
   "O, has he robb'd, or has he stown,
   Or has he killèd ony?
   Or what is the ill that he has done,
   That he's gaun to be hang'd sae shortly?"

4. "He hasna robb'd, he hasna stown,
He hasna killèd ony;
But he has hunted the king's deer and rae,
And he will be hangèd shortly."
"Come saddle to me the bonny brown steed,
For the black never rade sae bonny;
And I will gae on to Edinboro' town
To borrow the life o' my Geordie."

5. The first water-side that she cam' to,
The boatman wasna ready;
She gae anither skipper half-a-crown,
To boat her o'er the ferry.
When she cam' on to Edinboro' town,
The poor stood thick and mony;
She dealt them money roun' and roun',
Bade them pray for the life o' her Geordie.

6. When she gaed up the Tolbooth stair,
She saw there nobles mony;
And ilka noble stood hat on head,
But hat in hand stood Geordie.
Then out it spak' an English lord,
And vow but he spake bonny,—
"If ye pay down ten thousand crouns,
Ye'll get the life o' your Geordie."

7. Some gae her marks, some gae her crouns,
Some gae her guineas rarely;
Till she paid down ten thousand crouns,
And she got the life o' her Geordie.
Then out it spak' an Irish lord,
O wae befa' his body,—
"It's a pity the knicht didna lose his head,
That I micht hae gotten his lady."

8. But out it spak' the lady hersel',
And vow but she spak' bonny,—
"The pock-marks are on your Irish face,
You could not compare wi' my Geordie."
When she was in the saddle set,
And on ahint her Geordie,
The bird on the bush ne'er sang sae sweet,
As she sung to her love Geordie:—

9. "First I was mistress o' bonny Auchindown,
And then I was lady o' a' Cairnie;
But now I have come to the bonny Bog o' Gight
The wife o' my true love Geordie.
If I were in the high Hielans,
I would hear the white kye lowing;
But I'd rather be on the bonny banks o' Spey
To see the fish boaties rowing."

Christie's text = Child's H.

GROUP B

8. "Georgie"

Percy Grainger MS., NYPL MS. *MO+(English), No. 137. Also in Grainger, *JFSS*, III, No. 12 (1908), p. 191. Sung by Joseph Taylor, Brigg, Lincolnshire, August 4, 1906.

p Æ (inflected VII)

The singer did not recall the words when Grainger first noted the tune, but did so subsequently, and recorded the whole song for the Gramophone Company, on a record the Editor failed to obtain.

9. [Geordie]

Sharp MSS., 317/430. Also in Sharp, *JFSS*, II, No. 6 (1905), p. 27(2). Sung by Mrs. Lucy White, Hambridge, July 18, 1904.

p D/Æ

O Georgie shall be hanged in a golden chain
And that's a chain of many:
For he has confessed and die he must
And the Lord have mercy on him!

O Georgie never stoled no ducks nor no geese
And he never murdered any
But he stole sixteen of the King's royal deer
And sold them under vally (value).

10. "Geordie"

Sharp MSS., 1874/. Sung by Mrs. Callow (75), Stockham Cross, September 9, 1908.

p D

As I walked over London Bridge
One morning very early
I overtook a fair pretty maid
Lamenting for her Geordie

11. "Georgie"

Vaughan Williams MSS., III, p. 394; also I, p. 436. Also in Sharp MSS., 980/; and Sharp, 1908-12, II, p. 47. From Cambridgeshire, c. 1906.

p D/Æ

1. As I walked over London Bridge
One midsummer morning early,
There I spied a pretty fair maid,
She was ?mounted for her Georgie.

2. Georgie has stole no house nor land [horse nor cow?],
Nor has he murdered any.
He has stole six of the ?crowns ?white deer
And has sold [them] ?in Den Caney.

3. Come bridle my milk white steed,
Come saddle me my pony
That I might ride to the Goodluck bridge [judge?],
There I'll beg for the life of Georgie.

4. When she arrived at the ?red shire hall,
Where people there were many,
Down on her bended knees did fall,
Crying spare me the life of Georgie.

5. The judge looked over his left shoulder,
?When [he] saw her grief of ?misery,
He said young woman you are too late,
For he is condemned already.

6. She turned her heavy eyes around
And fixed them upon Georgie.
As you are ?confessed and die you must,
May the Lord have mercy on you.

7. Georgie shall be hung in the chains of gold,
Such chains as [his?] never be any,
And he is one of the royal blood
And he courted a royal lady.

8. He shall be buried in a coffin of gold,
Such coffin as there never was any.
Then on his tombstone it shall be wrote,
He's ?long ?won the heart of a lady.

9. I wish I were on yonder hill,
Where oft times I've been many,
With a sword and pistol all by my side,
There I'd fight for the life of Georgie.

The text given is that which accompanies the tune at I, p. 436 of the MSS., since only one stanza of text is found with the tune at III, p. 394. The latter differs from the first stanza above only in line three, which reads "O there I spied a fair pretty maid."

12. [Geordie]

Sharp MSS., 980/. Also in Sharp, *JFSS*, IV, No. 17 (1913), p. 333(3). Sung by William Mantle (72), Bridgwater, August 9, 1906.

p D/Æ

As I was walking over London Bridge
There I spied so many people
With the swords and pistols all in their hands
For to fight for the life of Georgy.

13. "Georgie"

Sung by Ada Jane Mehrten, Clements, Calif., October 26, 1952. LC/AAFS, rec. No. 11,335(A2). Collected by Sidney Robertson Cowell.

p M

Go bridle me my milk-white steed,
Go saddle him in a hurry,
That I may ride to the Orphans' court
To plead for the life of Georgie.

O Georgie never robbed on the King's highway,
Or never murdered any;
But he stole sixteen of the King's white steeds
And conveyed them away to the Army.

O Georgie was hung with a silken cord,
Such cords as these aren't many,
Because he was of a noble blood
And loved by a virtuous lady.

14. "Georgie"

Sung by Dorothy Mehrten, Oakland, Calif., October 14, 1952. LC/AAFS, rec. No. 11,334(A2). Collected by Sidney Robertson Cowell.

p M

Dorothy Mehrten's text is identical with that of Ada Jane Mehrten (variant 13), save for stanza 3, line 2, which she sings as follows:

Such cords there be not many.

15. "Geordie"

Sung by Mrs. Tiny Gaunt, Sperryville, R.I. LC/AAFS, rec. No. 9981(A11). Collected by MacEdward Leach and Horace P. Beck.

p π^1

Go saddle me my milk-white steed,
  Go saddle him quite steady,
That I may ride to King Henry's hall
  To plead for the life of Georgie.

As she drew near King Henry's hall
  She placed herself quite steady.
King Henry says, You're a day too late,
  For young Georgie's condemned already.

Young George never robbed on the King's highway,
  Nor he never murdered any;
But he stole sixteen of the King's horses
  And he sold them in Bokenny.

Go dig my grave both wide and deep,
  Way down beneath yon willow.
One grave can do for to hold a soul,
  And my arms can do for pillow.

16. "Geordie"

Sharp MSS., 1876/. Sung by James Fudge (78), East Combe, September 10, 1908.

p Æ

17. "Geordie"

Hammond MSS., No. 238; text, D.VI, p. 46. Sung by Henry Way, Bridport, Dorset, 1905-08.

p D/Æ

1. As we rode over London Bridge
   One Midsummer morning so early
   Oh! there I behold a lady fair
   Lamenting for her Georgie.
2. George never stole ox nor sheep
   Nor cattle he stole nor any
   But he stole six of the King's fat deer
   And sold them undervally.
3. I wish I were on yonder hills
   Where kisses they are plenty
   With my sword and pistol in my hand
   I will fight for the life of Georgie.
4. So have you got some nice little boy
   That will run an errand so early
   That will run five miles in one half hour
   With a letter to my Georgie.
5. George be hunged in golden chains
   And as due to him as any
   Because he was one of the royal royal blood
   And he married with a gay young lady.

18. "Geordie"

Sharp MSS., 312/423. Also in Sharp, *JFSS*, II, No. 6 (1905), p. 27(1); Sharp and Marson, 2nd series, 1905, p. 5; Sharp, 1916, p. 24; and Sharp, Selected Ed. [1920], I, p. 24. Sung by Mrs. Overd, Langport, August 17, 1904.

p D/Æ

1. Come bridle me my milk white steed,
Come bridle me my pony,
That I might ride to fair London town } Bis
To plead for the life of Geordie.

2. And when she entered in the hall
There were lords & ladies plenty.
Down on her bended knee she fall
To plead for the life of Geordie.

3. Then Geordie look round the court,
And saw his dearest Polly.
He said my dear you've come too late,
For I'm condemned already.

4. Then the people[1] lookèd down on him
And said I'm sorry for thee.
'Tis thine own confession hath hangèd thee
May the Lord have mercy upon thee.

5. O Geordie stole no cow nor calf
Nor he never stoled any money
But he stole sixteen of the King's white steeds
And sold them in Bohenny.

6. Let Geordie hang in golden chains,
His crimes was never many,
Because he came from the royal blood
And courted a virtuous lady.

7. I wish I was in yonder grove
Where times I have been many,
With my broad sword & pistol too,
I'd fight for the life of Geordie.

[1] "Judge he" is written above this in the MS.

19. "Georgie"

Sung by Mrs. Kendall Sigmund, Butler's Fork, Ark., September 17, 1955. LC/AAFS, rec. No. 11,899(A12). Collected by Mary Celestia Parler.

p π[4] (–III)

Georgie was hung with silken rope,
Such ropes there were not many,
For George was of a noble race,
And was loved by a [virtuous] lady.

20. "Georgie"

Sung by Mrs. Evelyn Skaggs, Wayton, Ark., October 2, 1954. LC/AAFS, rec. No. 11,896(A13). Collected by Mary Celestia Parler.

p π[3]

1. As I was acrossing London's bridge
One misty morning early,
There I spied a pretty fair miss
A-lamenting for her Georgie.

2. She said, Go saddle me my black,
And bridle him most gaily,
And I will ride this livelong night
And plead for the life of Georgie.

3. She rode, she rode till she came there,
'Twas in the morning early,
And on her bended knees she fell,
Saying, Spare me the life of Georgie.

4. She pulled out her purse of gold,
Said, Lawyers, money plenty;
Just fee yourselves and think on me,
And plead for the life of Georgie.

5. And Georgie's lawyer he rose up,
Said, I've nothing at all against him,
But his own confession he must die,
O the Lord have mercy on him.

6. The Judge looked over his left shoulder,
He looked both sad and sorry,
Said, My pretty fair Miss, you came too late,
Georgie has to be hung tomorrow.

7. Georgie was of a noble race,
And loved a virtuous lady,
Georgie was hung with silken ropes,
Such ropes there were not many.

8. Georgie walked up and down the halls,
A-bidding adieu to many.
But when he came to his own true love,
That grieved him worse than any.

9. George was buried in ?Holland ?Harlem ?Highland state,
And over him grew a willow,
With a marble stone to his head and feet
And his true love's arm for his pillow.

The overlinings in the text indicate syllables emphatically prolonged by the singer.

21. "Georgie"

Hammond MSS., No. 466. Sung by Mrs. Davis, Dorchester, Dorset, 1905-08.

p D/Æ

22. "Georgie"

Hammond MSS., No. 213. Also in Hammond, *JFSS*, IV, No. 17 (1913), p. 333(1). Sung by Mrs. R. Gale, Powerstock, Dorset, 1905-08.

p D

23. "Geordie"

Creighton and Senior, 1950, p. 73. Sung by John Bray, Glencoe, N.S. Tune collected by Helen Creighton.

p D/Æ

1. As I went over London bridge
   Was in the morning early,
   And there I met a fair lady
   Lamenting for her Geordie.

2. I then stepped up to this fair young one,
   Saying, "Where are you going so early?"
   "I'm going to my good lord judge," she cried,
   "To plead for the life of Geordie."

3. The judge looked over his right shoulder
   And said to this fair lady,
   "Fair lady, fair lady you came too late,
   Your Geordie is condemned forever."

4. "Has my Geordie been robbing all along,
   Or has he wounded any?"
   "Oh no, but he stole three of the king's gold rings
   And sold them in Virginny."

5. "Then my Geordie shall be hung with a golden chain,
   These chains they are not many,
   For he was born of royal blood
   And courted by a loyal lady.

6. "Then my Geordie shall be buried in a marble tomb,
   Such tombs there are not many,
   For he was born of noble blood
   And courted by a loyal lady."

24. "Georgie"

Sung by Harry Cox, Yarmouth, Norfolk. Caedmon LP rec. No. TC 1146(A9). Collected by Peter Kennedy and Alan Lomax.

p D (inflected III)

1. As I walked over London Bridge
   One midsummer's morning early,
   And there I beheld a fair lady,
   Lamenting for her Georgie.

2. "I pray can you send me a little boy
   Who can go an errand swiftly?
   Who can go ten miles in one hour
   With a letter for a lady."

3. "So come saddle me my best black horse,
   Come saddle it quite swiftly,
   So I may ride to the King's Castle Gaol
   And beg for the life of me Georgie."

4. So when she got to the castle door
   The prisoners stood many;
   They all stood around with their caps in their hands
   Excepting her bonny, bonny Georgie.

5. "My Georgie never stole neither horse nor cow,
   Nor done any harm to any;
   He stole sixteen of the King's fat deers
   Which grieved me most of any."

6. "Now six pretty babes that are born by him,
   The seventh lay at my bosom;
   I would freely part with six of them
   To spare the life of me Georgie."

7. Now the judge he looked over his left shoulder,
He seemed so very hard-hearted;
He said, "Fair lady, you are too late,
Your Georgie is condemned already."

8. Now me Georgie shall be hanged in the chains of gold,
Such gold as they don't hang many.
Because he come of the royal blood,
And courted a very rich lady.

9. Now me Georgie shall be hanged in the chains of the gold,
Such gold as you don't see any;
And on the tombstone these words should be wrote—
"Here lays the heart of a lady."

25. "Georgie"

Vaughan Williams MSS., I, p. 35. Also in Vaughan Williams, *JFSS*, IV, No. 15 (1910), p. 89. Sung by Walter Debbidge, Bridge Inn, Acle, Norfolk, April 15, 1908.

p D/Æ

(*Verse* 2)
"O six bravè children have I had by him
And the seventh lies in my bosom
I would freely part from them every one,
If you spare me the life of my Georgie."

"Now your Georgie shall be hangèd in the chains of gold,
Such a gold that never was any;
For he was a one of the royal blood,
And he courted a rich young lady."

The MSS. refer to five stanzas on a pasted sheet: these were not discovered. The text above is given with the tune in *JFSS*.

26. "Georgie"

Hammond MSS., No. 393. Also in Hammond, *JFSS*, IV, No. 17 (1913), p. 332(3). Sung by Mrs. Bartlett, Halstock, Leigh, Dorset, 1905-08.

p Æ

As I was going o'er fair London bridge,
On a midsummer morning so early,
Oh! there I spied a fair pretty maid
Lamenting for her Georgie. (*bis*)

27. "Geordie"

Sharp MSS., 1840/. Also in Sharp, *JFSS*, IV, No. 17 (1913), p. 333(2). Sung by Charles Neville, East Coker, September 3, 1908.

p D

For Geordie shall be hung in chains of gold
For scarce there can be any
For he was one of the nobble [*sic*] Lords
And he courted a rich young lady

28. "Geordie"

Vaughan Williams MSS., I, p. 124. Also in Vaughan Williams, *JFSS*, IV, No. 17 (1913), p. 332(2). Sung by Mr. Jeffries, Mitcham Fair, Surrey, August 13, 1907.

p D/Æ

He's stol'n neither sheep nor cow
Nor oxen has he any,
But he has stol'n six of the King's fat deer
And sold them in Low Daney.

29. "As I walked over London Bridge"

Vaughan Williams, *JFSS*, II, No. 8 (1906), p. 208. Sung by Mr. Deadman, Rodmell, Sussex, January 1906.

If C tonic, p I/Ly; if A tonic, p D/Æ, ending on III

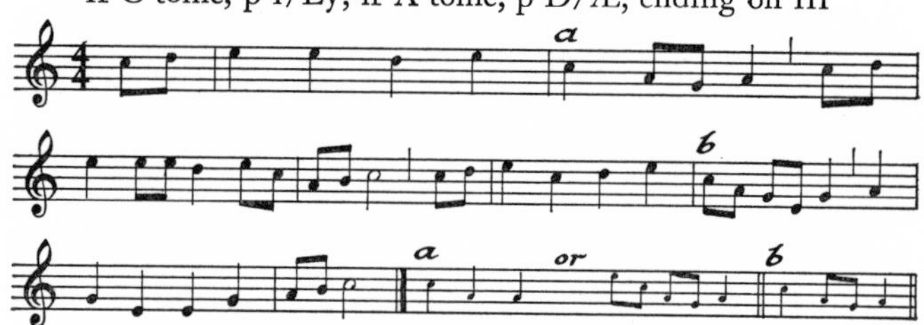

N.B. that this variant somewhat resembles a descant pitched a third above the usual tune.

As I walked over London Bridge
One midsummer's morning early
O there I spied a fair lady
Lamenting for her Geordie.

30. [Geordie]

Sharp MSS., 4336/3096. Also in Sharp and Karpeles, 1932, I, p. 242(D); and Davis, 1929, p. 592(B); text, p. 437. Sung by Mrs. Laura V. Donald, Dewey, Va., June 6, 1918.

p D

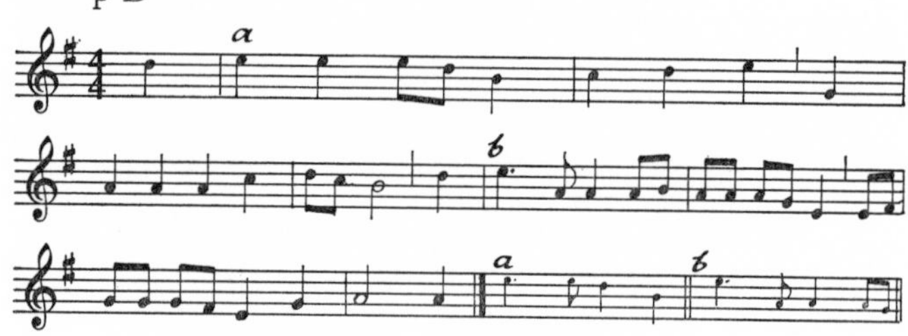

As I came over new London Bridge
One misty morning early,
I overheard a tenderhearted girl
A-pleading for the life of Georgie.

Come saddle unto me my milk-white steed,
Come saddle unto me quite gaily,
That I might ride the livelong night
A-pleading for the life of Georgie.

Georgie was hung with a silken rope,
Such ropes they was not many,
But Georgie come of a noble race
And was loved by a virtuous lady.

31. [Geordie]

Sharp MSS., 3451/2542. Also in Sharp and Karpeles, 1932, I, p. 241(B). Sung by Mrs. Jane Gentry, Hot Springs, N.C., September 14, 1916.

p D/Æ

1. As I went over London's Bridge
One morning bright and early,
I saw a maid for-bide the way
Lamenting for poor Charlie.

2. It's Charlie's never robbed the king's high court,
Nor he's never murdered any,
But he stole sixteen of his milk white steeds
And sold them in old Virginia.

3. Go saddle me my milk white steed,
The brown one ain't so speedy,
And I'll ride away to the king's high court
Enquiring for poor Charlie.

4. She rode, she rode to the king's high court
Enquiring for poor Charlie.
Fair lady you have come too late,
For he's condemned already.

(Repeat 2nd stanza here.)

5. It's will you promise me she said,
O promise me, I beg thee,
To hang him by a white silk cord
That never has hung any.

32. "Georgie"

Vaughan Williams MSS., I, p. 359. Also in Vaughan Williams and Butterworth, *JFSS*, IV, No. 17 (1913), p. 332(1). Sung at Newby Almshouses, Reydon, Suffolk, October 25, 1910.

p D/Æ, ending on IV

The printed form supplies an F♮ in the last phrase, doubles the note-values, and gives the antepenultimate bar as 3/2. There are other minor differences of reading.

33. "Charlie Condemned"

Thomas and Leeder, 1939, p. 42. Sung by Mrs. Martha Williams, Morgan County, Ky., June 1911.

p D (–II)

As I rode over London Bridge
One morning bright and early,
With my sword and pistol by my side
A-hunting for my Charlie.

I rode up to the King's high court
That looks so wonderful sorry
Is there where you call the King's high court
Or is any one here named Charlie?

The King looked around over his right shoulder
And this he said, "Fair Ladee,
Fair Ladee you have come too late
For Charlie's condemned already."

By permission of the author, Jean Thomas, The Traipsin' Woman, from *The Singin' Gatherin'* (published in New York by Silver Burdett in 1939).

34. "The Lady o' Gight"

Greig MSS., III, p. 102; text, Bk. 751, XLI, p. 93. Also in Greig and Keith, 1925, p. 133(2). Sung by Mrs. Corbet, New Deer.

p D

1. I choose my bonnie love in the woods o' Gight
Where the birds and the trees are many
And pleasures, pleasures had I never nane
But my crosses were thick, thick & many.

2. First I was Lady o' Bonnie Ythanside
And next I was Madame o' Kincraigie
But now I am Lady o' the Bonnie Hoose o' Gight
And my true love's name's aye Geordie.

3. He never adored me as his wife
Nor cheered me as his Lady
But every other day he saiddle the grey
And he's off to see Begnot's Lady.

4. Begnot he'd gotten word o' this
That Lord Gight had been wi' his lady
And he's ridden in to bonnie Aberdeen
And he's had him present shortly.

5. O where can I get a bonnie clever boy
That will rin my eeran shortly
That will rin on to the bonnie House o' Gight
Wi' a letter to my Lady.

6. Oh here you'll get a bonnie clever boy
That will rin your eeran' shortly
That will rin on to the bonnie Hoose o' Gight
Wi' a letter to your Lady.

7. When she got the letter into her hand
It's oh but she was sorry
She hadna read it to the foot
Till the tears cam trinkling mony.

8. Come saiddle me the black black steed
For the brown never rode so bonnie
Till I ride in to bonnie A(i)berdeen
And see fat they're deein wi' my Geordie.

9. As she gaed by the Well o' Spa
The poor things met she many
And some she gae shillins to
And some she gae croons
And some she gae red guineas many
When she'd gaen her red guineas them among
She bade them pray for her Geordie.

10. When she gaed up the Tolbooth stair
The nobles met she many
And every one wi' their hat on their head
But hat in hand stood her Geordie.

11. Oh has he robbed or has he slain
Or has he murdered any
Or what ill deed is this that he's done
That ye're going to behead my Geordie.

12. Out then spake the Earl of Aboyne
And oh but he spake bravely
Saying I would wish that Lord Gight might lose his head
That I could enjoy his Lady.

13. Oh woe be to your ill faurt face
And as much to your body
Ere you would compare your ill faurt face
Wi' mine or wi' my Geordie's.

14. Out then spoke the Earl of . . . .
And oh but he spake boldly
Saying: "Pay ye doon ten thousand croons
And buy up the life o' yer Geordie."

15. She's ta'en his hat into her hand
And thro' the nobles many
And some gae her shillins
And some gae her crowns
And some gae her red guineas many
And she's paid doon ten thoosand croons
Says: "Put on your hat my Geordie."

16. When she went down the Tolbooth stair
It's oh but she was cheerie
The nightingale ne'er sang sae sweet
As she sang to her Geordie.

17. None when she's on her saiddle set
And in behind her Geordie
The nightingale ne'er sang so sweet
As she sang that night to her Geordie.

GROUP C

35. "The Lady o' Gight"

Christie, I, 1876, p. 52. From Buchan, Aberdeenshire.

m Æ

"First I was Lady o' Black Riggs,
And then into Kincraigie;
Now I am the Lady o' Gight,
And my love he's ca'd Geordie.
I was the mistress o' Pitfan,
And madam o' Kincraigie;
And now my name is Lady Anne,
And I am Gight's own lady."
[*Etc.*]

Christie's text was "epitomized" from Peter Buchan's *Ancient Ballads and Songs of the North of Scotland*, 1828, I, p. 133.

36. "The Life of Georgie"

Randolph, I, 1946, p. 161(A). Also in Randolph, 1932, p. 224. Sung by George Underwood, Jane, Mo., March 7, 1928.

p π^4

1. Go saddle me my black, said she,
An' saddle him most gaily,
An' I'll ride over to Kingstall town,
An' plead for th' life of Georgie.
Li toodel ondel adel ondel,
Andel ondel ay ay da.

2. She rode right over to Kingstall town,
An' she was wore an' weary,
An' she knelt right down on her bended knee
Sayin' spare me the life of Georgie.
Li toodel ondel adel ondel,
Andel ondel ay ay da.

3. The judge looked over his left shoulder,
Sayin' Miss, I'm sorry for you,
But it's by his own confession
That Georgie must hang tomorrow.

4. She pulled out her purse of gold,
Sayin' here is money plenty,
Lawyers, come an' fee yourselves,
But spare me the life of Georgie.

5. Georgie rose up to plead for his-self,
Sayin' I've not murdered any,
But I stole sixteen of the King's best steeds
An' sold 'em in Bohemy.

6. Georgie walked up an' down the street,
A-biddin' adieu to many,
But when he come to his own true love
It grieved him the worst of any.

7. Georgie was hung by a silken rope,
Such ropes there are not many,
But Georgie was born of a noble race,
An' loved by a virtuous lady.

8. Georgie was buried at Highland Church,
An' over his head grew a willow,
With a marble stone at his head an' feet,
An' his true love's arm for a pillow.

37. "Geordie"

Greig and Keith, 1925, p. 133(1b); from Duncan MS., No. 415. Sung by Isaac Troup, Ythanwells.

a Æ

38. "Geordie"

Kinloch, 1827, App'x. to p. 187; text, p. 192.

a π^4

1. There was a battle in the North,
And rebels there were monie;
And monie ane got broken heads,
And taken was my Geordie.

My Geordie O, my Geordie O,
O the love I bear to Geordie;
For the very grund I walk upon
Bears witness I loe Geordie.

2. As she gaed up the tolbooth stair,
The cripples there stood monie;
And she dealt the red gowd them among,
To pray for her love Geordie.

3. And whan she cam into the hall,
The nobles there stood monie;
And ilka ane stood hat on head,
But hat in hand stood Geordie.

4. Up bespak a Norlan lord,
I wat he spak na bonnie,—
"If ye'll stay here a little while,
Ye'll see Geordie hangit shortly."

5. Then up bespak a baron bold,
And O but he spak bonnie;—
"If ye'll pay doun five hundred crowns,
Ye'se get you[r] true-love Geordie."

6. Some lent her guineas, some lent her crowns,
Some lent her shillings monie;
And she's paid doun five hundred crowns,
And she's gotten her bonnie love Geordie.

7. When she was mounted on her hie steed,
And on ahint her Geordie;
Na bird on the brier e'er sang sae clear,
As the young knight and his ladie:—

"My Geordie O, my Geordie O,
O the love I bear to Geordie;
The very stars in the firmament,
Bear tokens I loe Geordie."

39. "Geordie"

Kidson, 1891, p. 25. Collected by Charles Lolley, of Leeds, in the district of Howden, Yorkshire.

a D

"My Geordie he shall hang in chains,
In chains of gold and silver,
For stealing of the king's white deer."
. . . .

40. "Georgie"

Sung by Mrs. Georgia Dunaway, Fayetteville, Ark., May 10, 1951. LC/AAFS, rec. No. 10,821(A7). Also in Randolph, I, 1946, p. 164(D). Learned from her father, c. 1900. Collected by Mrs. Irene Carlisle.

a π^3

1. As I went over London's bridge,
'Twas early in the morning,
There I spied a pretty fair maid
Pleading for the life of Georgie.

2. Go saddle up my milkswhite steed,
And bridle them so gaily,
That I may ride to the King's castle town
And plead for the life of Georgie.

3. She rode all day and she rode all night
Till she was weak and weary;
While throwing back her fine yellow hair
She pleads for the life of Georgie.

4. She took from her pocket a purse of gold,
Saying here is money a-plenty.
Lawyers, lawyers, fee yourselves,
And spare me the life of Georgie.

5. George stepped up then unto the lawyer,
Saying, I have not murdered any,
But I've stole sixteen of the king's white steeds
And sold 'em in Boheeny.

6. Up stepped the lawyer then to George,
Saying, George, I'm sorry for you,
For your own confession has condemned you to die,
May the Lord have mercy upon you.

7. George walking up and down the street
A-bidding adieu to many,
A-bidding adieu to his own dear girl,
Which grieved him the most of any.

8. George shall be hung with a golden cord,
For of such there is not many,
Because he came from a royal race,
And he courted a handsome lady.

9. I wish I were over on yon hillside
Where kisses are a-plenty;
With a sword and a pistol by my side
I would fight for the life of Georgie.

41. [Geordie]

Sharp MSS., 4750/3309. Also in Sharp and Karpeles, 1932, I, p. 243(F). Sung by Mrs. Julie Boone, Micaville, N.C., October 3, 1918.

a π³

She rode up in the court-house yard,
Lawyers' money plenty.
Fee yourselves if it takes it all,
To save the life of my Georgie.

It's rise up, George, and plead for yourself,
For I cannot plead any longer.
Your own confession's hang-ed you,
The Lord have mercy on me.

It's I've not robbed no store-houses,
Nor done any murder,
But I stole sixteen of the king's fair steeds,
And I stole them in I-O-Bandy.

The own free cash was paid in my hand,
It all be paid in style-ee,
The own free cash was paid in my hand
To save the life of my Georgie.

42. "As I Walked Over London's Bridge"

Sung by S. F. Russell, Marion, Va., 1936. LC/AAFS, rec. No. 3159(B1). Collected by Sidney Robertson Cowell.

a π³

1. As I walked over London's bridge
   So early in the morning,
I overheard some fair one say,
   O spare me the life of Georgie,
I overheard some fair one say,
   O spare me the life of Georgie.

2. Go saddle and bridle my milk-white steed,
   Go saddle and bridle him { ?swiftly / quickly }
I'll ride away to the lone castle Carr (?Ker)
   A-pleading for the life of Georgie,
I'll ride away to the lone castle Carr
   A-pleading for the life of Georgie.

3. She rode all day and she rode all night
   Till she came wet and weary
A-combing back her long yellow locks
   A-pleading for the life of Georgie,
A-combing back her long yellow locks
   A-pleading for the life of Georgie.

4. And out her father drew his purse of gold,
   The like I never saw any,
Saying, Lawyers, Lawyers come ?fee yourselves
   And spare me the life of Georgie,
Saying, Lawyers, Lawyers come ?fee yourselves
   And spare me the life of Georgie.

5. Georgie was a-[standing by?]
   And he never killed anybody
But 'a stole sixteen of the King's white steeds
   And sold them in ?Golandie,
But 'a stole sixteen of the King's white steeds
   And sold them in ?Golandie.

6. The oldest lawyer [at the Bar?]
   Saying, George I'm sorry for you
That your own confession has condemned you to die
   May the Lord have mercy upon you,
That your own confession has condemned you to die
   May the Lord have mercy upon you.

7. As George was looking up through the street
   He bid farewell to many.
He bid farewell to his own true love
   Which grieved him worse than any.
He bid farewell to his own true love
   Which grieved him worse than any.

8. George was hung with a golden chain,
   The like I never saw any,
Because he came from a royal race
   And courted a virtuous lady,
Because he came from a royal race
   And courted a virtuous lady.

9. I wish I was on yonder hill
   Where kisses I've had many,
My sword and pistol all on my side,
   I'd fight for the life of Georgie,
My sword and pistol all on my side,
   I'd fight for the life of Georgie.

43. "Geordie"

Sharp MSS., 447/563. Sung by Mrs. Glover, Huish Episcopi, December 24, 1904.

p I

This seems a willful majorizing of a minor tune.

1. Georgie never stole no cows nor calves
Nor he never murdered any
But he did stole two of the king's fat deers
And sold them under vally.

2. Come bridle me my new marriage wife (*sic*)
Come bridle me my pony
That I may ride to the new Castle way
And fight for the life of Geordie.

3. Geordie was a walking over London Bridge
'Twas one morning early
There he met his fair pretty maid
Lamenting for her Geordie.

4. Geordie wished he was on yonder hill
Of kisses he had many
With a sword & pistol by my side
I am condemned already.

5. Georgie looked over his left shoulder
Sawed his sweetheart coming
He tossed his yaller gold lock behind
Come fight for the life of Geordie.

6. The Judge looked down on poor Geordie
I'm very sorry for you
Your own confections hanged you
And the Lord have mercy on you.

7. Geordie's coffin shall be made of the chains of gold
Such gold we could not valli
We know he came from a real good sort
And courted a French young lady.

8. He don't go very high but he
Will be passable in company
I'll get round him soon (*sic*).

GROUP D

44. "A Lamentable Ditty on the Death of Geordie"

Hogg, 2nd series, 1821, p. 104.

m I/Ly

In *JFSS*, I, No. 4 (1902), p. 165, Kidson observes that Hogg's air and text were received from David Constable; that Playford's *Dancing Master* (edition not specified) has a tune called, like Hogg's refrain, "Hey ho, my honey"; and notes that the Straloch lute-MS., 1687 (NL Scotland MS. Adv. 5.2.18), has a tune called "God be wi' the(e), Geordie."

1. Come, all you lusty northern lads,
That are so blythe and bonnie,
Prepare your hearts to be full sad,
To heare the end of Geordie.
Heigh-ho! heigh-ho! my bonnie love!
Heigh-ho! heigh-ho! my honey!
Heigh-ho! heigh-ho! my owne deare love!
And God be with my Geordie!

2. When Geordie to his triall came,
A thousand hearts were sorry;
A thousand lasses wept full sore,
And all for love of Geordie.
Heigh-ho, &c.

3. Some did say he would escape,
Some at his fall did glory;
But these were clownes and fickle louns,
And none that loved Geordie.
Heigh-ho, &c.

4. Might friends have satisfied the law,
Then Geordie would find many;
Yet bravely did he plead for life,
If mercy might be any.
Heigh-ho, &c.

5. But when this doughty carle was cast,
He was full sad and sorry;
Yet boldly did he take his death,
So patiently dyde Geordie.
Heigh-ho, &c.

6. As Geordie he went up the gate,
He tooke his leave of many;
He tooke his leave of his laird's wife,
Whom he lov'd best of any.
Heigh-ho, &c.

7. With thousand sighs and heavy looks,
Away from her he parted,
With whom he often blyth had beene,
Though now so heavy-hearted.
Heigh-ho, &c.

8. He writ a letter with his owne hand,
He thought he writ it bravely;
He sent it to Newcastle towne,
To his beloved lady.
Heigh-ho, &c.

9. Wherein he did at large bewaile
The occasion of his folly,
Bequeathing life unto the law,
His soule to heaven holy.
Heigh-ho, &c.

10. "Why, lady, leave to weep for me;
"Let not my ending grieve ye:
"Prove constant to the man you love,
"For I cannot relieve ye.
Heigh-ho, &c.

11. "Out upon thee, Withrington!
"And fie upon thee, Phœnix!
"Thou hast put down the doughty,
"That led the men from Anix.
Heigh-ho, &c.

12. "And fie on all such cruell carles,
"Whose crueltie's so fickle,
"To cast away a gentleman
"In hatred for so little!
Heigh-ho, &c.

13. "I would I were on yonder hill,
"Where I have been full merry;
"My sword and buckler by my side,
"To fight till I be weary.
Heigh-ho, &c.

14. "They well should know that took me first,
"Though hopes be now forsaken:
"Had I but freedome, arms, and health,
"I'd dye ere I'd be taken.
Heigh-ho, &c.

15. "But law condemns me to my grave;
"They have me in their power:
"There's none but Christ that can me save,
"At this my dying houre."
Heigh-ho, &c.

16. He call'd his dearest love to him,
When as his heart was sorry;
And speaking thus with manly heart,
"Deare sweeting, pray for Geordie."
Heigh-ho, &c.

17. He gave to her a piece of gold,
And bade her give't her bairns;
And oft he kiss'd her rosie lip,
And laid her in his armes.
Heigh-ho, &c.

18. And coming to the place of death,
He never changed colour;
The more they thought he would look pale,
The more his veins were fuller.
Heigh-ho, &c.

19. And with a cheereful countenance,
(Being at that time entreated
For to confesse his former life,)
These words he straight repeated:
Heigh-ho, &c.

20. "I never lifted oxe nor cow,
"Nor never murder'd any;
"But fifty horse I did receive
"Of a merchant-man of Gary;
Heigh-ho, &c.

21. "For which I am condemn'd to die,
"Though guiltlesse I stand dying.
"Deare gracious God, my soule receive,
"For now my life is flying!"
Heigh-ho, &c.

22. The man of death a part did act,
Grieves me to tell the story.
God comfort all the comfortlesse,
That did so well as Geordie!
Heigh-ho! heigh-ho! my bonnie love!
Heigh-ho! heigh-ho! my honey!
Heigh-ho! heigh-ho! mine owne true love!
Sweet Christ receive my Geordie!

45. "Georgie," or "Banstead Downs"

Broadwood, *JFSS*, I, No. 4 (1902), p. 164. Also in Broadwood, 1908, p. 32. Sung by Henry Burstow, Sussex, 1893.

p I/Ly

1. As I rode over Banstead Downs,
One mid-May morning early,
There I espied a pretty fair maid
Lamenting for her Georgie.

2. Saying "Georgie never stood on the King's highway,
He never robbèd money,
But he stole fifteen of the King's fat deer,
And sent them to Lord Navey.

3. "Oh, come and saddle my milk-white steed,
And bridle it all ready,
That I may go to my good Lord Judge
And ask the life of my Georgie!"

4. And when she came to the good Lord Judge
She fell down upon her knees already,
Saying, "My good Lord Judge, come pity me,
Grant me the life of my Georgie!"

5. The Judge looked over his left shoulder,
He seemed as he was very sorry:
"My pretty fair maid, you are come too late,
For he is condemned already.

6. "He will be hung in a silken cord
Where there has not been many,
For he came of royal blood,
And courted a virtuous lady."

7. "I wish I was on yonder hill,
Where times I have been many!
With a sword and buckler by my side
I would fight for the life of my Georgie!"

46. "Geordie"

Vaughan Williams MSS., III, p. 305. Sung at Hedgerley, June 1905.

p I/M

47. "Geordie"

Wilkinson MSS., 1935-36, p. 85. Sung by Mrs. Lucy McAllister, Harriston, Va., October 17, 1935.

p I/M

1. Saddle up, saddle up, my milk-white steed,
And bring to me my bonny.
It's I may ride to the new cast town,
To plead for the life of Georgie.

2. In comes this young lady riding amongst them all,
Saying: Georgie, I'm sorry for you.
If you don't come fast they will hang you Georgie,
And the Lord have mercy on you.

3. If I was a-standing on yonders hill,
Where kisses I've had many,
Bright swords and pistols by my side
I would fight for the life of Georgie.

4. In came the soldier a-walking amongst them all,
Looking both sad and sorry.
I'm afraid young lady you have come too late,
For Georgie is condemned already.

5. Speak for yourself George, speak for yourself,
For ain't you the face of many?
O speak for yourself George, speak for yourself,
For ain't you the face of many?

6. I'm sure that I never killed no one,
Although I have robbed many.
I stolen sixteen of the King's best teams
And sold them in Bo-valley.

7. George he was hung with a golden chain,
The chain did ring for many.
George he came from a noble race
And his mother was an honorable lady.

48. "Georgie"

Vaughan Williams MSS., III, p. 112.

p I

49. "Johnny Wedlock"

Chappell, 1939, p. 37. Contributed by Charles Tillett, Wanchese, N.C.; words 1924, tune 1935.

p π^1 (–II)

O Johnny Wedlock is my name,
And many a man does know me.
Of all the crimes I ever done
This crime will overcome me.

I've not robbed no man of his bride,
Nor have I took no man's money;
I stole three steeds from the king's wife
And sold them over in Virginia.

This old judge he stood there
With his head down over his left shoulder;
He ordered ten thousand to be paid down:
Dear, spare the life of Georgie.

50. [Geordie]

Sharp MSS., 3416/2507. Also in Sharp and Karpeles, 1932, I, p. 240(A). Sung by William F. Wells, Swannanoah, N.C., September 9, 1916.

p I, ending on II

1. As I crossed over London's Bridge
One morning bright and early,
I spied a maid for bide the way
Lamenting for poor Charlie.

2. Charlie was the son of a poor man
Who was loved by a fair lady.
It's by his own confession he must die.
May the Lord have mercy on him.

3. Charlie never murdered any one.
He stole sixteen of the king's white staff
And sold them in Virginee.

4. The king looked over his right shoulder
And thus he says to Charlie:
It's by your own confession you must die.
May the Lord have mercy on you.

5. The king looked over his left shoulder
And thus he says to Charlie:
It's by your own confession you must die.
Jinny have mercy on you.

51. [Geordie]

Sharp MSS., 3504/. Also in Sharp and Karpeles, 1932, I, p. 241(C). Sung by Mrs. Sarah Buckner, Black Mountain, N.C., September 19, 1916.

m π^1

She saddled up her milk white steed
She rode bright and gaily
She rode till she came to the King's High Court
Lamenting for poor Charlie

GROUP E

52. [Geordie]

Sharp MSS., 1011/. Sung by Charles Young, Puriton, August 14, 1906.

p I (–VI, inflected VII)

As I was a-walking over London Bridge
One morning O so early
There I beheld a most lady fair
Lamenting for her Georgie.

53. [Geordie]

Sharp MSS., 2119/2008. Sung by Mrs. Wixey (90), Buckland, April 6, 1909.

p I

The MS. ends the tune on A, but this is probably a slip of the pen.

1. As I was going over London Bridge
It was one morning early
There I met a fair lady
Lamenting for her Georgie.

2. Come fetch to me some little boy
That can go quick & early
The [*sic*] will go down ten miles in one hour
With a letter for a lady.

3. But when she came to the new Castle Gold (gaol?)
She bowed her head so slowly
Three times on her bended knees did fall
Saying Spare me the life of Georgie.

4. The Judge looked over his left shoulder
And he seem-ed very sorry
He said I think you've come too late
Georgie is condemned already.

5. It's six pretty babes that I have got
The seventh lies in my body
I freely part with them every one
If you'll spare me the life of Georgie.

6. It is not much Georgie have done
He have not killed any
But stole sixteen of the King's best steeds
And sold them in Bohenny.

7. My Georgie shall be hung in golden chains
Because there are not many
And because he came of a noble breed
And married a virtuous lady.

54. [Geordie]

Sung by Mrs. Mary Bird McAllister, Brown's Cove, Va., October 31, 1959. LC/AAFS, rec. No. 11,868(A11). Collected by Paul C. Worthington and George Foss.

p I/M

1. Saddle up, saddle up my milk-white steed
   And bring to me my bonny;
   It's I may ride to the new cast town
   For to plead for the life of Georgie.

2. In came this young lady, riding amongst them all,
   [With looks? loath? lawyers?] both sad and sorrow,
   I'm afeard, young lady, you have come too late,
   For Georgie's condemned already.

3. If I was a-standing on yonders hill
   Where kisses I've had many,
   Bright swords and pistols by my side,
   I would fight for the life of Georgie.

4. Speak for yourself, George, speak for yourself,
   O ain't you the fates of many?
   Speak for yourself, George, speak for yourself,
   O ain't you the fates of many?

5. I'm sure 'at I never killed no one,
   Although I have robbed many;
   I stole sixteen of the King's best team
   And sold them in Bovalley.

6. George he was hung with a golden chain,
   The chain did ring for many.
   O George he came of a noble race,
   And his mother was a honorable lady.

As Georgie was a-walking up and down the aisle
Bidding adieu to many
But when he came to his own true love,
Lord! it grieved him the want of any.

55. [Geordie]

Sharp MSS., 4384/. Also in Sharp and Karpeles, 1932, I, p. 242(E). Sung by Mrs. Molly E. Bowyer, Villamont, Va., June 10, 1918.

p M (inflected VII)

56. "Geordie," or "As I strolled over London Bridge"

Vaughan Williams MSS., I, p. 110. Sung at Fortune (?), August 1907.

p I

57. [Geordie]

Sharp MSS., 924/. Sung by William Bailey (60), Cannington, April 20, 1906.

a M, ending on II; or p I, ending on *VI*

[Third and fourth phrases:]
For George shall be hung in a chain of gold
For he courted a virtuous lady

"Cf. 'Girl I've left behind me.'" [*Sharp's MS. note.*]

58. "I'd fight for the life of Georgie"

Brown MSS., 16 b IV. Also in Schinhan, *Music, Brown Collection*, IV, 1957, p. 94(4). Sung by Miss Hattie McNeill.

p I (–VI)

Bonnie James Campbell

CHILD NO. 210

The tune which has the best claim to traditional association with this poignantly beautiful elegy appeared with it about fifty years after the first extant (fragmentary) text. Where it came from one cannot say, or even whether R. A. Smith arbitrarily set it to the words. It has been reprinted in later collections so often that it is unlikely to be dislodged. The rhythm of the song is so powerful in any case as almost to compel its tunes, despite varying contours, into a mutual resemblance.

The first tune is clearly related to other Scottish melodies, in particular "Todlen hame," which, as Glen has noted, goes under various names: "My ain fireside," "Armstrong's Farewell," "Robie douna gorrach," "Earl Douglas's Lament," "Lude Lament," and so forth. The same stuff went into the making of "Whistle and I'll come to you, my lad." In its earliest form, it appears to be a π^1 plagal tune, ending on the second to avoid the immediate restatement of the tonic at the opening of the next stanza. It seems likely that the final ending was a feminine one, like that of the first phrase:

This ending can be seen in a number of comparable tunes, e.g., "Todlen butt and Todlen ben" in *Orpheus Caledonius*, 1733, II, No. 41.

The melody, like those of other dactylic ballads (e.g., "Queen Jane," Child No. 170), has (four) long phrases, which confirms one's judgment that the words should be printed as long couplets.

The Vermont tune (variant 3) probably sprang out of a faded recollection of the genuine tune by coarse familiarity with "Vilikens." There may be echoes also of "Little Mohea."

According to the Gray-Muir MS. (NL Scotland MS. 2254), there is a tune for this ballad in Barsanti's collection called *Lyric Gems*, 1784, II, p. 123, a publication which I have not seen. 1784 would be a surprisingly early date for the song, since the earliest printed *text* found by Child was Finlay's in 1808. Only Herd's MSS. (Child A) antedate this.

LIST OF VARIANTS

1. "Bonnie George Campbell." Robert Archibald Smith, *The Scotish Minstrel* [1820-24], V, p. 50. Also in Robert Maver, *Genuine Scottish Melodies*, 1866, No. 303, p. 152; Alfred Moffat, *The Minstrelsy of Scotland*, 2nd ed. [1896], p. 68; and George Eyre-Todd, *Ancient Scots Ballads* [1894], p. 20.
2. "Bonnie George Campbell." Bascom Lamar Lunsford, LC Archive of American Folk Song, recording No. 9474(A2).
3. "Bonnie George Campbell." Phillips Barry, *JAF*, XVIII (1905), p. 294. Also in Phillips Barry, Fannie H. Eckstorm, and Mary W. Smyth, *British Ballads from Maine*, 1929, p. 284(D). (R.J.P.)
4. "James Campbell." Frank Proffitt, recorded by Evelyn K. Wells. Also (with other variations) on Folk-Legacy recording No. FSA-1, 1962.
5. "Bonnie George Campbell." Rory and Alex McEwen, H.M.V. recording No. 1143.

TUNES WITH TEXTS

1. "Bonnie George Campbell"

Smith [1820-24], V, p. 50. Also in Maver, 1866, No. 303, p. 152; Moffat, 2nd ed. [1896], p. 68; and Eyre-Todd [1894], p. 20.

p π^1, ending on II

Hie upon Hielands, and laigh upon Tay,
Bonnie George Campbell rode out on a day;
He saddled, he bridled, and gallant rode he,
And hame cam his guid horse, but never cam he.

Out cam his mother dear, greeting fu' sair,
And out cam his bonnie bryde riving her hair,
"My meadow lies green, and my corn is unshorn,
My barn is to build, and my baby's unborn."

In the second edition, Smith changed lines three and four of the second stanza to:

"The meadow lies green, the corn is unshorn,
But bonnie George Campbell will never return!"

and added a third stanza, as follows:

Saddled and bridled and booted rode he,
A plume in his helmet a sword at his knee,
But toom cam his saddle, all bloody to see,
Oh hame cam his guid horse but never cam he.

2. "Bonnie George Campbell"

Sung by Bascom Lamar Lunsford of Turkey Creek, N.C., March 1949, in the Library of Congress, Washington, D.C. LC/AAFS, rec. No. 9474(A2). Collected by Mrs. Rae Korson and Duncan Emrich.

m π^1

1. High upon Highlands, low upon Tay
   Bonnie George Campbell rode out on one day.
2. All saddled all bridled and booted rode he
   And home came the saddle but never came he.
3. My barn is to build, my baby's unborn
   But Bonnie George Campbell will never return.
4. Well, high upon Highlands, low upon Tay
   Bonnie George Campbell rode out on one day.
5. All saddled all bridled and booted rode he
   And home came the saddle but never came he.
6. Home came the saddle all bloody to see
   And home came the good horse but never came he.

3. "Bonnie James Campbell"

Barry, *JAF*, XVIII (1905), p. 294. Also in Barry, Eckstorm, and Smyth, 1929, p. 284(D). Sung by Mrs. R. J[ean] P[arker] of Bury, Quebec, at Newbury, Vt., August 15, 1905; learned a few years previously from Mrs. Jones (80), wife of a sea captain.

a I (inflected II)

Saddled and bridled and booted rode he,
Soon home came the saddle, but never came he.

4. "James Campbell"

Sung by Frank Proffitt, August 1961, at Pinewoods Camp, Plymouth, Mass. Recorded by Evelyn K. Wells. Also (with other variations) on Folk-Legacy rec. No. FSA-1, 1962.

a π^2

Booted and spurred and bridled rode he,
A plume in his saddle and a sword at his knee.
Back come his saddle, all bloody to see,
Back come the steed but never come he.

A-ridin' in the Highlands, steep was the way,
Ridin' in the Lowlands, hard by the Tay.
Out come his mother, with feet all so fair,
Out come his sweetheart, a-reivin' of her hair.

The meadow's all a-fallin' and the sheep is unshorn,
The house is a-leakin' and the baby's unborn,
But bonny James Campbell nowhere could be seen,
For back come the saddle but never come he.

Booted and spurred and bridled rode he,
A plume in his saddle and a sword at his knee.
Home come the saddle all bloody to see,
Home come the steed but never come he.

5. "Bonnie George Campbell"

Sung by Rory and Alex McEwen, Berwick, H.M.V. rec. No. 1143. Recorded by Peter Kennedy.

a I

Bewick and Graham

CHILD NO. 211

The single tune which has been preserved for this fine ballad comes apparently from Northumbrian tradition, and is printed only in Bruce and Stokoe, without information as to source. It is not among James Telfer's tunes in manuscript. What makes one more confident that it was derived from tradition is the fact that whoever set it down (?Stokoe) had trouble in noting the time of bars two and four. As they are given, they look like an attempt to fit free singing into the strait jacket of regular barring. If these two bars are lengthened to 4/4, we should probably have something closer to what was sung. The same thing may have occurred at the cadence of phrase three, or the singer may not have found a pause necessary.

There are not very many ballad-airs in genuine triple time. This one suggests the "Young Beichan" (Child No. 53) tradition. The final cadence makes it Mixolydian, but up to that point it could as well be major and plagal.

LIST OF VARIANTS

"The Bewick and the Græme." John Collingwood Bruce and John Stokoe, *Northumbrian Minstrelsy*, 1882, p. 25.

TUNE WITH TEXT

"The Bewick and the Græme"

Bruce and Stokoe, 1882, p. 25.
a M

1. Gude Lord Græme is to Carlisle gane,
    Sir Robert Bewick there met he,
And arm in arm to the wine they did go,
    And they drank till they were baith merrie.

2. Gude Lord Græme has ta'en up the cup—
    "Sir Robert Bewick and here's to thee!
And here's to our twa sons at hame!
    For they like us best in our ain countrie."—

3. "O were your son a lad like mine,
    And learn'd some books that he could read,
They might hae been twa brethren bauld,
    And they might hae bragg'd the Border side.

4. But your son's a lad, and he's but bad,
    And billie to my son he canna be."
. . . .
. . . .

5. "Ye sent him to the schools and he wadna learn,
    Ye bought him books and he wadna read."—
"But my blessing shall he never earn
    Till I see how his arm can defend his head."

6. Gude Lord Græme has a reckoning call'd,
    A reckoning then called he;
And he paid a crown, and it went roun',
    It was all for the gude wine and free.

7. And he has to the stable gane,
    Where there stude thirty steeds and three,
He's ta'en his ain horse amang them a',
    And hame he rade sae manfullie.

8. "Welcome, my auld father!" said Christie Græme,
    "But where sae lang frae hame were ye?"—
"It's I hae been at Carlisle town,
    And a baffled man by thee I be.

9. "I hae been at Carlisle town,
    Where Sir Robert Bewick he met me;
He says ye're a lad, and ye are but bad,
    And billie to his son ye canna be.

10. "I sent ye to the schools and ye wadna learn,
    I bought ye books and ye wadna read,
Therefore, my blessing ye shall never earn,
    Till I see with Bewick thou save thy head."

11. "Now God forbid, my auld father,
    That ever sic a thing suld be;
Billie Bewick was my master and I was his scholar,
    And aye sae weel as he learned me."

12. "O hald thy tongue, thou limmer loon,
    And of thy talking let me be;
If thou disna end me this quarrel soon
    There is my glove, I'll fight wi' thee."

13. Then Christie Græme he stooped low,
    Unto the ground you shall understand—
"O father put on your glove again,
    The wind has blown it from your hand."

14. "What's that thou says, thou limmer loon,
How dares thou stand to speak to me?
If thou do not end this quarrel soon,
There's my right hand, thou shalt fight with me."

15. Then Christie Græme's to his chamber gane,
To consider weel what then should be,
Whether he should fight with his auld father,
Or with his billie Bewick, he.

16. "If I suld kill my billie dear,
God's blessing I shall never win;
But if I strike at my auld father,
I think 'twould be a mortal sin.

17. "But if I kill my billie dear,
It is God's will, so let it be;
But I make a vow ere I gang frae hame,
That I shall be the next man's dee."

18. Then he's put on his back a gude auld jack,
And on his head a cap of steel,
And sword and buckler by his side,
O gin he did not become them weel!

19. We'll leave off talking of Christie Græme,
And talk of him again belyve,
And we will talk of bonnie Bewick,
Where he was teaching his scholars five.

20. When he had taught them well to fence,
And handle swords without any doubt,
He took his sword under his arm,
And he walk'd his father's close about.

21. He looked atween him and the sun,
And a' to see what there might be,
Till he spied a man in armour bright,
Was riding that way most hastilie.

22. "O wha is yon that cam this way,
Sae hastilie that hither came?
I think it be my brother dear!
I think it be young Christie Græme.—

23. "Ye're welcome here, my billie dear,
And thrice ye're welcome unto me!"
"But I'm wae to say I've seen the day
When I am come to fight wi' thee.

24. "My father's gane to Carlisle town
Wi' your father Bewick there met he:
He says I'm a lad and I am but bad,
And a baffled man I trow I be.

25. "He sent me to schools and I wadna learn;
He gae me books and I wadna read;
Sae my father's blessing I'll never earn
Till he see how my arm can guard my head."—

26. "O God forbid, my billie dear,
That ever such a thing suld be;
We'll take three men on either side,
And see if we can our father's agree."

27. "Oh haud thy tongue now, billie Bewick,
And of thy talking let me be;
But if thou'rt a man, as I'm sure thou art,
Come o'er the dyke and fight wi' me."—

28. "But I hae nae harness, billie, on my back,
As weel I see there is on thine,"—
"But as little harness as is on thy back,
As little, billie, shall be on mine."—

29. Then he's thrown off his coat o' mail,
His cap of steel awa flung he;
He stuck his spear into the ground,
And he tied his horse unto a tree.

30. Then Bewick has thrawn aff his cloak,
And's psalter-book frae's hand flung he;
He laid his hand upon the dyke,
And ower he lap most manfullie.

31. O they hae fought for twa lang hours,—
When twa lang hours were come and gane
The sweat drapp'd fast frae aff them baith,
But a drop o' blude could not be seen.

32. Till Græme gae Bewick an akward stroke,
An akward stroke strucken sickerlie;
He has hit him under the left breast,
And dead-wounded to the ground fell he.

33. "Rise up, rise up, now, billie dear!
Arise and speak three words to me!—
Whether thou's gotten' thy deadly wound,
Or if God and good leeching may succour thee?"—

34. "O horse, O horse, now, billie Græme,
And get thee far from hence with speed,
And get thee out of this country,
That none may know who has done the deed."—

35. "O I have slain thee, billie Bewick,
If this be true thou tellest to me;
But I made a vow ere I came frae home,
That aye the next man I wad be."—

36. He has pitched his sword in a moodie hill,
And he has leap'd twenty lang feet and three,
And on his ain sword's point he lap,
And dead upon the ground fell he.

37. Twas then came up Sir Robert Bewick,
And his brave son alive saw he.
"Rise up, rise up, my son," he said,
"For I think ye hae gotten the victorie."—

38. "O haud your tongue, my father dear!
Of your pridefu' talking let me be!
Ye might hae drunken your wine in peace,
And let me and my billie be.

39. "Gae dig a grave baith wide and deep,
And a grave to haud baith him and me;

But lay Christie Græme on the sunny side,
For I'm sure he wan the victorie."

40. "Alack! a wae!" auld Bewick cried,
"Alack, was I not much to blame?
I'm sure I've lost the liveliest lad
That e'er was born unto my name."—

41. "Alack! a wae!" quo gude Lord Græme,
"I'm sure I hae lost the deeper lack!
I durst hae ridden the Border through,
Had Christie Græme been at my back.

42. "Had I been led through Liddesdale,
And thirty horsemen guarding me,
And Christie Græme been at my back,
Sae soon as he had set me free!

43. "I've lost my hopes, I've lost my joy,
I've lost the key but and the lock;
I durst hae ridden the world around,
Had Christie Græme been at my back."

Bruce and Stokoe take their text from Scott's *Minstrelsy* (e.g., Scott, *Poetical Works*, 1833-34, III, p. 69).

The Duke of Athole's Nurse

CHILD NO. 212

For all these late romantic Scottish ballads which employ the favorite feminine ending in the second and fourth phrases, we are very likely to find the same two or three tunes being handed about in abundantly variant forms. The commonest, probably, are the "Binorie" type and the "Gypsy Laddie."

The A-group of the present ballad belongs to the first of these, the "Binorie" family. Telfer's tune has not (to my knowledge) been printed hitherto, as this ballad was not included in *Northumbrian Minstrelsy*. Greig's 1b and 1c tunes (variants 2 and 3 below) are in a very characteristic form of it; his 1a (variant 7) in a form only a little less familiar. Christie's tune is so tinkered up that it is hard to recognize, the original alternations between the Æolian and Dorian sixths being, however attractive, untypical of Scottish folk melody as we know it. But, as Keith observes, Christie's second strain has clear affiliations with Greig's 1b and 1c, which come from the same geographical area. All four tunes properly belong in the Æolian camp; they are plagal, but the lower range reaches to the octave in Christie's variant, and to lower III in others, and hence they may alternatively be regarded as authentic tunes ending an octave above.

The second class is represented by only one example, Greig's 2 (variant 9). The second and third phrases of it are closely paralleled in Greig's first "Geordie" (No. 209) tunes, 1a and 1b. Those tunes are M/D and Æolian, the present one clearly Mixolydian. All belong to the "Gypsy Laddie" family, but the present tune is farther than usual from the traditional center.

LIST OF VARIANTS

GROUP Aa

1. "The Duke of Athol's Nurse." James Telfer MS. ('Mr. Telfer's tunes'), No. 39, p. 19; in MS. C 30, Society of Antiquaries Library, Newcastle-upon-Tyne.
2. "The Duke of Athole's Nurse." Greig MSS., I, p. 129, King's College Library, Aberdeen. Also in Gavin Greig and Alexander Keith, *Last Leaves of Traditional Ballads and Ballad Airs*, 1925, p. 136(1b). (Ritchie)
3. "The Duke of Athole's Nurse." Greig MSS., IV, p. 142, and Bk. 772, LXII, p. 67. Also in Greig and Keith, 1925, p. 136(1c). (Imlah)
4. "The Duke o' Athole's Nurse." Greig MSS., IV, p. 129, and Bk. 717, VII, p. 74. (Robb)
5. "The Duke of Athole's Nurse." Miss M. Douglas Gordon (singer), Archive, School of Scottish Studies, University of Edinburgh.

GROUP Ab

6. "The Duke of Athole's Nurse." Greig MSS., I, p. 159, and Bk. 764, LIV, p. 30. (J. W. Spence)
7. "The Duke o' Athole's Nurse." Greig MSS., III, p. 22. Also in Greig and Keith, *Last Leaves*, 1925, p. 136(1a). (J. W. Spence, Sr.)

GROUP Ac

8. "The Duke of Athole's Nurse." W. Christie, *Traditional Ballad Airs*, I, 1876, p. 80.

GROUP B

9. "The Duke of Athole's Nurse." Greig and Keith, *Last Leaves*, 1925, p. 136(2). From Duncan MS., No. 11. (Gillespie)

TUNES WITH TEXTS

GROUP Aa

1. "The Duke of Athol's Nurse"

Telfer MS., No. 39, p. 19.

p P/Æ (on mediant octave)

2. "The Duke of Athole's Nurse"

Greig MSS., I, p. 129. Also in Greig and Keith, 1925, p. 136(1b). Sung by Miss Annie Ritchie, Whitehill, March 1906.

p D/Æ

Oh wisna she a wily wily wife
And wisna she weel worth the reesin'
Wisna she a wily wily wife
She set the young squire to the bakin'.

3. "The Duke of Athole's Nurse"

Greig MSS., IV, p. 142; text, Bk. 772, LXII, p. 67. Also in Greig and Keith, 1925, p. 136(1c). Sung by Mrs. Imlah, Weetingshill, New Deer, November 29, 1911.

p D/Æ

Oh, I am the Duke o' Athole's Nurse,
And my trade is very well becoming;
And I would gie a' my half-year's fee
For one sight o' my leman.

If ye be the Duke o' Athole's Nurse,
Your trade is very well becoming;
Keep well, keep well your half-year's fee,
Ye'll get two sights o' your leman.

. . . .

They socht but, & they socht ben,
And spared nae the curtains a-tearin'
But a' that they socht, & a' that they wrocht,
They kissed the young squire at his bakin'.

. . . .

Aye as she gaed but & ben
She said, Lassie, mind your bakin'.

4. "The Duke of Athole's Nurse"

Greig MSS., IV, p. 129; text, Bk. 717, VII, p. 74. From Alexander Robb; learned from his grandmother, who was born c. 1780 at Mill of Crimond.

p D/Æ

1. As I cam in by the Duke of Atholl's (Athole's) gates
I heard his yule nurse singin
And aye as she sang and her bonnie voice rang
Till hills and dales were ringin

2. Oh, I am the bonnie Duke of Atholl's nurse
And the post it does well become me
And I would gie a' my half-year's fee
For a kiss and a sicht o' my Johnny.

3. He leant him in over his saddle bow
And he has gien her kisses mony,
Says, Keep weel, keep weel your half year's fee
You'll get twa sichts o' your Johnny.

4. But ye have my heart and another has my hand,
And what can I do wi' ye?
But gin I hae your heart and another has your hand
What the better will I be of you?

5. But you'll go doon to yonder ale house
And drink or the day be a-dawnin'
And spare nae the beer tho' it be dear
And the wine keep constantly drawin.
And gin I be a woman as surely as I am
I will come and clear ye o' your lawin.

6. Her seven brothers were standin' near by
And they heard them thus talkin
And they hae said amon' themselves
We'll go and clear this lawin.

7. So he went down to yonder ale house
And drank till the day was a-dawnin'
And he spared nae the beer although it was dear
And the wine he kept constantly drawin.

8. But he lookit over the castle wa'
To see gin the day was a-dawnin
And there he spied seven well armed men
They were comin wi' their swords well drawn.

9. O Landlady, O Landlady what shall I do
For my life it is nae worth a farthin
For here they come seven well armed men
I'll be dead or the day be a-dawnin.

10. But she's castin aff her petticoat
Likewise her goon & her apron
And she has gien him the mutch frae aff her heid
And she set the young squire to the bakin.

11. Oh when they came up to the gates
Sae loudly as they rappit
Oh when they came up to the door
Sae loudly as they chappit.

12. Oh cam there a stranger here last night
To drink or the day was a-dawnin
Come show us the room that the stranger is in
For we've come to clear his lawin.

13. Oh there cam a stranger here last night
But he went ere the day was a-dawnin
For he bocht but a pint and he paid it ere he went
So he didna leave ony lawin.

14. But they socht him up & they socht him doon
And they spared nae the feather beds a-turnin
And aye as they gaed but and aye as they gaed ben
They said Bonnie lassie are ye bakin'.

15. They socht him up and they socht him doon
And spared nae the curtains a-rivin
And aye as the auld wife gaed but and ben
She scolded her maid at the bakin'
And she said I have had mony a maid
But the marrows o' you I never had bakin'.

16. They socht him up and they socht him doon
Through kitchie and ha' a-rankin'
But for a' that they ca'd and a' that they socht
They left the young squire busy bakin.

5. "The Duke of Athole's Nurse"

Archive, School of Scottish Studies. Sung by Miss M. Douglas Gordon, 1953. Collected by Francis M. Collinson for the School of Scottish Studies. Transcribed by the collector.

a Æ, ending on the octave

Oh it's I am the Duke of Athole's nurse
And the post as weel becoming,
But I would gie' my half year's fee
For the sight of my true love's . . . ?*

* Collinson suggests that the last words may be "love Johnnie."

GROUP Ab

6. "The Duke of Athole's Nurse"

Greig MSS., I, 159; text, Bk. 764, LIV, p. 30. Sung by J. W. Spence, Rosecroft, Fyvie, April 1906.

m D/Æ

1. As I came in by the Duke o' Athole's gates
I heard a fair maid singing
She sang sae sweet, & so very complete
Till the hills & the dales were ringing.

*2. A lang lang mile e'er he cam near
She heard his bridles ringin'
A lang lang mile e'er she cam' near
He heard her sweet voice singin'

3. O I am the Duke o' Athole's nurse
And I'm sure it weel does fa' me
I wad gie a' my half year's fee
For ae sicht o' my *Geordie*.

4. He's leant him over his saddle bows
And he's gi'en her kisses mony
Says "Keep weel, keep weel your half year's fee
Ye'll get twa sichts o' your *Geordie*."

5. "Ye hae my hand & anither has my heart
And fat mair can I dae wi' ye"?
Gin ane hae yer hand & anither has yer heart
It's what better will I be o' ye?"

6. Yell gang ye doon to yon tavern high
And drink till the day it be dawning
And ye'll spare no the beer although it be dear
And ye'll cause the wine to be drawn
And aye ye'll drink to bonnie lassie's health
That's comin' to clear up the lawin'.

7. He's gane him doon to yon tavern high
And he drank till the day it was dawin'
And aye he drank to the bonnie lassie's health
That was comin' to clear up the lawin'.

8. He's ta'en him up to yon window high
To see gin the day it was dawin'
And there he spied her seven brithers comin'
Wi' their swords a' weel drawn.

9. O landlady, landlady what shall I do
For my life it's nae worth a farthin'
For they're comin' in revenge o' my fair maid's vows
And I'll ne'er see the day dawing.

10. She's casten aff her petticoats
Likewise her gown & her apron
And she has put them all on upon him
And she's set the young squire to the bakin'.

11. When they cam up to the gate
Sae loudly as they rappit
And when they cam up to the door
Sae loudly as they chappit.

12. Cam' there a stranger here last nicht,
Drank he till the day it was dawin'?
Come show us the room that your stranger is in
We are come to clear up his lawin'.

13. There cam a stranger here last night
But he drankna till the day it was dawin'
He called for a pint & he paid it e'er he went
So there's no more to clear of the lawin'.

14. They sought but & they sought ben
And they kissed the bonnie lassie bakin'
But for a' that they wrought, & for a that they sought
They left the young squire busy bakin'.

15. The wife scauled but, & she scauled ben
And she scauled the bonnie lassie bakin'
But for a that they wrought, & for a that they sought
They left the young squire busy bakin'.

* Greig noted this stanza as "unique."

7. "The Duke o' Athole's Nurse"

Greig MSS., III, p. 22. Also in Greig and Keith, 1925, p. 136(1a). Sung by J. W. Spence, Sr. (85), Rosecroft, Fyvie, September 1907.

m D/Æ

It's I am the Duke o' Athole's nurse,
And I'm sure it weel does fa' me,
I wad gie a' my half-year's fee
For ae sicht o' my Geordie.

GROUP AC

8. "The Duke of Athole's Nurse"

Christie, I, 1876, p. 80. From Christie's maternal grandfather.

a D/Æ (inflected VI), ending on the octave

In this case Christie may have invented the first strain and left the second fairly close to the traditional form of the one-strain tune.

As I gaed in yon greenwood side,
I heard a fair maid singing;
Her voice was sweet, she sang sae complete,
That all the woods were ringing.
"O, I am the Duke o' Athole's nurse,
My post is well becoming;
But I would gi'e a' my half year's fee,
For ae sight o' my leman."

[*Etc.*]

Text, with some alterations by Christie, from Peter Buchan's *Ancient Ballads and Songs of the North of Scotland*, 1828, II, p. 23.

GROUP B

9. "The Duke of Athole's Nurse"

Greig and Keith, 1925, p. 136(2); from Duncan MS., No. 11. Sung by Mrs. Gillespie.

a M

1. As he cam in by yon toon en',
She heard his bridles ringin,
An' when he cam in by the Castle wa',
He heard her bonnie voice singin.

2. "O I'm the Duke o' Athole's nurse,
My post is very weel becomin,
But I wad gie a' my half year's fee
For ae sicht o my leman."

3. "Ye say ye're the Duke o Athole's nurse,
An' your post it is very weel becomin;
Keep weel, keep weel your half year's fee,
Ye'll get twa sichts o your leman."

4. He leaned him ower his saddle bow,
An' cannily kissed his dearie;
Said, "Ye hae my heart, but another has my han',
What better can ye be o me?"

5. "Gin I hae your heart, an' another has your han',
These words hae fairly undone me;
But let us set a time, an' tryst to meet again,
Then in good friendship ye'll twine me.

6. "Ye'll do ye doon to yon tavern house,
An' drink till it be dawin,
An' as sure as I'm a woman true,
I'll come an' clear your lawin.

7. "Ye'll spare not the wine, although it be fine,
Nor any drink though it be rarely;
But ye'll aye drink to the bonnie lassie's health
That's to clear your lawin fairly."

8. Then he's done him doon to yon tavern house,
An' drank till the day was dawin,
An' ilka gless he drank, he drank the lassie's health,
That was comin to clear his lawin.

9. "It's a wonder to me," the squire he did say,
"That my bonnie lassie's sae delayin;
She promised as sure as she loved me,
She wad be here by the dawin."

10. He's teen him up to a shott window,
A little before the dawin,
An' there he spied her brothers three
Wi' their swords a' weel drawn.

11. "O where shall I rin, or where shall I gang,
Or where shall I gang an' hide me?
She that was to meet me in friendship this day
Has sent her brothers to slay me."

12. He's gane to the landlady o the house,
To see gin she could save him.
She dressed him in her ain clothin,
An' she set him to the bakin.

13. She gae him a suit o her ain female claes,
An' set him to the bakin;
The birds never sang mair sweet on the bush,
Than the young squire sang at his bakin.

14. As they came in at the ha' door,
Sae loodly as they rappit,
An' when they cam upon the floor,
Sae loodly as they chappit.

15. "O had ye a quarterer here last nicht,
Who drank till the day was dawin?
Come show us the room where the quarterer lies in,
An' we'll shortly clear his lawin."

16. "There was nae quarterer here last nicht
That drank till the day was dawin.
He called for a pint, an' he paid it ere he went,
Ye've got naething to do wi his lawin."

17. One of them bein in a very merry mood,
To the young squire fell a-talkin;
The wife took her foot an' she gae him a kick,
Says, "Haste ye, bonnie Annie, wi your bakin."

18. They socht the house up, an' they socht the house doon,
An' they spared nae the curtains for the rivin,
An' ilka ane o them, as they passed by,
They kissed the bonnie lassie at her bakin.

Sir James the Rose

CHILD NO. 213

OF THIS rather tasteless ballad, not popular but popularized, and apparently much affected in Scotland, the melodic tradition is fairly consistent and perhaps basically one. With the exception of Christie's first tune ("Old way"), which he claims to be able to trace back traditionally for a century and a quarter, it is obvious that all the tunes were meant for texts that had a masculine rhyme at 2 and 4—that is, for the ballad generally attributed to Michael Bruce. Inasmuch as the other form, too, was "made for print," we need not be careful to exclude the favored ballad from the traditional canon. Christie's tune, incidentally, appears to have a strong infusion of the later form of the song "Ewe-buchts, Marion," widely printed in the last quarter of the eighteenth century and after. But Christie is so untrustworthy that he may himself have introduced the feminine cadence; and his tune, stripped down, may probably derive from the same tradition as the rest.

The main line of the melodic tradition belongs in the D to Æ province, inclining uneasily in a few exceptional cases toward the major. The latter look as though they had forgotten their earlier outlines and their true tonic; and viewing them in isolation, one would hardly relate them to the others.

Perhaps a more general observation is in order at this point. In connection with these abnormal variants, particularly Greig's 1d and 1e (variants 20 and 19 below, respectively), it is natural, in the light thrown by the large majority of examples, to conclude that the final here is not the true tonic. The cast of the tune still remains recognizably the same, with the same modal feeling, when we put it into the context to which it belongs. But just here we must be on guard. We ought probably to be cautious in restoring or imposing that earlier tonic-final when the tune has shown a tendency to adopt a different one. For a song is not sung in a context of variants: it is a solitary. When we meet it so, the (new) final may make an entirely satisfactory resting-point for our now ignorant ears, so that we class the tune unquestioningly in the mode of that final. Or we may be in doubt between the final and one or even two or three alternative possibilities, according to whether the emphases and cadences of earlier phrases have made us aware of certain pivotal notes. But doubtless it is in just this way that modal changes often occur. There is a weakening of the tonal center; and from the various possibilities which the phrases of the tune successively offer, sometimes one will be chosen for anchor, sometimes another. But the choice is not unlimited: it will naturally be among the notes important to the tune as it stands—resting places which, when final, generate a mode close at hand, and out of corresponding segments of the same scale, whether pentatonic, hexatonic, or heptatonic.

Thus, for example, in Greig's 1d (variant 20) below, the mass of evidence shows that the tune "ought" to end on G. The cadence A-G would have been perfectly natural. But the lower seventh (here F) has been planted at strategic points throughout, and that note's own fourth above and fifth below make melodic pivots which reinforce its importance. By the time we reach the end of the third phrase, the "lower seventh" has thus established itself as a quite satisfactory anchor for the tune, and is so stated in the final cadence. Thus the tune has changed from P/Æ to M/D, both plagal. We should, I believe, be wary of denying this new development because of previous knowledge, and of insisting that the "true" tonic is still G. The temptation, I repeat, is strong to do so—nor have I been able to resist it; but to yield is to make our melodic sensibilities slaves to historical event and accidental knowledge which in the next instance may probably be denied us. Thus all our judgments as to mode become more, instead of less, subjective, in comparison with the solid objectivity of a rule that the final is tonic. I believe, therefore, that we should give up that anchorage only when driven from it by the strongest pressures.

The main tradition here, to revert to our starting-point, is closely tied up with that of "Gil Morrice" (Child No. 83). The tune was used also with "Young Johnstone" (No. 88), "Fause Foodrage" (No. 89), and with the notorious "Hardyknute," to which it is mated in Johnson's *Museum* (see variant 21 below). It is often π^4, and plagal; not seldom D/Æ, plagal.

Several variants have been collected in the Maritime Provinces which are hard to align with the rest. One of these looks like the relative minor of another (cf. Karpeles MSS. Nos. 5317 and 5320); and two are of the "Come-all-ye" pattern, having stronger affiliations elsewhere, perhaps among the bothy songs and ballads.

LIST OF VARIANTS

GROUP A

1. "Sir James the Rose." Greig MSS., II, p. 147, King's College Library, Aberdeen. (Farquhar)
2. "Sir James the Rose." Greig-Duncan MS. 785 (transcription of W. Walker), p. 106, King's College Library, Aberdeen. From Duncan MS., No. 351. (Harper)
3. "Sir James the Rose." Greig MSS., III, p. 46. (Quirrie)
4. "Sir James the Rose." Greig MSS., III, p. 21. (R[ae])
5. "Sir James the Rose." Greig MSS., IV, p. 141. (Keith)
6. "Sir James the Rose." W. Christie, *Traditional Ballad Airs*, I, 1876, p. 18.
7. "Sir James the Rose." Gavin Greig and Alexander Keith, *Last Leaves of Traditional Ballads and Ballad Airs*, 1925, p. 140(1a). From Duncan MS., No. 6. (Duncan)
8. "Sir James the Rose." Greig MSS., III, p. 37. Also in Greig-Duncan MS. 785 (Walker), p. 106. (Hall)
9. "Sir James the Rose." Robert Maver, *Genuine Scottish Melodies*, 1866, No. 286, p. 143.
10. "Sir James the Rose." Greig MSS., III, p. 119. Also in Greig-Duncan MS. 785 (Walker), p. 106. (Thain)
11. "Sir James the Rose." Greig MSS., III, p. 11. Also in Greig and Keith, *Last Leaves*, 1925, p. 141(1c). (Rettie)
12. "Sir James the Rose." Greig MSS., III, p. 116. Also in Greig and Keith, 1925, p. 140(1b). (Lee)
13. "Sir James the Rose." Greig MSS., IV, p. 186. Also in Greig and Keith, 1925, p. 141(2). (Angus)
14. "Sir James the Rose." James Telfer MS. ('Mr. Telfer's

tunes'), No. 18, p. 9; in MS. C 30, Society of Antiquaries Library, Newcastle-upon-Tyne.

15. "Sir James the Rose." Christie, *Traditional Ballad Airs*, I, 1876, p. 16.
16. "Sir James the Rose." W. Roy MacKenzie, *Ballads and Sea Songs from Nova Scotia*, 1928, pp. 394 and 48.
17. "Sir James the Ross." Maud Karpeles MSS., No. 5317, and p. 4867. Also in Karpeles, *JEFDSS*, III, No. 1 (1936), p. 58(3).
18. "Sir James the Rose." Karpeles MSS., No. 5319, and p. 4874. Also in Karpeles, *JEFDSS*, III, No. 1 (1936), p. 58(4).
19. "Sir James the Rose." Greig MSS., III, p. 203. Also in Greig and Keith, *Last Leaves*, 1925, p. 141(1e). (Towers)
20. "Sir James the Rose." Greig MSS., III, p. 63. Also in Greig and Keith, 1925, p. 141(1d). (Robb)

GROUP A APPENDIX

21. "Hardyknute." James Johnson, *The Scots Musical Museum*, III, [1790], No. 280, p. 289 (repr. 1853).

GROUP B

22. "Sir James the Rose." Anne G. Gilchrist, *JEFDSS*, III, No. 1 (1936), p. 55.

GROUP C

23. "Sir James the Ross." Robert Archibald Smith, *The Scotish Minstrel* [1820-24], II, p. 30.

GROUP D

24. "Sir James the Rose." Karpeles MSS., No. 5320. Also in Karpeles, *JEFDSS*, III, No. 1 (1936), p. 59(5).

GROUP E

25. "Sir James, the Rose." Helen Hartness Flanders and Marguerite Olney, *Ballads Migrant in New England*, 1953, p. 148. Also in Helen Hartness Flanders, *Ancient Ballads Traditionally Sung in New England*, III, 1963, p. 245(B).
26. "Sir James the Ross." Helen Creighton and Doreen H. Senior, *Traditional Songs from Nova Scotia*, 1950, p. 78(B).
27. "Sir James the Ross." Creighton and Senior, 1950, p. 75(A).

TUNES WITH TEXTS

GROUP A

1. "Sir James the Rose"

Greig MSS., II, p. 147. From Mrs. Farquhar, Maud, September 1907.

p π^4

Of all the Scottish northern chiefs,
Of high & warlike name,
The bravest was Sir James the Rose,
A knight o' meikle fame.

2. "Sir James the Rose"

Greig-Duncan MS. 785 (Walker transcript), p. 106; from Duncan MS., No. 351. Sung by Mrs. Harper, Cluny; learned from her mother.

p π^4

O'er hills and dales the page he ran
Until a lonely glen,
And there he met Sir John the Graeme
Wi' twenty o' his men.

3. "Sir James the Rose"

Greig MSS., III, p. 46. From J. Quirrie, Turriff.

p π^4

Of all the Scottish northern chiefs
Of high & mighty name
The bravest was Sir James the Rose,
A knicht o' muckle fame.

4. "Sir James the Rose"

Greig MSS., III, p. 21. From J. S. Rae, Banff, September 1907.

m π^4

Of all our northern Scottish chiefs
Of high & warlike name,
The bravest was Sir James the Rose
Of meikle worth & fame.

5. "Sir James the Rose"

Greig MSS., IV, p. 141. Sung by A. Keith.

p π^4

6. "Sir James the Rose"

Christie, I, p. 18. From Aberdeenshire tradition.

m π^4

Of all the Scottish northern chiefs,
Of high and warlike name,
The bravest was Sir James the Rose,
A knicht of meikle fame.
The chieftain of the brave clan Ross,
A firm, undaunted band;
Five hundred warriors drew their sword,
Beneath his high command.
[*Etc.*]

Christie's text is "epitomized" from that of Michael Bruce in Alexander Whitelaw, *The Book of Scottish Ballads*, 1844, p. 41.

7. "Sir James the Rose"

Greig and Keith, 1925, p. 140(1a); from Duncan MS., No. 6. Sung by Rev. J. B. Duncan, who learned it from his father.

p π^4

Of all the Scottish northern chiefs,
Of high and warlike name,
The bravest was Sir James the Rose,
A Knicht o muckle fame.

8. "Sir James the Rose"

Greig MSS., III, p. 37. Also in Greig-Duncan MS. 785 (Walker transcript), p. 106. Sung by Miss Hall, New Deer, October 1907.

p π^4

Of all the Scottish northern chiefs
Of high and mighty name,
The bravest was Sir James the Rose,
A knicht o' muckle fame.

9. "Sir James the Rose"

Maver, 1866, No. 286, p. 143 ("Hardy knute").

p D/Æ

In nearly identical form and metre, this tune is given for "Edom o Gordon" (No. 178) in the 1869 edition of Ritson's *Scotish Songs*, II, p. 362.

10. "Sir James the Rose"

Greig MSS., III, p. 119. Also in Greig-Duncan MS. 785 (Walker transcript), p. 106. Sung by Mrs. Thain, New Deer.

p D/Æ

11. "Sir James the Rose"

Greig MSS., III, p. 11. Also in Greig and Keith, 1925, p. 141(1c). Sung by Mrs. Rettie, Milbrex, September 1907.

p π^4

Comparison may be made here with S. Fraser, *Highland Airs* [1816], p. 99 ("Macdonald Lord of the Isles").

They spurred their steeds & furious flew
Like lightning o'er the lea,
And reached Lord Buchan's lofty towers
By dawning of the day.

12. "Sir James the Rose"

Greig MSS., III, p. 116. Also in Greig and Keith, 1925, p. 140(1b). Sung by Mrs. Lee, Strichen, June 1908.

p π4

Of all the Scottish northern chiefs,
Of high & mighty name,
The bravest was the good Sir James,
A knicht o' mickle fame.

13. "Sir James the Rose"

Greig MSS., IV, p. 186. Also in Greig and Keith, 1925, p. 141(2). Sung by James Angus, 1913; learned from W. Blow, a cooper, c. 1870.

a π4

14. "Sir James the Rose"

Telfer MS., No. 18, p. 9.

a Æ

15. "Sir James the Rose"

Christie, I, 1876, p. 16. Christie arranged the tune "from two copies got in Buchan" by his father; in tradition from 120 years before.

p D/Æ

Oh heard ye o' Sir James the Rose,
The young heir o' Buleichan?
For he has killed a gallant squire,
Whase friends are out to tak' him.

Now he's gane to the house of Mar,
Whare the nourice was his leman;
To seek his dear he did repair,
Weening she might befriend him.

[*Etc.*]

Christie took his text from Alexander Whitelaw, *The Book of Scottish Ballads*, 1844, p. 39.

16. "Sir James the Rose"

Mackenzie, 1928, p. 394; text, p. 48. Sung by Robert Reid, River John, Pictou County, N.S.

p D/Æ

1. Of all the Scottish northern chiefs
Of high and warlike name,
The bravest was Sir James the Rose,
A knight of muckle fame.

2. His growth was like the youthful oak
That crowns the mountain brow,
And waving o'er his shoulders broad
The locks of yellow flew.

3. Wide were his fields, his herds were large,
And large his flocks of sheep,
And numerous were his goats and deers
Upon the mountains steep.

4. In bloody fight thrice had he stood
Against the English keen,
Ere two and twenty opening springs
The blooming youth had seen.

5. The fair Matilda dear he loved,
A maid of beauty rare;
Even Margaret on the Scottish throne
Was never half so fair.

6. Long had he wooed, long she refused
With seeming scorn and pride.
At length her eyes confessed the love
Her fearful words denied.

7. Her father, Buchan's cruel lord,
Their passion disapproved;
He bade her wed Sir John the Graeme,
And leave the youth she loved.

8. One night they met as they were wont,
Down by a shady wood,
Where on the bank beside the burn
A blooming saught tree stood.

9. Concealed beneath the underwood
The crafty Donald lay,
A brother to Sir John the Graeme,
To hear what they might say.

10. And thus the maid began, "My sire
Our passion disapproves.
He bids me wed Sir John the Graeme,
So here must end our loves.

11. "My father's will must be obeyed,
Naught boots me to withstand.
Some fairer maid in beauty's bloom
Shall bless thee with her hand.

12. "Soon will Matilda be forgot
And from thy mind effaced,
But may the happiness be thine
Which I can never taste."

13. "What do I hear? Is this thy vow?"
Sir James the Rose replied,
"And will Matilda wed the Graeme,
Though sworn to be my bride?"

14. "His sword shall sooner pierce my heart
Than reave me of my charms"—
Then clasped her to his throbbing breast,
Fast locked within his arms.

15. "I spoke to try thy love," said she,
"I'll ne'er wed man but thee.
The grave shall be my bridal bed
Ere Graeme my husband be.

16. "Take then, dear love, this faithful kiss
In witness of my troth.
May every plague become thy lot
The day I break my oath!"

17. They parted thus, the sun was set,
Up hasty Donald flies;
Then, "Turn thee, turn thee, beardless youth!"
He loud, insulting cries.

18. Then turned about the fearless chief,
And soon his sword he drew,
For Donald's blade before his face
Had pierced his tartans through.

19. " 'Tis for my brother's slighted love,
His wrongs sit on my arm."
Three paces back the youth retired,
And saved himself from harm.

20. Returning swift his sword he reared
Fierce Donald's head above,
And through the head and crashing bone
The furious weapon drove.

21. Life issued at the wound. He fell
A lump of lifeless clay.
"So fall my foes!" quoth valiant Rose,
And stately strode away.

22. Through the green woods in haste he passed
Unto Lord Buchan's hall,
Beneath Matilda's window stood,
And thus on her did call:

23. "Art thou asleep, Matilda dear?
Awake, my love, awake!
Behold, thy lover waits without,
A long farewell to take.

24. "For I have slain fierce Donald Graeme,
His blood is on my sword;
And far, far distant are my men,
Nor can assist their lord.

25. "To Skye I will direct my flight,
Where my brave brothers bide,
To raise the mighty of the Isles
To combat on my side."

26. "Oh do not so," the maid replied,
"With me till morning stay,
For dark and dreary is the night,
And dangerous is the way.

27. "All night I'll watch you in the park,
My faithful page I'll send
In haste to raise the brave clan Rose
Their master to defend."

28. He laid him down beneath a bush,
And wrapped him in his plaid,
While trembling for her lover's sake
At distance stood the maid.

29. Swift ran the page o'er hill and dale,
Till in a lonely glen
He met the furious John the Graeme
With twenty of his men.

30. "Where goest thou, little page?" he said,
"So late who didst thou send?"
"I go to raise the brave clan Rose,
Their master to defend.

31. "For he has slain fierce Donald Graeme,
His blood is on his sword,
And far, far distant are his men
Nor can assist their lord."

32. "And he has slain my brother dear,"
The furious chief replied;
"Dishonour blast my name, but he
By me ere morning dies!

33. "Say, page, where sleeps Sir James the Rose,
And I'll thee much reward."
"He sleeps in Lord Buchan's park,
Matilda is his guard."

34. They spurred their steeds and furious flew
Like lightning o'er the lea;
They reached Lord Buchan's lofty towers
By dawning of the day.

35. Matilda stood without the gate
Upon a rising ground,
And viewed each object in the dawn,
All ear to every sound.

36. "Where sleeps the Rose?" began the Graeme,
"Or has the villain fled?
This hand shall lay the wretch on earth
By whom my brother's bled."

37. At this the valiant knight awoke,
The virgin shrieking heard.
Straight he rose and drew his sword
When the fierce band appeared.

38. "Your sword last night my brother slew,
His blood yet dims its shine,
But ere the sun shall gild the morn
Your blood shall reek on mine."

39. "Your words are brave," the chief replied,
"But deeds approve the man.
Set by your men, and hand to hand
We'll try what valour can."

40. Four of his men, the bravest four,
Fell down beneath his sword,
But still he scorned the poor revenge,
But sought their haughty lord.

41. Till basely behind him came the Graeme
And pierced him in the side;
Out spouting came the purple stream,
And all his tartans dyed.

42. But yet his hand dropped not the sword,
Nor sank he to the ground,
Till through his enemy's heart the steel
Had pierced a mortal wound.

43. Graeme like a tree by wind o'erthrown
Fell breathless on the clay,
While down beside him sank the Rose,
Who faint and dying lay.

44. Matilda saw and fast she ran.
"Oh spare his life!" she cried.
"Lord Buchan's daughter begs his life;
Let her not be denied."

45. Her well-known voice the hero heard,
And raised his death-closed eyes,
And fixed them on the weeping maid,
And weakly this replies:

46. "In vain Matilda begs a life
By death's arrest denied.
My race is run. Adieu, my love!"
Then closed his eyes and died.

47. The sword yet warm from his left side
With frantic hand she drew.
"I come, Sir James the Rose," she cried,
"I come to follow you!"

48. The hilt she leaned against the ground
And bared her snowy breast,
And fell upon her lover's face,
And sank to endless rest.

17. "Sir James the Ross"

Karpeles MSS., No. 5317; text, p. 4867. Also in Karpeles, *JEFDSS*, III, No. 1 (1936), p. 58(3). Sung by Pat Kiley, Gaskiers, St. Mary's, Newfoundland, July 29, 1930.

p D/Æ

1. It's all those Scottish lords and chiefs
Of high war-like name,
The bravest is Sir James the Ross
That knight of many fame.

2. His growth was of the tuft that firmed
[like the tufted fir]
That crowned the mountain air,
And waving over his shoulder flew
His locks of yellow hair.

3. The chief then of the high clan Ross,
That firm undaunted being;
Five hundred warriors drew their swords
Beneath his high command.

4. In blood to fight twice hard he stood
Against the English king
And two and twenty opening springs
This blooming youth had seen.

5. And fair Mathilda dear he loved,
That maid of beauty rare,
Yet Margaret on the Scottish throne
Was never half so fair.

6. Long had he woo'd and long she refused
With seeming scorn and pride,
Yet oft her eyes confessed the love
His fearful words denied.

7. At last she dressed his well-tried feat
And allowed his tender claim,
And vow'd to him her virgin heart
That owned an equal fame.

8. One night they met as they did walk
Close in a shady wood,
And on the bank beside this brook,
A blooming culting stood.

9. Concealed beneath this underwood
A crafty Daniel lay,
A brother to Sir John Graham,
To hear what they would say.

10. Thus the maid began: Dear sir,
Our passions disapproves
And bids me wed Sir John Graham
And leave the youth I love.

11. What do I hear is this I vow,
Sir John the Ross replied,
And will Mathilda wed Graham
When sworn to be my bride?

12. His sword shall sooner pierce my heart
Than rob me of my charm.
He pressed her to his beating breast
Fast locked within his arms.

13. I spoke to try thy love, she said,
I'll never wed man but thee,
The grave shall be my bridegroom bed
If Graham my husband be.

14. They parted thus the sun was set;
Up hasty Daniel flies
And turn thee, turn thee beardless youth
His loud insulting cries.

15. And turned around this fearless chief
And soon his sword he drew,
For Daniel bled before his breast
And pierced his tartans through.

16. It's for my brother's spited love,
His wrong sits on my arm
Three paces back this youth retired
To save himself from harm.

17. And turning swift his hand he raised,
Pierced Daniel's head above,
And through the brain and crashing bone
His sharp-edged weapon drove.

18. He staggered and reeled and tumbled down
Like a lump of breathless clay.
You follow my foe, cries gallant Ross,
And stately drove away.

19. To the green woods he gave read [quickly hy'd]
Unto Lord Bolden's hall,
And at Mathilda's window stood,
And this began to call:

20. Is thou asleep, my dear,
Awake, my love, awake.
A luckless lover calls on thee
A long farewell to take.

21. For I have slain fierce Daniel Graham,
His blood it's on my sword
And far, far distant are my men
That shall desist their lord.

22. To Skye I'll now direct my way
Where my two brothers bides;
I'll raise the valiants of that isle
To combat on my side.

23. Do not go, the maid replied,
With me till morning stay,
For dark and dreary is the night
And dangerous is the way.

24. All night I'll watch you in the park,
My foot-page back I'll send
In hopes to rouse the Ross's men
Their master to defend.

25. Beneath the bush she laid him down,
Wrapped warm within his plaid,
And trembling for her lover's fate
A distance stood the maid.

26. Swift flew the page over hills and dales
Till in the lonely glen
He met the furious John Graham
And twenty of his men.

27. Where do you go, little page, he said,
So late who do descend?
I go to rouse the Ross's men
Their master to defend.

28. For he have slain fair Daniel Graham
His blood it's on his sword,
And far, far distant are his men
That should assist their lord.

29. And has he slain my brother dear,
The furious Graham replied,
His honour blast my name, he said,
By me at morning dies.

30. Tell me where is Sir James the Ross,
I will thee well reward.
He sleeps unto Lord Bolden's park,
Mathilda is his guard.

31. They picked their stage (stave?) with furious moves
[spurred their steeds in furious mood]
And scoured along the way,
They reached Lord Bolden's lofty tower
By the dawning of the day.

32. Mathilda stood outside the gate,
To whom Graham did say:
Have you Sir James the Ross last night
Or did he pass this way?

33. Last day at noon, Mathilda cries,
Sir James the Ross passed by,
He picked his staves with furious moves
And onward past did drive.

34. By this he is at Edinburgh town,
If horse and men him good.
Your page then lied who said he was
Here sleeping in this wood.

35. She wrung her hands and tore her hair.
Brave Ross thou art betrayed,
And ruined by those very means
For whence I helped thy name.

36. By this the valiant knight awoke,
The virgin's shriek he heard,
He then rose up and drew his sword
When this fierce band appeared.

37. Your sword last night my brother slain,
His blood yet dims its shine,

And e'er the setting of the sun
Your blood shall reek on mine.

38. Your word is well, the chief replied,
But deeds will prove the men
Set by your men and hand to hand
I'll try what valour can.

39. O boasting high those cowards heard,
My hearty (haughty?) sword he fear.
In showing from those folding fields
If he'll keep in the rear.

[Oft boasting hides a coward's heart,
My weighty sword you fear
Which shone in front in Flodden field
When you kept in the rear.]

40. With dauntless steps he onward drove,
And dared him to the fight,
Graham gave back and from his aim
For well he knew its might.

41. Up comes his foe, his bravest foe,
And sank down beneath his sword
And still they scorn the poor revenge
And sought this hearty (haughty?) lord.

42. Behind him basely came Graham,
And pierced him through the side.
Out spouting comes the crimson tide
And all his tartans dyed.

43. But still the sword cut not the grip
Nor felled him to the ground
Till through his enemy's heart with steel
He had forced this mortal wound.

44. Graham like a tree overthrown with wind
Fell breathless on the clay
And down beside him sinks brave Ross
A-fainting dying lay.

45. The sad Mathilda saw him fall.
To spare his life, she cries.
Lord Bolden's daughter begs his life
Let her not be denied.

46. Her well-known voice the hero knew,
He raised his half closed eyes,
And fixes them on the weeping maid
And weakly this replied:

47. In vain Mathilda begs the life,
My debt shall rest to-night.
My race is run, here doom, my love [Adieu]
Then closed his eyes and died.

48. The sword yet warm from his left side
With frantic hand she drew,
I come, Sir James the Ross, she cries,
I come to follow you.

49. She lain the hilt against the ground,
And bared her snow-white breast,
And fell upon her lover's face
To sink to endless rest.

"Words in square brackets from Gavin Greig's *Last Leaves*, p. 137." [*Miss Karpeles' note.*] The parenthesized conjectures are Miss Karpeles'.

18. "Sir James the Rose"

Karpeles MSS., No. 5319; text, p. 4874. Also in Karpeles, *JEFDSS*, III, No. 1 (1936), p. 58(4). Sung by Mrs. James Welsh, Ferryland, Newfoundland, August 1, 1930.

m D

1. Of all the Scottish northern chiefs
Of high and warlike fame,
The bravest was Sir James the Ross,
A knight of mighty fame.

2. The fair Mathilda dear he loved,
A maid of high renown
. . . .
And bid her wed Sir James the Ross.

. . . .

3. Art thou asleep Mathilda dear?
Awake, my love, I say,
A luckless lover on thee calls
A long farewell to take.

4. For I have slain Sir Donald Graham,
His blood lies on my sword,
And far, far distant are my men,
They can't assist their lord.

5. To Skye I'll now direct my way
Where my two brothers abide
And rouse the combat of the . . .
And combat on my side.

6. O do not go, the maid replied,
With me till morning stay,
For dark and distant is the road
And dangerous is the way.

7. All night I'll watch you in the park,
My faithful page I'll send
To run and raise the Ross's clan
Their master to defend.

8. Swift ran the page o'er hill and dale
Till in a lonely glen
He met the fierce Sir John Graham
With fifth of his men.

9. Where goest thou, little page, he said,
So late who did thee send.
I have to raise the Ross's clan
Their master to defend.

10. For he have slain Sir Donald Graham,
His blood lies on his sword,
And far, far distant are his men
That can't assist their lord.

11. Tell me where is Sir John the Ross,
I will thee well reward.
He sleeps within Lord Bohun's park
Mathilda is his guide.

12. Outside the gate Mathilda stood,
To her the Graham did say:
Saw you Sir John the Ross
Last night did he pass this way?

13. Last day at noon, Mathilda said,
Sir John the Ross passed by,
He spurred his steed with furious move,
'Tis onward fast did hie.

14. By this he's in Edinburgh
If horse and men holds good.
'Tis false, said he, your page told me
He sleeps within your wood.

15. She wrung her hands and tore her hair,
Brave Ross you are betrayed
And wounded by those means, she cried,
Of when I hoped thine aid.

16. By this the gallant knight awoke,
The virgin's squeaks he heard,
And up he rose and drew his sword
As the undaunted band appeared.

17. Last day your sword my brother slew,
His blood yet dim with shine,
And e'er the setting of the sun,
Yours will reek on mine.

18. Your words are great, replied the chief,
But deeds approve the man,
Set by your band and hand to hand
We'll try what valour can.

19. Four of his men, the bravest four,
Fell down beneath his sword,
But still he scorned the high revenge
That sought their hearty lord.

20. Behind him beastly came the Graham
And pierced him through the side
And spurting came the purple blood
. . . .

21. The sad Mathilda saw him fall.
O spare his life, she cried.
Lord Bohun's daughter begs his life,
Let her not be denied.

22. Her loving voice the hero heard,
And raised his death-closed eyes
And fixed them on the weeping maid
And weakly thus replied:

23. In vain Mathilda begs the life
Of death's arrest denied,
My race is run, adieu my love,
And closed his eyes and died.

19. "Sir James the Rose"

Greig MSS., III, p. 203. Also in Greig and Keith, 1925, p. 141(1e). Sung by T. S. Towers, Sanday, Orkney.

a D

And has he slain my brother dear?
The furious Graeme replies

20. "Sir James the Rose"

Greig MSS., III, p. 63. Also in Greig and Keith, 1925, p. 141(1d). Sung by A. Robb, New Deer, December 1907.

p P/Æ, ending on *VII*

Of all the Scottish northern chiefs
Of high & mighty name
The bravest was Sir James the Rose,
A knicht o' mickle fame.

GROUP A APPENDIX

21. "Hardyknute"

Johnson, III [1790], No. 280, p. 289 (repr. 1853).

p π^4

GROUP B

22. "Sir James the Rose"

Gilchrist, *JEFDSS*, III, No. 1 (1936), p. 55. From the Edinburgh MS. ("a sheet of manuscript airs . . . found amongst the papers of the late Frank Kidson.")

a M/D

GROUP C

23. "Sir James the Ross"

Smith [1820-24], II, p. 30.

a I/M (nearly π^1)

Of all the Scottish northern chiefs,
Of high and mighty name,
The bravest was Sir James, the Ross,
A Knight of meikle fame.
His growth was like a youthful Oak
That crowns the mountain's brow,
And waving, o'er his shoulders broad,
His locks o' yellow flew.

The Chieftain of the brave clan Ross,
A firm undaunted band;
Five hundred Warriors drew the sword
Beneath his high command.
In bloody fight thrice had he stood
Against the English keen,
Ere two-and-twenty op'ning springs
This blooming youth had seen.

GROUP D

24. "Sir James the Rose"

Karpeles MSS., No. 5320. Also in Karpeles, *JEFDSS*, III, No. 1 (1936), p. 59(5). Sung by Bill Kennedy, Trepassey, Newfoundland, August 2, 1930.

p π^1

O yes, sir, he's at London Cross,
If man and horse prove good.
'Tis false, said he, your page told me
He sleeps here in this wood.

GROUP E

25. "Sir James, the Rose"

Flanders and Olney, 1953, p. 147. Also in Flanders, III, 1963, p. 245(B). Sung by Hanford Hayes, Staceyville, Me., September 22, 1940; learned in the Maine woods. Collected by Helen Hartness Flanders and A. C. Beal. From *Ballads Migrant in New England*, edited by Helen Hartness Flanders and Marguerite Olney; copyright 1953 by Helen Hartness Flanders.

p I (inflected VII)

1. Of all the northern Scottish Chiefs
That live as warlike men,
The bravest was Sir James, the Rose,
A knight of muckle fame.

2. His growth was like the thrifty fir
That crowns the mountain's brow
And wavering o'er his shoulders broad
Bright locks of yellow flow.

3. Three years he fought on bloody fields
Against their English king.
Scarce two and twenty summers yet
This fearless youth had seen.

4. It was fair Mathildy that he loved—
That girl with beauty rare—
And Margaret on the Scottish throne
With her could not compare.

5. Long he had wooed, long she'd refused
It seemed, with scorn and pride
But after all confessed her love;
Her faithful words, denied.

6. "My father was born a cruel lord.
This passion does approve.
He bids me wed Sir John a Grame
And leave the one I love.

7. "My father's will I must fulfill,
Which puts me to a stand.
Some fair maid in her beauty bloom
May bless you with her hand."

8. "Are those the vows, Mathildy dear,"
Sir James, the Rose, did say,
"And would Mathildy wed the Grame
When she's sworn to be my bride?"

9. "I only spoke to try thy love.
I'll ne'er wed man but thee.
The grave shall be my bridal bed
Ere Grames my husband be.

10. "You take this kiss, fair youth," she said,
"In witness of my love,
May every plague down on me fall
The day I break my vows."

11. Ere they had met and there embraced,
Down by a shady grove,
It was on a bank beside a burn
A blooming shelltree stood.

12. Concealed beneath the undie wood
To hear what they might say,
A brother to Sir John the Grame
And there concealed he lay.

13. Ere they did part the sun was set.
At haste, he then replied,
"Return, return, you beardless youth,"
He loud insulting cries.

14. "O it's of my brother's slight love
Rests softly on your arm."
Three paces back the youth retired
To save himself from harm.

15. Then turned around the beardless youth
And quick his sword he drew
And through his enemy's crashing blows
His sharp-edged weapon drew.

16. Grame staggered back. He reeled and fell
A lifeless lump of clay.
"So falls my foes," said valiant Rose,
And straightly walked away.

17. Through the green woods he then did go
Till he reached Lord Bohan's Hall
And at Mathildy's window stood
And thus began to call.

18. "Art thou asleep, Mathildy dear?
Awake, my love, awake.
Your own true lover calls on you
A long farewell to take.

19. "For I have slain fair Donald Grame.
His blood is on my sword
And distant are my faithful men.
They can't assist their lord.

20. "To the Isle of Skye, I must awa'
Where my twa brothers abide.
I'll raise the gallyants of that Isle.
They'll combat on my side."

21. "Don't do so," the maid replied,
"With me 'til morning stay,
For dark and rainy is the night
And dangerous is the way.

22. "All night I'll watch you in my park.
My little page I'll send.
He'll run and raise the Rose's clan
Their master to defend."

23. She laid him down beneath the bush
And rolled him in his plaid.
At a distance stood the weeping maid;
A-weeping for her love.

24. O'er hills and dales, the page he ran,
Till lonely in the Glen,
'Twas there he met Sir John the Grame
And twenty of his men.

25. "Where art thou going, my little page?
What tidings dost thou bring?"
"I'm running to raise the Rose's clan
Their master to defend.

26. "For he has slain fair Donald Grame,
His blood is on his sword,
And distant are his faithful men
They can't assist their lord."

27. "Tell me where he is, my little page,
And I will thee well reward."
"He sleeps now in Lord Bohan's Hall.
Mathildy, she's his guard."

28. He spurred his horse at a furious gait
And galloped o'er the lea
Until he reached Lord Bohan's Hall
At the dawning of the day.

29. Without the gate, Mathildy stood
To whom the Grame replied,
"Saw ye Sir James, the Rose, last night,
Or did he pass this way?"

30. "Last day at noon fair James, the Rose,
I seen him passing by.
He was mounted on a milk-white steed
And forward fast did fly.

31. "He's in Edinborotown now by this time
If man and horse proves good."
"Your page now lies who said he was
A-sleeping in the wood."

32. She wrung her hands and tore her hair
Saying, "Rose, thou art betrayed,
Thou art betrayed all by those means
I was sure you would be saved."

33. The hero heard a well-known voice;
This valiant knight awoke,
Oh, he awoke and drew his sword
As this brave band appeared.

34. "So you have slain my brother dear;
His blood as dew did shine
And by the rising of the sun
Your blood shall flow or mine."

35. "You speak the truth," the youth replies,
"That deeds can prove the man.
Stand by your men and hand to hand
You'll see our valiant stand."

36. "If boasting words a coward hide,
It is my sword you fear,
It's seen the day on Flodden's Field
When you sneaked in the rear."

37. "Oh, at him, men, and cut him down!
Oh, cut him down in twain.
Five thousand pounds onto the man
Who leaves him on the plain."

38. Four of his men—the bravest four—
Fell down before that sword,
But still they scorned that mean revenge
And sought the cowardly Lord.

39. Till cowardly behind him stole the Grame
And wound him in the side.
Out gushing came his purple gore
And all his garments dyed.

40. But ne'er of his sword did he quit the grip
Nor fell he to the ground
Till through his enemy's heart his steel
Had pierced a fatal wound.

41. Grame staggered back. He reeled and fell
A lifeless lump of clay
Whilst down beside him sank the Rose
That fainting, dying lay.

42. O when Mathildy seen him fall,
"O spare his life," she cried,
"Lord Bohan's daughter begs his life.
She shall not be denied."

43. The hero heard a well-known voice
And raised his death-closed eyes
And fixed them on the weeping maid,
And faintly this replies,

44. "In vain, Mathildy, you beg my life.
By death's, it's been denied;
My race is run. Good-bye, my love,"
He closed his eyes and died.

45. She drew his sword from his left side
With frantic hands, she drew.
"I come, I come, brave Rose," she cried,
"I'm going to follow you."

46. She leaned the hilt upon the ground
And pressed her snow-white breast;
Laid down upon her lover's face
And endless went to rest.

47. So come all indulging parents,
By this warning take
And never encourage your children dear
Their sacred vows to break.

26. "Sir James the Ross"

Creighton and Senior, 1950, p. 78(B). Sung by Oswald Gorman, Burnt Cote, N.S.

p π^1

Of all the Scottish northern chiefs of high and warlike name
The bravest was Sir James the Ross, that knight of muckle fame.
His growth was like the tufted fern that crowns the mountain brow,
And waving o'er his shoulder broad those locks of yellow flew.

That chieftain of that brave clan Ross, a high undaunted band,
Five hundred warriors drew their sword beneath his high command,
In bloody fights thrice had he stood against the English king
When two and twenty . . . his blooming youth had seen.

The fair Matilda did he love, a maid of beauty rare,
Queen Margaret on her Scottish throne was never half so fair,
Long time he wooed, long she refused with seeming scorn and pride,
At length her youthful heart confessed those fearful words denied.

27. "Sir James the Ross"

Creighton and Senior, 1950, p. 75(A). Tune from William Nelson, Kinsac, N.S.; sung by A. E. Ettinger, Halifax, N.S.

? a I, ending on V

1. Of all the northern Scottish chiefs of high and warlike name,
The bravest is Sir James the Ross a knight of mighty fame.
His growth was like the trumpled fir that crowns the mountains brow,
And waving o'er Ross's shoulders broad the locks of yellow flew.

2. He was chieftain of the brave clan Ross, a firm undaunted band,
Five hundred warriors drew their swords beneath his high command,
And bloody fights thrice had he stood against the English king
E'er two and twenty opening springs this blooming youth had seen.

3. One fair Matilda he dearly loved, a maid of beauty rare,
Queen Margaret on the Scottish throne was never half so fair,
Long had he wooed, long she refused with seeming scorn and pride,
But oft her eye confessed the love her faithless tongue denied.

4. They met one night as they were wont down by a shady wood,
And on the bank it's near a burn where those two lovers stood,
With this the maid began, "My sire our passions disapprove
And bids me wed Sir John the Graeme and quit the youth I love.

5. "My father's will must be obeyed, I cannot him withstand,
Some fairer maid in beauty's bloom will grace thee with her hand."
"What's this I hear Matilda say?" Sir James the Ross replied,
"And will Matilda wed the Graeme who's sworn to be my bride?

6. "Sooner his sword would pierce my breast than rob me of my charmer,"
He clasped her to his beating breast close locked in both their arms.
"It was to try your love," said she, "I'll ne'er wed none but thee,
The grave shall be my bridal bed e'er Graeme my husband be.

7. "So take, dear youth, this faithful kiss in witness of my troth,
May every plague become my lot the day I break my oath."
Concealed beneath the undergrowth the crafty Donald lay,
A brother to Sir John the Graeme to hear what they might say.

8. They parted e'er the sun had set, up swift young Donald flies,
"Return, return, you beardless youth," he loud insulting cries,
"It's for my brother's slighted love the wrong rests on my arm."
Three paces back the youth retires to save himself from harm.

9. Then turning round his sword he drew o'er Donald's head so fierce,
Then through his brain with crushing blows the sharp edged weapon pierced,
Graeme staggered, reeled and tumbled down a lump of lifeless clay,
"So falls my foes," cried valiant Ross and straightway strode away.

10. Then through the woods he quickly went unto Lord Buchan's hall,
And at Matilda's window stood and there began to call,
"Matilda dear art thou asleep? Awake, my love, awake,
Your luckless lover calls on you a long farewell to take,

11. "For I have slain fierce Donald Graeme, his blood is on my sword,
And far far distant is the men who would assist their lord,
To Skyes I would direct my steps where my two brothers lie,
To raise the valiant of the isle to combat on my side."

12. "Oh do not go," Matilda cried, "with me till morning stay,
For dark and dreary is the night, and dangerous is the way,
All night I'll guard you in the park, my faithful page I'll send
To go and raise the Ross' clan their master to defend."

13. She laid him down beneath the wood and wrapped him in her plaid,
And fearing for her lover's fate at a distance stood the maid,
Away the little page boy he flew and scoured along the glen
Until he met Sir John the Graeme with twenty of his men.

14. "Where goest thou, my little page, or who so late doth send?"
"I go to raise the Ross' clan their master to defend,
For he has slain fierce Donald Graeme, his blood is on his sword,
And far far distant is the men that would defend their lord."

15. "Tell me where is Sir James the Ross? I will thee well reward."
"He's sleeping in Lord Buchan's park, Matilda is his guard."
Away then the Graeme he flew and scoured along the lea
Until he reached Lord Buchan's park at the dawning of the day.

16. Matilda stood without the gate to whom the Graeme did say,
"Saw you Sir James the Ross last night or did he pass this way?"
"At last night's tide," Matilda said, "Sir James the Ross passed by,
He pricked his steed with furious mood as onward he did hie.

17. "He's by this time in Edinburgh if horse and man prove good."
"Your page then lies who said he was here sleeping in this wood."
She wrung her hands and tore her hair, "Brave Ross you are betrayed
And ruined by the very means that wished you most to aid."

18. With this the fearless chief awoke, her well known voice he heard,
And starting on towards the gate he heard the insulting words,

"Your sword last night my brother slew, his blood it dims the shine,
And before the rising of the sun your blood shall reek on mine."

19. "My blood it shall," the chieftain cries, "but deeds prove best the man,
Put by your men and arm to arm we'll try what valour can,
Oft boasting hides the coward heart, my weighty blade you fear,
Which stood in front in Flodden's field while yours hung in the rear."

20. Four of his men, the bravest four, they fell beneath his sword,
But still he made a brave retreat and sought the haughty lord,
Up behind him came the Graeme and wound him in the side,
Out spouting came the purple gore and all his tartan dyed.

21. The sword it never lost its grip nor cast it on the ground
Until his enemy his steel did prove a mortal wound,
Graeme staggered, reeled and tumbled down, a lump of lifeless clay,
And down behind him fell the Ross who faint undying lay.

22. Matilda saw her lover fall, "Oh spare his life," she cried,
"Lord Buchan's daughter claims his life, let her not be denied,"
With this the fearless chief arose, he heard Matilda's cry,
"Farewell, farewell my loving dear," and closed his eyes and died.

23. The sword yet warm from his left side with frantic hands she drew,
She said, "I come Sir James the Ross, I come to follow you,"
She leaned the hilt upon the ground and pierced her snowy breast,
And fell upon her lover's form and sword to endless rest.

The Braes o Yarrow

CHILD NO. 214

Although the textual tradition of this ballad cannot be followed very far into the eighteenth century, it seems clear that a ballad lay behind Hamilton of Bangor's overwrought piece on the subject ("Busk ye, busk ye"); and the ramifications of the tunes which in one way or another are connected with the ballad are ancient and honorable.

It will be well to begin with the steadiest and best established, even if most recent, tradition. This is that of the North-East of Scotland, where Greig and Duncan collected no less than twenty-two examples, of which Keith printed six. The tune is very characteristic and fairly consistent. It is always plagal; almost always D/Æ, but sometimes π^4 or Æ; and all the variants are in triple time. It generally opens with a phrase that divides into two identical, or very similar, descending figures, but sometimes opens with an upward sequence. As Keith has noted, it is found with a number of ballads: "Geordie," "Barbara Allan," "Willie's Drown'd" (all in Christie), Greig's "Tifty's Annie," and others.

The tunes of this group that start with an ascending figure have a discernible allegiance to the simpler forms (many examples of which we have already encountered) of "Boyne Water" in its second strain. Tunes with fuller and more unmistakable affiliation form our second, small group. The traditional connection of this family with the ballad, however, rests on early hearsay and late evidence. Kidson's tune (variant 36), which came from Eskdale tradition, was sung by Mrs. Calvert of Gilnockie, who was the granddaughter of Scott's Tibbie Shiel, from whom she seems to have got it. Perhaps on the strength of Kidson's note (*Traditional Tunes*, 1891, p. 22), J. C. Dick asserts that Tibbie Shiel sang the ballad to this tune (Dick, ed., 1903, p. 379). As Kidson gives it, it is the second strain of "Boyne Water." But the tune which Dick prints (*op. cit.*, p. 79) is a form of "Boyne Water" with both strains. He gives it as from Oswald's *Caledonian Pocket Companion*, V [c. 1753],* p. 26, where it was called "The Rashes" (variant 34). Oswald, Dick notes (*ibid.*, p. 379), also printed the tune in *Caledonian Pocket Companion*, XI [c. 1759],* p. 23, with the title "When the King comes o'er the water." The tune, with the song last named, is printed by Hogg, *The Jacobite Relics of Scotland*, 1st series, 1819, p. 45. Dick observes that the tune is "now best known as 'The wee wee German Lairdie,'" the words of which were first printed by Cromek in *Remains of Nithsdale and Galloway Song*, 1810. This song is also given by Hogg, *op.cit.*, p. 85. But it is curious that there the tune consists of the old second strain plus a new and spirited second strain not earlier associated with "Boyne Water." As Dick also notes, Burns sent Johnson his song of "O May thy morn," to be sung to "The Rashes" in Oswald's version, but it is printed in Johnson's *Museum* with the tune in its "Wee German Lairdie" guise (variant 35). The "Boyne Water" tune in an older form is printed by Moffat from a MS. of 1730-35 (*Minstrelsy of Ireland* [1897], p. 340, App'x., No. XII), but the signature of one flat ought surely to be changed to three sharps to make sense: then the tune at once reassumes its familiar appearance.

* Dates according to Dick, *op.cit.*, p. xli.

Moffat's next following tune, "The Watter of Boyne" (*ibid.*, No. XIIa), which he gives as from the Leyden MS. for lyra-viol, c. 1690-92, is a quite different tune, popular on late seventeenth-century broadsides and elsewhere as "The Bog-trotter's March," "The Northumberland Bagpipes," etc. But the tune which Moffat prints (p. 339, No. XI) from D'Urfey's *Pills*, 1719-20, V, p. 112, where it went to a version of "The Baffled Knight," is certainly a form of "Boyne Water" with the opening strain rather perversely twisted.

It remains to say that the "Boyne Water" tradition has also been found in connection with the "Yarrow" ballad in New England. Cf. Barry, Eckstorm, and Smyth, *British Ballads from Maine*, 1929, pp. xxxvi, 195, and 291 (variant 37). But that tradition is associated with such a multitude of ballads in this country that we need not be so impressed with the fact as Barry appears to have been.

Our third class consists of a single example, given from the 1833 edition of Scott's *Minstrelsy* (variant 38). It is not, as we might have hoped, anything like Tibbie Shiel's version, but is a form of "Leader Haughs and Yarrow," which Thomson printed in *Orpheus Caledonius*, 1733, II, No. 11, and which has since been many times reprinted. The only justification for associating it with the ballad, so far as I am aware, is that Herd's fragment (*Ancient and Modern Scottish Songs*, 1776, I, p. 145), printed as Child's O text, is directed to be sung "to the tune of Leaderhaughs and Yarrow." The tune is very interesting and full of beauty. Technically, it is a wide-ranging Dorian; but it has strong Mixolydian feeling throughout and for that reason I prefer to consider the final as a dropped close a fourth below the true tonic.

The fourth type is found with the words of Hamilton's poem "Busk ye, busk ye" in Thomson, 1733 ("The Braes of Yarrow"); with Ramsay's verses in Johnson's *Museum*, and Rimbault, 1850; with Hamilton again in Maver, 1866; with Scott's *Minstrelsy* ballad-text in Eyre-Todd [1894]; and doubtless appears in many other collections with insignificant alterations. The best reason for associating it with the ballad lies in a traditional version printed in the *Rymour Club Miscellanea*, by Duncan Fraser, as from his father (variant 40). This tune is a bright 6/8 plagal, in I/M, of a type not uncommon. Editorial annotation connects it with Greig's "The Scauldin Wife," "The Back o' Benachie," "The Lion's Den" (cf. *JFSS*, V, No. 19 [1915], p. 114). It should also be compared with the following ballad, No. 215. But it appears to me to follow the outline of the older "Busk ye" tune. The latter, in turn, is certainly sib to the still older "An thou wert mine ain thing," familiar in its *Beggar's Opera* form ("O what pain it is to part"), and of which an ancestor appeared in Gordon of Straloch's lute MS., c. 1627 (NL Scotland MS., Adv. 5.2.18). An early version of it, transcribed from the Leyden MS. and bearing the name of "The lady's goune," is given by G. F. Graham, *The Songs of Scotland* (variant 41).

In a final category is placed a tune that I cannot connect with any of the preceding. It suggests the "Babe of Bethlehem" or "Lazarus" tradition (cf. *ante*, Vol. I, No. 56).

214. THE BRAES O YARROW

LIST OF VARIANTS

GROUP A

1. "The Dowie Dens o' Yarrow." Lucy Broadwood, *JFSS*, V, No. 19 (1915), p. 113(B). Also in Greig MSS., II, p. 6, King's College Library, Aberdeen. (Gillespie)
2. "The Dowie Dens o' Yarrow." John Ord, *The Bothy Songs and Ballads*, 1930, p. 426.
3. "The Dowie Dens o' Yarrow." Greig MSS., IV, p. 160. Also in Gavin Greig and Alexander Keith, *Last Leaves of Traditional Ballads and Ballad Airs*, 1925, p. 143(a). (Spence)
4. "Dowie Dens o' Yarrow." Greig MSS., II, p. 2. (Stuart)
5. "Yarrow." Greig MSS., II, p. 56. (Gordon)
6. "Yarrow." Greig MSS., IV, p. 47. (Dunbar)
7. "Yarrow." Greig MSS., III, p. 168. (Gray)
8. "Yarrow." Greig MSS., II, p. 144. (Fowlie)
9. "Dowie Dens o' Yarrow." Greig MSS., I, p. 111. (Rennie)
10. "Dowie Dens o' Yarrow." Greig MSS., I, p. 181. (Riddell)
11. "Dowie Dens o' Yarrow." Greig MSS., III, p. 10. (Brown)
12. "Dowie Dens o' Yarrow, & Tiftie's Annie." Greig MSS., III, p. 30. (A. Greig)
13. "Dowie Dens." Greig MSS., II, p. 131. (Knox)
14. "Yarrow." Greig MSS., III, p. 115. (Lee)
15. "Dowie Dens o' Yarrow." Greig MSS., II, p. 3. Also in Greig and Keith, *Last Leaves*, 1925, p. 144(f). (Findlay)
16. "The Dowie Dens o' Yarrow." Greig and Keith, 1925, p. 143(b). From Duncan MS., No. 70. Also in Duncan, *JFSS*, V, No. 19 (1915), p. 113(A). (J. Greig)
17. "The Dowie Dens o' Yarrow." Greig-Duncan MS. 785 (transcription of W. Walker), p. 112, King's College Library, Aberdeen. From Duncan MS., No. 307. (Christie)
18. "The Dowie Dens o' Yarrow." Greig MSS., IV, p. 157. Also in Greig and Keith, *Last Leaves*, 1925, p. 144(d). (New Leeds woman)
19. "The Dowie Dens o' Yarrow." Jean Matthew, Sound Archives of the British Broadcasting Corporation, London, recording No. 18785.
20. "The Dowie Dens." Greig MSS., I, p. 110; and Bk. 716, VI, p. 29. (Barron)
21. "The Dowie Dens o' Yarrow." Greig MSS., I, p. 110. Also in Greig and Keith, *Last Leaves*, 1925, p. 144(e). (Ritchie)
22. "The Dowie Dens of Yarrow." Margaret Stewart (singer), Archive, School of Scottish Studies, University of Edinburgh.
23. "Yarrow." Greig MSS., IV, p. 38, and Bk. 766, LVI, p. 104. (Fotheringham)
24. "The Dowie Dens of Yarrow." Davy Stewart, Caedmon recording No. TC 1146(A10).
25. "The Dowie Dens o' Yarrow." Greig-Duncan MS. 785 (Walker), p. 112; from Duncan MS., No. 242. Also in Duncan, *JFSS*, V, No. 19 (1915), p. 113(C). (Mackay)
26. "The Dowie Dens o' Yarrow." Broadwood, *JFSS*, V, No. 19 (1915), p. 111(2).
27. "The Dowie Dens o' Yarrow." J.C.M. Campbell (singer), Archive, School of Scottish Studies.
28. "The Dowie Dens o' Yarrow." Greig MSS., III, p. 34, and Bk. 721, XI, p. 3. Also in Greig-Duncan MS. 785 (Walker), p. 112; and Lucy E. Broadwood, *JFSS*, V, No. 19 (1915), p. 110. (Potts)
29. "The Dowie Dens o' Yarrow." P. N. Shuldham-Shaw, *JEFDSS*, V, No. 2 (1947), p. 77.
30. "The Derry Downs of Arrow." Mrs. Lola Stanley, LC Archive of American Folk Song, recording No. 11,905 (B14).
31. "The Dowie Dens o' Yarrow." Greig MSS., I, p. 181 (first set). Also in Greig and Keith, *Last Leaves*, 1925, p. 144(c). (Riddell)
32. "Dewy Dewy Dens of Yarrow." May Kennedy McCord, LC Archive of American Folk Song, recording No. 11,875(A7).
33. "Dowie Dens o' Yarrow." Ewan MacColl, Riverside recording No. RLP 12-625(B1), *The English and Scottish Popular Ballads*, III, ed. Kenneth S. Goldstein. Also on Columbia recording No. SL 209(A1), No. 6.

GROUP B

34. "The Rashes." James Oswald, *The Caledonian Pocket Companion*, V [c. 1753], p. 26. Also in James C. Dick, ed., *The Songs of Robert Burns*, 1903, No. 82, p. 79.
35. "O May thy morn." James Johnson, *The Scots Musical Museum*, V [1796], No. 464, p. 477 (repr. 1853). Also in James Hogg, *The Jacobite Relics of Scotland*, 1st series, 1819, p. 85.
36. "The Dowie Dens of Yarrow." Frank Kidson, *Traditional Tunes*, 1891, p. 22.
37. "The Braes of Yarrow." Phillips Barry, Fannie H. Eckstorm, and Mary W. Smyth, *British Ballads from Maine*, 1929, p. 291. (Young)

GROUP C

38. "The Dowie Dens o' Yarrow." Sir Walter Scott, *The Poetical Works of Sir Walter Scott*, 1833-34, III, opp. p. 150, and p. 147. Also in Robert Maver, *Genuine Scottish Melodies*, 1866, No. 79, p. 40.

GROUP D

39. "The Braes of Yarrow." W. Thomson, *Orpheus Caledonius*, 1733, II, p. 34. Also in Johnson, *The Scots Musical Museum*, I [1787], No. 64, p. 65 (repr. 1853); Edward F. Rimbault, *Musical Illustrations of Bishop Percy's Reliques*, 1850, p. 86; Maver, *Genuine Scottish Melodies*, 1866, No. 18, p. 9; and George Eyre-Todd, *Ancient Scots Ballads* [1894], p. 70.
40. "The Dowie Dens o' Yarrow." Duncan Fraser, *Rymour Club Miscellanea*, I (1910), p. 44.

GROUP D APPENDIX

41. "The lady's goune." G. F. Graham, *The Songs of Scotland*, 1848-49, I, p. 162.

GROUP E

42. "The Dewy Dens of Darrow." Helen Hartness Flanders and Marguerite Olney, *Ballads Migrant in New England*, 1953, p. 235. Also in Helen Hartness Flanders, *Ancient Ballads Traditionally Sung in New England*, III, 1963, p. 257.

TUNES WITH TEXTS

GROUP A

1. "The Dowie Dens o' Yarrow"

Broadwood, *JFSS*, V, No. 19 (1915), p. 113(B). Also in Greig MSS., II, p. 6. Sung by Mrs. Gillespie, Glasgow; learned in Aberdeenshire in the 1850's from Alexander Cruickshank, Redburn, Byth. Communicated by James B. Duncan.

p D/Æ

"O father, dear, I've dreamt a dream,
I fear it will prove sorrow,
I dreamt I was puin' the heather bells,
In the dowie dens o' Yarrow."

2. "The Dowie Dens o' Yarrow"

Ord, 1930, p. 426.

p D/Æ

1. There lived a lady in the south,
   You could scarce have found her marrow;
   She was courted by nine gentlemen,
   And the ploughman laddie o' Yarrow.

2. As he came ower yon high, high hill,
   And down yon glen so narrow,
   There he spied nine gentlemen
   Come to fight with him on Yarrow.

3. If I see all, there's nine to ane,
   And that's an unequal marrow;
   But I will take you three by three,
   And I'll slay you all on Yarrow.

4. Then three he slew, and three withdrew,
   And three lay deadly wounded,
   Till her brother John stepped in behind
   And pierced his body through.

5. Go home, go home, ye false young man,
   And tell your sister sorrow,
   That her true love John lies dead and gone
   In the dowie dens o' Yarrow.

6. As she came ower yon high, high hill,
   And down yon glen so narrow,
   It's there she spied her brother John
   Returning home from Yarrow.

7. O, brother, dear, I've dreamt a dream,
   And I fear it will prove sorrow,
   For I dreamt that you were spilling blood
   In the dowie dens o' Yarrow.

8. O, sister, dear, I'll read your dream,
   And I'm sure it will prove sorrow,
   Your true love John lies dead and gone,
   A bloody corpse in Yarrow.

9. She wrung her hands and tore her hair
   Wi' muckle grief and sorrow,
   For she dearly loved her true love John,
   The ploughman laddie o' Yarrow.

10. This lady's hair being three-quarters long,
    And the colour of it was yellow,
    She's tied it round her middle jimp,
    And she carried him home from Yarrow.

11. O, daughter, dear, dry up your tears,
    And dwell no more in sorrow,
    And I'll wed you to one of a higher degree
    Than the ploughman laddie o' Yarrow.

12. O, father, ye hae seven sons,
    Ye can wed them a' to-morrow,
    But a fairer flower than my true love John
    There never bloomed in Yarrow.

13. Now this lady, she being in distress
    For her love who died on Yarrow,
    She flung herself in her father's arms,
    And died through grief and sorrow.

3. "The Dowie Dens o' Yarrow"

Greig MSS., IV, p. 160. Also in Greig and Keith, 1925, p. 143(a). Sung by J. W. Spence, Rosecroft, Fyvie.

p D/Æ

4. "Dowie Dens o' Yarrow"

Greig MSS., II, p. 2. Sung by Mrs. Stuart, Auchmaliddie, New Deer, July 1906.

p D/Æ

There lived a lady in this place,
Ye wad scarcely find her marrow,
She was courted by nine gentlemen
And the ploughman lad o' Yarrow.

There lived a lady in the south,
You cd scarcely find her marrow;
She was courted by nine gentlemen,
And the ploughman lad o' Yarrow.

5. "Yarrow"

Greig MSS., II, p. 56. Sung by Mrs. Gordon, May 1906.

p D/Æ

6. "Yarrow"

Greig MSS., IV, p. 47. Sung by Mrs. Dunbar.

p D/Æ

7. "Yarrow"

Greig MSS., III, p. 168. Sung by W. Gray.

p D/Æ

8. "Yarrow"

Greig MSS., II, p. 144. Sung by Mrs. Fowlie, Bonnykelly, New Deer, September 1907.

p D/Æ

9. "Dowie Dens o' Yarrow"

Greig MSS., I, p. 111. Sung by J. C. Rennie, Milladen, Mintlaw, 1905.

p D/Æ

10. "Dowie Dens o' Yarrow"

Greig MSS., I, p. 181 (second set). Collected by George Riddell, Rosehearty.

p D/Æ

11. "Dowie Dens o' Yarrow"

Greig MSS., III, p. 10. Sung by George Brown, Turriff, September 1907.

p D/Æ

There lived a lady in the south,
You cd scarcely find her marrow;
She was courted by nine gentlemen,
And the ploughman lad o' Yarrow.

12. "Dowie Dens o' Yarrow, & Tiftie's Annie"

Greig MSS., III, p. 30. Sung by Alexander Greig, Oldwhat, New Deer, September 1907.

p D/Æ

There lived a lady in the south,
You cd scarcely find her marrow;
She was courted by nine gentleman,
And a ploughman lad in Yarrow.

13. "Dowie Dens"

Greig MSS., II, p. 131. Sung by Mrs. Knox, New Deer, August 1907.

p D/Æ

14. "Yarrow"

Greig MSS., III, p. 115. Sung by Mrs. Lee.

m D/Æ

15. "Dowie Dens o' Yarrow"

Greig MSS., II, p. 3. Also in Greig and Keith, 1925, p. 144(f). Sung by Andrew Findlay, New Deer, May 1906.

p D/Æ

There lived a lady in the north,
Ye wad scarcely find her marrow;
She was courted by nine gentlemen,
And a servant lad in Yarrow.

16. "The Dowie Dens of Yarrow"

Greig and Keith, 1925, p. 143(b); from Duncan MS., No. 70. Also in Duncan, *JFSS*, V, No. 19 (1915), p. 113(A). Sung by James Greig, of Strichen, c. 1893; noted by his daughter, Mrs. Harper, Cluny.

p D/Æ

There was a lady lived in the north,
Her name it was called Sarah;
She was coorted by nine noblemen
An' a plooman lad fae Yarrow.

17. "The Dowie Dens o' Yarrow"

Greig-Duncan MS. 785 (Walker transcript), p. 112; from Duncan MS., No. 307. Sung by Frank Christie, Cluny, Aberdeenshire.

p D/Æ

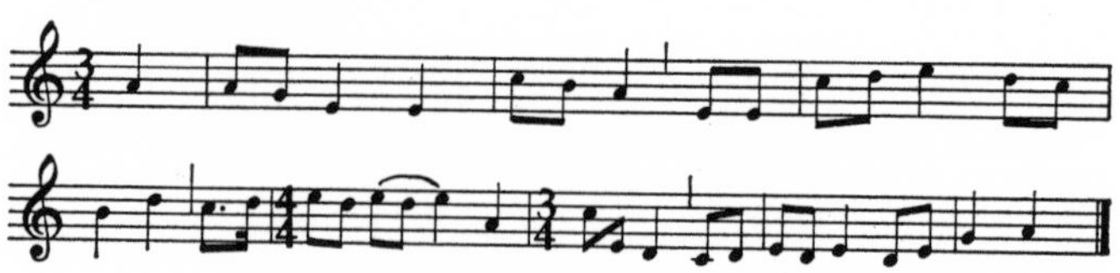

There was a maid and she was fair
There was few that was her marrow
She was coorted by nine gentlemen
And a plouman lad in Yarrow

18. "The Dowie Dens o' Yarrow"

Greig MSS., IV, p. 157. Also in Greig and Keith, 1925, p. 144(d). Sung by a New Leeds woman.

p D/Æ

19. "The Dowie Dens o' Yarrow"

BBC Sound Archives, rec. No. 18785. Sung by Jean Matthew, Aberdeenshire, July 18, 1952. Collected by Seamus Ennis.

p D/Æ

1. There lived a lady in the South,
Ye could scarcely find her marrow;
She was courted by nine gentlemen
And a plowman lad in Yarrow.

2. There was nine o' them sat drinkin wine
And nine o' them in Yarrow.
And there fell oot a great dispute
Of which should be her marrow.

3. As they gaed up yon high high hill
And doun yon glen sae narrow,
It's they did spy her true-love John
Come to fight with them in Yarrow.

4. "There's nine o' you and ane of me,
That's an unequal marrow.
But I will take you three by three
And I'll slay you all in Yarrow."

5. There's three he slew and three withdrew,
And three lay deidly wounded,
Till her brother John came in behind,
And pierced his body through [thoro'].

6. "Go home, go home, ye false young man,
And tell your sister sorrow
That her true-love John lies dead and gone
In the dowie dens o' Yarrow."

7. As he gaed up yon high high hill
And doun yon glen so narrow,
It's there he spied his sister dear
Come to meet her love in Yarrow.

8. "O Brother dear, I hae dreamed a dream,
I fear it will prove sorrow,
I dreamed I pu'd a red red rose
In the dowie dens o' Yarrow."

9. "O Sister dear, I can rede your dream,
And I know it will prove sorrow:
Your true-love John lies dead and gone,
A bloody corpse in Yarrow."

10. She wrung her hands and she tore her hair
Wi' muckle grief and sorrow,
For well she loved her plowman lad,
Love's dearest flower in Yarrow.

11. This lady's hair bein' three quarters long,
And the color of it was yellow,
She tied it round his middle small
And she carried him hame frae Yarrow.

12. "O daughter dear, dry up your tears,
And weep nae mair for sorrow.
I'll wed ye to a fairer flower,
Than ever sprung in Yarrow."

13. "O Father dear, ye hae seven sons,
Ye can wed them a' tomorrow
But ye'll never wed me to a fairer flower
Than the plowman lad in Yarrow."

20. "The Dowie Dens"

Greig MSS., I, p. 110; text, Bk. 716, VI, p. 29. Sung by Arthur Barron, Whitehill, February 1906.

p D/Æ

1. There lives a lady in this place
You scarce could find her marrow
She's courted by nine gentlemen
The ploughman lads o' Yarrow.

2. It's nine o' them sat drinkin wine
Sat drinkin' wine in Yarrow
And there fell a contest amang the crew
It's wha wad fight in Yarrow.

3. There's nine o' you & but ane o' me
Makes an unequal marrow
And I'll fight ye a' one by one
For the sake o' my love Sarah.

4. There's three he slew and three withdrew
And three lay badly wounded
And her brother John, he stepped in behind
And pierced his body thorough.

5. Go home, go home, you're a false young man
And tell your sister Sarah
That her true love John, he's dead & gone
On the bloody dens o' Yarrow.

6. O father dear I've dreamed a dream
I'm afraid it will prove sorrow.
I dreamed that I was puin the heather bells
In the dowie dens o' Yarrow.

7. O daughter dear I'll read your dream
I'm afraid it will prove sorrow
Your true love John lies dead & gone
A bloody corpse in Yarrow.

8. O daughter dear, dry up your tears
I'll wed you to some other
I'll wed you to some higher match
Than the one you've lost in Yarrow.

9. O father dear you have seven sons
You can wed them all tomorrow
But a fairer flower never sprang in June
Than the one we've lost in Yarrow.

10. She wrung her hands & she tore her hair
Wi muckle grief and sorrow
She's torn the ribbon frae her hair
And she's away to Yarrow.

11. She's gone over yon high high hill
And down yon glen so narrow
And there she spied her true love John
His bloody corpse in Yarrow.

12. She's washed his face & she's combed his hair
Wi muckle grief & sorrow
And she's washed the red blood frae his wounds
In the dowie dens o' Yarrow.

13. This lady's hair being three quarters long
And the colour o' t was yellow
She's tied it roon his middle sma'
And carried him hame frae Yarrow.

14. This fair maid she being great with child
To the one she lost in Yarrow
She took him in her arms twa
And died wi' him in Yarrow.

21. "The Dowie Dens o' Yarrow"

Greig MSS., I, p. 110. Also in Greig and Keith, 1925, p. 144(e). Sung by Miss Annie Ritchie, Whitehill, February 1906.

p D/Æ

There was a lady lived in the south,
You scarce cd find her marrow
She was courted by nine armèd men,
And the ploughman lad o' Yarrow.

22. "The Dowie Dens of Yarrow"

Archive, School of Scottish Studies. Sung by Margaret Stewart. Collected by Hamish Henderson for the School of Scottish Studies; transcribed by the Editor.

m D/Æ

O son, O son do you take your gun,
Or do you take your arrow
Or do you take your gey broad sword
To fight your . . . in Yarrow.

Stanza one was indecipherable. The above is stanza two.

23. "Yarrow"

Greig MSS., IV, p. 38; text, Bk. 766, LVI, p. 104. Sung by J. A. Fotheringham, Orkney.

p Æ

1. There lived a lady in the North
You scarce could find her marrow
She was courted by nine noble men
And a plooman lad from Yarrow.

2. As this nine noblemen sat drinking wine
Sat drinking wine in Yarrow
They made a bargain 'tween them a'
To fight wi' me in Yarrow.

3. As I walked up yon high high hill
And doon yon lane so narrow
It's there I met the nine noble men
Come to fight wi' me in Yarrow.

4. There are nine of you & but one of me
And that's not equal marrow
But come one by one & I'll slay you all
In the Dowie Den o' Yarrow.

5. It's three he slew & three withdrew
And three lay dead in Yarrow
But her brother John he came up behind
And he pierced him with an arrow

6. Go home, go home you false young man
And tell your sister sorrow
Her true love John he lies dead & gone
In the Dowie Dens of Yarrow.

7. Oh father dear I have dreamed a dream
Wi' muckle grief & sorrow
I dreamt I was pu'ing heather bells
In the Dowie Dens o' Yarrow.

8. O daughter dear, I can read your dream
Wi' muckle grief & sorrow
Your true love John he lies dead & gone
In the dowie dens o' Yarrow.

9. She wrung her hands, she tore her hair
Wi' muckle grief & sorrow
She's ta'en the red ribbon off her hair
And she's awa to Yarrow.

10. She washed his face, she combed his hair
Wi' muckle grief & sorrow
She tied the ribbon aroond his waist
And she carried him home from Yarrow.

11. Oh daughter, dear dry up your tears
And weep no more in sorrow
For I'll wed ye [MS.: yet] to a far fairer one
Than the one ye lost in Yarrow.

12. Oh father dear ye have seven sons
Ye can wed them all tomorrow
But ye'll ne'er wed me to a fairer one
Than the one I lost in Yarrow.

13. This lass's heart being so full of grief
For the lad she lost in Yarrow,
Her tender heart it broke in two,
And she died upon the morrow.

[*alternate for stanza ten*]

This lass' hair being three quarters long
And the colour of it was yellow
She tied it roon his middle so sma'
And she carried him home from Yarrow.

24. "The Dowie Dens of Yarrow"

Sung by Davy Stewart, Dundee, Angus. Caedmon rec. No. TC 1146(A10). Collected by Alan Lomax.

p D/Æ

1. There were a lady into the North,
You could scarcely find her marrow.
She was courted by nine noblemen,
In the dowie dens of Yarrow.

2. Her father had a young ploughboy,
O him she loved most dearly;
She dressed him up like a noble lord,
And sent him off to Yarrow.

3. As these nine noblemen sat drinking wine,
Drinking to their sorrows;
That the fairest maid they ever saw
Was in the dowie dens of Yarrow.

4. "Did you come here to play cards or dice?
Did you come here for sorrow?
Did you come here to slay us all
In the dowie dens of Yarrow?"

5. "I neither come here to play cards or dice,
I didn't come here for sorrow.
But one by one, as long as ye'll stand
In the dowie dens of Yarrow."

6. It's three he drew and three he slew
And three he deadly wounded.
Till her false brother, John, came running in
And pierced him through the middle.

7. "Go home, go home now, ye false young man,
And tell of your sister's sorrow,
That her true lover, John, lie dead and gone
In the dowie dens of Yarrow."

8. "O mother dear, come read my dream,
I hope it will prove sorrow;
That my true lover John lie dead and gone
In the dowie dens of Yarrow.

9. "O daughter now I will read thy dream,
The blood it proves of sorrow;
That your true lover, John, lie dead and gone
In the dowie dens of Yarrow."

10. Her hair being of three-quarters long,
And the colour of it was yellow,
She wrapped it round his middle so small,
And she carried him home from Yarrow.

11. "O mother dear, come make my bed,
Make it long and narrow,
My true love John, died for me today,
And I will die for him tomorrow."

25. "The Dowie Dens o' Yarrow"

Greig-Duncan MS. 785 (Walker transcript), p. 112; from Duncan MS., No. 242. Also in Duncan, *JFSS*, V, No. 19 (1915), p. 113(C). Sung by Mrs. Mackay, Alford, Aberdeenshire, c. 1907, from 40 years' recollection.

p π^4

There lived a lass into the Sooth,
Ye wad scarcely find her marrow,
She was coorted by nine gentlemen
And a plooman lad in Yarrow.

26. "The Dowie Dens o' Yarrow"

Broadwood, *JFSS*, V, No. 19 (1915), p. 111(2). From a recording made in London by John MacLennan, of West Ross-shire, May 23, 1908.

p D/Æ

There was a lady in the West,
Some say she had no marrow;
She was courted by nine gentlemen
And a ploughman lad in Yarrow.

27. "The Dowie Dens o' Yarrow"

Archive, School of Scottish Studies. Sung by J. C. M. Campbell, of Wester Ross, in London, October 22, 1951; learned from his mother. Collected by Francis M. Collinson for the School of Scottish Studies; transcribed by the collector.

p D/Æ

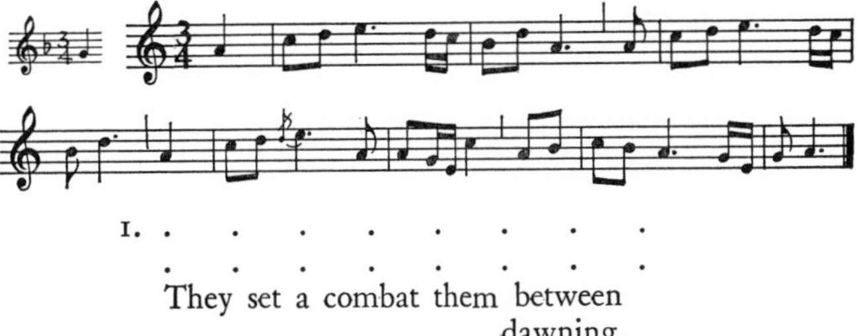

1. . . . .
. . . .
They set a combat them between
. . . . . . dawning.

2. O stay at hame my noble lord
O stay at hame my marrow
My cruel brother will you betray
On the dowie Holms o' Yarrow.

3. O fare ye weel my lady fair
O fare ye weel my sailor,
For I maun gae or ne'er return
Frae the dowie Banks o' Yarrow.

4. She kissed his cheeks, she kaimed his hair
As she had done before-o
She's belted on his noble brand
And he's away to Yarrow.

5. O he's gane up yon high high hill
I watched him gae wi' sorrow
An' in that den spied nine armed men
In the dowie Holms o' Yarrow.

6. O are ye come to drink the wine
As ye hae done before-o?
Or are ye come to wield the brand
On the dowie Holms o' Yarrow.

7. Four he hurt and five he slew
On the dowie Holms o' Yarrow
Till that stubborn knight came him behind
And ran his body through.

8. Gae hame, gae hame, good brother John
And tell your sister Sarah
To come and lift her noble lord
Who's sleeping sound on Yarrow.

9. Yestreen I dreamed a doleful dream
I bent there wad be sorrow
I dreamt I pu'd the heather green
On the Dowie Dens o' Yarrow.

10. She gaed up yon high high hill
I wit she gaed wi' sorrow,
And in the den spied nine dead men
On the dowie Dens o' Yarrow.

11. She kissed his cheek, she kaimed his hair
As oft she'd done before-o
She drank the red-bluid frae him ran
On the dowie dens o' Yarrow.

12. O haud your tongue my daughter dear
For what needs a' this sorrow
I'll wed you to a better lord
Than him you lost on Yarrow.

13. O haud your tongue my father dear
An' dinna grieve your Sarah
A better lord was never born
Than him I lost on Yarrow.

14. Tak' hame your oosen, tak hame your kye
For they hae bred down (on?) sorrow
I wish that they had a' gane wad
When they came first to Yarrow.

28. "The Dowie Dens o' Yarrow"

Greig MSS., III, p. 34; text, Bk. 721, XI, p. 3. Also in Greig-Duncan MS. 785 (Walker transcript), p. 112; and Broadwood, *JFSS*, V, No. 19 (1915), p. 110. Sung by John Potts, Peebleshire, September 3, 1907; noted by Lucy E. Broadwood.

p π^4

1. There lived a lady in the West,
Some said she had no marrow
She was courted by nine gentlemen
And a plowman lad in Yarrow.

2. Late at e'en and drinking wine
As oft they'd done before o
They made up a plot themsells amang
To fight for her in Yarrow.

3. "Oh bide at hame my true love John
Oh bide at hame my marrow.
For my cruel brother will thee betray
In the dowie dens o' Yarrow.["]

4. As he gaed up yon lang lang bog
He gaed wi dool and sorrow
He spied ten men all watering their steeds
In the dowie dens o' Yarrow.

5. Oh, are ye come to sell your land
Come here to beg or borrow
Or are ye come to wield your brand
In the dowie dens o' Yarrow.

6. I'm neither come to sell my land
Come here to beg or borrow
But I am come to wield my brand
In the dowie dens o' Yarrow.

7. Oh three he slew and three he drew
And three he did lay low
When her brother John came by a bush
And ran his body thorough.

8. O lady hie thee to yon glen
Hi thee wi' dool and sorrow
For your true love John lies dead and gone
In the dowie dens o' Yarrow.

9. Oh sister sister make my bed
Oh make it long and narrow
For my true love died for me yestreen
I'll die for him the morrow.

29. "The Dowie Dens o' Yarrow"

Shuldham-Shaw, *JEFDSS*, V, No. 2 (1947), p. 77. From the singing of Mr. A. Sutherland, Caithness, March 20, 1947.

m D

Two he slew and two withdrew
On the Dowie Dens o' Yarrow.

The above were the only lines recalled.

30. "The Derry Downs of Arrow"

Sung by Mrs. Lola Stanley, Fayetteville, Ark., December 30, 1958. LC/AAFS, rec. No. 11,905(B14). Collected by Mary Celestia Parler.

a D/Æ

1. I knew a lady of the North,
 A fair a fair O was she.
 She was courted by nine noble cowboys
 On the derry downs of Arrow.

2. Her father hired a noble cowboy,
 She loved him she did dearly.
 She dressed him up as a nobleman,
 And sent him away to Arrow.

3. As he rode over those high high hills,
 Those high high hills and valleys,
 These nine noble men was waiting his coming,
 On the derry downs of Arrow.

4. There's nine of you and one of me,
 No taller slender bravery.
 I'll fight you all it's one by one,
 On the derry downs of Arrow.

5. It's three he slew and three they flew,
 And two he left them wounded.
 Her brother Jim slipped up behind
 And pierced his heart on Arrow.

6. Go home, go home, you false-hearted lad
 And tell your sister Saro
 Her sweetheart John got killed last night
 On the derry downs of Arrow.

7. She went to bed it was early that night,
 And rose before the morrow:
 O Father dear, ' had a dream last night,
 I'm afraid it will bring to me sorrow.

8. O daughter dear, I will read your dream,
 I will read it all for sorrow.
 Your sweetheart John got killed last night
 On the derry downs of Arrow.

9. She wrung her hands all through her hair,
 Her jewels being many,
 She pulled them off and laid them down,
 And started away for Arrow.

10. As she rode over those high high hills,
 Those high high hills and valleys,
 Until she came to her sweetheart John,
 Got killed last night on Arrow.

11. She washed his face and combed his hair,
 And wiped away her weeping tears,
 And laid him it's all in his grave
 On the derry downs of Arrow.

12. O Father dear, seven sons have you,
 You can wed them all tomorrow.
 But the very old bloom that sprung in June
 Is the one I lost on Arrow.

13. O Daughter dear, dry up your tears,
 And weep no more for sorrow.
 I'll lead you to a better lad
 Than the one you lost on Arrow.

31. "The Dowie Dens o' Yarrow"

Greig MSS., I, p. 181 (first set). Also in Greig and Keith, 1925, p. 144(c). Collected by George Riddell, Rosehearty, 1903.

p Æ

32. "Dewy Dewy Dens of Yarrow"

Sung by Mrs. May Kennedy McCord, 1960(?). LC/AAFS, rec. No. 11,875(A7). Collected by Sherman Lee Pompey.

a π^4

O tell my Willie to come down
 And hear the mavis singing,
And see the birds all flying round,
 And hear the church bells ringing.

She sought him up, she sought him down,
 By rivers broad and narrow;
She sought him by the river-side
 And found him dead in Yarrow.

33. "Dowie Dens o' Yarrow"

Sung by Ewan MacColl, Riverside rec. No. RLP 12-625(B1), ed. K. S. Goldstein. Also on Columbia rec. No. SL 209(A1), No. 6. Learned from singer's mother.

a D/Æ

1. There was a lady in the North,
   I ne'er could find her marrow;
   She was courted by nine gentleman
   And a ploughboy lad frae Yarrow.

2. These nine sat drinking at the wine,
   Sat drinking wine on Yarrow;
   They ha'e made a vow amang themselves
   To fecht for her on Yarrow.

3. As he walked up yon high, high hill
   And doon by the houns o' Yarrow,
   There he saw nine armed men
   Come to fecht wi' him on Yarrow.

4. And there they flew and there he slew
   And there he wounded sairly,
   Till her brither, John, cam' in beyond
   And pierced his heart maist foully.

5. "O faither, dear, I dreamed a dream,
   A dream o' dule and sorrow;
   I dreamed I was pu'ing the heather bells
   On the dowie dens o' Yarrow."

6. As she walked up yon high, high hill
   And doon by the houms o' Yarrow;
   There she saw her ain true love
   Lying pale and wan on Yarrow.

7. Her hair it being three-quarters lang,
   The color it was yellow,
   She wrappit it roond his middle sae sma'
   And bore him doon to Yarrow.

8. "O, faither dear, ye've sieven sons,
   Ye may wed them a' tomorrow,
   For the fairest flooer amang them a'
   Was the lad I looed on Yarrow."

GROUP B

34. "The Rashes"

Oswald, V [c. 1753],* p. 26. Also in Dick, ed., 1903, No. 82, p. 79.

m D/Æ, ending on *V*

* Date according to Dick, *op.cit.*, p. xli.

35. "O May thy morn"

Johnson, V [1796], No. 464, p. 477 (repr. 1853). Also in Hogg, 1st series, 1819, p. 85 ("The wee wee German Lairdie").

a D

Stenhouse cites "Andrew and his Cutty Gun" as the parent of this (cf. *Museum*, I [1787], p. 405 and No. 180).

36. "The Dowie Dens of Yarrow"

Kidson, 1891, p. 22. Sung by Mrs. Calvert, Gilnockie, Eskdale; learned from her grandmother, Tibbie Shiel.

a D

1. There lived a lady in the west—
   I ne'er could find her marrow;
   She was courted by nine gentlemen,
   And a ploughboy lad in Yarrow.

2. These nine sat drinking at the wine,
   Sat drinking wine in Yarrow;
   They made a vow among themselves,
   To fight for her in Yarrow.

3. She washed his face, she kaimed his hair,
   As oft she'd done before, O!
   She made him like a knight sae bright,
   To fight for her in Yarrow.

4. As he walked up yon high, high hill,
And down by the holmes of Yarrow;
There he saw nine armèd men,
Come to fight with him in Yarrow.

5. "There's nine of you, there's one of me,
It's an unequal marrow;
But I'll fight you all one by one,
On the dowie dens of Yarrow."

6. There he slew, and there they flew,
And there he wounded sorely;
Till her brother, John, he came in beyond,
And pierced his heart most foully.

7. "Go home, go home, thou false young man,
And tell thy sister, Sarah,
That her true love, John, lies dead and gone,
On the dowie dens of Yarrow."

8. "Oh, father, dear, I dreamed a dream,
I'm afraid it will bring sorrow;
I dreamed I was pulling the heather bell,
In the dowie dens of Yarrow."

9. "Oh, daughter, dear, I read your dream,
I doubt it will prove sorrow;
For your true love, John, lies dead and gone,
On the dowie dens of Yarrow."

10. As she walked up yon high, high hill,
And down by the holmes of Yarrow,
There she saw her true love, John,
Lying pale and dead on Yarrow.

11. Her hair it being three quarters long,
The colour it was yellow;
She wrapped it round his middle sma',
And carried him hame to Yarrow.

12. "Oh, father, dear, you've seven sons,
You may wed them a' to-morrow;
But a fairer flower I never saw,
Than the lad I loved in Yarrow."

13. This fair maid being great with child,
It filled her heart with sorrow;
She died within her lover's arms,
Between that day and morrow.

37. "The Braes of Yarrow"

Barry, Eckstorm, and Smyth, 1929, p. 291. Sung by Mrs. Susie Carr Young, Brewer, Me. Tune recorded by George Herzog in 1928.

a D

This singer used the same tune for "Barbary Allen" (No. 84).

1. . . . .
Wherever it is ranging,
For my true love is like the moon,
That ev'ry month is changing.

2. O my lover roves, he trips the groves,
He trips both groves and valley,
Scarce in the dew there could I view
The tracks of my loved Molly.

3. She has a heart would gain love's might,
'Twould gain the heart of any:
And the darkest night she'll show me a light,
And that is known to many.

4. Last night I made my bed so wide,
To-night I'll make it narrow:
With a pretty baby by my side,
And a dead man for its father.

5. Love is the cause of my downfall,
Which leaves me broken hearted.

GROUP C

38. [The Dowie Dens o' Yarrow]

Scott, 1833-34, III, opp. p. 150; text, p. 147. Also in Maver, 1866, No. 79, p. 40.

m M (inflected VII), ending on *V*

1. Late at e'en, drinking the wine,
And ere they paid the lawing,
They set a combat them between,
To fight it in the dawing.

2. "O stay at hame, my noble lord,
O stay at hame, my marrow!
My cruel brother will you betray
On the dowie houms of Yarrow."—

3. "O fare ye weel, my ladye gaye!
O fare ye weel, my Sarah!
For I maun gae, though I ne'er return
Frae the dowie banks o' Yarrow."

4. She kiss'd his cheek, she kaim'd his hair,
As oft she had done before, O;
She belted him with his noble brand,
And he's away to Yarrow.

5. As he gaed up the Tennies bank,
I wot he gaed wi' sorrow,
Till, down in a den, he spied nine arm'd men,
On the dowie houms of Yarrow.

6. "O come ye here to part your land,
The bonnie Forest thorough?
Or come ye here to wield your brand,
On the dowie houms of Yarrow?"—

7. "I come not here to part my land,
And neither to beg nor borrow;
I come to wield my noble brand,
On the bonnie banks of Yarrow.

8. "If I see all, ye're nine to ane;
And that's an unequal marrow;
Yet will I fight, while lasts my brand,
On the bonnie banks of Yarrow."

9. Four has he hurt, and five has slain,
On the bloody braes of Yarrow,
Till that stubborn knight came him behind,
And ran his body thorough.

10. "Gae hame, gae hame, good-brother John,
And tell your sister Sarah,
To come and lift her leafu' lord;
He's sleepin sound on Yarrow."—

11. "Yestreen I dream'd a dolefu' dream;
I fear there will be sorrow!
I dream'd I pu'd the heather green,
Wi' my true love, on Yarrow.

12. "O gentle wind, that bloweth south,
From where my love repaireth,
Convey a kiss from his dear mouth,
And tell me how he fareth!

13. "But in the glen strive armed men;
They've wrought me dole and sorrow;
They've slain—the comeliest knight they've slain—
He bleeding lies on Yarrow."

14. As she sped down yon high high hill,
She gaed wi' dole and sorrow,
And in the den spied ten slain men,
On the dowie banks of Yarrow.

15. She kissed his cheek, she kaim'd his hair,
She searched his wounds all thorough,
She kiss'd them, till her lips grew red,
On the dowie houms of Yarrow.

16. "Now haud your tongue, my daughter dear!
For a' this breeds but sorrow;
I'll wed ye to a better lord,
Than him ye lost on Yarrow."—

17. "O haud your tongue, my father dear!
Ye mind me but of sorrow;
A fairer rose did never bloom
Than now lies cropp'd on Yarrow."

GROUP D

39. "The Braes of Yarrow"

Thomson, 1733, II, p. 34. Also in Johnson, I [1787], No. 64, p. 65 ("Busk ye, Busk ye") (repr. 1853); Rimbault, 1850, p. 86; Maver, 1866, No. 18, p. 9; and Eyre-Todd [1894], p. 70.

p I

Busk ye, busk ye, my bonny, bonny Bride,
Busk ye, busk ye, my winsom Marrow;
Busk ye, busk ye, my bonny, bonny Bride,
And let us leave the Braes of *Yarrow*.
Where got ye that bonny, bonny Bride,
Where got ye that winsom Marrow?
I got her where I durst not well be seen,
Puing the Birks on the Braes of *Yarrow*.
[*Etc.*]

Thomson gives as text the poem "Busk ye, busk ye" by William Hamilton of Bangour.

40. "The Dowie Dens o' Yarrow"

Fraser, *Rymour Club Miscellanea*, I (1910), p. 44. Fraser learned it from his father.

p I/M

"O sister dear, I've dream'd a dream,
It is with grief and sorrow;
I dream'd I was pu'in the birk sae green,
Wi' my true love on Yarrow."

"Oh, sister dear, I'll read your dream,
It is with grief and sorrow;
It's you may go fetch your gay Lord hame,
For he's lying slain on Yarrow."

Sometimes she rode, and sometimes she ran,
It was wi' grief and sorrow;
But aye she fainted when she thocht on
The dowie dens o' Yarrow.

Her hair it was three hand-fu's lang,
It was with grief and sorrow;
She tied it round aboot his middle,
And dragg'd him hame from Yarrow.

"This is a traditional tune sung many years ago by my father, and now transcribed from memory for the first time.

"The words, unfortunately, have not left such a vivid impression as the air, so that only a few isolated stanzas can be recalled. They differ from the 'minstrelsy' set and other forms of the ballad known to me." [*Fraser's note.*]

GROUP D APPENDIX

41. "The lady's goune"

Graham, 1848-49, I, p. 162. Transcribed from Leyden MS. for lyra-viol (1692).

a I

This would appear to be a sort of simplified instrumental counterpart to the *Orpheus Caledonius* form of the vocal melody.

GROUP E

42. "The Dewy Dens of Darrow"

Flanders and Olney, 1953, p. 235. Also in Flanders, III, 1963, p. 257. Sung by Mrs. Lily Delorme, Cadyville, N.Y., December 4, 1941; learned from her father. Collected by Marguerite Olney and Marjorie Porter. From *Ballads Migrant in New England*, edited by Helen Hartness Flanders and Marguerite Olney; copyright 1953 by Helen Hartness Flanders.

m I

1. Now a father had a young ploughboy,
Whom this lady loved most dearly;
She dressed him as a galliant knight
To fight for her on Darrow.

2. Then he went up this high, high hill,
And on the lane so narrow,
And there he saw nine noble knights
On the Dewy Dens of Darrow.

3. "O it's will you try the hunting hound?
Or will you try the arrow?
Or will you try the single sword
On the Dewy Dens of Darrow?"

4. "No, I won't try the hunting hound,
Nor will I try the arrow,
But I will try the single sword
On the Dewy Dens of Darrow."

5. His sword he drew—three knights he slew,
And was fighting with the other,
When her brother sprang from behind a tree
And they shot him with their arrow.

6. And she went up this high, high hill,
And on the lane so narrow,
And there she saw her noble knight
On the Dewy Dens of Darrow.

7. Her hair was about three-quarters long,
And the color being yellow,
She tied it round his waist so strong,
And she carried him home to Darrow.

8. "O daughter, dear, dry up those tears,
And give no more to sorrow,
For tomorrow you'll wed with a handsomer knight
Than the one you lost on Darrow."

9. "O father, dear, you have nine sons,
And you may wed them all tomorrow;
But you'll never find a handsomer knight,
Than the one I lost on Darrow."

Rare Willie Drowned in Yarrow, or, The Water o Gamrie

CHILD NO. 215

Keith has pertinently declared that there is no compelling need to identify the song of "Willie drowned in Yarrow" with the ballad of "Willie drowned in Gamrie" (Greig and Keith, *Last Leaves*, 1925, p. 145). But I find myself not disposed to part company with Child on the point. If we add to the fact that there is no water of Gamrie (unless the sea) the further significant, almost total, absence of rhyme in the Gamrie forms of the ballad, we shall conclude, I believe, that Child was not making a long shot. There is the connection in subject and the sharing of stanzas; and comparing two of the latter, we are likely to infer a substitution of name in the second:

She sought him east, she sought him west,
She sought him brade and narrow;
Sine, in the clifting of a craig,
She found him drowned in Yarrow. (Child 215 A4)

She sought it up, she sought it down,
She sought it braid and narrow;
An in the deepest pot of Gamerie,
There she got sweet Willie. (Child 215 D13)

Cf. also stanzas F9, G8, H15, and Greig's own stanza 14. There is, at any rate, equally no compelling need to separate the two, as Keith does; and we may properly reckon the tunes printed with "Rare Willie" as belonging to the tradition of this ballad.

There is a long continuity in the musical tradition so understood. Our earliest records of the tune go back to the Blaikie MSS. of 1683 and 1692. The line runs through the eighteenth- and nineteenth-century collections with divergences enough to show that tradition has not depended solely on print; and turns up finally in Ohio, in the twentieth century. Everywhere the tune is I/M and plagal, with three exceptions. R. A. Smith's is π^1 but sufficiently close. Christie gives, in addition to a version of "Rare Willie," a tune for "Gamrie" that had been published in the 1820's in his father's *Collection of Strathspeys.* Since Maver gives an almost identical form in 1866 (No. 425), as well as the usual form (No. 416), we may assume that he printed from Christie's father.

The tune lately collected from Miss Gordon (variant 8) may probably be made over out of Smith's tune and cloudy recollections of Christie, with whose book she was pretty certainly acquainted in youth. Her tune also has suggestions of "Waly, Waly" (cf. No. 204).

This "Gamrie" tune is out of line with all the others as to mode, but its melodic contour is close enough for Christie to call the other (the usual tune) a "major set" of this. As I have said before, I do not believe that our tradition often passes from minor to relative major (nor vice versa), and the weight of tradition here is anyhow altogether on the major side. If we supposed Christie's father to have modified the final cadence of the "Gamrie" tune, from an original tonic in G, we should find it restored to the major without violence to its general cast.

The only tune left outside the main group, then, is Mrs. Gillespie's, which is a plagal Dorian that she sang as well for "Barbara Allan" (No. 84), and which Keith has printed with that ballad.

It should be mentioned again that Duncan Fraser's tune for No. 214 belongs to the main tradition of the present ballad.

LIST OF VARIANTS

GROUP A

1. "Sweet Willy." Blaikie MS., National Library of Scotland MS. 1578, No. 1, p. 1.
2. "Sweet Willie." Blaikie MS., NL Scotland MS. 1578, No. 1a, p. 1.
3. "Willie was drowned in Yarrow." Greig MSS., III, p. 34, and Bk. 721, XI, p. 6, King's College Library, Aberdeen. Also in Greig-Duncan MS. 785 (transcription of W. Walker), p. 121, King's College Library, Aberdeen; and Lucy E. Broadwood, *JFSS*, V, No. 19 (1915), p. 115. (Potts)
4. "Yarrow." Mary O. Eddy, *Ballads and Songs from Ohio*, 1939, p. 69.
5. "Willy's rare, and Willy's fair." W. Thomson, *Orpheus Caledonius*, 1733, II, p. 110. Also in Joseph Ritson, *Scotish Songs*, 1794, I, p. 142; James Johnson, *The Scots Musical Museum*, VI [1803], No. 525, p. 542 (repr. 1853); Robert Maver, *Genuine Scottish Melodies*, 1866, No. 416, p. 208; W. Christie, *Traditional Ballad Airs*, I, 1876, p. 64; and George Eyre-Todd, *Ancient Scots Ballads* [1894], p. 136.
6. "Willie's Drowned at Gamery." Christie, *Traditional Ballad Airs*, I, 1876, p. 66. Also in Maver, *Genuine Scottish Melodies*, 1866, No. 425, p. 213.
7. "Willie's Rare." Robert Archibald Smith, *The Scotish Minstrel* [1820-24], VI, p. 76.
8. "Willie's Drowned in Yarrow." Miss M. Douglas Gordon (singer), Archive, School of Scottish Studies, University of Edinburgh.

GROUP B

9. "Willie's Drowned in Gamrie." Gavin Greig and Alexander Keith, *Last Leaves of Traditional Ballads and Ballad Airs*, 1925, pp. 70(3) and 145. (Gillespie)

TUNES WITH TEXTS

GROUP A

1. "Sweet Willy"

Blaikie MS., NL Scotland MS. 1578, No. 1, p. 1.

p I/M

2. "Sweet Willie"

Blaikie MS., NL Scotland MS. 1578, No. 1a, p. 1.

m I/M

3. "Willie was drowned in Yarrow"

Greig MSS., III, p. 34; text, Bk. 721, XI, p. 6. Also in Greig-Duncan MS. 785 (Walker transcript), p. 121; and Broadwood, *JFSS*, V, No. 19 (1915), p. 115. Contributed by Lucy Broadwood, as sung by John Potts, Whitehope Farm, Innerleithen, Peebleshire, September 3, 1907.

p I/M

The variant reading is given in the *Journal*, *loc.cit.*, above.

Her hair it was five quarters long
    The colour of it was yellow
She tied it round his middle sae sma'
    And she dragged him out o' Yarrow.

Oh mother mother make my bed
    Oh make it long and narrow
For never a young man shall lie by my side
    Since Willie was drowned in Yarrow.

4. "Yarrow"

Eddy, 1939, p. 69. Sung by Mrs. Jane Small, Canton, Ohio; learned from a cousin in Stonehouse, Lanarkshire, Scotland.

m I/M

1. My Willie's rare, my Willie's fair,
    My Willie's wondrous bonny,
He promised he would marry me,
    If ever he married ony.
Ony, ony,
If ever he married ony,
He promised he would marry me,
If ever he married ony.

2. My Willie's tae the huntin' gane,
    Afraid that he would tarry;
He sent a letter back to me
    That he was too young to marry.
Marry, marry, *etc.*

3. Last night I had a dreary dream,
    It caused me pain and sorrow;
I dreampt I was pulling the heather so green
    High up on the braes of Yarrow.
Yarrow, Yarrow, *etc.*

4. She wandered up, she wandered down,
    High up on the hills of Yarrow,
And right beneath a rock she found
    Her true lover drowned in Yarrow.
Yarrow, Yarrow, *etc.*

5. Her hair it was three quarters long,
    The color of it was yellow;
She turned it 'round her Willie's waist
    And pulled him out of Yarrow.
Yarrow, Yarrow, *etc.*

5. "Willy's rare, and Willy's fair"

Thomson, 1733, II, p. 110. Also in Ritson, 1794, I, p. 142; Johnson, VI [1803], No. 525, p. 542 (repr. 1853); Maver, 1866, No. 416, p. 208; Christie, I, 1876, p. 64; and Eyre-Todd [1894], p. 136 (as from *The Caledonian Musical Repository*, 1809).

p I (VII in grace-note)

Willy's rare, and *Willy*'s fair,
    And *Willy*'s wond'rous bony;
And *Willy* heght to marry me,
    Gin e'er he marry'd ony.

Yestreen I made my Bed fu' brade,
The Night I'll make it narrow;
For a' the live-long Winter's Night,
I lie twin'd of my Marrow.

O came you by yon Water-side,
Pu'd you the Rose or Lilly;
Or came you by yon Meadow green,
Or saw you my sweet *Willy?*

She sought him East, she sought him West,
She sought him brade and narrow;
Sine in the clifting of a Craig,
She found him drown'd in *Yarrow.*

6. "Willie's Drowned at Gamery"

Christie, I, 1876, p. 66. Also in Maver, 1866, No. 425, p. 213. From the *Collection of Strathspeys* published by Christie's father in the early 1820's.

m Æ (or m I, ending on *VI*)

"O Willie's fair, and Willie's rare,
And Willie's wondrous bonny;
And Willie says he'll marry me,
Gin e'er he marry ony."
"O ye'll get James, or ye'll get George,
Or ye'll get bonny Johnny;
Ye'll get the flower o a' my sons,
Gin ye'll forsake my Willie."
[*Etc.*]

Text "epitomized" from Peter Buchan's *Ancient Ballads and Songs of the North of Scotland*, 1828, I, p. 245.

7. "Willie's Rare"

Smith [1820-24], VI, p. 76. "Written from the singing of Mr. William Chalmers, Paisley."

p π^1

Willie's rare, and Willie's fair,
And Willie's wond'rous bonnie,
And Willie hecht to marry me,
Gin e'er he married ony.

Yestreen I made my bed fu' braid,
The night I'll make it narrow;
For a' the live-lang winter's night
I lie twin'd o' my marrow.

O! cam you by yon water side?
Pu'd you the rose or lily?
Or, cam you by yon meadow green?
Or, saw you my sweet Willie?

She sought him east, she sought him west,
She sought him braid and narrow,
And in the clifting o' a craig,
She fand him drown'd in Yarrow.

8. "Willie's Drowned in Yarrow"

Archive, School of Scottish Studies. Sung by Miss M. Douglas Gordon, 1953. Collected by Francis M. Collinson for the School of Scottish Studies. Transcribed by the collector.

a I

O Willie's fair and Willie's rare,
And Willie's wondrous bonny;
And Willie's haed(?) to marry me,
Gin 'ere he marries any.

But noo my Willie's gone awa';
He doesnd hear me greeting,
He doesna' hear me sob alane
When a' the world is sleeping.

GROUP B

9. "Willie's Drowned in Gamrie"

Greig and Keith, 1925, p. 70(3) ["Barbara Allan"]; text, p. 145. Sung by Mrs. Gillespie in the early twentieth century.

p D

215. RARE WILLIE DROWNED IN YARROW, OR, THE WATER O GAMRIE

1. On Monday morning at twelve o'clock
   Willie's company convenèd;
Three score an' ten brave gentlemen
   To convoy him on to Gamery.

2. When they were a' in saddle set,
   An' a' in good order,
He said, "Stay ye still, my merry men a',
   For I've forgotten something.

3. "I hae forgotten my mother's blessing,
   Her malison will go wi me;
Never an hour but bare sixteen,
   This day I mean to marry."

[He returns and receives her curse instead of her blessing.]

4. They rode on an' farther on,
   Till they came to the water o Gamery;
Every one rode safely through,
   But never yet came Willie.

5. The firstan step Willie's horse stepped in,
   He stepped in to the belly:
The water's strong, Willie's horse gaed wrong,
   An' the water's taen sweet Willie.

6. The firstan step Willie's horse stepped in,
   He stepped in to the belly:
The saiddle snapt, an' a' did brak,
   An' the water's taen sweet Willie.

7. They rode on an' farther on,
   Till they came to the kirk o Gamery;
An' the bonniest bride among them a'
   Said, "Where is my love Willie?"

8. Oot it spak his old father,
   Said, "Maid, I'll tell ye plainly:
The water's strong, Willie's horse gaed wrong,
   An' the water's taen your Willie.

9. "But ye'se get James, or ye'se get George,
   Or ye'll get bonnie Johnnie,
Or ye'll get ony o a' my sons
   For the loss o your sweet Willie."

10. "I winna hae James, I winna hae George,
   Nor I winna hae bonnie Johnnie,
Nor I winna hae ane o a' your sons
   For the loss o my dear Willie."

11. She put her hand unto her head,
   Where the ribbons they hung bonnie;
She pu'd them doon an' let them fa',
   An' sae fast she ran to Gamery.

12. "O came ye by yon bonnie water side?
   Pu'd either rose or lily?
Or did ye see another man
   Whose name was callèd Willie?"

13. "I came in by yon bonnie water side,
   Pu'd neither rose nor lily,
Nor did I see another man
   Whose name was callèd Willie."

14. She sought up an' she sought down,
   An' O but she sought him bonnie,
An' in a pot, below a bank,
   An' there she's found her Willie.

15. She's taen oot her siller comb,
   Combed down his locks sae yellow,
An' thrice she's kissed his claycold lips:
   "Farewell, my dearest Willie."

The Mother's Malison, or, Clyde's Water

CHILD NO. 216

ELEMENTS of this ballad are common to certain other ballads earlier in the canon, and have foreign analogues as well. The most prominent is "Annie of Lochryan" (No. 76), with which, however, it would be too fanciful to claim a connection in the melodic tradition.

For the present ballad there is clearly but one melodic family, and no useful purpose is served by subscribing to Keith's four. But the tune-type is, as he says, met in other associations: "The Gardener" (No. 219), "Lang Johnnie More" (251), "Pitcaithly's Wells," "There cam a Laddie frae the North," "The False Lover Won Back" (218) and elsewhere. It should be observed how even here there is an occasional infusion of the "Gypsy Laddie's" second strain ("Lady Cassilis"). It is very notable that in the present series of variants, the second half of the tune is much more stable than the first, and that the last phrase is the firmest of all. It may be relevant that that phrase has much in common with the most characteristic phrase in the well-known "Comin' thro' the Rye." The tune stays safely within the major galaxy, being variously π^1, I, I/M, and M. It is always plagal, or, alternatively, authentic with an ending on the octave.

A distinct and beautiful tune, unrelated to the rest, has recently been found in traditional use in the Northeast of Scotland: it will soon be familiar through recordings.

LIST OF VARIANTS

GROUP A

1. "Clyde's Water." Greig MSS., III, p. 97, and Bk. 731, XXI, p. 36, King's College Library, Aberdeen. Also in Gavin Greig and Alexander Keith, *Last Leaves of Traditional Ballads and Ballad Airs*, 1925, p. 150(4). (Mowat)
2. "Clyde's Water." Greig MSS., I, p. 76, and Bk. 711, I, p. 31. Also in Greig and Keith, 1925, p. 149(2a). (Watson)
3. "The Drowned Lovers." W. Christie, *Traditional Ballad Airs*, II, 1881, p. 250(1).
4. "Clyde's Water." Greig MSS., IV, p. 71. Also in Greig and Keith, *Last Leaves*, 1925, p. 149(2b). (Sangster)
5. "Clyde's Waters." Greig-Duncan MS. 785 (transcription of W. Walker), p. 122, King's College Library, Aberdeen. From Duncan MS., No. 386. (Lyall)
6. "The Drowned Lovers." Christie, *Traditional Ballad Airs*, II, 1881, p. 250(2).
7. "Clyde's Water." Greig and Keith, *Last Leaves*, 1925, p. 149(1a), and 147. From Duncan MS., No. 14. (Gillespie)
8. "Clyde Waters." Greig MSS., II, p. 46. Also in Greig-Duncan MS. 785 (Walker), p. 122. (Rettie)
9. "Clyde's Water." Greig MSS., III, p. 13. Also in Greig and Keith, *Last Leaves*, 1925, p. 149(1b). (Fowlie)
10. "Clyde Waters." Greig MSS., IV, p. 20. (Greig)
11. "Clyde's Water." Greig MSS., I, p. 76. Also in Greig and Keith, *Last Leaves*, 1925, p. 149(1c). (Pyper)
12. "Clyde's Water." Greig MSS., IV, p. 168. Also in Greig and Keith, 1925, p. 150(2c). (Spence)
13. "Clyde's Water." Greig and Keith, 1925, p. 150(3). From Duncan MS., No. 31. (Duncan)

GROUP B

14. "Clyde's Water." Ewan MacColl, Riverside recording No. RLP 12-627(B3), *The English and Scottish Popular Ballads*, IV, ed. Kenneth S. Goldstein.

TUNES WITH TEXTS

GROUP A

1. "Clyde's Water"

Greig MSS., III, p. 97; text, Bk. 731, XXI, p. 36. Also in Greig and Keith, 1925, p. 150(4). Sung by John Mowat, Craigmaud, New Pitsligo, May 1908.

p I/M; or a I/M, ending on the octave

1. Spare me, spare me, Clyde's waters,
   Oh spare me as I gang;
   Mak' me your prey as I come back,
   But spare me as I gang.

2. He is on to Maggie's bowers,
   And tirlin' at the pin.—
   "Oh sleep ye, waulk ye, Maggie dear,
   Oh rise & lat me in."

3. "Who is this at my bower,
   And tirlin' at the pin?["]
   "It's I, it's I, your true love,
   Oh rise & lat me in.

4. "The soberest bed in a' your bowers,
   Mysel' for to lie in;
   The meanest sta' in a' your stable
   For my steed to stand in."

5. "My stables they are fu' o' horse,
And my barns fu' o' hay;
And my bowers are full o' gentlemen,
And they'll not remove till day."

2. "Clyde's Water"

Greig MSS., I, p. 76; text, Bk. 711, I, p. 31. Also in Greig and Keith, 1925, p. 149(2a). Sung by Miss N. Watson, Whitehill, New Deer, October 1905.

p π^1

1. Young Willie stands in his stable
And combing down his steed
And looking through his white fingers
His nose began to bleed.

Repeat last two lines

2. Bring corn, corn to my horse
And meat unto my men
For I'm awa to Maggie's bowers
I'll win or she lie doon.

Repeat

3. O stay, O stay this ae nicht Willie
O stay and dinna gang
For there is a noise in Clyde Waters
Wid fear a thousand men.

Repeat

4. It's I've a steed in my stable
Cost me twice twenty pounds
And I'll put trust in his fore legs
Tae carry me safe along.

Repeat

5. As I rode o'er yon high high hill
And down yon dreary glen
It's o spare me spare me Clyde waters
O spare me as I gang
Make me the wreck as I come back
But spare me as I gang.

6. As I rode o'er yon high high hill
And down yon dreary glen
It's I hae reached at Maggie's window
Rise up and lat me in
For my boots are full of Clyde waters
And I'm frozen tae the chin.

7. It's up arose her mother dear
A' for tae speak tae him
It's my stable's full of horse she says
My barn's full of hay.
And my bowers are full of gentlemen
So ye can't get in till day.

8. He turned his horse right round about
Wi' the saut tear in his e'e
I never thought tae come here this nicht
And be denied by thee.

9. As he rode o'er yon high hill
And down yon dreary glen
The rush that ran in Clyde waters
Took Willie's can[e] frae him. *Rep[eat]*

10. As Willie he sat saddle o'er
To catch his cane again
The rush that ran in Clyde waters
Took Willie's hat frae him. *Rep[eat]*

11. His brother being on the other side
Cries Willie will ye droon.
Oh had ye tae yer high horse heid
He'll learn ye how to swim.

12. It's up she rose her Maggie dear
All in a frightful dream
For she dreamt that Willie was here last nicht
And she widna lat him in.

13. Go to yer bed my daughter dear
Lie doon and tak yer rest
For it's nae the space of half an hour
Since Willie left yer gate.

14. Then to her chamber she went with speed
And how quickly she put on
Now she is off tae Clyde waters
As fast as she can run.

3. "The Drowned Lovers"

Christie, II, 1881, p. 250(1). Sung by Bellie Cumine, Monquhitter.

p π^1

Willie stands in his stable door,
Clapping his coal-black steed;
And doubting of his Marg'ret's troth,
His nose began to bleed.
[*Etc.*]

Christie's text for both this tune and that in variant 6 below generally follows Buchan's (*Ancient Ballads and Songs*, 1828, I, p. 140) as it was modified by the anonymous editor of *The Ballad Minstrelsy of Scotland*, 1871.

4. "Clyde's Water"

Greig MSS., IV, p. 71. Also in Greig and Keith, 1925, p. 149(2b). Sung by Mrs. Sangster, Cortiecram, Mintlaw, September 1907.

p π^1

5. "Clyde's Waters"

Greig-Duncan MS. 785 (Walker transcript), p. 122; from Duncan MS., No. 386. Sung by Mrs. Lyall, Skene.

p π^1 (VII in grace-note)

Rise up rise up my Maggie dear
Rise up an' let me in;
My boots are fu' o' Clyde's water
An' I'm shiverin' to the chin.

6. "The Drowned Lovers"

Christie, II, 1881, p. 250(2). From Buchan tradition.

p I/M

Willie stands in his stable door,
Clapping his coal-black steed;
And doubting of his Marg'ret's troth,
His nose began to bleed.
"Gi'e corn to my horse, mother,
And meat to my man John;
And I'll awa' to Marg'ret's bower,
Before the night comes on."
[*Etc.*]

Christie uses the same text for this tune as for variant 3 above.

7. "Clyde's Water"

Greig and Keith, 1925, p. 149(1a); text, p. 147. From Duncan MS., No. 14. Sung by Mrs. Gillespie; learned from her mother.

p I

1. Willie stands in his stable door,
An' clapping his milk-white steed,
An' looking ower his white fingers,
His nose began to bleed.

[*Ll. 3 and 4 of each verse repeated when singing.*]

2. "Gie corn to my horse, mother,
An' meat to my young man,
An' I'll awa to Maggie's bowers,
I'll win or she lie doon."

3. "O bide this night wi me, Willie,
O bide this night wi me:
The bestan cock o a' the reest
At your supper shall be."

4. "O, a' your cocks an' a' your hens,
I value not a pin;
For I'll awa to Maggie's bowers,
I'll win or she lie doon."

5. "O stay this night wi me, Willie,
O stay this night wi me:
The bestan sheep o a' the flock
At your supper shall be."

6. "O, a' your sheep an' a' your flocks
I value not a pin;
For I'll awa to Maggie's bowers,
I'll win or she lie doon."

7. "O gin ye gang to Maggie's bowers
Sae sair against my will,
The deepest pot in Clyde's waters
My malison you'll feel."

8. "The gweed steed that I ride upon
Cost me thrice thirty poun',
An' I'll put trust in his firm feet
To bring me safe to lan'."

9. As he rode ower yon high high hill,
An' down yon dowie den,
The rush that was in Clyde's water
Wad feart five hundred men.

10. "O roaring Clyde, ye roar ower loud,
Your streams seem wondrous strang;
Mak me your wrack as I come back,
But spare me as I gang."

11. Then he's gane on to Maggie's bowers,
An' tirled at the pin:
"O sleep ye, wake ye, Maggie dear,
O rise an' lat me in."

12. "O wha is that at my bower door,
That calls me by my name?"—
"It is your first love, Willie dear,
This night come newly hame."

13. "I hae nae lovers without," she said;
"As few hae I within;
The bestan love that e'er I had
Was here just late the streen."

14. "The warstan stall in a' your stables
For my peer steed to stan';
The warstan bower in a' your bowers
For me to lie therein;
For my boots are fu' o Clyde's waters,
An' I'm shivering to the skin."

15. "My barns are fu' o corn, Willie,
My stables are fu' o hay;
My bowers are fu' o gentlemen,
An' they winna be teem till day."

16. "O fare ye weel, my fause Maggie,
O fareweel an' adieu,
I've gotten my mother's malison
This night for coming to you."

17. As he rade ower yon high high hill,
An' down yon dowie den,
The rush that was in Clyde's water
Made Willie lose his cane.

18. He leaned him ower his saddle-bow,
To catch his cane again,
But the rush that was in Clyde's water
Took Willie's hat fae him.

19. He leaned him ower his saddle-bow
To catch his hat through force;
The rush that was in Clyde's water
Took Willie fae his horse.

20. His brother stood upon the bank,
Says, "Fye man, will ye droon?
O turn ye to your high horse head,
An' learn how to soom."

21. "How can I turn to my high horse head
An' learn how to soom?
For I've got my mother's malison,
An' it's here that I maun droon."

22. The very hour this young man sank,
Into the pot sae deep,
Up wakened his love Maggie
Out o her drowsy sleep.

23. "Come here, come here, my mother dear,
An' read this drowsy dream:
I dreamt love Willie was at our gates,
An' neen wad lat him in."

24. "Lie still, lie still now, Maggie dear,
Lie still an' tak your rest;
Sin Willie he was at our gates,
It's but twa quarters past."

25. Sadly, sadly, rase she up,
An' nimbly pat she on;
The higher that the lady cries,
The louder blew the win'.

26. The firstan step that she stept in,
She stept in to the queet:
"O how, alas!" the lady said,
"This water's wondrous deep."

27. The nextan step that she stept in,
She stept in to the knee:
Says she, "I could wade farther in
If my true love I could see."

28. The nextan step that she stept in,
She stept in to the chin;
The deepest pot in Clyde's water
She gat sweet Willie in.

29. "Ye've had a cruel mother, Willie,
An' I have had another,
But we shall sleep in Clyde's water
Like sister an' like brother."

8. "Clyde Waters"

Greig MSS., II, p. 46. Also in Greig-Duncan MS. 785 (Walker transcript), p. 122. Sung by Mrs. Rettie, Milbrex, September 1906.

p I

Oh stay at hame, my Willie dear,
O stay at hame wi' me,
And the best fed lamb in a' my flock
Shall be weel dressed for thee—
And the best fed lamb in a' my flock
Shall be weel dressed for thee.

9. "Clyde's Water"

Greig MSS., III, p. 13. Also in Greig and Keith, 1925, p. 149(1b). Sung by Mrs. A. Fowlie, Bonnykelly, New Deer, September 1907.

p I

Oh stay at hame, my Willie dear,
Oh stay at hame wi' me;
And the best fed lamb o' a' my flock
Shall be weel dressed for thee, thee,
[And the best fed lamb o' a' my flock
Shall be weel dressed for thee.]

10. "Clyde Waters"

Greig MSS., IV, p. 20. From Miss Agnes Greig, Pundlercroft, New Deer.

p I

Oh stay at hame, my Willie dear,
Oh, stay at hame wi' me;
And the best fed lamb in a' my flock,
Shall be weel dressed for thee
And the &c.

11. "Clyde's Water"

Greig MSS., I, p. 76. Also in Greig and Keith, 1925, p. 149(1c). Sung by Mrs. Pyper, Whitehill, New Deer, December 1905.

p M

Oh Willie stood in his stable door,
Kaimed doon his milk white steed,
And looking o'er his white fingers
His nose began to bleed.

12. "Clyde's Water"

Greig MSS., IV, p. 168. Also in Greig and Keith, 1925, p. 150(2c). Sung by J. W. Spence, Rosecroft, Fyvie.

p I/M

13. "Clyde's Water"

Greig and Keith, 1925, p. 150(3); from Duncan MS., No. 31. Text from Greig-Duncan MS. 785 (Walker transcript). Sung by William Duncan, Rothienorman.

m I/M

Corn Corn to my horse
An' meat unto my man
An' I'll awa to Maggie's boures
I'll win 'ere she lie down O.

GROUP B

14. "Clyde's Water"

Sung by Ewan MacColl, Riverside rec. No. RLP 12-627 (B3), ed. K. S. Goldstein. MacColl learned the tune and three stanzas of text (10, 11, and 13) from Jeannie Robertson, Aberdeen; the rest of the text he learned from his mother.

a I

1. Oh, Willie stands at his ha' door,
And aye he straiked his milk-white steed,
And then oot ower his white fingers
His nose begun to bleed.

2. "O Mither, gie my horse its corn,
And gie some meat to my servant man;
For I'm awa' to Maggie's bowers,
I'll in ere she lies doon."

3. "O bide this nicht at hame, Willie,
Bide this nicht at hame wi' me;
And the bestan sheep in a' the fauld
At your supper it shall be."

4. "You can ha'e your sheep and a' your flocks,
For them I wouldna gie a pin;
For I'm awa' to Maggie's bowers
And this nicht I'll win in."

5. "Gin ye should gang to Maggie's bowers,
It shall be sair against my will;
The deepest hole in Clyde's waters
My malison you'll fill."

6. Then he rode up yon high, high hill,
And he rode doon yon dowie glen;
The rush that was in Clyde's waters
Would feart five hundred men.

7. "O, Clyde, ye roar ower loud this night,
Your waters they seem wondrous strang;
You can wrack me when I come back this way,
Gin you spare me as I gang."

8. Then he's rode on to Maggie's door,
And he has turled at the pin;
"O, sleep ye or wake ye, Maggie dear,
But rise and let me in."

9. "O, wha's that stands at my ha' door?
Wha's that ca's me by my name?"
"It is your ain true love, your Willie
That's newly come frae hame.

10. "Open the door, O, Maggie dear,
Open the door and let me in.
For my boots are full of Clyde's waters
And I'm shivering to the chin."

11. "My barns are fu' o' corn, Willie,
And a' my byres are fu' o' hay;
My bowers are fu' o' gentlemen
And they'll no' come oot till day."

12. "Then fare ye weel, my fause Maggie,
Fare ye weel and a lang adieu;
I got my mither's malison
This nicht when I came to you."

13. Then he rode up yon high, high hill,
And he rode doon yon dowie glen,
The rush that was in Clyde's waters
Took the whup frae Willie's hand.

14. The rush that was in Clyde's water
Took his hat from him by force;
The rush that was in Clyde's water,
Took Willie frae his horse.

15. Noo at the hour young Willie fell
Into the hole sae wide and deep,
It was then awoke his ain true Maggie
Oot o' her droosy sleep.

16. "Come here, come here, my mother dear,
Come here and read to me this dream;
I dreamed my love stood at oor ha' door
And nane would let him in."

17. "Lie still, lie still, O Maggie dear,
Maggie, lie still and tak' your rest;
For your ain true love was at our ha' door,
Scarce twa quarters are past."

18. Then sadly, sadly rose she up,
No word she spak but her cla'es put on;
But the higher that the lady cried,
The louder blew the wind.

19. The firstan step that she did tak',
She stepped in unto the queet;
The nextan step, the lady cried,
This water's wondrous deep!

20. The nextan step that she stepped in,
She stepped in unto the chin;
The deepest hole in Clyde's water
She found sweet Willie in.

21. "O, ye have had a cruel mither,
And a cruel one had I;
But we shall cheat them baith, Willie,
In Clyde's water we will lie."

The Broom of Cowdenknows

CHILD NO. 217

When this ballad first began to be recorded, in the second half of the eighteenth century, it had, apparently, no refrain or burden. Had it had the old familiar burden, "O the broom, the bonny bonny broom," etc., it seems probable that the transcribers would have set that down. The first appearance of a refrain in a dependable text is that in Child D, which was taken down by Motherwell from singing. There the refrain is merely a fifth-line repeat with a syllabic bridge: still no burden. The burden first appears with the ballad in Child G (from Scott's *Minstrelsy*), where, however, it is used only as an introductory stanza, not repeated. It is only with Buchan's texts, Child L and M, that the burden makes its conventional appearance, and with a few texts that succeed his in date.

Nevertheless, it is clear that the musical tradition of the ballad is integral with that of the old song-tune which is intimately associated with this burden from its first appearance in the middle of the seventeenth century. The tune is unmistakable, and we have a number of early records of it, some of them unfortunately hard to decipher from the tablature in which they are written. The tune, wherever it clearly appears, ends on the second degree and is major in cast, whether straight Ionian, π^1, I/M, or Mixolydian. It is also authentic. Of the early records, Playford's (1651) is very simple, and not particularly appealing. That in the Guthrie MS. [1675-80], as it has been deciphered by Nelly Diem (see variant 2 below) must be some sort of instrumental obbligato, and not a true representation of the tune. A flageolet version of the early eighteenth century (Drexel MS. 3909; variant 3 below) appears to be I/M with Mixolydian decoration. The tablature does not indicate barring or length of notes, and it is impossible to be quite sure of the tune. Possibly, also, it is inaccurately set down. The familiar reading in *Orpheus Caledonius* (variant 5 below) has been followed with simplified editorial treatment in a great number of later printings.

The tune in its authentic form enters the ballad tradition in the nineteenth century records, and continues into the present century (Group Ab). One of these variants is Christie's, who says he can follow it back for a hundred years in Buchan tradition.

Quite distinct appears to be the tune in Johnson's *Museum*, set to Herd's text, "Bonnie May." If this was a traditional tune for the ballad, it finds no support in the other records. This tune is plagal D/Æ. It is the same as R. A. Smith's "May Colvin" (No. 4), *The Scotish Minstrel* [1820-24], III, p. 92; and other parallels are noted by Gilchrist in *JFSS*, III, No. 12 (1908), p. 188.

The tune which Barry found in New Brunswick is so corrupted with "Of a' the airts" and other forgetfulness that it hardly needs to be seriously considered.

LIST OF VARIANTS

GROUP Aa

1. "Broome: The bonny bonny Broome." John Playford, *The English Dancing Master*, 1651, ed. Margaret Dean-Smith, 1957, p. 63. Also in W. Chappell, *Popular Music of the Olden Time* [1855-59], II, p. 461.
2. "The bony broom." Guthrie MS. [1675-80], fol. 7, Edinburgh University Library; transcribed in Nelly Diem, *Beitrage zur Geschichte der Schottischen Musik in XVII Jahrhundert*, 1919, p. 159.
3. "The bonie broom." Drexel MS. 3909 [1700-50], New York Public Library.
4. "The Broom of Cowdenknows." Allan Ramsay, *Musick for Allan Ramsay's Collection of Scots Songs*, c. 1726, pt. II, p. 26.
5. "The Broom of Cowdenknows." W. Thomson, *Orpheus Caledonius* [1725], fol. 10; and 1733, I, opp. p. 18.
6. "The Broom of Cowdenknows." James Johnson, *The Scots Musical Museum*, I [1787], No. 69, p. 70 (repr. 1853). Also in Joseph Ritson, *Scotish Songs*, 1794, I, p. 118; Robert Archibald Smith, *The Scotish Minstrel* [1820-24], II, p. 45; George Thomson, *The Select Melodies of Scotland* [1822-23], III, p. 32; G. F. Graham, *The Songs of Scotland*, 1848-49, I, p. 56; and George Eyre-Todd, *Ancient Scots Ballads* [1894], p. 40.

GROUP Ab

7. "The Maid of the Cowdenknowes." W. Christie, *Traditional Ballad Airs*, I, 1876, p. 126.
8. "The Ewe-buchts." Greig MSS., III, p. 142, King's College Library, Aberdeen. Also in Gavin Greig and Alexander Keith, *Last Leaves of Traditional Ballads and Ballad Airs*, 1925, p. 153(1c). (Milne)

GROUP AC

9. "Ochiltree Walls." William Motherwell, *Minstrelsy: Ancient and Modern*, 1827, App'x., No. 10 and p. xviii.
10. "The Maid of the Cowdenknowes." Christie, *Traditional Ballad Airs*, I, 1876, p. 284.
11. "The Cowdenknowes." Greig MSS., II, p. 36, and II, p. 99. Also in Greig and Keith, *Last Leaves*, 1925, p. 153(1d). (Rae)
12. "The Cowdenknowes." Greig MSS., II, p. 35. (Calder)
13. "The Cowdenknowes." Greig MSS., IV, p. 51. Also in Greig and Keith, 1925, p. 152(1a). (Dunbar)
14. "Bonnie Mary is to the ewe-buchts gane." Greig MSS., II, p. 150, and Bk. 729, XIX, p. 69. (Mowat)
15. "The Broom of Cowdenknowes." Ewan MacColl, Riverside recording No. RLP 12-623(B4), *The English and Scottish Popular Ballads*, II, ed. Kenneth S. Goldstein.
16. "The Ewe-Buchts." Greig MSS., III, p. 154. (Greig)
17. "The Ewe-Bughts." Greig MSS., III, p. 117, and Bk. 731, XXI, p. 87. (Robb)
18. "The Broom of Cowdenknowes." Greig and Keith, *Last Leaves*, 1925, p. 152(1b). From Duncan MS., No. 427. (Reid)
19. "The Ewe Bughts." Greig MSS., III, p. 116. Also in Greig and Keith, 1925, p. 153(3). (Lee)

GROUP B

20. "Bonnie May." Johnson, *The Scots Musical Museum*, II [1788], No. 110, p. 113 (repr. 1853).

APPENDIX

21. "The Broom of Cowden-Knowes." Phillips Barry, Fannie H. Eckstorm, and Mary W. Smyth, *British Ballads from Maine*, 1929, p. 293. (McGill)

TUNES WITH TEXTS

GROUP Aa

1. "Broome: The bonny bonny Broome"

Playford, 1651, ed. Dean-Smith, 1957, p. 63. Also in Chappell [1855-59], II, p. 461.

a I, ending on II

2. "The bony broom"

Guthrie MS. [1675-80], fol. 7; transcribed in Diem, 1919, p. 159.

3. "The bonie broom"

Drexel MS. 3909 [1700-50].

a M?

The tune has been presumptuously translated from flageolet tablature by one who knew not how to govern the ventages and therefore could not test the effect of the trills and mordents. Moreover, the tablature is far from precise. It bears no indication of time-values, and serves more for mnemonic device than for accurate interpretation. Besides, the signs for *agréments* are open to questions which such instruction-books as that of Thomas Greeting do not resolve. It is not clear which of the two notes of a decoration is the anchor of the melodic line. I have therefore abstained from arbitrary interpretation and given the notes simultaneously, which an expert may flourish according to his better wisdom, in the assurance that he must use both in every case. The timing is also conjectural but accords more or less clearly with other examples of the tune. Unfortunately, the little tune-book which contains the original has been lost or mislaid for a number of years. It had formerly belonged to David Laing and William Motherwell before it entered the collection of Mr. Drexel and eventually came to the New York Public Library. It contains many Scottish tunes and some English ones of the Restoration period (e.g., "Duke of Monmouth's march," "The King shall enjoy his own again," "King James's march to Dublin") which seem to date it as a late seventeenth- or early eighteenth-century collection.

4. "Broom of Cowdenknows"

Ramsay, c. 1726, pt. II, p. 26. Text from Ramsay's *Tea-Table Miscellany*, ed. of 1871, I, p. 13.

a I (inflected VII), ending on II; or a D (inflected VI)

How blyth ilk morn was I to see
The swain come o'er the hill!
He skipt the burn and flew to me:
I met him with good will.

O the broom, the bonny bonny broom,
The broom of Cowdenknows;
I wish I were with my dear swain,
With his pipe and my ewes.

[*Etc.*]

5. "The Broom of Cowdenknows"

Thomson [1725], fol. 10; and (more simply) 1733, I, opp. p. 18.

a I/M, ending on II; or a D/Æ

O the Broom, the bonny Broom,
The Broom of Cowdenknows;
I wish I were at hame again,
To milk my Daddy's Ews.

How blyth ilk Morn was I to see,
The Swain come o'er the Hill!
He skip'd the Burn, and flew to me:
I met him with good Will.

O the Broom, &c.

[*Etc.*]

6. "The Broom of Cowdenknows"

Johnson, I [1787], No. 69, p. 70 (repr. 1853). Also in Ritson, 1794, I, p. 118; Smith [1820-24], II, p. 45; Thomson [1822-23], III, p. 32; Graham, 1848-49, I, p. 56; and Eyre-Todd [1894], p. 40.

a I, ending on II

GROUP Ab

7. "The Maid of the Cowdenknowes"

Christie, I, 1876, p. 126. In Buchan tradition from a hundred years before.

a π^1, ending on II

[It's] O the broom, and the bonnie bonnie broom,
The broom of the Cowdenknows!
And aye sae sweet as the lassie sang,
I' the bought, milking the ewes.
I' the bought, &c.

[*Etc.*]

Christie "epitomized" his text from Scott's *Minstrelsy*, 1833, I, p. 37.

8. "The Ewe-buchts"

Greig MSS., III, p. 142. Also in Greig and Keith, 1925, p. 153(1c). Contributed by George Ironside, as learned from Miss Mary Milne, New Deer, November 1908.

a I/Ly, ending on II; or a M/D

GROUP AC

9. "Ochiltree Walls"

Motherwell, 1827, App'x., No. 10; text, App'x., p. xviii.

a M/D

O May, bonnie May, is to the yowe buchts gane
For to milk her daddies yowes,
And ay as she sang her voice it rang
Out ower the tap o' the knowes, knowes, knowes,
Out ower the tap o' the knowes.

10. "The Maid of the Cowdenknowes"

Christie, I, 1876, p. 284.

a M/D

11. "The Cowdenknowes"

Greig MSS., II, p. 36, and II, p. 99 (fragment). Also in Greig and Keith, 1925, p. 153(1d). Sung by Miss H. Rae, Sandhaven, October 1906.

a D

Bonnie Mary's to the ewebuchts is gane
To milk her father's ewes,
And aye as she sang her bonnie voice it rang
Right over the tops o' the knowes, knowes,
Right over the tops o' the knowes.

Variants a and b are from the same singer, apparently on another occasion.

The following lines are given with the fragment of the tune (MSS. II, 99) also obtained from Miss Rae, at a different time:

She was milking her father's yowes,
She was milking her father's yowes.

12. "The Cowdenknowes"

Greig MSS., II, p. 35. From Rev. J. C. Calder, Crimond, July 1906.

a M/D

Bonnie Mary's to the ewe-buchts gane
To milk her daddie's yowes
And aye as she sang her bonnie voice it rang,
Right over the tops o' the knowes, knowes,
Right over the tops o' the knowes.

13. "The Cowdenknowes"

Greig MSS., IV, p. 51. Also in Greig and Keith, 1925, p. 152(1a). Sung by Mrs. Dunbar, Longhill of Crimond.

a M/D

14. "Bonnie Mary is to the ewe-buchts gane"

Greig MSS., II, p. 150; text, Bk. 729, XIX, p. 69. Sung by J. Mowat, Craigmaud, New Pitsligo, September 1907.

a M/D

1. Bonny Mary to the Ewe buchts did gang
To milk her daddie's ewe
And aye as she sang & her bonnie voice it rang
Right over the tops of the knowes, knowes,
Right over the tops of the knowes.

2. There came a troop o' merry gentlemen
All merrily riding by
And ane o' them to the ewe buchts did gang
To see Mary milkin her ewes, ewes
To see Mary milkin her ewes.

3. Milk on, milk on, my bonnie, bonnie lass
Milk on milk on said he
Ride on, ride on young man, she said
And do not tarry wi' me, me
And do not tarry wi' me.

4. He's taen her by the milk white hand
And by the waist gown sleeve
And he's kissed her owre & owre again
And asked no one's leave, leave
And asked no one's leave.

5. He mounted on his milk white steed
And he's ridden after his men
And all that his men ever said unto him
Oh master you've tarried long, long
Oh master you've tarried long.

6. I've ridden east, I've travelled west
I've ridden amongst the knowes
But the bonniest lassie that ever I saw
Was milkin her daddie's ewes, ewes
Was milkin her daddie's ewes.

7. She's taen the milk pail on her heid
And she's gaen singin hame
And all that her father ever said unto her
Oh daughter you've tarried long, long
Oh daughter you've tarried long.

8. But it fell on a day
On a bonnie simmer's day
She was ca'in out her father's kye
And who did she spy but the same gentlemen
All merrily riding by, by
All merrily riding by.

9. One of them did say unto her
Oh maid have you got a man
And the answer that she gave unto him
O I have got one at home, home
O I have got one at home.

10. You lie, you lie, you weel faur'd maid
And so loud as I hear you lie
Don't you mind on the dewy dewy night
You was in the ewe buchts wi' me me,
You was in the ewe buchts wi' me.

11. He has ordered one of his men to go down
And set her on behind
Says "Your father can ca' in his kye when he likes
For they'll never be ca'ed in by mine mine
For they'll ne'er be ca'ed in by mine.

12. I am the laird o' Logan Braes
I've got fify ploughs & three
And I'm sure that I've met wi' the ae bonniest lass
That's in all the north country countrie
That's in all the north countrie.

15. "The Broom of Cowdenknowes"

Sung by Ewan MacColl, Riverside rec., No. RLP 12-623(B4), ed. K. S. Goldstein. Learned from his father.

a M

O, the broom and the bonnie, bonnie broom,
The broom o' the Cowdenknowes,
And aye sae sweet the lassie sang,
In the ewe-buchts milkin' her yowes, her yowes,
In the ewe-buchts milkin' her yowes.
[*Etc.*]

Text conflated from Greig and Keith, 1925, and MacColl's father.

16. "The Ewe-Buchts"

Greig MSS., III, p. 154. Sung by Alexander Greig, Oldwhat, New Deer, February 1909.

a M/D

Bonnie Mary is to the ewe-buchts gane,
For to milk her daddy's ewes
And aye as she sang & her bonnie voice it rang,
Right over the tops o' the knowes,
Right over the tops o' the knowes.

17. "The Ewe-Bughts"

Greig MSS., III, p. 117; text, Bk. 731, XXI, p. 87. Sung by A. Robb, April 1908.

a M/D

1. Bonnie Mary to the ewe-bughts is gane
To milk her daddy's Ewes,
And aye as she sang & her sweet voice it rang
Right over the tops o' the knowes—knowes,
Right over the tops o' the knowes.

2. There was a troop of gentlemen,
Cam' merrily riding by
And ane o' them is to the Ewe-bughts gane
To see Mary milkin' her kye.

3. "Milk on, milk on, my bonnie bonnie lass,
Milk on, milk on," said he;
"Milk on, milk on, my bonnie bonnie lass,
And ye'll show me oot owre the lea."

4. "Ride on, ride on, stout rider," she said,
["]Your steed is baith stoot & strang,
It's oot o' the Ewe-bughts I winna gang
For fear ye do me wrang."

5. He has ta'en her by the milkwhite hand,
And by the grass-green sleeve,
And laid her doon on the dewy dewy grass
And never spiered her leave.

6. He's gien her a silver comb,
To comb doon her yellow hair,
And he has gien her guineas three,
For fear she'd never get mair

7. He has mounted his milk-white steed,
And after the rest o' his men;
And a' that they did say to him
Was, "Dear master, you've tarried lang."

8. She has pitten her milk pail on her head,
And she's gane singin' hame;
And a' that her father did say unto her,
Was, "Dear daughter you've tarried lang."

9. "There's been a tod in your bughts, father,
And the like o' 'im I never saw,
For afore he had ta'en the boggie that he's ta'en
I wad raither he had ta'en them a'.

10. "And the nicht it is misty & dark, father,
Come ye to the door & see,
And the Ewes gaed skippin' oot owre the knowes
And they widna bught in for me.

11. "Woe be to your shepherd, father,
Some ill death may he dee,
He's bigget the bughts owre far frae the hoose,
And he's trysted a man to me.

12. "And he was a man & a bonnie man,
And a bonnie man was he,
And aye as he spak & he lifted his hat,
And he had a bonnie blinkin' eé."

13. It fell once upon a day
She was cain' oot her father's kye,
And by cam' the same troop o' merry gentlemen,
And they winket the bonnie lassie by.

14. And one of them did say unto her
"Oh have ye got a man?"
So saucily she did reply,
Says, "Oh I've got one at home."

15. "Ye lee, ye lee, ye weel-faur'd maid,
Sae lood's I hear ye lee;
For don't ye mind on the dark & misty nicht
That I was in the bughts wi' thee?

16. ["]And I gave you a silver comb
To comb doon your bonnie yellow hair,
And I did give you guineas three
For fear ye'd never gotten mair?"

17. He's taen her by the waist sae sma',
And he's set her on ahin',
Says, "Your father can ca his kye when he likes,
But ye'll never ca them again.

18. "I am Laird o' Youghal Tree Wells,
I have 20 ploughs & 3,
And I hae gotten the bonniest lass,
That's in a' the north countrie."

18. "The Broom of Cowdenknowes"

Greig and Keith, 1925, p. 152(1b); from Duncan MS., No. 427. Sung by Robert Reid, Kemnay.

a M/D

Bonnie Mary to the ewebuchts has gane
To milk her daddie's yowes,
An' aye as she sang, her bonnie voice it rang
Richt over the tops o the knowes, knowes,
Richt over the tops o the knowes.

19. "The Ewe Bughts"

Greig MSS., III, p. 116. Also in Greig and Keith, 1925, p. 153(2). Sung by Mrs. Lee, Strichen, June 1908.

p I/M

O woe be to yon shepherd, she says,
And an ill death may he dee,
Biggin' the ewe bughts sae far frae hame,
And trystin' the young men to me.

GROUP B

20. "Bonnie May"

Johnson, II [1788], No. 110, p. 113 (repr. 1853).

a D/Æ, ending on the octave

1. It was on an ev'ning sae saft and sae clear,
A bonnie lass was milking the kye,
And by came a troop of gentlemen,
And rode the bonnie lassie by.

2. Then one of them said unto her,
Bonnie lassie, shew me the way
O if I do sae it may breed me wae,
For langer I dare na stay.

3. But dark and misty was the night
Before the bonnie lass came hame;
Now where hae you been, my ae doughter?
I am sure you was na your lane.

4. O father, a tod has come o'er your lamb,
A gentleman of high degree,
And ay whan he spake he lifted his hat,
And bonnie, bonnie blinkit his ee.

5. But when twenty weeks were past & gane,
O twenty weeks and three,
The lassie began to grow pale and wan,
And think lang for his blinkin ee.

6. O wae be to my father's herd,
An ill death may he die;
He bigged the bughts sae far frae hame,
And wadna bide wi' me.

7. It fell upon another fair evening,
The bonnie lass was milking her kye,
And by came the troop of gentlemen,
And rode the bonnie lassie by.

8. Then one of them stopt, and said to her,
Wha's aught that baby ye are wi'?
The lassie began for to blush, and think
To a father as gude as ye.

9. O had your tongue, my bonnie May,
Sae loud's I hear you lie;
O dinnae you mind the misty night
I was in the bught with thee.

10. Now he's come aff his milk-white steed,
And he has taen her hame:
Now let you father bring hame the kye,
You ne'er mair shall ca' them agen.

11. He was the laird of Auchentrone,
With fifty ploughs and three
And he has gotten the bonniest lass
In a' the south countrie.

APPENDIX

21. "The Broom of Cowden-Knowes"

Barry, Eckstorm, and Smyth, 1929, p. 293. Sung by Mrs. James McGill, Chamcook, New Brunswick, October 1927; learned in Kirkcudbrightshire, Scotland. Tune recorded by George Herzog.

p π^1

1. Bonny Maisry's to the yowe-buchts gane
Tae milk her daddy's yowes,
And aye as she sang, her bonny voice it rang
Oot o'er the taps o' the knowes.
O, the broom, the broom, the bonny, bonny broom,
The broom on the Cowden-knowes,
O, fain wud I be in my ain counterie
Milking my daddy's yowes.

2. There was a troop of merry gentlemen
Was riding atween twa knowes,
And they heard the voice of a bonny lass
In a bucht milking her yowes.

3. There's ane o' them lichted off his steed,
And has tyed him to a tree,
And he's gane to yon yowe-bucht
To hear what it might be.

4. "O, pity me, fair maid," he said,
"Tak pity upon me;
O, pity me and my milk-white steed
That's trembling at yon tree."

5. He's ta'en her by the waist sae small
And by the green gown-sleeve,
And he's led her into the yowe-bucht,
O' her freens he's spared no leave.

6. He has put his hand in his pocket,
And given her guineas three,
"If I dinna come back in half a year,
Then luke nae mair for me.

7. "Now show me to the king's hie street,
Now show to me the way;
Now show to me the king's hie street
And the fair water of Tay."

8. When she cam hame her feyther said:
"Come, tell to me richt plain,
I doot you've met some [one] in the way,
You hae na been your lain."

9. "The nicht it is baith mist and mirk,
Ye may gang oot and see;
The nicht is mirk and misty tae,
There's naebody been wi' me."

The False Lover Won Back

CHILD NO. 218

Greig showed that this pretty ballad, as both Child and Keith have called it, had a firm hold in his region, although Child had recovered but two texts. We might say it had 'sprung from the ashes,' to use Child's phrase for "Henry Martin," of the old and too cruel "Child Waters" (No. 63).

The main melodic tradition is perhaps plagal major. Christie's tune, which he derives from a Buchan singer about the opening of the nineteenth century, is a charming pentatonic. Greig's first tune (variant 1), mixed I/M, is recognizably close, although of course lacking Christie's second strain. In exchange, it has a fifth phrase, with bridge, for refrain.

Greig's Wallace tune (variant 3) is an interesting example of modal variation. Enough of the previous tune is left to establish a clear relationship, but this one ends convincingly on the lower sixth, and without other evidence would certainly be called Æolian. And so it probably ought to be considered. According to Keith this tune is found with other folk-songs, but I am unable to point to any close variants, except the one that follows it here. Phrases two and four are, however, common formulae. The Gordon variant lacks the indicative minor sixth but widens its range.

The remaining tune appears to be independent of the others. It has a close family resemblance to the first part of "I'm a' doun for lack o' Johnnie" (G. F. Graham, *The Songs of Scotland*, 1848-49, II, p. 36), an air made notable by its use in Max Bruch's "Scottish Fantasia." But possible other and older affiliations are with "O an ye were deid, guidman," and "Corn Riggs" (cf., e.g., Alfred Moffat, *The Minstrelsy of Scotland*, 2nd ed. [1896], pp. 100 and 236).

LIST OF VARIANTS

GROUP A

1. "The Place where my love Johnnie dwells." W. Christie, *Traditional Ballad Airs*, I, 1876, p. 144.
2. "The false lover won back." Greig MSS., IV, p. 56, and Bk. 759, XLIX, p. 88, King's College Library, Aberdeen. Also in Gavin Greig and Alexander Keith, *Last Leaves of Traditional Ballads and Ballad Airs*, 1925, p. 155(1). (Morrice)
3. "The False Lover won Back." Greig and Keith, 1925, p. 155(2). From Duncan MS., No. 510. (Wallace)
4. "The Fause Lover." Greig MSS., II, p. 56; and Bk. 719, IX, p. 107. (Gordon)

GROUP B

5. "The False Lover won Back." Greig and Keith, *Last Leaves*, 1925, p. 155(3). From Duncan MS., No. 286. (Gillespie)

TUNES WITH TEXTS

GROUP A

1. "The Place where my love Johnnie dwells"

Christie, I, 1876, p. 144. From a Buchan singer, c. 1800.

m π^1

1. The sun shines high on yonder hill,
   And low on yonder town;
   In the place where my love Johnny dwells,
   The sun gaes never down.

"O when will ye be back, bonny lad,
   O when will ye be hame?"
"When heather hills are nine times brunt,
   And a' grown green again."

2. "O that's ower lang awa', bonny lad,
   O that's ower lang frae hame!
   For I'll be dead and in my grave,
   Ere ye come back again."
   He put his foot into the stirrup,
   And said he maun gae ride;
   But she kilted up her green claithing,
   And said she wou'dna bide.

3. The firsten town that they came to,
   He bought her hose and sheen;
   And bade her rue and return again,
   And gang nae farther wi' him.
   "Ye likena me at a', bonny lad,
   Ye likena me at a'."
   "It's sair for you likes me sae weel,
   And me nae you at a'."

4. The nexten town that they came to,
   He bought her a braw new gown;
   And bade her rue and return again,
   And gang nae farther wi' him.

The nexten town that they came to,
He bought her a wedding ring;
And bade her dry her rosy cheeks,
And he would tak' her wi' him.

5. "O wae be to your bonny face,
And your twa blinkin' een!
And wae be to your rosy cheeks!
They've stown this heart o' mine.
There's comfort for the comfortless,
There's honey for the bee;
There's comfort for the comfortless,
There's nane but you for me."

2. "The false lover won back"

Greig MSS., IV, p. 56; text, Bk. 759, XLIX, p. 88. Also in Greig and Keith, 1925, p. 155(1). From Miss Annie Shirer, as learned from the singing of Miss Kate Morrice, a very old woman of Kininmonth.

m I/M

1. The sun shines high on yonder hill,
And low in yonder dell;
The place where me & my love dwells
The sun goes never doon, bonnie love,
The sun goes never doon.

2. Go saddle to me the bonnie black steed,
Or saddle to me the broon,
That I may ride all around, bonnie love,
That I may ride all around.

3. It's when will ye be back, bonnie love,
Or when will ye be hame?
When the heather hills are nine times brunt,
And a' growin' green again, bonnie love,
And a' growin' green again.

4. Oh, that's owre lang to bide awa',
Oh, that's owre lang frae hame;
The baby that's nae born yet
Will be owre lang wintin' its name, bonnie love,
Owre lang wintin' its name.

5. He turned aboot his high horse' [*sic*] heid,
And fast awa' rode he;
And she kilted up her gay clothing,
And fast, fast followed she, bonnie love,
And fast, fast followed she.

6. The first intoon[1] that they cam' till,
He bocht her hose & sheen;
And he bade her rue & return noo,
And nae mair follow him, bonnie love,
And nae mair follow him.

7. It's love for love that I do want,
And love for love again;
It's hard when I like you sae weel,
And you nae me again, bonnie love,
And you nae me again.

8. The neist in toon that they cam' till,
He bocht her a broch & a ring;
And he bade her rue & return noo,
And nae mair follow him, bonnie love,
And nae mair follow him.

9. It's love for love that I do want,
And love for love again;
It's hard when I like you sae weel,
And you nae me again, bonnie love,
And you nae me again.

10. The neist in[2] toon that they cam' till,
He bocht her a wedding goon;
And he bade her dry her rosy cheeks,
And he would tak' her wi' him, bonnie love,
And he would tak' her wi' him.

11. It's love for love that I do want,
An' love for love again;
And there's nane but you for me, bonnie love,
And there's nane but you for me.

12. There's comfort for the comfortless,
And honey for the bee;
And there's nane for you but me, bonnie love,
There's nane for you but me.

13. So it's love for love that I hae got
And love for love again;
So turn your high horse heid aboot,
And we will ride for hame, bonnie love,
And we will ride for hame.

[1] i.e., firsten toon
[2] i.e., niesten

3. [The False Lover won Back]

Greig and Keith, 1925, p. 155(2); from Duncan MS., No. 510. Sung by William Wallace, Leochel-Cushnie.

a Æ

The sun shines high on yonder hill,
An' low in yonder glen;
An' in the place where my love dwells
The sun gangs never doon.

4. "The Fause Lover"

Greig MSS., II, p. 56; text, Bk. 719, IX, p. 107. Sung by Mrs. Gordon, South Auchreddie, New Deer, May 1906.

m D/Æ

1. Come saddle to me the black steed, said he
Come saddle to me the broon
There is a place where my lovie dwells
And the sun he never goes down.

2. He's ta'en the horse by the bridle reins
And she's led him to a manger
She took the young man by the hand
And led him to her chamber.

3. She placed before him bread & wine
The wine it was like amber
There's cheese & breid for grenadiers
And corn & wine for horses.
[Alternative?:]
A glass o' wine for gentlemen
And bonnie lads for lasses.

4. Oh when will ye be back lovie
Oh when will ye be hame?
When the heather hills are nine times brunt
And a' grown green again.

5. Oh that's owre lang away love
Oh that's owre lang fae hame
For the baby that's nae born yet
Will be owre lang wantin its name.

6. He turnèd round his high horse heid
And fast awa rode he
She's kilted up her petticoats
And fast fast followed she.

7. At the firsten (in)toon that he cam to
He bought her hose and sheen
He bade her rue and return again
And nae mair follow him.

8. Oh love me once (again) young man she said
Oh love me once again
It's hard for me that I love you
And you nae me again.

9. He's turnèd round his high horse heid
And fast awa rode he
She's kilted up her petticoats
And fast fast followed she.

10. The next intoon that he came to
wedding gown
He bought her a brooch & a ring
He bade her rue & return again
And nae mair follow him.

11. Oh love me once young man said she
Oh love me once again
It's hard for me that I love you
And you nae me again.

12. There's comfort for the comfortless
And honey for the bee
Then comfort ye the comfortless
For there's nane but you for me.

GROUP B

5. [The False Lover won Back]

Greig and Keith, 1925, p. 155(3); from Duncan MS., No. 286. Sung by Mrs. Gillespie.

p I

It's love for love that I wad gie,
Love I wad tak again;
It's hard that I like you sae weel,
An' you nae me again, bonnie love,
An' you nae me again.

The Gardener

CHILD NO. 219

This piece rests uneasily in Child's collection. It is both too little of a ballad, generating virtually no story, and too sophisticated and fanciful in symbolism. It will perhaps do for a folksong which has been framed as situation. He says, "Be mine, fair maid." She retorts, "Indeed not!" For narrative this is hardly better than the dramatic prologue of which Joseph Addison was said to have been so inordinately fond: "A certain king said to a beggar, 'What hast to eat?' 'Beans,' quoth the beggar. 'Beans?' quoth the king. 'Yea, beans, I say,' and so forthwith we straight begin the play."

The earliest copy of a tune, Kinloch's, from Northern tradition, is the farthest from what appears to be normal. If the final be tonic, the tune is plagal D/Æ; but its feeling is definitely major, and the final is pretty certainly on the sixth. This brings it into closer relation with the other variants, which are all major (π^1, I/M), plagal, and with which it has other traits in common. Note that, without the tune tradition's being modified beyond recognition, these few members nevertheless vary in number of phrases from five to six to eight (ten, counting repetition). Greig's (b) tune (see variant 1 below) will suggest Christie's "The Place where my love Johnny dwells" (*ante*, No. 218); and, generally, the melodic tradition of this and the preceding ballad seem interconnected.

There is an ABBA tune in Christie called "The Gardener Lad"— "note for note as sung on the street by two blind men in the beginning of the century"—but of which he does not record the proper words (see variant 6 below). It probably belongs to another gardener song, not the present one, and is here relegated to an appendix. A song from recent tradition (Scots) seems not related to any hitherto known, and is similarly placed. Chambers' tune is of course a version of No. 199, *ante*.

It did not escape Child's notice that the textual tradition of this ballad had got mixed up with Mrs. Habergham's seventeenth century song, "The Seeds of Love," as handed down orally, and with "The Sprig of Thyme" ("Once I had plenty of thyme"): two very popular songs in the west of England and elsewhere. On these complications, see Chappell, *Popular Music* [1855-59], II, pp. 520-23; Baring-Gould and Sheppard, *Songs and Ballads of the West*, 1895, notes on Nos. VII and CVIII, pp. xv, xlii; Baring-Gould, Sheppard, and Bussell, *Songs of the West*, 1905, notes pp. 3-4; Child, 1882-98, V, pp. 258-60; also Sharp's *One Hundred English Folk Songs*, 1916, Nos. 33 and 34, and the notes on p. xxix. There is, however, no discernible connection between the numerous variants of the English song-tunes and those of our present, Scottish, "ballad."

LIST OF VARIANTS

1. "The Gardener and the Ploughman." Greig MSS., IV, p. 3, and Bk. 762, LII, p. 7, King's College Library, Aberdeen. Also in Gavin Greig and Alexander Keith, *Last Leaves of Traditional Ballads and Ballad Airs*, 1925, p. 158(b). (Jaffray)
2. "The Gardener." Greig MSS., IV, p. 89. (Miss Robb)
3. "The Gardener Lad." Greig MSS., III, p. 57. Also in Greig and Keith, *Last Leaves*, 1925, p. 157(a). (A. Robb)
4. "The Gardener Lad." Greig MSS., III, p. 94, and Bk. 729, XIX, p. 109. Also in Greig and Keith, 1925, p. 158(c). (Mackie)
5. "The Gardener." George R. Kinloch, *Ancient Scottish Ballads*, 1827, App'x. to p. 74, and p. 74.

APPENDIX

6. "The Gairdner Child." Ewan MacColl, Riverside recording RLP 12-625(B3), *The English and Scottish Popular Ballads*, III, ed. Kenneth S. Goldstein.
7. "The Gardener Lad." W. Christie, *Traditional Ballad Airs*, II, 1881, p. 206.
8. "False Love, and Ha'e You Played Me This?" Robert Chambers, *The Songs of Scotland Prior to Burns*, ed. of 1880, p. 444.
9. "The Gairdner and the Plooman." Hamish Henderson, *Scottish Studies*, I (1957), p. 182.

TUNES WITH TEXTS

1. "The Gardener and the Ploughman"

Greig MSS., IV, p. 3, and Bk. 762, LII, p. 7. Also in Greig and Keith, 1925, p. 158(b). Sung by Mrs. Jaffray, Mintlaw, April 1910.

m I/M

1. A gardener lad that lives nearby,
   Lang has he wooed me,
   An' he's gien me his hert to keep,
   A pledge o' love to be,—be,
   A pledge o' love to be.

2. Lang did I keep my gardener's hert,
   My ain was aye free;
   Or the blithe blink o' the plooman lad
   Has stown the hert frae me,—me,
   Has stown the hert frae me.

3. The firstant time I did him see,
   He was ploughin' in yon brae's brow,
   And I could neither haud nor ca,
   It was a' for love o' you,—you,
   It was a' for love o' you.

4. The next time that I did you see,
You was under a bush o' rue,
And aye the sweeter 'at ye sang,
The nearer the bush I drew,—drew,
The nearer the bush I drew.

5. Mak' up yer gown, my bonnie lass,
An' mak' it neat an' fine,
An' ye shall be the ploughman's wife,
For the gardener's changed his min',—min',
For the gardener's changed his min'.

6. The ploughman lad he's hearin' this,
Just in a bush nearby,
Said, Say nae mair, my bonnie love,
Or ye ken better why,—why,
Or ye ken better why.

7. The firstant time I did you see
You was under a bush of rue;
And aye the sweeter 'at ye sang,
The nearer the buss I drew,—drew,
The nearer the buss I drew.

2. "The Gardener"

Greig MSS., IV, p. 89. From Miss Annie Robb, Strichen.

p I

The relationship between this and the following tune, and those of the preceding No. 218, is obvious.

Wi' a red rose in his hand.

3. "The Gardener Lad"

Greig MSS., III, p. 57. Also in Greig and Keith, 1925, p. 157(a). Sung by Alexander Robb, New Deer, December 1907.

p I/M

Lady Margret stood in her bow'r door,
As straucht's a willow wand,
An' by there cam the gard'ner lad,
Wi a red rose in his hand;
An' by there cam the gard'ner lad,
Wi a red rose in his hand.

4. "The Gardener Lad"

Greig MSS., III, p. 94; text, Bk. 729, XIX, p. 109. Also in Greig and Keith, 1925, p. 158(c). Sung by James Mackie, Strichen, May 1908.

m π^1

The suggestion of "Comin' thro' the rye" will not escape notice.

1. There was a lass near by to this
Who many sweethearts had
And the gardener laddie view'd them a'
Just as they came and gaed
The Gardener laddie viewed them a'
And said he had nae skill
If I should go as oft's the rest
They'd say he was a feel

2. If I could think her worth my pains
Its to her I would go
And I would *wad* a thousand crowns
She would not say me no.
But she is not a proper girl
Neither handsome, tight nor tall
And another young man he spak out
Says Slight her none at all

3. For we of women all are come
If you will call to mind
And unto women for their sakes
We surely should prove kind

4. Lady Margaret stood in her bower door
As straight's a willow wand
And by it came the gardener lad
Wi' a red rose in his hand
Oh will ye fancy me fair maid
And will ye fancy me
Amo' the flowers o' my garden
I'll shape a wede for thee.

5. The lily white shall be your smock
Becomes your body neist
The marigold shall be your stays
With a red rose in your breast
Your gloves shall be the locran clover
What grows in yonder van
And I'll line them wi the blue Blevet
That grows amo' the lan'.

6. As you have shaped a weed for me
   Ammo your summer flowers
Its I will pay you back again
   Amo' the winter showers
The driven snow shall be your shirt
   Becomes your body neist
The coal black rain shall be your coat
   With a windgale in your breist

7. The steed that you shall ride upon
   Shall be the weathery snell
And I'll bridle in wi the Norlan blast
   And some sharp showers of hail
The hat that on your head you wear
   Shall be a stormy day
And when you come into my sight
   I'll wish you were away.

5. "The Gardener"

Kinloch, 1827, App'x. to p. 74; text, p. 74.

p D/Æ; or, if on C, a I/Ly, ending on VI

1. The gard'ner stands in his bouer door,
   Wi' a primrose in his hand,
And bye there cam a leal maiden,
   As jimp as a willow wand;
And bye there cam a leal maiden,
   As jimp as a willow wand.

2. "O ladie can ye fancy me,
   For to be my bride;
Ye'se get a' the flowers in my garden,
   To be to you a weed.

3. The lily white sall be your smock,
   It becomes your body best;
Your head sall be buskt wi' gelly-flower,
   Wi' the primrose in your breist.

4. Your gown sall be the Sweet William;
   Your coat the camovine;
Your apron o' the sallads neat,
   That taste baith sweet and fine.

5. Your hose sall be the brade kail-blade,
   That is baith brade and lang;
Narrow, narrow, at the cute,
   And brade, brade at the brawn.

6. Your gloves sall be the marigold,
   All glittering to your hand,
Weel spread owre wi' the blue blaewort
   That grows amang corn-land."

7. O fare ye weil, young man, she says,
   Fareweil, and I bid adieu;
Sin ye've provided a weed for me
   Amang the simmer flowers,
It's I'se provide anither for you,
   Amang the winter-showers:

8. The new fawn snaw to be your smock,
   It becomes your bodie best;
Your head sall be wrapt wi' the eastern wind,
   And the cauld rain on your breist.

APPENDIX

6. "The Gairdner Child"

Sung by Ewan MacColl, Riverside rec. No. RLP 12-625 (B3), ed. K. S. Goldstein. Learned from his mother.

m M

Proud Maisrie stands at her bower door,
As straicht as a willow wand,
And syne there cam' a gairdner child
Wi' a red rose in his hand, his hand,
   Wi' a red rose in his hand.

[*Etc.*]

MacColl's text is a conflation of lines from his mother's version and Greig's copies.

7. "The Gardener Lad"

Christie, II, 1881, p. 206.

a I

8. "False Love, and Ha'e You Played Me This?"

Chambers, ed. 1880, p. 444.

a I/M

False luve! and hae ze played me this,
   In the simmer, 'mid the flowers?
I sall repay ze back again,
   In the winter 'mid the showers.

Bot again, dear luve, and again, dear luve,
Will ze not turn again?
As ze look to ither women,
Shall I to ither men.

The words given by Chambers with this tune are taken from Herd, 1776, II, p. 6, where the accurate reading is as above. Child quotes them in his headnote to the preceding ballad (No. 218), and notes their partial occurrence in the present ballad, without assigning Herd's fragment either to one or the other.

9. "The Gairdner and the Plooman"

Henderson, *Scottish Studies*, I (1957), p. 182. Collected from Mrs. Elsie Morrison, Nether Dallachy, Spey Bay, April 5, 1956; learned during her youth spent working on Speyside farms.

p I/M

The final quarter-notes in bars 1, 2, and 5 are probably inadvertent misprints, since all else is regular.

When I was in my sixteenth year
From trouble I was free.
My hert my ain it did bide true,
But noo it'll hardly dee:
But noo it'll hardly dee, bonnie lad,
But noo it'll hardly dee.

A gairdener lad cam a-coortin' me
Amangst the rue an' thyme.
He has teen fae me my maidenheid,
And he gied me cause tae rue:
An' he gied me cause tae rue, bonnie lad,
An he's gien me cause tae rue.

O it's braw tae be wi' the gairdener lad
Amangst the rue an' thyme,
But it's better tae be wi' the plooman lad
Gyaun whistlin' at his ploo:
Gyaun whistlin' at his ploo, bonnie lad,
Gyaun whistlin' at his ploo.

Katharine Jaffray

CHILD NO. 221

This ballad, in late reshaping, whether Scots or Irish or English, has enjoyed a widespread popularity, for reasons not hard to guess. It has been found in our century in Aberdeen, Somerset (or Devon), County Connaught, Massachusetts (from County Tyrone), Vermont (from County Cork), New Brunswick, and Nova Scotia.

Phillips Barry has a valuable note on this ballad in connection with Irish tradition (Flanders, *et al.*, *The New Green Mountain Songster*, 1939, pp. 143-44). In it he calls attention to a tune in Petrie, *The Complete Collection of Irish Music*, 1902-05, No. 544, "The fairy troop." This is probably the first record of the tune that is still current with our ballad today. The title is explained by a phrase in a version that Child quotes in part in his headnote (1882-98, IV, p. 218):

> He smiled and this did say,
> 'They might have been some fairy troops,
> That rode along this way.'

One could easily be persuaded that all variants belong to the same tribe. All (save that from Vermont) are authentic, all except two are in the major domain, whether I/Ly, I/M, I, or M. All are long-phrase tunes, properly taking two lines of quatrain text before making a real cadence. All have a strongly marked rhythm, and more than half of them agree in a conspicuous mid-cadence on the major third.

The Vermont tune (variant 9) is perhaps ambiguous. Read in the light of other variants, it appears to end on the fourth. But if taken on its own terms, although the tune is worn-down and monotonously phrased, the final makes a satisfactory tonic. Thus the tune could be either authentic I/M or plagal I/Ly. But in spite of modality, its first two phrases oddly resemble the second and third of Greig's tune (variant 10) in reverse order.

The Greig tune and a recent one from Leitrim (variants 10 and 11) are alike in a mode different from all the rest, and the third phrase of one is like the first of the other. It is possible that they split off from the main family, but they have been assimilated to other patterns, and may stand as independent D/Æ authentic tunes.

LIST OF VARIANTS

GROUP A

1. "Katherine Janfarie." W. Christie, *Traditional Ballad Airs*, II, 1881, p. 16.
2. "The fairy troop." George Petrie, *The Complete Collection of Irish Music*, ed. Charles Villiers Stanford, 1902-05, No. 544.
3. "Katherine Joffray." Helen Creighton, *Songs and Ballads from Nova Scotia* [1933], p. 22.
4. "Katherine Jaffray." Helen Creighton and Doreen H. Senior, *Traditional Songs from Nova Scotia*, 1950, p. 79(A).
5. "The Squire of Edinboro' town." C. Milligan Fox, *Journal of the Irish Folk Song Society*, I (1904), p. 45.
6. "Green Wedding." Sharp MSS., 1119/1113, Clare College Library, Cambridge. (Parish)
7. "Give me a Kiss of the Pretty Bride." Phillips Barry, *JAF*, XXII (1909), p. 75.
8. "Squire of Edinborough town." Phillips Barry, Fannie H. Eckstorm, and Mary W. Smyth, *British Ballads from Maine*, 1929, p. 405. (Sprague)
9. "Katharine Jaffray." Helen Hartness Flanders, Elizabeth Flanders Ballard, George Brown, and Phillips Barry, *The New Green Mountain Songster*, 1939, p. 141. Also in Helen Hartness Flanders, *Country Songs of Vermont*, 1937, p. 20; and Flanders, *Ancient Ballads Traditionally Sung in New England*, III, 1963, p. 262(A).

GROUP B

10. "Katharine Jaffray." Gavin Greig and Alexander Keith, *Last Leaves of Traditional Ballads and Ballad Airs*, 1925, p. 161. From Duncan MS., No. 225. (Alexander)
11. "The Green Wedding." Thomas Moran, Sound Archives of the British Broadcasting Corporation, London, recording Nos. 22016 and 18759.

TUNES WITH TEXTS

GROUP A

1. "Katherine Janfarie"

Christie, II, 1881, p. 16. From Buchan tradition.

m I

> There was a may, and a weel far'd may,
> Liv'd high up in yon glen;
> Her name was Katherine Janfarie,
> She was courted by mony men.
> Up then came lord Lauderdale,
> Up frae the Lowland border;
> And he has come to court this may,
> A' mounted in good order.

[*Etc.*]

Christie takes his text from Scott's *Minstrelsy*, 1833, III, p. 122.

2. "The fairy troop"

Petrie, 1902-05, No. 544. From the MSS. (1840-50) of John Edward Pigot.

a I

Reprinted by permission of the publishers, Boosey & Hawkes, Inc.

3. "Katherine Joffray"

Creighton [1933], p. 22. Sung by Ben Henneberry, Devil's Island.

m I/Ly

1. It's of a farmer lived in the east,
He had one only son,
He courted of a counteree girl
Till he thought he had her won.
Till he thought he had her won,
He courted of a counteree girl
Till he thought he had her won.

2. He got consent from her father and mother
And the two young men likewise,
And then she cried, "I am undone,"
And the tears rolled from her eyes, etc.

3. She sent her love a love-letter,
Gave him to understand
This very night I am going to be wed
To a rich gentleman, etc.

4. He sent her back an answer
And sealed it with a ring,
"The suit that you wear at your wedding,
Be sure and put on green, etc.

5. "A suit of the same I will put on,
To your wedding I'll prepare,
And I'll wed you, my dearest, dear,
In spite of all that's there," etc.

6. Then he looked to the east and he looked to the west,
He espied far over the land,
He espied fourscore of his best young men
All under his command, etc.

7. Then he mounted them double on a milk-white steed,
And a single man rode he;
He rode till he came to the wedding house
Where the wedding was to be, etc.

8. She invited them all, both great and small,
"Have you been out all day?
Or have you seen those foreign troops
That have passed along this way?" etc.

9. He laughed at her, and he scoffed at her,
And then he seemed to say,
"There might have been some gentlemen
That have passed along this way," etc.

10. And he filled up a glass of the best port wine,
He drank to the company round,
Saying, "Here's a health to thee, young man,
The man they call the groom.

11. "But ten times happier is the man
That will enjoy the bride,
For another might love her as well as he
And take her from his side."

12. Then up spoke the intended groom,
And a rough spoken man was he,
"If it is for to fight that you came here
I am just the man for thee."

13. "Oh, it is not to fight that I came here,
But kind friendship for to show,
Grant me one kiss from your bonny, bonny bride,
And away from you I'll go."

14. He took her round the middle so small,
And a hold of her grass-green sleeve,
And he led her out of the wedding house,
Of the company asked no leave.

15. Where the drums did beat and the fife did play
And they did so merrily sing,
Now she's conveyed to fair Edinborough Castle
With her company dressed in green.

16. Now come all young fellows that are going to be wed,
A warning take by me,
Never be served as I've been served
All on my wedding day.
All on my wedding day,
At catching fish instead of flesh
I always had foul play.

4. "Katherine Jaffrey"

Creighton and Senior, 1950, p. 79(A). Sung by Mrs. Thomas Osborne, South East Passage, N.S.

m I

1. There was a farmer lived in the east,
He had one only son,
He courted of a country girl
Till he thought he had her won.

2. He won consent from her father and her mother
And those two young men likewise,
Until she cries, "I am undone,"
And the tears rolled from her eyes.

3. She wrote a letter to her love
And sealed it with a ring,
"This very night I am going to be wed
Unto a farmer's son."

4. The few first lines he gazed upon
He smiled and thus did say,
"I may deprive him of his bride
All on his wedding day."

5. He wrote her back an answer
It was both sharp and keen,
Saying, "The suit you wear at your wedding
Be sure to put on green.

6. "A suit of the same I will put on,
For your wedding I'll prepare,
And I'll wed you, my dearest dear
In spite of all that's there."

7. He looked to the east, he looked to the west,
He looked all over his land,
He espied threescore of his best young men
And of his noble band.

8. Then he mounted them double on milk-white steeds
And a single man rode he,
He rode till he came to the wedding house
Where the wedding was to be.

9. They welcomed them all both great and small
Saying, "Have you been out all day?
Or have you seen those foreign troops
That rode along this way?"

10. He laughed at them and he scoffed at them
And unto them did say,
"Yes, I have seen those foreign troops
That passed along this way."

11. He filled up a glass of the best port wine,
Drank a health to all in the room,
Saying, "Here's another to the man,
The man they call the groom.

12. "But ten times happier is the man
That will enjoy the bride,
For another might like her as well as he
And take her from his side."

13. Then up spoke the intended groom,
An angry man was he,
Saying, "If it is for to fight that you came here
I am just the man for thee."

14. "It is not to fight that I came here
But kind friendship to show,
Grant me one kiss from your bonny bonny bride
And away from you I'll go."

15. He threw his arms around her waist,
Took hold of her grass green sleeve,
And out of the wedding house went they
When the company asked no leave.

16. Where the drums did beat and the fife did play
Most glorious to be seen,
And now she's conveyed to fair Edinborough Castle
With her company dressed in green.

5. "The Squire of Edinboro' town"

Fox, *JIFSS*, I (1904), p. 45. Sung by Ann Carter, Belfast, 1904, who learned it in childhood from her grandmother in County Galway. Tune recorded by Mrs. Fox, text by Mrs. Elizabeth Wheeler.

a I

1. There was a Squire of Edinboro' Town,
A Squire of high degree;
He fell in love with a country girl,
And a comely girl was she.

2. There was a farmer in the East
That had an only son;
He fell in love with this comely girl,
Till he thought he had her won.

3. He got consent from father and mother,
From old and young likewise;
And still she cried, "I am undone,"
And the tears fell from her eyes.

4. She wrote her love a letter,
And sealed it with a ring,
That she was to be married,
And to a farmer's son.

5. He wrote her back an answer,
To be sure to dress in green;
A suit of the same he would put on,
Her wedding for to see.

6. He lookèd East and he lookèd West,
And looked all round his land;
And mounted four-and twenty men,
All of the Scottish clan.

7. He rode East and he rode West,
He rode all round his lands,
Until he rode to the wedding-house door;
Of the company he asked no leave,

8. Saying, "Happy is the man they call the groom,
And he who enjoys the bride;
But another young man may love her as well,
And take her from his side."

9. Then out spake the angry groom,
And an angry man was he:
"If 'tis for fight that you come here,
I am the man for thee!"

10. "It's not for fight that I come here,
But friendship for to show.
Give me one kiss from your bonny bride's lips,
And away from you I'll go."

11. He took her by the waist so small,
And by the grass-green sleeves,
And led her outside of the wedding-house door,
Of the company he asked no leave.

12. The drums did beat, the fifes did play—
So glorious to be seen—
And he brought her away to Edinboro' Town,
With the company dressed in green.

6. [Green Wedding]

Sharp MSS., 1119/1113. Sung by Robert Parish (84), Exford, September 5, 1906.

a I

1. There was a squire lived in the East
A squire of high degree
Came courting of a country girl
A comely girl was she
Until her father he heard of it
And an angry man was he
He requested of his daughter dear
To shun his company.

2. There was a farmer lived close by
Who had an only son
Came courting of this country girl
Until he thought he had her won
He gained consent from her father & mother
The old & young likewise
Until at last she cried I am undone
And the tears fell from her eyes.

3. She wrote the squire a letter
And sealed it with her hand
Saying this very day I am to wed
Unto another young man
The first few lines that he looked on
He smiled & thus did say
O I may deprive him of his bride
All on his wedding day.

4. He wrote her back another
To be sure to be dressed in green
A suit of the same I will put on
At yr wedding I'll be seen
A suit of the same I will put on
To yr wedding I'll prepare
Saying my dearest dear I'll have you yet
In spite of all that's there.

5. He looked the East he looked the West
He looked all over his land,
He mounted them all eight score men
All of a Scottish band
He mounted them on milk white steed
And a single man rode he
Then all the way to the wedding hall went
The company dressed in green.

6. When he got to the wedding hall
They unto him did say
You are welcome Sir, you are welcome Sir
Where have you spent the day?
He laughed at them he scorned at them
He unto them did say
O you might have seen my tars of troop [*sic*]
Come riding by this way.

7. The Squire he took a glass of wine
And filled it to the brim.
Here is health unto the man, said he
The man they call the groom.
Here's health unto the man said he
The man who may enjoy his bride
For another might love her just as well
And take her from [*sic*] his Bride.

8. Then up spoke he the intended one
And an angry man was he
If it's to fight that you come here
Why it's I'm the man for thee
No it's not to fight that I come here
But merely friendship for to show
So give me a kiss from your bonny young Bride
And away from thee I'll go.

9. He took her by the waist so small
And by the grass green sleeve
He led her from the wedding hall
To the company asked not leave.
The band did play and the bugles did sound
Oh, most glorious to be seen.
Then all the way to Headingbourn Town
Went the company dressed in green.

"The words I copied from an M.S. copy which Parish lent me." [*Sharp's MS. note.*]

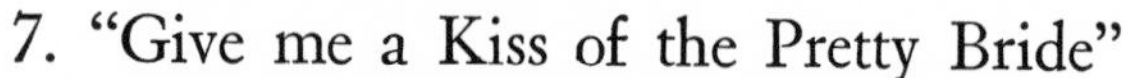

7. "Give me a Kiss of the Pretty Bride"

Barry, *JAF*, XXII (1909), p. 75. Sung by Mrs. Sarah Carson, Boston, Mass., November 30, 1907, and March 1908; learned in County Tyrone.

a M

8. "Squire of Edinborough town"

Barry, Eckstorm, and Smyth, 1929, p. 405. Sung by John Sprague, Milltown, New Brunswick, October 1928.

a I/Ly

9. "Katharine Jaffray"

Flanders, *et al.*, 1939, p. 141. Also in Flanders, 1937, p. 20; and Flanders, III, 1963, p. 262(A). Sung by Mrs. E. M. Sullivan, Springfield, Vt.; learned in childhood in County Cork. Transcribed by Elizabeth F. Ballard. From *The New Green Mountain Songster*, edited by Helen Hartness Flanders, Elizabeth Flanders Ballard, George Brown, and Phillips Barry; copyright 1939 by Helen Hartness Flanders.

a I/M, ending on IV

1. There was a squire in Edinboro town
A squire of high degree.
He fell in love with a country girl
And a comely girl was she.

2. Till at length her father came to hear
And an angry man was he.
He requested of his daughter dear
To shun his company.

[Then she promised to marry someone else.]

3. She wrote her love a letter
And she sealed it with her ring,
Saying, "I'm going to be wedded
To a farmer's son."

4. He wrote her back an answer
And to her did say
"Be sure you dress in green
And a suit of the same I will put on*
For your wedding I will prepare."

5. He rode east and he rode west
And he rode all around his land.
Then he smiled and thus did say,
"I might deprive his bride all on his wedding day."

6. He mounted then on a milk-white steed
And a single man rode he
Until he came to the wedding house door
With his company dressed in green.

7. "You are welcome, you are welcome!
Where have you been all day
Or have you seen those horsemen
That rode along this way?"

8. He looked at her, he laughed at her
And thus to her did say,
"They might have been some fairy troops
That rode along this way."

9. She filled him a glass of the new port wine
And he drank to the company round
Saying, "Happy is the man who will enjoy the bride
For another might like her as well as he*
And take her from his side."

10. Then up spoke the intended groom
And an angry man was he,
"If it was to fight that you came here
I am the man for thee."

11. "It was not to fight that I came here
But friendship for to show.
Give me one kiss from your bonny, bonny bride
And away from your wedding I will go."

12. He took her by the middle so small
And by the grass green sleeve
And out of the wedding house door they marched—
Of the company asked no leave.

13. The drums did beat, the trumpets sound
Most glorious to be seen
And back they marched to Edinborotown
With his company dressed in green.

* Tune to third line is repeated for fourth line.

GROUP B

10. "Katharine Jaffray"

Greig and Keith, 1925, p. 161; from Duncan MS., No. 225. Sung by Robert Alexander, Udny.

a D/Æ

With this tune, cf. those of "The Duke of Gordon's Daughters" (No. 237).

1. Lochnagar cam fae the West
Into the low countrie,
An' he had coorted Katharine Jaffray,
An' stole her heart away.

2. Hame he cam, ane Amosdale,
Cam fae the north countrie,
An' he has gained her father's heart,
But an' her mother's tee.

3. A bridal day it then was set,
An' the bridal day cam on,
An' who appeared among the guests
But Lochnagar himsel?

4. A glass was filled o good red wine,
Weel drunk between them twa:
Said he, I'll drink wi you, bridegroom,
An' syne boun me awa.

5. "A few words wi your bridesmaiden
I hope you'll grant me then:
I'm sure before her wedding day
I would have gotten ten."

6. Out spoke then the first groomsman,
An' an angry man was he,
Says, "I will keep my bonnie bride
Until the sun gae tee;

7. "Until the sun gae tee," he said,
"Until the sun gae tee,
An' deliver her ower to her bridegroom,
Which is my duty to dee."

8. But he's taen her by the middle jimp,
An' never stoppit to ca',
He's taen her by the milk-white han'
An' led her through the ha'.

9. He leaned him ower his saiddle-bow,
An' kissed her cheek an' chin,
An' then he wissed them a' good nicht,
An' hoised her on ahin.

10. He drew a trumpet fae his breist,
An' blew baith lood an' shrill;
A hunner o well-airmed men
Cam Lochnagar until.

11. A hunner o weel-airmed men,
Wi milk-white steeds an' grey,
A hunner o weel-airmed men
Upon his wedding day.

12. Horsemen rode, an' bridesmen ran,
An' ladies in full speed,
But you wadna hae seen his yellow locks
For the dust o his horse' [*sic*] feet.

13. She turned in the saiddle-bow,
Addressed her late bridegroom,
Says, "The compliments I got fae you,
I'll return them back again."

14. So Katharine Jaffray was mairriet at morn,
An' she was mairriet at noon;
She was twice mairriet in ae day,
Ere she keest aff her goon.

11. "The Green Wedding"

BBC Sound Archives, rec. Nos. 22016 and 18759. Sung by Thomas Moran, Mohill, County Leitrim, December 1954. Collected by Seamus Ennis.

a D/Æ

1. There was a Squire in Edinburgh town
And a wealthy Squire was he
And he hadn courted a country girl
And a comely lass was she.

2. He got consent from father and mother
From old and young likewise
But still she cried I am undone
While the tears roll from my [*sic*] eyes.

3. She wrote her love a letter and
   She sealed it with her hand
That she was going to be wed
   Unto another man.

4. The very first line that he looked over
   He smiled and this did say:
Well, I might deprive him of his bride
   All on his wedding day.

5. He wrote her back a letter to
   Be sure and dress in green
And a suit of the same I will put on
   For your wedding I'll prepare.

6. He looked East and he looked West
   He looked all over his land
And he had a-mounted eight score men
   All of ?his Scottish land.

7. He mounted two on every steed
   And a single man rode he
So now they are gone to Edinburgh town
   With the company dressed in green.

8. You're welcome, you are welcome, Lord,
   Where have you been all day,
Or did you see those fairy troops
   That rode along this way?

9. They filled him a glass of the new port wine
   He drank to the company round.
O happy is the man, he says,
   The man they call the groom.

10. Happier is the man, he said,
   That will enjoy the bride,
For another might like her as well as him
   And take her from his side.

11. Oh and out he spoke the young bridegroom,
   And an angry man was he.
If it was to fight that you come here,
   I am a man for thee.

12. It was not to fight that I come here,
   For friendship I mean to show.
Give me one kiss from your bonny bonny bride,
   And away from you I'll go.

13. He took her by the middle so small
   And by the green grass sleeve
And he marched her out of the wedding-house-door
   Of the company he asked no leave.

14. They laughed at him, they scoffed at him,
   They smiled and this did say,
Well it must have been some fairy troop
   That stole your bride [spoken] away.

Bonny Baby Livingston

CHILD NO. 222

CHILD'S A-text of this ballad is from Mrs. Brown, and she gave it in two variant forms. It is another example of the re-creative practice of a singer immersed in oral tradition. (Cf. "Mrs. Brown and the Ballad," *California Folklore Quarterly*, IV [1945], p. 129.) Child remarks: ". . . the fact seems to be that, at the time when she recited to Jamieson [i.e., her version 222 Ab, printed in Jamieson, *Popular Ballads and Songs*, 1806, II, p. 135], she was not in good condition to remember accurately" (1882-98, IV, p. 231). But it is not a matter of accurate memory when there is no ultimate text to which to be faithful.

It is a noteworthy fact that all Child's other texts (B-E and the unnumbered text of C. K. Sharpe in App'x., V, p. 261) contain something like the following stanzas from Buchan's MS. (Child B 13, 14):

> 'O day, dear sir! O day, dear sir!
> O dear! if it were day,
> And me upon my father's steed,
> I soon shoud ride away.'
>
> 'Your father's steed is in my stable,
> Eating good corn and hay,
> And ye are in my arms twa;
> What needs you lang for day?'

So also does Greig's text (Greig MSS., Bk. 762, LII, p. 89; *Last Leaves of Traditional Ballads and Ballad Airs*, 1925, p. 162). Now, it has not been remarked that Mrs. Brown's unique text of "The Bonny Birdy" (Child No. 82) contains the equivalent of these stanzas, where in part they are used as a burden. "The Bonny Birdy" is a sort of moralized and refined "Little Musgrave" (No. 81), for which we lack any corroborative tradition. Since Mrs. Brown's version of No. 222 departs from otherwise universal traditional testimony on the point just quoted, we may presume that what she added to No. 82 she subtracted from No. 222. Her copy of the latter also departs from all other copies in its happy, romantic conclusion, which we may tentatively credit to the singer's temperamental bias.

The only tune which has been recovered is that of C. K. Sharpe—a characteristic one of π^3 mode. It might be argued, however, that the tune ends on the second, in which case it would be a π^1 tune. According to the Gray-Muir MS. (NL Scotland MS. 2254), there is a tune for this ballad in the Bunyan MS., 1877, p. 116—wherever that MS. may be. It is also interesting that in Motherwell's notebook in Harvard College Library, there is a list of tunes to be got, among which is "Barbra Livingston," with a cross before it, possibly indicating success. But Motherwell never printed the tune.

LIST OF VARIANTS

"Bonnie Baby Livingston." Francis James Child, *The English and Scottish Popular Ballads*, 1882-98, V, pp. 421 and 261.

TUNE WITH TEXT

[Bonny Baby Livingston]

Child, 1882-98, V, p. 421; text, p. 261. From C. K. Sharpe's "first MS. collection, p. 24" (=William Macmath transcript, p. 32, Harvard College Library).

a π^3

1. Bonny Anny Livieston
 Went out to see the play,
By came the laird of Glenlion,
 And [he's] taen hir quite away.

2. He set hir on a milk-white steed,
 Himself upon a gray,
He's teen hir oer the Highland hills,
 And taen hir quite away.

3. When they came to Glenlion's gate,
 The[y] lighted on the green;
There was mony a bonny lad and lass
 To wolcome the lady hame.

4. They led hir through high towers and bowers,
 And through the buling-green,
And ay when they spake Erse to hir
 The tears blinded hir een.

5. Says, The Highlands is no for me, kind sir,
 The Highlands is no for me;
If that ye would my favour win,
 Take me unto Dundee.

6. "Dundee!" he says, "Dundee, lady!
 Dundee you shall never see;
Upon the laird of Glenlion
 Soon wadded shall ye be."

7. When bells were rung, and mas was sung,
 And all were bound for bed,
And bonny Annie Livieston
 By hir bridegroom was laid.

8. "It's O gin it were day!" she says,
 "It's O gin it were day!
O if that it were day," she says,
 "Nae langer wad I stay."

9. "Your horse stands in a good stable,
 Eating both corn and hay,
And you are in Glenlion's arms,
 Why should ye weary for day?"

10. "Glenlion's arms are good enough,
But alais! the'r no for me;
If that you would my fevour win,
Taike me unto Dundee.

11. "Bat fetch me paper, pen and ink,
And candle that I may see,
And I'll go write a long letter
To Geordie in Dundee.

12. "Where will I get a bonny boy,
That will win hose and shoon,
That will gang to my ain true-luve,
And tell him what is done?"

13. Then up then spake a bonny boy,
Near to Glenlion's kin,
Says, Many time I hae gane his erand,
But the lady's I will rin.

14. O when he came to broken brigs
He bent his bow and swame,
And when he came to grass growing
Set down his feet and ran.

15. And when he came to Dundee gate
Lap clean outoer the wa;
Before the porter was thereat,
The boy was in the haa.

16. "What news? what news, bonny boy?
What news hes thou to me?"
"No news, no news," said bonny boy,
"But a letter unto thee."

17. The first three lines he looked on,
A loud laughter gied he,
But or he wan to the hinder en
The tears blinded his eie.

18. "Gae saddle to me the black," he says,
"Gae saddle to me the broun,
Gae saddle to me the swiftest steed
That eer took man to towen."

19. He burst the black unto the slack,
The browen unto the brae,
But fair fa on the siller-gray
That carried him ay away!

20. When he came to Glenlion's yett,
He tirled at the pin,
But before that he wan up the stair
The lady she was gone.

21. "O I can kiss thy cheeks, Annie,
O I can kiss thy chin,
O I can kiss thy clay-cold lips,
Though there be no breath within.

22. "Deal large at my love's buriell
The short bread and the wine,
And gin the morn at ten o clock
Ye may deal as mukle at mine."

23. The taen was biried in Mary's kirk,
The tither in St. Mary's quire,
And out of the taen there grew a birk,
And the ither a bonny brier.

24. And ay they grew, and ay they threw,
Till they did meet aboon,
And a' that ere the same did see
Knew they had true lovers been.

Eppie Morrie

CHILD NO. 223

MR. EWAN MacColl is the sole authority for a tune of this very spirited, if brutal, ballad of bride-stealing. He learned his tune from his father; the text has come mostly from Maidment by way of Child, with some help from Samuel Wylie of Falkirk. I am unable to point to any analogies for the melody, which does splendid service in MacColl's vigorous rendition.

LIST OF VARIANTS

"Eppie Morrie." Ewan MacColl, Riverside recording No. RLP 12-621(A1), *The English and Scottish Popular Ballads*, I, ed. Kenneth S. Goldstein.

TUNE WITH TEXT

"Eppie Morrie"

Sung by Ewan MacColl, Riverside rec. No. RLP 12-621(A1), ed. K. S. Goldstein. Tune learned from his father; text conflated.

p D/Æ

1. Four and twenty hielan' men
Cam' frae the Carron side,
To steal awa' Eppie Morrie,
For she wadna' be a bride, a bride,
She wadna' be a bride.

[*Repeat last line throughout.*]

2. Then oot it's came her mither, then,
It was a moonlicht nicht;
She couldna see her dochter
For the waters shone sae bricht, sae bricht.

3. "Haud awa' frae me, mither,
Haud awa' frae me!
There's no' a man in a' Strathdon
Shall wedded be wi' me, wi' me."

4. They've taken Eppie Morrie, then,
And a horse they've bound her on;
And they ha' rid to the minister's hoose
As fast as horse could gang, could gang.

5. Then Willie's ta'en his pistol out
And set it to the minister's breist;
"O, marry me, marry me, minister,
Or else I'll be your preist, your preist."

6. "Haud awa' frae me, Willie!
Haud awa' frae me!
I daurna avow to marry you,
Except she's willing as thee, as thee."

7. "Haud awa' frae me, good sir,
Haud awa' frae me!
There's no' a man in a' Strathdon
Shall married be by me, by me."

8. They've taken Eppie Morrie, then,
Sin better couldna be,
And they hae rid ower Carron side
As fast as horse could flee, could flee.

9. Then mass was sung and bells were rung
And they're awa' to bed,
And Willie and Eppie Morrie
In ane bed they were laid.

10. He's ta'en the sark frae off his back
And kicked awa' his shoon,
And thrawn awa' the chaumer key,
And naked he lay doon, lay doon.

11. "Haud awa' frae me, Willie,
Haud awa' frae me!
Before I lose my maidenhead
I'll try my strength with thee, with thee."

12. He's kissed her on the lilly breist
And held her shouthers twa,
And aye she grat and aye she spat
And turned to the wa', the wa'.

13. "Haud awa' frae me, Willy,
Haud awa' frae me!
There's no' a man in a' Strathdon
Shall married be wi' me, wi' me."

14. A' through the nicht they warssled there
Until the licht o' day,
And Willie grat and Willie swat
But he couldna streitch her spey, her spey.

15. Then early in the morning
Before the licht o' day,
In came the maid o' Scallater,
Wi' a gown and shirt alane, alane.

16. "Get up, get up, young woman!
And drink the wine wi' me."
"You micht hae ca'd me maiden
For I'm sure as hale as thee, as thee."

17. "Weary fa' you, Willie, then,
That ye couldna prove a man;
You micht hae ta'en her maidenhead,
She would hae hired your hand, your hand."

18. "Haud awa' frae me, lady,
Haud awa' frae me!
There's no a man in a' Strathdon
Shall wedded be wi' me."

19. Then in there came young Breadalbane
With a pistol on each side.
"O, come awa', Eppie Morrie
And I'll mak' you my bride, my bride."

20. "Go, get to me a horse, Willie,
Get it like a man,
And send me back to my mither
A maiden as I cam', I cam'."

21. The sun shines o'er the westlin hills
By the lamplicht o' the moon;
"O, saddle your horse, young John Forsythe
And whistle and I'll come soon, come soon."

Rob Roy

CHILD NO. 225

THERE seems, at first blush, no very settled melodic tradition for this ballad. The Gray-Muir MS. (NL Scotland MS. 2254) gives a rather imposing array of references ("Christie, Finlay Dun c. 1840, Muir, *Old Sc. Songs* 1811, Johnson M M., Thomson, N. Gow, Oswald, etc.") but if they can be confirmed, they must probably be first translated into the names of other songs. None of these authorities that I have seen has a tune under the name of "Rob Roy."

But Motherwell's copy (Child C) is directed to be sung to two tunes, "The Gipsy Laddy" for the first twelve stanzas, and thereafter "Haud awa fra me, Donald." The first seven stanzas of Child E go to "The Bonny House of Airly," and the remainder to "Haud awa frae me, Donald." (Both texts came from traditional rendition.) Child G, sent to William Tytler by Robert Burns, was sung to "a rude set of Mill, Mill O," for four stanzas or so; changing thenceforward to "something like Jenny dang the weaver." The first fourteen stanzas of C. K. Sharpe's text (Child L) went to "The Gipsy Laddy"; the rest to "Had away frae me, Donald." It is to be noticed that at some point in the text there enters a kind of lyrical repetitive formula, e.g.,

Be content, be content,
Be content to stay, lady &c.

I'm as bold, I'm as bold,
I'm as bold as he, lady &c.
(Child C, sts. 14, 16.)

Cf. D 8, 12; E 8 ff.; F 6, 7, 10, 11, 12; G 7, 9; H 3, 6, 7; I 5, 7, 9, 11, 13, 15, 17, 18; K 18, 20, 22, 24, 26, 28; L 16, 18, 20, 22, 23, 24. These noteworthy stanzas go naturally with the first strain of "Haud awa," for an early form of which see W. Thomson's *Orpheus Caledonius*, 1733, II, p. 104; R. A. Smith [1820-24], III, p. 73; and for historical discussion, G. F. Graham, *Songs of Scotland*, 1848-49, I, p. 77; J. C. Dick, ed., *The Songs of Robert Burns*, 1903, p. 500.

Graham says that "Haud awa" was published in Playford's *English Dancing Master*, 1657, under the title "Welcome home, old Rowley." I have not seen that edition of Playford, but the date, one would think, must be too early for a tune of that name. Graham prints the tune, at any rate, and there is no doubt about its identity. The interesting thing is that the second half of it is a form of the old "Gypsy Laddie" tune. In Child's A, B, C, and D are stanzas (A 4-5, B 3-4, C 5-6, D 3-4) themselves highly suggestive of many "Gypsy Laddie" variants. It would appear, then, that this late ballad, influenced perhaps by kindred subject-matter, had borrowed a form or forms of the old "Gypsy Laddie" tune in its first strain for the earlier stanzas, and moved to the second strain in its later ones, the hypnotic rhythm of the "Haud awa" first strain then influencing the pattern of some of the stanzas.

As to the tunes named above, "The Mill, Mill O" (Thomson, 1733, I, opp. p. 40; Johnson's *Museum*, No. 242; and elsewhere), "Jenny dang the weaver" (Thomson, 1733, II, opp. p. 83 ["Jenny beguil'd the Webster"]; *Museum*, No. 127; and elsewhere), "The Bonny House o' Airly" (cf. *ante*, No. 199): all are recognizable variations of the same melodic stock and could be (and were) easily interchanged in traditional transmission.

In the face of this "Gypsy Laddie" association, the tune introduced by R. A. Smith (variant 2, below) has less traditional standing in connection with "Rob Roy." Yet it may belong to a Gaelic tradition connected with the subject, as it is the same tune as one called "Rob Ruadh Mac'Ghrigair," printed in S. Fraser's *The Airs and Melodies peculiar to the Highlands of Scotland and the Isles* [1816]. It is, moreover, a good vigorous tune, and deserves to be remembered.

A tune learned by Mr. Ewan MacColl from family tradition for this ballad has affiliations with other Scottish romantic ballads, e.g., Child Nos. 236, 251.

LIST OF VARIANTS

GROUP A

1. "Rob Ruadh Mac'Ghrigair." S. Fraser, *The Airs and Melodies peculiar to the Highlands of Scotland and the Isles* [1816], p. 88.
2. "Rob Roy McGregor." Robert Archibald Smith, *The Scotish Minstrel* [1820-24], I, p. 1.

GROUP B

3. "Rob Roy." Ewan MacColl, Riverside recording No. RLP 12-626(B1), *The English and Scottish Popular Ballads*, III, ed. Kenneth S. Goldstein.

TUNES WITH TEXTS

GROUP A

1. "Rob Ruadh Mac'Ghrigair"

Fraser [1816], p. 88.

m Æ, ending on V

2. "Rob Roy McGregor"

Smith [1820-24], I, 1.

m Melodic minor, ending on V

1. Rob Roy frae the Highlands cam,
   And to the Lawland border,
To steal awa a gay Ladie
   To haud his house in order.
And he cam o'er the Lough o' Linn,
   Twenty men his arms did carry,
Himsel gaed in to fetch her out,
   Insisting she would marry.

2. "Oh will ye gae wi' me?" he says,
   "And will ye be my honey?
And will ye be my wedded wife?
   I loe ye best o' ony."
'I winna gae wi' you,' she says,
   'Ye ne'er can be my honey;
I winna be your wedded wife,
   Ye lo'e me for my money.'

3. "But ye sal gang wi' me," he said,
   "And nae mair words about it;
And sin' ye'll no gang wi' your will,
   Ye sall gang without it."
He set her on a gude black steed,
   Himsel lap on ahint her,
And he's awa to the Hieland hills
   Whare her friends canna find her.

4. "Rob Roy was my faither ca'd,
   McGregor was his name, Lady,
He led a band o' heroes bauld,
   An' I am here the same, Lady.
Be content, be content,
   Be content, and bide, Lady;
For thou art my wedded wife
   Until thy dying day, Lady.

5. "He was a hedge unto his friends,
   A heckle to his faes, Lady,
And every ane that durst him wrang,
   They had gude cause to rue, Lady.
I'm as bauld, I'm as bauld,
   I'm as bauld, and mair, Lady;
And he that dares dispute my word,
   Sal feel my gude claymore, Lady."

GROUP B

3. "Rob Roy"

Sung by Ewan MacColl, Riverside rec. No. RLP 12-626(B1), ed. K. S. Goldstein. Learned from his father.

m π^1

Rob Roy frae the Hielands came,
Doon tae the Lowland border,
To steal awa' a bonnie lass,
To keep his hoose in order.
   Wi' a fal dal diddle um a di dum doo
   Wi' a fal dal diddle um a did doh.
[*Etc.*]

MacColl conflated the fragmentary text he learned from his father with variants from Child.

Lizie Lindsay

CHILD NO. 226

The most characteristic and familiar setting of this still favorite song is the one contributed by Robert Burns to the *Scots Musical Museum* (variant 1). It is a major tune in triple time, the second phrase of which—elsewhere the first also—takes off on a plagal up-beat. There is something of "Ewe-Buchts, Marion" in this tune: that is, it has well-established traditional connections. Some copies lack the fourth, some the fourth and seventh, but the variations are not wide. A tune (variant 6) collected by Barry in New Brunswick, and deriving from Scotland, c. 1911, is plagal, I/M, and in common time. It has a second strain. Its total effect is quite different, and we may consider it a willful substitution for the traditional tune. The reason for that substitution will appear if the first strain be compressed into triple time. The resemblance in general outline then becomes sufficiently close. But the common metre does violence to the strong anapaestic beat of the words.

In the other branch of the melodic tradition for this song, represented by Christie and Greig, the mode is D/Æ and Æolian. Greig's tune is closer to the major tradition, but neither his nor Christie's is a mere transposition into the relative minor. Here, too, the presumable laws of traditional modal change have operated, though we lack evidence of intermediary stages.

There is again a copy off the beaten track to be accounted for: Mrs. Gillespie's double-strain plagal tune in D/Æ, properly 9/8, but frequently wrongly barred in 6/8 time. This seems to be a cross between two related tunes, one of which has supplanted the other as a setting for one of Burns's best-known songs, "Tam Glen." The earlier copies were variously called: "The muckin o' Geordy's byre" ("My Daddy's a Delver of Dykes"), e.g., W. Thomson, *Orpheus Caledonius*, 1733, I, p. 69; and "Old Hewson the Cobbler," for which cf. J. C. Dick, ed., *The Songs of Robert Burns*, 1903, p. 415. The tune was popular in England in the seventeenth century, and seems related to "The Rant" (Gay's "How happy could I be with either").

The Gray-Muir MS. (NL Scotland MS. 2254) gives references for the present ballad to the Bunyan MS., 1877, pp. 65, 84, 116.

LIST OF VARIANTS

GROUP Aa

1. "Leezie Lindsay." James Johnson, *The Scots Musical Museum*, V [1796], No. 434, p. 446 (repr. 1853). Also in Robert Archibald Smith, *The Scotish Minstrel* [1820-24], II, p. 100; and George Eyre-Todd, *Ancient Scots Ballads* [1894], p. 148.
2. "Leezie Lindsay." John Harrington Cox, *Traditional Ballads Mainly from West Virginia*, 1939, p. 36; and 1964 (ed., George Boswell), p. 46. Also, with slight difference, in George W. Boswell, *Tennessee Folklore Society Bulletin*, XVI (1950), p. 26.
3. "Lizzie Lindsay." Francis James Child, *The English and Scottish Popular Ballads*, 1882-98, V, p. 421, and IV, p. 524.
4. "Leezie Lindsay." Smith, *The Scotish Minstrel*, 2nd ed. [1825], II, p. 101 (2nd set). Also in G. F. Graham, *The Songs of Scotland*, 1848-49, II, p. 82.
5. "Leezie Lindsay." Robert Maver, *Genuine Scottish Melodies*, 1866, No. 330, p. 165.

GROUP Aa APPENDIX

6. "Leezie Lindsay." Phillips Barry, Fannie H. Eckstorm, and Mary W. Smyth, *British Ballads from Maine*, 1929, p. 297.

GROUP Ab

7. "Donald Macdonald." Gavin Greig and Alexander Keith, *Last Leaves of Traditional Ballads and Ballad Airs*, 1925, p. 164. From Duncan MS., No. 258. (Innes)
8. "Bonnie Lizzie Lindsay." W. Christie, *Traditional Ballad Airs*, II, 1881, p. 88.

GROUP Ab APPENDIX

9. "Lizzie Lindsay." Greig-Duncan MS. 785 (transcription of W. Walker), p. 138, King's College Library, Aberdeen. From Duncan MS., No. 495. (Gillespie)

TUNES WITH TEXTS

GROUP Aa

1. "Leezie Lindsay"

Johnson, V [1796], No. 434, p. 446 (repr. 1853). Also in Smith [1820-24], II, p. 100; and Eyre-Todd [1894], p. 148. From Robert Burns.

m I

The variant readings a and b are from R. A. Smith's copy.

Will ye go to the Highlands Leezie Lindsay,
Will ye go to the Highlands wi' me
Will ye go to the Highlands Leezie Lindsay
My pride and my darling to be.

2. "Leezie Lindsay"

Cox, 1939, p. 36; and 1964 (ed. Boswell), p. 46. Also, slightly different and from a different singer, in Boswell, *TFSB*, XVI (1950), p. 26. Communicated by Iris McClure, Morgantown, W.Va., November 1925; learned from her uncle, J. F. McClure.

m I/Ly

1. "Will ye gang to the Hielands, Leezie Lindsay?
Will ye gang to the Hielands wi' me?
Will ye gang to the Hielands, Leezie Lindsay,
My wife and my darling to be?"

2. "To gang to the Hielands wi' you, sir,
I dinna ken how that may be;
For I ken na the land that ye live in,
Nor ken I the lad I'm gaun wi'."

3. Then up bespake Leezie's best woman,
A bonnie young lassie was she:
"Had I but a mark in my pocket,
It's Donal that I wad gaun wi'."

4. She has kilted her coats o' green satin,
She has kilted them up to her knee,
And she's aff to the Hielands wi' Donald,
His bride and his darling to be.

5. He has led her high up on a mountain,
And bade her look out on the sea;
"These isles are Lord Ronald McDonald's,
And his bride and his darling are ye."

3. "Lizzie Lindsay"

Child, 1882-98, V, p. 421; text, IV, p. 524. Sent by W. Walker; from the singing of George Nutchell (*sic*), Edzell Castle, Forfarshire, October 5, 1891. He learned it 58 years before from his step-grandmother, who was then 80.

m I/Ly

1. "Will ye gang to the Highlands, Lizzie Lindsay?
Will ye gang to the Highlands wi me?
Will ye gang to the Highlands, Lizzie Lindsay,
My bride an my darling to be?"

2. She turned her round on her heel,
And a very loud laugh gaed she:
"I'd like to ken whaur I'm ganging,
An wha I am gaun to gang wi."

3. "My name is Donald Macdonald,
I'll never think shame nor deny;
My father he is an old shepherd,
My mither she is an old dey.

4. "Will ye gang to the Highlands, bonnie Lizzie?
Will ye gang to the Highlands wi me?
For ye shall get a bed o green rashes,
A pillow an a covering o grey."

5. Upraise then the bonny young lady,
An drew till her stockings an sheen,
An packd up her claise in fine bundles,
An away wi young Donald she's gaen.

6. When they cam near the end o their journey,
To the house o his father's milk-dey,
He said, Stay still there, Lizzie Lindsay,
Till I tell my mither o thee.

7. "Now mak us a supper, dear mither,
The best o yer curds an green whey,
An mak up a bed o green rashes,
A pillow an covering o grey.

8. "Rise up, rise up, Lizzie Lindsay,
Ye have lain oer lang i the day;
Ye should hae been helping my mither
To milk her ewes an her kye."

9. Out then spak the bonnie young lady,
As the saut tears drapt frae her ee,
"I wish I had bidden at hame;
I can neither milk ewes or kye."

10. "Rise up, rise up, Lizzie Lindsay,
There is mair ferlies to spy;
For yonder's the castle o Kingussie,
An it stands high an dry."

11. "Ye are welcome here, Lizzie Lindsay,
The flower o all your kin,
For ye shall be lady o Kingussie,
An ye shall get Donald my son."

4. "Leezie Lindsay"

Smith, 2nd ed. [1825], II, p. 101 (2nd set). Also in Graham, 1848-49, II, p. 82.

m π^1

1. 'Will ye gang to the Hielands, Leezie Lindsay?
Will ye gang to the Hielands wi' me?
Will ye gang to the Hielands, Leezie Lindsay?
My pride and my darling to be.'

2. "To gang to the Hielands wi' you, Sir,
I dinna ken how that may be,
For I ken nae the road I am gaeing,
Nor yet wha I'm gaun wi'."

3. 'Oh, Leezie, lass, ye maun ken little,
Syn ye dinna ken me,
For I am Lord Ronald Mac Donald,
A chieftain o' high degree.'

4. "Oh, if ye're the laird o' Mac Donald,
A great ane I ken ye maun be;
But how can a chieftain sae mighty
Think o' a puir lassie like me."

5. She has gotten a gown o' green satin,
She has kilted it up to her knee,
And she's aff wi' lord Ronald Mac Donald,
His bride and his darling to be.

5. "Leezie Lindsay"

Maver, 1866, No. 330, p. 165.

m I/Ly

Throughout the second phrase and at the start of the third, Maver's barring has been corrected by delaying it one beat.

"Will ye gang to the Hielan's, Leezie Lindsay,
Will ye gang to the Hielan's wi' me?
Will ye gang to the Hielan's, Leezie Lindsay,
My bride and my darlin' to be?"

[*Etc.*]

Maver's text is from R. A. Smith.

GROUP Aa APPENDIX

6. "Leezie Lindsay"

Barry, Eckstorm, and Smyth, 1929, p. 297. Words sent by Mrs. James McGill, Chamcook, New Brunswick, November 1927 and July 1928. Melody recorded by George Herzog, September 1928.

p I/M

The abbreviated pauses at the phrase-endings are as in Herzog's careful transcription.

1. "Will ye gang tae the Hielans, Leezie Lyndsay,
Will ye gang tae the Hielans wi' me?
Will ye gang tae the Hielans, Leezie Lyndsay,
My bryde an' my darling tae be?"

2. "O, what hae ye got in the Hielans, sir,
O, what hae ye got?" quoth she.
"O, what hae ye got in the Hielans, kind sir,
Gin I gang tae the Hielans wi' thee?"

3. "O, I hae got a hoose, Leezie Lyndsay,
O, I hae got a fine ha',
O, I hae got a hoose, Leezie Lyndsay,
A hoose in the Hielans for thee."

4. "I'll no gang tae the Hielans wi' thee, sir,
I'll no gang tae the Hielans wi' thee;
For dark is the nicht, an' the road it is lang,
I'll no gang tae the Hielans wi' thee."

5. "Will ye gang tae the Hielans, Le[e]zie Lindsay,
Will ye gang, bonnie Le[e]zie wi' me?
Will ye gang tae be wife tae Macdonell,
His bride and his darlin' tae be?"

GROUP Ab

7. "Donald Macdonald"

Greig and Keith, 1925, p. 164; from Duncan MS., No. 258. Sung by George Innes, Portnockie; learned in Banffshire, mid-nineteenth century.

a D/Æ

Up spoke Lady Dysie's old mother,
An' a rude spoken woman was she:
"I would like to know where she is gaun,
Or wha she is gaun to gang wi."

"My father he's laird o Kinkussie,
My mother she's lady the same,
My name it is Donald Macdonald,
To tell it I never think shame."

Then oot spak young Lady Dysie,
An' a weel spoken lady was she:
"Ye'll pack my clothes in small bundles,
An' awa wi young Donald I'll gae."

8. "Bonnie Lizzie Lindsay"

Christie, II, 1881, p. 88. Sung by Jamie Coul, Port-Gordon; from Aberdeen and Banff tradition.

a Æ

There was a braw ball in Edinbro',
And mony braw ladies were there;
But nae ane at a' the assembly
Could wi' Lizzie Lindsay compare.
In cam' the young laird o' Kingcaussie,
And a bonnie young laddie was he,—
"Will ye lea' ye're ain kintra, Lizzie,
And gang to the Hielands wi' me?"
[*Etc.*]

Text "epitomized" from "the recitation of a lady in Glasgow."

GROUP Ab APPENDIX

9. "Lizzie Lindsay"

Greig-Duncan MS. 785 (Walker transcript), p. 138; from Duncan MS., No. 495. Sung by Mrs. Gillespie.

m D/Æ

The MS. is barred in straight 6/8 time throughout.

O lassie but ye ken little
In sae be ye dinna ken me
For I am Lord Ronald Macdonald
Your pride and your darling to be

She's kilted her coats o' green satin
Kilted them up to her knee
An' she's off wi' Lord Ronald Macdonald
His pride and his darling to be.

Bonny Lizie Baillie

CHILD NO. 227

This ballad appears not to have held its ground so well in tradition as others intrinsically no better. So far as I know, no new copies have appeared since Buchan's day, and Christie did not include it in his collection.

For our copy of an air, we are indebted to Burns and the *Museum* (No. 456). But according to Glen, *Early Scottish Melodies*, 1900, p. 201, the tune and six stanzas had earlier appeared in William Napier's *Selection of Scots Songs*, 1792, Vol. II. Technically, if the final be tonic, the mode is Dorian; but the tune has more Æolian feeling, and a more comfortable tonic would be the fourth below the final. R. A. Smith (IV, p. 90) gives the same tune, with a slight change in timing at the mid-cadence.

LIST OF VARIANTS

"Lizae Baillie." James Johnson, *The Scots Musical Museum*, V [1792], No. 456, p. 469 (repr. 1853). Also in Robert Archibald Smith, *The Scotish Minstrel* [1820-24], IV, p. 90.

TUNE WITH TEXT

"Lizae Baillie"

Johnson, V [1792], No. 456, p. 469 (repr. 1853). Also in Smith [1820-24], IV, p. 90. From Robert Burns.

p D; or, if tonic D, a Æ

1. [Lizae Baillie's to Gartartan gane,
 To see her sister Jean;
And there she's met wi' Duncan Graeme,
 And he's convoy'd her hame.]

2. My bonny Lizae Baillie,
 I'll row ye in my plaidie
And ye maun gang alang wi' me
 And be a Highland Lady.

3. "I am sure they wad nae ca' me wise,
 Gin I wad gang wi' you, Sir;
For I can neither card nor spin,
 Nor yet milk ewe or cow, Sir."

4. "My bonny Lizae Baillie,
 Let nane o' these things daunt ye.
Ye'll hae nae need to card or spin,
 Your mither weel can want ye."

5. Now she's cast aff her bonny shoen,
 Made o' the gilded leather,
And she's put on her highland brogues,
 To skip amang the heather:

6. And she's cast aff her bonny gown,
 Made o' the silk and sattin,
And she's put on a tartan plaid,
 To row amang the braken:

7. She wad nae hae a Lawland laird,
 Nor be an English lady;
But she wad gang wi' Duncan Graeme
 And row her in his plaidie.

8. She was nae ten miles frae the town,
 When she began to weary;
She aften looked back, and said,
 "Farewell to Castlecarry.

9. "The first place I saw my Duncan Graeme
 Was near yon holland bush.
My father took frae me my rings,
 My rings but and my purse.

10. "But I wad nae gie my Duncan Graeme
 For a' my father's land,
Though it were ten times ten times mair
 And a' at my command."

11. Now wae be to you, logger-heads,
 That dwell near Castlecarry,
To let awa sic a bonny lass,
 A Highlandman to marry.

The *Museum* text is that of Herd, *Ancient and Modern Scottish Songs*, 1776, II, p. 3, except for lacking the first stanza, which is here supplied therefrom.

Glasgow Peggie

CHILD NO. 228

The center of the melodic tradition for this ballad appears to be an authentic Dorian tune. Christie establishes this tradition with his tune from Banffshire. (We may disregard his second strain, as usual.) In succeeding examples collected by Greig there is a slighter emphasis on III and VI, and III is entirely absent from several copies. In a tune-variant set to different words ("Says I my dear," variant 14, below), the third has become major except for its last occurrence. Although that note is not metrically stressed, it is particularly striking because it occurs on the so-called "snap," and because of the Lydian downward run of the first and third cadence. But in spite of its Mixolydian inclination it has kept well its original cast. Greig's Crighton (c) tune (variant 12), however, although technically M/D, has much more of a major feeling. It has extended its range another degree upward, and its strong emphasis on a major triad anchored on the fourth degree would cause it to be classified as an I/M plagal tune, if there were no other variants by which to test it. Miss Macmath's tune (variant 13) has quite succumbed to the major, keeping the added degree upward, and anchoring on the degree just below the old tonic, so as to be authentic I/M. It is now almost unrecognizable, but may instructively be compared with the "Says I my dear" variant that immediately follows it and has already received comment.

It should be mentioned that for the present need, Keith's secondary ballad of "Kilboggie" (*Last Leaves*, p. 167) has been considered together with "Glasgow Peggie," since the tune tradition is identical and the textual theme the same.

Moffat's nursery version of the ballad is very distinct from the foregoing, both in text and tune. The tune seems related to "A Hundred Pipers an' a'." Copyright claims prevent its inclusion here ("a" in the List of Variants).

There is said to be a tune in the Bunyan MS., 1877, p. 117 (cf. Gray-Muir MS., NL Scotland MS. 2254).

LIST OF VARIANTS

GROUP Aa

1. "Glasgow Peggy." W. Christie, *Traditional Ballad Airs*, I, 1876, p. 70.
2. "Glasgow Peggie." Ewan MacColl, Riverside recording No. RLP 12-623(B3), *The English and Scottish Popular Ballads*, II, ed. Kenneth S. Goldstein.
3. "The Highland Lads." Greig MSS., I, p. 33, and Bk. 726, XVI, p. 26, King's College Library, Aberdeen. (Spence)
4. "Highland Lads." Greig MSS., II, p. 49. Also in Gavin Greig and Alexander Keith, *Last Leaves of Traditional Ballads and Ballad Airs*, 1925, p. 166(b). (Stuart)
5. "Kilboggie." Greig and Keith, 1925, pp. 168(a) and 167. From Duncan MS., No. 180. (Chree)
6. "Kilboggie." Greig and Keith, 1925, p. 169(b). From Duncan MS., No. 180. (Alexander)
7. "Highland Lads." Greig MSS., II, p. 48, and Bk. 752, XLII, p. 1. (Rettie)
8. "Highland Laddie." Greig MSS., I, p. 32. (Barron)
9. "Bonnie Peggy." Greig MSS., I, p. 33. (J. Greig)
10. "Glasgow Peggy." Greig MSS., I, p. 182. Also in Greig and Keith, *Last Leaves*, 1925, p. 166(a). (Riddell)
11. "Highland Lads." Greig MSS., III, p. 38. (A. Greig)
12. "A Highland Laddie." Greig MSS., III, p. 138. Also in Greig and Keith, *Last Leaves*, 1925, p. 166(c). (Crighton)

GROUP Ab

13. "Glasgow Peggie." Macmath MS., pp. 115 and 93, Harvard College Library. Also in Francis James Child, *The English and Scottish Popular Ballads*, 1882-98, V, pp. 422 and 266(G).

APPENDIX A

14. "Says I my dear." Greig MSS., I, p. 82. Also in Greig-Duncan MS. 785 (transcription of W. Walker), p. 140(a), King's College Library, Aberdeen. (Clark)

GROUP B

a. "Glasgow Peggie." Alfred Moffat, *Fifty Traditional Scottish Nursery Rhymes* [1933], p. 28.

TUNES WITH TEXTS

GROUP Aa

1. "Glasgow Peggy"

Christie, I, 1876, p. 70. Sung by an old woman from Keith, Banffshire.

a D

1. The Hielan' lads sae brisk and braw,
    The Hielan' lads sae brisk and gaudie,
Ha'e gane awa' to Glasgow town,
    To steal awa' the bonny Peggy.
As they cam' on to Glasgow town,
    And pass'd the banks and braes sae bonny;
There they espied the weel-faur'd may,
    And she said to them her name was Peggy.

2. Their Chief did meet her father soon,
And O but he was wondrous angry;
Says, "Ye may steal my owsen and kye,
But ye maunna steal my bonnie Peggy."
"O haud your tongue, ye gude auld man!
For I've got cows and ewes already;
I come na' to steal your owsen and kye,
But I will steal your bonny Peggy."

3. He set her on a milk-white steed,
And he himsel' rode a gude grey naigie,
And they are on mony miles to the north,
And nane wi' them but the bonny Peggy.
"I ha'e fifty acres o' gude red lan',
And a' weel plough'd and sawn already;
And why should your father be angry wi' me,
And ca' me naething but a Hielan' laddie.

4. "I ha'e twenty weel mounted steeds,
Black, and brown, and grey, already;
And ilk ane o' them is tended by a groom,
Altho' I be but a Hielan' laddie.
I hae now ten thousand sheep,
A' feeding on yon braes sae bonny;
And ilka hundred a shepherd has,
Altho' I be but a Hielan' laddie.

5. "I hae a castle on yonder hill,
It's a' set roun' wi' windows mony;
I'm Lord M'Donald o' the whole Isle of Skye,
And why shouldna Peggy be ca'd my Lady?"
Now a' that Peggy had before,
Was a wee cot house and a little kail yairdie;
But now she is Lady o' the whole Isle of Skye,
And now bonny Peggy is ca'd my Lady.

2. "Glasgow Peggie"

Sung by Ewan MacColl, Riverside rec. No. RLP 12-623(B3), ed. K. S. Goldstein. Learned from his father.

a D

1. Hielan' lads are young and braw,
Hielan' lads are young and merry,
And I'll awa' tae Glesca toon,
To steal awa' my bonnie Peggy.

2. Her faither he's got word o' this,
And, O, but he was wondrous angry;
"Ye may tak' my owsen and a' my kye
But leave to me my bonnie Peggy."

3. "Ye can keep your owsen and a' your kye,
For I ha'e cows and ewes already;
I'll no' tak' your owsen and a' your kye,
But I'll steal awa' your bonnie Peggie."

4. He's mounted on his milk white steed,
And she is on his wee grey naigie,
And they hae rid tae the break o' day,
And he has ta'en awa' the bonnie lassie.

5. They rid ower hills and they rid ower dales,
They rid through moors and mosses mony,
Until they met wi' the Earl o' Hume,
A-ridin' wi' his young son Johnnie.

6. Then oot and spak' the Earl o' Hume,
And, O, but he was wondrous sorry,
"The bonniest lass in Glesca toon,
And she's awa' wi' a hielan' laddie."

7. They rode on through moss and moors,
Through bog and up through mountains mony,
Until they cam' to yonder glen,
And she's lain doon wi' her hielan' laddie.

8. Her bed was o' the gweed green grass,
Their blankets o' the brackens bonnie,
Wi' her tartan plaid beneath her heid,
And she's lain doon wi' her hielan' laddie.

9. "There are blankets and sheets in my faither's hoose,
Sheets and blankets a' made ready,
And wouldna he be angry at me
For lyin' doon wi' a highland laddie!"

10. He's ta'en her up yon high, high hill,
When that the sun was shinin' clearly,
Says "A' that ye see belongs to thee,
For lying doon wi' a hielan' laddie.

11. "A' that ye ha'e left behind
Was a wee cot-hoose and a wee kail-yairdie,
But noo you're the lady o' a' my lands,
For lyin' doon wi' a hielan' laddie."

3. "The Highland Lads"

Greig MSS., I, p. 33; text, Bk. 726, XVI, p. 26. Sung by J. W. Spence, Rosecroft, Fyvie, July 1905.

a M/D

1. Highland lads are brisk and braw
Highland lads are young and airy
But I'll awa to Glesga toon
And steal awa yon bonnie lassie.

2. When her father got word o' this
   Oh but he was wondrous angry
Says "Ye may steal awa my ousen & my kye
   But ye winna steal awa my lovely Peggy."

3. Keep weel aul' man your ousen & your kye
   For I've got cows and ewes already
I winna steal awa your ousen & your kye
   But I'll steal awa your lovely Peggy.

4. He's mounted her on his milk-white steed
   Jumped up himself on his little gray nagie
And they rode thirty miles afore it was lang
   So he's ta'en awa his lovely Peggy.

5. They rode o'er hills & they rode o'er dales
   They rode through moors & mosses many
Until that they met the Earl o' Argyle
   He was ridin' oot wi' his young son bonnie.

6. It's oot & spak the Earl o' Argyle
   And oh but he was wondrous angry
To see the bonniest lass in a' the countryside
   Gaun ridin awa wi' a Hielan laddie.

7. They rode o'er hills, they rode through dales
   They rode through moors & mosses money
Until that they came to yon low glen
   There he's lighted down wi' his lovely Peggy.

8. Their bed was o' the good green grass
   Their blankets & sheets o' the ferns bonnie
He's rolled up his plaid, laid it below her head
   And she's lain her doon wi' her Hielan' laddie.

9. There is blankets & sheets in my father's hoose
   And they're a' washed & dried already
And oh, wadna he right angry be at me
   For lyin' doon wi' a Hielan' laddie.

10. There is 500 acres of good land
   And it's a' ploughed & sown already
And oh wadna he richt angry be at me
   For lyin' doon wi' a Hielan' laddie.

11. He's ta'en her up to yon high hill
   When that the sun was yet shining clearly
Says "A' that is yours as far as ye can see
   For lyin' doon wi' a Hielan laddie.

12. A' that I promised you at the first
   Was a wee-cot hoose & a little kail yardie
But noo ye are the lady o' all the Isle of Skye
   For lyin' doon wi' the Hielan laddie.["]

4. "Highland Lads"

Greig MSS., II, p. 49. Also in Greig and Keith, 1925, p. 166(b). Sung by Mrs. Stuart, Auchmaliddie, July 1906.

a D

they're
(The) Highland lads (are) brisk & braw,
Highland hills are bricht and airy,
But to see the bonniest lass in a' the countryside
Gang ridin' awa' wi' a Highland laddie.

5. [Kilboggie]

Greig and Keith, 1925, p. 168(a); text, p. 167. From Duncan MS., No. 180. Sung by Robert Chree, Alford; learned in Glenbuchat, c. 1866.

a M/D

1. First when I cam to Kilboggie's toon,
   Wi my short coat an' my tartan plaidie,
First when I cam my bonnie love to see,
   She lay in her bed till her breakfast was ready.

2. When she got up an' put on her clothes,
   She said she had been on the hill wi her daiddy,
But weel kent I by her milk-white hands
   She lay in her bed till her breakfast was ready.

3. When her breakfast was set doon,
   It was set doon an' it was made ready;
Oot spoke her mother unto her,
   "Have ye any regard for a Highland laddie?"

4. "It's I wad gie you a' my silk goons,
   A' my silk goons an' my Glasgow plaidie,
It's I wad leave them a' wi you,
   An' gae far far awa wi my Highland laddie."

5. It's they went oot to tak a walk,
   To tak a walk till the dinner was ready;
He's mounted her on his high horse back,
   An' she's far far awa wi her Highland laddie.

6. The first true love that they did meet,
   She said, "Who is this that ye hae wi ye?"
"It is my sister," he did reply,
   "An' I'm takin her to the Highlands wi me."

7. They rode on an' farther on,
   There was nothing there fittin for a lady;
There was nobody there for to welcome her hame
   But an aul carl an' a cankered wifie.

8. The one o them called her Lowlan Kate,
   The other called her Lowlan Jinny,
But she gae them a far properer name,
   It was her Highland mam an' her Highland daiddy.

9. They rode on an' farther on,
There was nothing there fittin for a lady;
There was nothing there for to lay her on
But a wee puckle heather an' his Highland plaidie.

10. "In my father's ha' there's sheets an' blankets enew,
They're a' sewed an' made ready,
An' wouldn't they be richt angry to see
Me lyin here wi a Highland laddie?"

11. "In the Highlands there's flocks an' sheep enew,
They are very thick an' mony;
It's ye'll get woo, an' ye can spin,
An' mak ye a blanket instead o a plaidie."

12. "Flocks an' sheep they're good an' good enough,
Corn stacks are muckle better;
They will stand in drift an' snaw,
When the sheep will die wi the wind an' the weather."

13. "In the Highlands I've got fifty acres o land,
It's a' ploughed an' sown already;
I am Ardonald o a' the Isles,
An' why should not Peggy be called my lady?

14. "In the Highlands I've got fifteen milk cows,
They're a' tied to the sta's already;
I am Ardonald o a' the Isles,
An' why should not Peggy be called my lady?

15. "A coach an' six to me prepare."—
A coach an' six they soon made ready;
"A coach an' six to me prepare,
An we'll go once more an' see your daiddy."

6. [Kilboggie]

Greig and Keith, 1925, p. 169(b); from Duncan MS., No. 180. Sung by Robert Alexander, Udny; learned from his mother, of Strathdon, c. 1836.

a M/D

7. "Highland Lads"

Greig MSS., II, p. 48; text, Bk. 752, XLII, p. 1. Sung by Mrs. Rettie, Millbrex, Fyvie, September 1906.

a D

1. The Hielan' lads are brisk an' braw
The Hielan' lads are brisk an' airy
But I'll awa to Glesca toon
An' wile awa yon bonnie lassie.

2. Her father he got word o' this
And oh but he was wondrous angry
Says Ye maun steal awa my oxen or my kye
But ye winna wile awa my lovely Peggie

3. Guide weel aul' man your oxen & your kye
For I hae cows and yowes already
I winna steal awa your oxen & your kye
But I will wile awa your lovely Peggy

4. He set her on a milk white steed
And himsel' on a little gray naigie
And he's rode thirty miles frae the toon
Wi' nane but himsel' and his lovely Peggie.

5. They rode ower hills, they rode through dales
And over moors and mosses many.
And fa' did they meet but the Earl o' Argyle
And wi' him his young son ridin' bonnie.

6. Then oot it spak the Earl o' Argyle
And oh but he was wondrous angry
To see the bonniest lass in a' the countree
A ridin' awa wi' a Hielan' laddie

7. They rode owre hills they rode through dales
And over moors and mosses many
Until that they came to the foot of yonder glen
And he's lien doon wi' his lovely Peggie

8. Their bed was o' the good green grass
The blankets & sheets o' the ferns bonnie
He folded up his plaid an' he laid below her head
And he's lien doon wi' his lovely Peggie.

9. There is blankets & sheets into my father's hoose
And they're a' washen and dried already
An' how could he be but angry at me
For the lyin' doon wi' a Hielan' laddie.

10. I have hundreds o' acres o' good land
And they're a' ploughed & sown already
And why should he be angry at thee
For the lyin' doon wi' a Hielan' laddie

11. He's ta'en her up to yon high hill
When the moon & the stars were shining clearly
Says 'A' that's yer ain noo, as far as ye see
For the ridin awa wi a Hielan laddie.

12. A' that I was promised at the first
Was a wee cot hoose & a little kail yardie
And noo I am Lady o' a' the Isle o' Skye
For the ridin' awa wi' a Hielan' laddie.

8. "Highland Laddie"

Greig MSS., I, p. 32. Sung by Arthur Barron, Mains of Whitehill, New Deer, April 1906.

a D

A' that I promised you at first
Was a wee cot-hoose & a little kail yairdie
But noo ye are lady o'er a the Isle o' Skye
For the lyin' doon wi' a Highland laddie.

9. "Bonnie Peggy"

Greig MSS., I, p. 33. Sung by James Greig, Oldwhat, New Deer, 1904.

a D

The highland lads they're bright & braw,
The highland hills they're light & airy;
But I maun awa' to bonnie Glasgow toon,
And steal awa' yon bonnie lassie.

10. [Glasgow Peggy]

Greig MSS., I, p. 182. Also in Greig and Keith, 1925, p. 166(a). From George Riddell, Rosehearty, 1903.

a M/D

11. "Highland Lads"

Greig MSS., III, p. 38. Sung by Alexander Greig, Oldwhat, New Deer, October 1907.

a M/D

Hielan lads are brisk & braw,
Hielan hills are light & airy.
But I maun awa to bonnie Glasgow toon
To steal awa' my bonnie Peggy.

12. "A Highland Laddie"

Greig MSS., III, p. 138. Also in Greig and Keith, 1925, p. 166(c). Sung by Miss Lizzie Crighton, Bonnykelly.

a D/M; or, if on G, p I/M

As the troops gied up thro' Glasgow toon,
The Highland clan they were a' lively,
The bonniest lass that e'er I saw
Was a Glasgow girl & her name was Peggy.

GROUP Ab

13. "Glasgow Peggy"

Macmath MS., p. 115; text, p. 93. Also in Child, 1882-98, V, p. 422; text, p. 266(G). Sung by Miss Jane Webster, Kirkcudbrightshire, 1892; learned more than 50 years before.

a I/M

1. It was on a day, and a fine summer's day,
When the Lowlands they were making ready,
There I espied a weelfar'd lass,
She was gaun to Glasgow, and they ca' her Peggy.

2. It's up then spak a silly auld man,
And O but he spak wondrous poorly!
Sayin, Ye may steal awa my cows and my ewes,
But ye'll never steal awa my bonny Peggy.

3. "O haud yer tongue, ye silly auld man,
For ye hae said eneugh already,
For I'll never steal awa yer cows and yer ewes,
But I'll steal awa yer bonny Peggy."

4. So he mounted her on a milk-white steed,
Himsel upon a wee grey naigie,
And they hae ridden ower hill and dale,
And over moors and mosses many.

5. They rade till they cam to the head o yon glen,
It might hae frightened anybody;
He said, Whether will ye go alongst with me,
Or will ye return back again to your mammie?

. . . .

6. Their bed was o the green, green grass,
And their blankets o the bracken sae bonnie,
And he's laid his trews beneath their head,
And Peggy's laid doun wi her Heilan laddie.

7. They lay till it cam to the break o day,
Then up they rose and made them ready;
He said, Whether will ye go alongst with me,
Or will ye return back again to your mammie?

8. "I'll follow you through frost and snow,
I'll follow you through dangers many,
And wherever ye go I will go alongst with you,
For I'll never return back again to my mammie."

9. "I hae four-and-twenty gude milk-kye,
They're a' bun in yon byre sae bonny,
And I am the earl o the Isle o Skye,
And why should not Peggy be called a lady?

10. "I hae fifty acres o gude land,
A' ploughed ower and sawn sae bonny,
And I am young Donald o the Isle o Skye,
And wherever I'm laird I'll make ye lady."

Stanzas 2 through 10 are from Child.

APPENDIX A

14. "Says I my dear"

Greig MSS., I, p. 82. Also in Greig-Duncan MS. 785 (Walker transcript), p. 140(a). Sung by Mrs. Clark, Bruckley, November 1905.

a M (inflected III)

Says I my dear what brought you here
So early in a summer morning
I been pulling the sloes I was mining [*sic*] my yowes
Gatherin' a' my yowes and lambs together.

Could ye fancy me my weel faured lass
Could ye fancy me my dearest darling
Could ye fancy me my weel faured lass
And leave a' your yowes & lambs together.

For to fancy you, Sir, that winna do
I am only (but) a poor shepherd's daughter
For to fancy you, Sir, that winna do
For to leave a' my yowes and lambs together.

[*Etc.*]

Earl Crawford

CHILD NO. 229

Greig did not find this ballad, and it has left but a meager record. To the unique tune preserved by Christie, one may be added from the Blaikie MS., of unknown provenience. These are certainly related, though not very obviously. The Blaikie tune, although it lacks its fourth, is distinctly Mixolydian; the other lacks the Mixolydian note and is I/M. Blaikie's tune lacks the repetition of the second half which appears to be indicated in Buchan's text, as also in Christie's.

Christie's note on this ballad contains an interesting generalization, which will go far to justify his editorial practice. He says he "has known instances where one person, who had the Air from another, sung it in a different and more melodious style from having a finer musical taste. It is, therefore, almost impossible to find out the true set of any traditional air, unless the set can be traced genuinely to its composer" (*Traditional Ballad Airs*, I, p. 68). And if it can be so traced, how traditional is it?

LIST OF VARIANTS

1. "Earl of Crawford." Blaikie MS., National Library of Scotland MS. 1578, No. 126, p. 39.
2. "Earl Crawford." W. Christie, *Traditional Ballad Airs*, I, 1876, p. 68. Text, Francis James Child, *The English and Scottish Popular Ballads*, 1882-98, IV, pp. 277(Aa), 280(Ab).

TUNES WITH TEXTS

1. "Earl of Crawford"

Blaikie MS., NL Scotland MS. 1578, No. 126, p. 39.

a M (–IV)

2. It was at fifteen that I was married,
And at sixteen I had a son;
And wasna that an age ower tender
For a lady to hae her first-born!
And wasna, etc.

3. But it fell ance upon a day
I gaed into the garden green,
And naebody was therein walking
But Earl Crawford and his young son.

4. 'I wonder at you, ye Earl Crawford,
I wonder at you wi your young son;
Ye daut your young son mair than your Lillie;
[I'm sure you got na him your lane.']

5. [He turned about upon his heel,
I wite an angry man was he;
Says, If I got nae my young son my lane,
Bring me here the one that helpet me.]

6. ['O hold your tongue, my Earl Crawford,
And a' my folly lat it be;
There was nane at the gettin o oor son,
Nae body only but you and me.']

7. He set her on a milk-white steed,
Her little young son her before;
Says, Ye maun gae to bonny Stobha,
For ye will enter my yates no more.

8. When she cam to her father's bowers,
She lichtit low down on the stane,
And wha sae ready as her auld father
To welcome Lady Lillie in?

9. 'O how's a' wi you, my daughter Lillie,
That ye come here sae hastilie?
And how's a' wi' the Earl o Crawford,
That he didna send a boy wi thee?'

2. "Earl Crawford"

Christie, I, 1876, p. 68; text, Child, 1882-98, IV, pp. 277 (Aa), 280(Ab). From Mrs. Mary Thomson, the nurse of Christie's children, 1867; learned from her mother.

a I/M

1. O we were sisters, sisters seven,
We were a comely crew to see,
And some got lairds, and some got lords,
And some got knichts o hie degree;
And I mysel got the Earl o Crawford,
And wasna that a great match for me!

10. 'O haud your tongue now, my old father,
And ye'll lat a' your folly be;
For ae word that my merry mou spak
Has parted my good lord and me.'

11. 'O haud your tongue, my daughter Lillie,
And a' your follies lat them be;
I'll double your portion ten times ower,
And a better match I'll get for thee.'

12. 'O haud your tongue now, my old father,
And a' your folly lat it be;
I wouldna gie ae kiss o Crawford
For a' the goud that ye can gie.

13. 'Whare will I get a bonny boy,
That's willin to win meat and fee,
What will gae on to Earl Crawford
And see an 's heart be fawn to me?'

14. 'O here am I, a bonny boy,
That's willin to win meat and fee,
That will go on to Earl Crawford's,
And see an 's hairt be faen to thee.'

15. When he cam to the yates o Crawford,
They were a' sitting down to dine:
'How comes it now, ye Earl Crawford,
Ye arena takin Lady Lillie hame?'

16. 'Ye may gae tell her Lady Lillie,
And ye maun neither lee nor len,
She may stay in her father's bowers,
For she'll not enter my yates again.'

17. When he cam back to her father's yates,
He lichtit low down on his knee:
'What news, what news, my bonny boy?
What news, what news hae ye to me?'

18. 'I'm bidden tell you, Lady Lillie—
I'm bidden neither to lee nor len—
She may stay in her father's bowers,
For she'll not enter my yates again.'

19. She stretched out her lily hand,
Says, 'Adieu, adieu to ane and a!
Adieu, adieu to Earl Crawford!'
Wi that her sair heart brak in twa.

20. Then dowie, dowie her father raise up,
And dowie, dowie the black put on,
And dowie, dowie he mounted the brown,
And dowie, dowie sat thereon.

21. And dowie rade to the yates o Crawford,
And when to Crawford's yates he came,
They were a' dressd in the robes o scarlet,
Just gaun to tak Lady Lillie hame.

22. 'Ye may cast aff your robes o scarlet—
I wyte they set you wondrous weel—
And now put on the black sae dowie,
And come and bury your Lady Lill.'

23. He took his hat into his hand,
And laid it low down by his knee:
'An it be true that Lillie's dead,
The sun shall nae mair shine on me.'

Child's Aa text consists of the text printed by Christie (I, p. 290) from the recitation c. 1867 of Mrs. Mary Robertson, mother of Mrs. Thomson, with bracketed additions (st. 4^4, 5, 6) from a version contributed by Mrs. Thomson in 1890 (Ab). (The text possessed by Christie apparently also included these lines, but he did not print them.) Stanza 14, interpolated here from a note in Child (IV, p. 280), is likewise from Ab.

The Earl of Errol

CHILD NO. 231

THE melodic tradition for this ballad falls easily into three groups—if we admit the Blaikie tunes to the canon on the strength of the title "Kate Carnagie." The first group has the strongest claim to be considered the proper tune, although it is found elsewhere as well, as Keith has noted ("Laird o' Drum," No. 236; "Lang Johnnie More," No. 251; and "Maybe I'll be married yet"). Here there is always a second strain or burden. Both Christie's tunes are intrinsically (*bar* editing) π^1 plagal; Greig's 2 (variant 3 below) is I/M, plagal.

Mrs. Gillespie's tune was also sung by her to "The Broomfield Hill" (No. 43). It is made out of similar strongly rhythmical, rollicking stuff, but has no close support from other variants. It is an authentic tune, in I/M.

The Blaikie tunes are very much alike. Here there is question of the true tonic. To me, the feeling is major, with no inclination toward the Mixolydian; and I suppose the tonic to be properly a fifth below the final, therefore authentic and I/Ly. There is no burden or second strain.

LIST OF VARIANTS

GROUP A

1. "What needs I my apron wash?" or "The Countess of Errol." W. Christie, *Traditional Ballad Airs*, I, 1876, p. 206.
2. "Errol's Place," or "The Countess of Errol." Christie, II, 1881, p. 40.
3. "Errol." Greig MSS., IV, p. 125, King's College Library, Aberdeen. Also in Gavin Greig and Alexander Keith, *Last Leaves of Traditional Ballads and Ballad Airs*, 1925, p. 171 (2). (Gordon)

GROUP B

4. "The Earl of Errol." Greig and Keith, 1925, p. 170(1). From Duncan MS., No. 3. (Gillespie)

GROUP C

5. "Kate Carnagie." Blaikie MS., National Library of Scotland MS. 1578, No. 48(a), p. 17.
6. "Kate Carnagie." Blaikie MS., NL Scotland MS. 1578, No. 48, p. 17.

TUNES WITH TEXTS

GROUP A

1. "What needs I my apron wash?" or "The Countess of Errol"

Christie, I, 1876, p. 206.

p π^1

Christie took the tune from his father's *Collection of Strathspeys*, c. 1820, there given as "The Countess of Errol." Since the words of this ballad were deemed "unsuited" to his own work, Christie substituted a sentimental text for the true words.

2. [Errol's Place, or The Countess of Errol]

Christie, II, 1881, p. 40. From tradition of the northeastern counties.

p π^1

Again Christie has substituted an alien text.

3. "Errol"

Greig MSS., IV, p. 125. Also in Greig and Keith, 1925, p. 171(2). Sung by P. R. Gordon, Brisbane, as heard in the Quilquox district, Buchan, 1830-50.

p I/M

(*To the second strain*)

Wi' the rantin' o't, An' the dantin' o't,
Accordin' as ye ken,
The thing we ca' the dantin' o't,
Lady Errol lies her lane.

Errol O, Errol O,
Errol o the green,
The lady's lost the richts o it,
An' noo she lies her leen, O.

GROUP B

4. "The Earl of Errol"

Greig and Keith, 1925, p. 170(1); from Duncan MS., No. 3. Sung by Mrs. Gillespie, 1905; from 50 years' recollection.

a I/M

Errol it's a bonnie place,
It stands upon a green, O;
The roses they grow red an' white,
An' the apples red an' green, O.

GROUP C

5. "Kate Carnagie"

Blaikie MS., NL Scotland MS. 1578, No. 48(a), p. 17.

a I/Ly, ending on V

6. "Kate Carnagie"

Blaikie MS., NL Scotland MS. 1578, No. 48, p. 17.

a I/Ly, ending on V

Richie Story

CHILD NO. 232

ALL the tunes recorded for this ballad are related. They are mainly authentic major, but may lack either the seventh or the fourth, and may extend their range downward to the plagal limit. To the same family belongs "Galla Water" (*Scots Musical Museum*, No. 125), for which we should expect earlier records, there being apparently none prior to that in Oswald's *Caledonian Pocket Companion*, VIII [1756],* p. 28, according to Glen, *Early Scottish Melodies*, 1900, p. 102. To the same melodic tradition seem likewise to belong "Ay wakin O" (cf. Johnson's *Museum*, Nos. 382, 213, etc.) and a tune, undeniably close to ours, in D'Urfey, *Pills*, 1719-20, V, p. 42, to which J. Muir Wood called attention (see Child, 1882-98, IV, p. 299). The latter therefore would be the tribal progenitor. Keith has observed an Irish relative in Joyce, *Ancient Irish Music*, 1873, No. 11, p. 12 (repr. 1912).

Dick's references for "Galla Water" are given in *The Songs of Robert Burns*, 1903, pp. 397-98. He remarks: "In many modern copies it is corrupted by closing on the key-note, with the introduction of the leading note." If these are the signs of corruption, most copies of the *ballad*-tune display them.

The text printed with Maver's tune, as it happens, belongs to the modern popular song of "Huntingtower," which derives from "Richie Story." The musical traditions of the older ballad and the secondary form are identical, so far as they are known. Another example is the variant from Nova Scotia.

* Date according to Dick, ed., *The Songs of Robert Burns*, 1903, p. xli.

LIST OF VARIANTS

1. "Richie Story." Greig MSS., I, p. 96, King's College Library, Aberdeen. Also in Greig-Duncan MS. 785 (transcription of W. Walker), p. 198, King's College Library, Aberdeen. (Ritchie)
2. "Richie Story." Gavin Greig and Alexander Keith, *Last Leaves of Traditional Ballads and Ballad Airs*, 1925, pp. 173 (1) and 172. From Duncan MS., No. 19. (Gillespie and Duncan)
3. "Richie's Lady." W. Christie, *Traditional Ballad Airs*, I, 1876, p. 72.
4. "Richie Story." Ewan MacColl, Riverside recording No. RLP 12-622(A5), *The English and Scottish Popular Ballads*, I, ed. Kenneth S. Goldstein. Also by Ewan MacColl and Peggy Seeger, Folkways LP recording No. FW 8755(A2).
5. "Castle Norie." Greig MSS., I, p. 153, and Bk. 714, IV, p. 28. Also in Greig and Keith, *Last Leaves*, 1925, p. 173(2). (Robb)
6. "Ritchie's Lady." Greig MSS., II, p. 106, and Bk. 719, IX, p. 16. Also in Greig and Keith, 1925, p. 174(3). (Littlejohn)

APPENDIX

7. "The Scotch Wedding." Thomas D'Urfey, *Wit and Mirth: Or Pills to Purge Melancholy*, 1719-20, V, p. 42.
8. "The Duke of Athol's Courtship." Robert Maver, *Genuine Scottish Melodies*, 1866, No. 390, p. 195.
9. "When Will Ye Gang Awa'?" Helen Creighton and Doreen H. Senior, *Traditional Songs from Nova Scotia*, 1950, p. 217.

TUNES WITH TEXTS

1. "Richie Story"

Greig MSS., I, p. 96. Also in Greig-Duncan MS. 785 (Walker transcript), p. 198. Sung by Miss Annie Ritchie, Whitehill, January 1906.

a I

I was your waiting man, Madam,
I made your bridle shine, Madam,
And ye wot not that your own true love
Was England's royal King, Madam.

2. [Richie Story]

Greig and Keith, 1925, p. 173(1); text, p. 172. From Duncan MS., No. 19. Sung by George F. Duncan, Glasgow; text, attributed to him and his sister, Mrs. Gillespie, learned from their mother's singing in the 1860's and later.

a I/M

1. "Here's a letter to you, madam,
Here's a letter to you, madam,
Here's a letter fae the Earl o the Wemyss,
An' it's a' in suit o you, madam."

2. "Say not so to me, Richard,
Say not so to me, Richard;
For I've made a voo, an' I will keep it true,
To marry none but you, Richard."

3. "Say not so to me, madam,
Say not so to me, madam;
For I have neither lan's nor rents,
For to maintain you wi, madam."

4. "Say not so to me, Richard,
Say not so to me, Richard;
For I want neither lan's nor rents,
For to maintain me wi, Richard."

5. Oot it spak her ae brother,
"O dear sister, weel may we be sorry,
That you should wed your ain servant man,
An' lose a' your right to bonnie Castle Norrie.

6. "O dear sister, weel may we be sorry,
O dear sister, weel may we be sorry;
The gardens they are fine, an' they're a' laid wi thyme,
An' a' the walks o bonnie Castle Norrie."

7. "O dear brother, how could I be sorry?
O dear brother, how could I be sorry?
I wadna gie my Richard wi his laced coat
For a' the lans o bonnie Castle Norrie."

8. "O I am gaun fae hame, madam,
I am gaun fae hame, madam;
I'm gaun awa sae far awa,
I'm gaun across the sea, madam."

9. "I will go wi you, Richard,
I will go wi you, Richard;
I'll go wi you sae far awa,
I'll go across the sea, Richard."

10. "Ye canna go wi me, madam,
Ye canna go wi me, madam;
I'm gaun awa to London toon,
My friends long me to see, madam."

11. "Yes, I'll go wi you, Richard,
Yes, I'll go wi you, Richard;
I'll go wi you to London toon,
Your friends I long to see, Richard."

12. When they went doon through London toon,
O but the bells were ringin bonnie,
An' mony a ane did look at them,
But little did they think it was Richard's lady.

13. When they cam in at the Parliament gate,
The marriage bells they were ringing bonnie,
An' mony a knight an' mony a squire
Stood there to welcome Richard's lady.

14. "Sae dearly's ye loved me, madam,
Sae dearly's ye loved me, madam,
Ye left your lan' an' a' your rents
Your servant to go wi, madam.

15. "But sae dearly's I loved you, madam,
Sae dearly's I loved you, madam,
I left the sceptre an' the throne,
An' was your waitin man, madam.

16. "An' was your waitin man, madam,
Made a' your bridles ring, madam;
An' little did ye think that your waitin boy
Was England's royal King, madam.

17. "But since it's so ye loved me, madam,
Since it's so ye loved me, madam,
Ye shall be queen o a' England,
An' happy shall ye be, madam."

3. "Richie's Lady"

Christie, I, 1876, p. 72. In Buchan tradition "from time immemorial."

a I

1. There were ladies in yon ha',
Seven ladies in Cumbernaudie;
The youngest and fairest o' them a'
Has faun in love wi' her footman laddie.
He gaed down the garden green,
In amang the birks sae bonnie;
And there he saw his lady gay,
Wi' ribbons on her shoulders mony.

2. "Here's a letter to thee, Madam;
Here's a letter to thee, Lady;
With Earl Hume's humble desire,
Your servant for to be, Lady."
"I'll ha'e nane o' his letters, Richie;
Nane from Earl Hume, Richie;
But I'll ha'e him that I like best,
And I'll ha'e nane but you, Richie."

3. "Say na' that to me, Lady,
Say na' that to me, Lady;
For I ha'e neither lands nor rents,
For to maintain you wi', Lady."
"Say na' that again, Richie,
Say na' that again, Richie;
The House o' Athole it is mine,
Taranadie shall be thine, Richie."

4. He gaed from the garden green,
Thinking he would shun his lady;
But quickly she follow'd after him,—
Says, "Ye maun leave your comrades, Richie.
To the Borders we maun gae,
I'll gae to them wi' thee, Richie;
For gin my father hear o' our love,
High hangèd ye will be, Richie."

5. "To the Borders we will gae,
We will to them gang, Lady;
But tho' your father hear o' our love,
It's me he daurna' hang, Lady."
As they rode by her sister's bowers,
Her sisters they were wondrous sorry;
They bade her cast off her robes o' silk,
And gang and beg wi' her Richard Storie.

6. As they rode thro' yon burrow town,
   Her gold watch, it shone sae bonny,
   And mony a ane saluted her;
   But nane thought that she was to be his Lady.
   As they were riding up yon high hill,
   The Lady, she grew wondrous weary;
   She lookèd over her left shoulder,
   Says, "I wish I were at the Cumbernaudie!"

7. "Oh, are ye not sorry, Lady?
   Oh, are ye not sorry, Lady?
   To leave your home and kindred dear,
   And follow Richard Storie, Lady!"
   "What needs I be sorry, Richie?
   What needs I be sorry, Richie?
   When I get him that I like best,
   And what is laid before me, Richie."

8. As they rode by yon bonny House,
   They heard music sounding bonny;
   And four-and-twenty gallant knichts,
   Came out to welcome Richie's Lady.
   A coach and four was soon prepar'd,
   A coach and four was soon made ready;
   And now she rides in her coach and four,
   And blesses the day that made her his Lady.

4. "Richie Story"

Sung by Ewan MacColl; learned from his mother. Riverside rec. No. RLP 12-622(A5), ed., K. S. Goldstein. Also sung by Ewan MacColl and Peggy Seeger, Folkways LP rec. No. FW 8755(A2).

a I

"Here's a letter to you, madam,
Here's a letter to you, madam,
Here's a letter fae the Earl o' the Wemyss,
And it's a' in suit o' you, madam."

"Say not so to me, Richard,
Say not so to me, Richard;
For I've made a voo, and I'll keep it true,
To marry none but you, Richard."
[*Etc.*]

Mr. MacColl's text is conflated from his mother's singing and Greig's copy, *ante*, variant 2.

5. "Castle Norie"

Greig MSS., I, p. 153; text, Bk. 714, IV, p. 28. Also in Greig and Keith, 1925, p. 173(2). Sung by Alexander Robb, New Deer, March 1906.

m I/Ly

O dear sister how could ye be sad
O dear brother how could ye be sorry
For I hae promised my ain true love
To leave a' my riches to you at Castle Norrie.
I'm sure I've chosen a very pretty lass
And she is the prettiest in a' Castle Norrie

6. "Ritchie's Lady"

Greig MSS., II, p. 106; text, Bk. 719, IX, p. 16. Also in Greig and Keith, 1925, p. 174(3). Sung by Miss Littlejohn, Banchory, January 1907.

a I/Ly, ending on VI

1. There were seven bonnie ladies in yonder ha',
   There were seven bonnie ladies in Campernandie,
   And the youngest o' them and the fairest o' them a'
   She's fa'en in love wi' her footman laddie.

2. He has ta'en him up the stair
   Wi' a letter for his lady—
   "It's the Earl o' Doune has his service for to gie,
   But ye'll follow me your footman laddie,
   And ye'll follow me your footman laddie."

3. "That I daurna do Ritchie,
   That I daurna do laddie,
   For gin my father get word o' this
   It's you that he will hang, Ritchie,
   It's you that he will hang, laddie."

4. "That he daurna do, lassie,
   That he daurna do, lady,
   For tho' your father get word o' this
   It's me he daurna hang, lassie,
   It's me he daurna hang, lady."

5. "To the Borders we maun gang, Ritchie,
To the Borders we maun gang, laddie,
For gin my father gets word o' this
It's you that he will hang, laddie,
And it's you that he will hang, laddie."

6. As they gaed by yon bonnie castle wa'
O but her silk goon it hung bonnie,
"It's ye'll tak' aff this goon o' silk,
And ye'll muck the byres wi' Ritchie Torrie,
And ye'll muck the byre wi' Ritchie Torrie."

7. As they gaed up yon bonnie hillside,
O but her gold watch it shone bonnie,
She turned aboot and gave a sigh—
"Wish an I were back to Campernandie,
Wish an I were back to Campernandie."

8. "Dear me! aren't ye sorry, lassie?
Dear me! aren't ye sorry, lady?
That ye maun forsake your ain true love,
And follow me your footman laddie?"

9. "What needs I be sorry, Ritchie?
What needs I be sorry, laddie?
For the thing that's before me I must undergo,
So I'll follow you, my footman laddie,
And I'll follow you, my footman laddie."

10. As they gaed up yon bonnie hillside,
O but the sun was settin' bonnie,
There were four-and-twenty Englishmen
Cam' a' to welcome Ritchie Torrie,
And cam' a' to welcome Ritchie Torrie.

11. A coach an' six an' they did prepare,
A coach an' six an' they soon made ready,
An' now she rides in her coach an' six
An' blesses the day she was Ritchie's lady,
An' blesses the day she was Ritchie's lady.

APPENDIX

7. "The Scotch Wedding"

D'Urfey, 1719-20, V, p. 42.

a I

8. "The Duke of Athol's Courtship"

Maver, 1866, No. 390, p. 195.

a I

"I am gaun awa, Jeanie,
I am gaun awa, Jeanie,
I'm gaun ayont the saut seas,
I'm gaun sae far awa, Jeanie."
[*Etc.*]

Cf. the references in Child, 1882-98, IV, p. 299 (Appendix).

9. "When Will Ye Gang Awa'?"

Creighton and Senior, 1950, p. 217. Sung by Mrs. Edward Gallagher, Chebucto Head, N.S.

m I

1. "When will ye gang awa', Jamie,
Far across the sea, laddie,
When will ye gang to Germanie,
What will ye bring to me, laddie."

2. "I'll bring a brand new goon, Janie,
The brawest in the toon, lassie,
It shall be made with silken thread
With ruffles all aroound, lassie."

3. "That's nae girt at all, Jamie,
Silken goon and all, laddie,
There's nae a gift in all the toon
I'll have when you're awa', laddie."

4. "When I come back again, Janie,
Frae a foreign land, lassie,
I'll bring with me a gallant gay
To be your own guid man, lassie."

5. "Be my guid man yourself, Jamie,
Marry me yourself, laddie,
Take me back to Germanie,
At hame with ye to dwell, laddie."

6. "Canna see hoo that could be, Janie,
Canna see hoo that could be, lassie,
For I've a wife and bairns, three,
Canna see how you'd agree, lassie."

7. "Why couldn't ye a telt me that afore, Jamie,
Why couldn't ye a telt me long ago, laddie?
For had I ken all your false heart,
You'd ne'er ha got in mine, laddie."

8. "Dry the tearful 'ee, Janie,
Weep nae mair for me, lassie,
For I have no wife nor bairns, three,
I'll wed no one but thee, lassie.

9. "All Loch Voil is mine, Janie,
All Loch Voil is mine, lassie,
St. Johnston's Tower and Hunting Bower,
They all are mine and thine, lassie."

Andrew Lammie

CHILD NO. 233

According to Jamieson, *Popular Ballads and Songs*, 1806, I, p. 128, the music to which this ballad usually went "is of that class which, in Teviotdale, they term a *Northern Drawl*; and a Perthshire *set* of it, but two notes lower than is commonly sung, is to be found in Johnson's *Scots Musical Museum* [i.e., No. 175], to the song 'How lang and drearie is the night, &c.'"

If Jamieson is correct, the recent tradition, which, thanks to Greig, is fairly full for this ballad, is not of great age. The tune to which he refers does conform to the rhythmical scheme of traditional variants, and agrees (necessarily, of course, because of the verbal pattern) in the feminine cadence at 2 and 4. But, melodically, it is too far removed from the rest to trace a connection. Presumably, he did not mean pitch by "two notes lower," for folk-singing has little to do with pitch. He could hardly have meant that there was a Teviotdale tune in the same key literally two degrees higher; but he may have meant that such a tune would approximate what he had in mind. If he meant to imply a shift from major to minor, the tune would be impossible to reconstruct with any assurance.

The tradition as it has been recovered is sufficiently consistent, but diverse in its over-all unity, so that it makes a fine study in variation, ranging all the way from π^4 to π^1 in modal change, and keeping rhythmically steady.

The variants fall without too much forcing into three groups, of which the middle one is perhaps most characteristic. The first is typically D/Æ, plagal, with mid-cadence moving up from minor III to IV, and feminine; first-phrase cadence on the lower flat seventh. The second group swings from Dorian to π^2, plagal. Both Motherwell's and Christie's variants are M/D, and agree so closely that one wonders if Christie (or his father, who published it earlier) did not follow Motherwell, only adding a Dorian third in his second strain. The third group is major and π^1, again plagal. Perhaps the most typical medial and final cadence throughout is that of a fall from a fourth above; but some copies rise one degree, instead. The opening phrases are quite unstable.

Some variants, e.g., Greig 2d and 4 (variants 1 and 14, below), have ambiguous finals. The first may be heard as a π^1 tune ending on the sixth; but if it be considered after the D/Æ variants, its final will probably be felt to be the true tonic.

As Keith has pointed out, the tune family occurs elsewhere: with "Barbara Allan" (No. 84) and, especially, with "Yarrow" (cf. No. 214).

There is in the Gray-Muir MS. (NL Scotland MS. 2254) reference to a tune in the Bunyan MS., 1877, p. 22.

LIST OF VARIANTS

GROUP Aa

1. "Tiftie's Annie." Greig MSS., II, p. 100, King's College Library, Aberdeen. Also in Gavin Greig and Alexander Keith, *Last Leaves of Traditional Ballads and Ballad Airs*, 1925, p. 179(2d). (Rae)
2. "Tiftie's Annie." Greig MSS., IV, p. 179. Also in Greig and Keith, 1925, p. 178(2b). (Corbet)
3. "Tiftie's Annie (& Dowie Dens)." Greig MSS., III, p. 30. (Greig)
4. "Tiftie's Annie." Greig MSS., I, p. 58. Also in Greig-Duncan MS. 785 (transcription of W. Walker), p. 150, King's College Library, Aberdeen. (Barron)
5. "Tifty's Annie." Jeannie Robertson, Sound Archives of the British Broadcasting Corporation, London, recording No. 20183-20184.
6. "Tiftie's Annie." Greig MSS., IV, p. 98. Also in Greig and Keith, *Last Leaves*, 1925, p. 178(2c). (Sangster)
7. "Tifty's Annie." Otto Andersson, *Budkavlen*, XXXIII (1954), p. 42.
8. "Tiftie's Annie." Greig MSS., II, p. 102. Also in Greig and Keith, *Last Leaves*, 1925, p. 179(2e). (McBoyle)

GROUP Ab

9. "Tiftie's Annie." Greig MSS., IV, p. 76. Also in Greig and Keith, 1925, p. 178(1c). (Johnstone)
10. "Mill o' Tiftie's Annie." William Motherwell, *Minstrelsy: Ancient and Modern*, 1827, App'x., No. 28 and p. xxii. Also in Robert Maver, *Genuine Scottish Melodies*, 1866, No. 398, p. 199; and W. Christie, *Traditional Ballad Airs*, I, 1876, p. 48.
11. "Tifty's Annie." Greig and Keith, *Last Leaves*, 1925, pp. 178(1b) and 175. From Duncan MS., No. 351. (Duncan and Gillespie)
12. "Tifty's Annie." Greig-Duncan MS. 785 (Walker), p. 149. From Duncan MS., No. 294. (Harper)

GROUP Ac

13. "Mill o' Tifty." Greig MSS., III, p. 119. Also in Greig and Keith, *Last Leaves*, 1925, p. 178(2a). (Thain)
14. "Tifty's Annie." Greig and Keith, 1925, p. 179(4). (Goodall)
15. "Tiftie's Annie." Greig MSS., I, p. 110. Also in Greig and Keith, 1925, p. 177(1a). (Ritchie)
16. "Tiftie's Annie." Greig MSS., IV, p. 5. Also in Greig and Keith, 1925, p. 179(3). (Coutts)

TUNES WITH TEXTS

GROUP Aa

1. "Tiftie's Annie"

Greig MSS., II, p. 100. Also in Greig and Keith, 1925, p. 179(2d). Sung by Miss H. Rae, Sandhaven, October 1906.

m π^4

At Mill o' Tiftie lived a man
In the neighbourhood o' Fyvie,
He had a lovely daughter fair
Was callèd bonnie Annie.

2. "Tiftie's Annie"

Greig MSS., IV, p. 179. Also in Greig and Keith, 1925, p. 178(2b). Sung by George Corbet, Weetingshill, 1913; from his mother.

p D/Æ

3. "Tiftie's Annie (& Dowie Dens)"

Greig MSS., III, p. 30. Sung by Alexander Greig, September 1907.

p D/Æ

4. "Tiftie's Annie"

Greig MSS., I, p. 58. Also in Greig-Duncan MS. 785 (Walker transcript), p. 150. Sung by Arthur Barron, Whitehill, 1905.

p D/Æ

It's up and down in Tiftie's glen
Where the burn rins clear and bonnie,
I've often gane to meet my love,
My bonnie Andrew Lammie.

5. "Tifty's Annie"

BBC Sound Archives, rec. No. 20183-20184. Sung by Jeannie Robertson, London, November 1953. Collected by Peter Kennedy.

p D/Æ

At the Mill o' Tifty there lived a man,
In the neighborhood o' Fyvie.
He had a lovely daughter fair
Whose name was bonnie Annie.

6. "Tiftie's Annie"

Greig MSS., IV, p. 98. Also in Greig and Keith, 1925, p. 178(2c). Sung by Mrs. Sangster, Cortiecram, Mintlaw, September 1910.

m D/Æ

7. "Tifty's Annie"

Andersson, *Budkavlen*, XXXIII (1954), p. 42. Sung by Mrs. Ethel Findlater, Dounby, Orkney, in the summer of 1938.

p D/Æ

At mill o Tifties lived a man
In the neighbourhood of Fyvie.
He had a lovely daughter fair
Who was called Bonnie Annie.

Her bloom was like the springing flower
That salutes the rosy morning,
With innocence and graceful smile
Her beauteous form adorning.

8. "Tiftie's Annie"

Greig MSS., II, p. 102. Also in Greig and Keith, 1925, p. 179(2e). Sung by Peter McBoyle, New Deer, July 1907.

p D/Æ

It's up & doon in Tiftie's glen,
Where the burn rins clear & bonnie,
It's there I've often gane to meet
My bonnie Andrew Lammie.

GROUP Ab

9. "Tiftie's Annie"

Greig MSS., IV, p. 76. Also in Greig and Keith, 1925, p. 178(1c). Sung by John Johnstone, New Deer.

p D

It's up & doon in Tiftie's glen,
Where the burn rins clear and bonnie,
I've aften gane to meet my love,
My bonnie Andrew Lammie.

10. "Mill o' Tiftie's Annie"

Motherwell, 1827, App'x., No. 28; text, App'x., p. xxii. Also in Maver, 1866, No. 398, p. 199; and Christie, I, 1876, p. 48. Tune from A. Blaikie, Paisley.

p D/M

At Mill o' Tiftie liv'd a man,
In the neighbourhood o' Fyvie;
He had a lovely daughter fair,
Was called bonnie Annie.
Her bloom was like the springing flower,
That salutes the rosy morning,
With innocence and graceful mein [*sic*]
Her beauteous form adorning.

Variant a is the only significant difference between Christie's tune and Motherwell's. In this phrase Christie concurs with Maver.

11. "Tifty's Annie"

Greig and Keith, 1925, p. 178(1b); text, p. 175. From Duncan MS., No. 351. Tune from George F. Duncan, from a MS. of his parents, c. 1886; text from his sister, Mrs. Gillespie, Glasgow, as learned in Buchan in the 1850's.

p M

1. At Mill o Tifty there lived a man
In the neighbourhood o Fyvie;
He had a lovely daughter fair,
Was callèd bonnie Annie.

2. Her bloom was like the springing flower
That hails the rosy morning,
With innocence and graceful mien
Her beauteous face adorning.

3. Lord Fyvie had a trumpeter
Whose name was Andrew Lammie;
He had the airt to gain the heart
O' Mill o Tifty's Annie.

4. Proper he was, baith young an' gay,
His like was not in Fyvie,
Nor was there one that could compare
Wi this same Andrew Lammie.

5. Lord Fyvie he rode by the door
Where livèd Tifty's Annie;
His trumpeter rode him before,
Even this same Andrew Lammie.

6. Her mother called her to the door,
Said, "Come here to me, Annie;
Did ye ever see a prettier man
Than the trumpeter o Fyvie?"

7. Naething she said, but sighed fu' sore,
Alas for bonnie Annie!
She durst not own her heart was won
By the trumpeter o Fyvie.

8. At nicht when a' gaes to their bed,
A' sleeps fu' soun but Annie;
Love so oppressed her tender breast,
Thinking on Andrew Lammie.

9. "Love comes in at my bedside,
An' love lies doon beyond me,
Love so oppressed my tender breast,
An' love will waste my body.

10. "The first time me an' my love met
Was in the woods o Fyvie;
His lovely form an' gracefu mien
Soon gained the heart o Annie.

11. "He called me mistress; I said No,
I'm Mill o Tifty's Annie;
Wi apples sweet he did me treat,
An' kisses soft an' many.

12. "It's up an' doon in Tifty's den,
Where the burn rins clear an' bonnie,
I've often gane to meet my love,
My bonnie Andrew Lammie."

13. But alas! her father came to know
That the trumpeter o Fyvie
Had had the airt to gain the heart
O' his daughter bonnie Annie.

14. Her father soon a letter wrote,
An' sent it to Lord Fyvie,
To say his daughter was bewitched
By his servant Andrew Lammie.

15. Then up the stair his trumpeter
He called him soon an' shortly:
"Pray tell to me what's this you've done
To Tifty's bonnie Annie?"

16. "Woe be to Mill o Tifty's pride,
For it has ruined many;
He'll not have it said that she should wed
The trumpeter o Fyvie.

17. "In wicked airt I had nae pairt,
Nor therein was I canny;
True love alone the heart has won
O' Tifty's bonnie Annie.

18. "Where will I get a boy so kind
That'll carry a letter canny
An' will rin on to Tifty's toon,
Gie it to bonnie Annie?

19. "Tifty he has daughters three,
An' they're a' wondrous bonnie,
But ye'll ken her amo' them a',
Gie it to bonnie Annie.

20. "It's up an' doon in Tifty's den
Where the burn rins clear an' bonnie,
There will ye gang, an' I'll attend;
My love, I long to see ye.

21. "Thou must gang to the brig o Sleuch,
An' there I'll gang an' meet ye,
An' there we will renew our love,
Before I gang an' leave ye."

22. "My love, I go to Edinburgh toon,
An' for a while maun leave ye":
She sighed fu' sair, an' said nae mair
But "I wish that I were wi ye."

23. "I'll buy to you a bridal goon,
My love, I'll buy it bonnie;
I will thee wed when I come back
To see my bonnie Annie.

24. "If ye'll be true an' constant too,
As I am Andrew Lammie,
I will thee wed when I come back
To view the lands o Fyvie."

25. "I'll be true an' constant too
To thee, my Andrew Lammie;
But my bridal bed it will be made
In the green churchyard o Fyvie."

26. "The time is gone, an' now comes on,
My dear, that I must leave ye;
If longer here I should appear,
Mill o Tifty he wad see me."

27. "I now for ever bid adieu
To thee, my Andrew Lammie;
Ere ye come back, I will be laid
In the green churchyard o Fyvie."

28. He hied him to the head o the house
To the high house-top o Fyvie;
He blew his trumpet loud an' shrill,
Twas heard at Mill o Tifty.

29. Her father locked the door at nicht,
Laid up the keys fu canny;
An' when he heard the trumpet sound,
Said, "Your coo is lowing, Annie."

30. "My father dear, I pray forbear,
Reproach nae mair your Annie,
For I wadna gie that ae coo's low
For a' the kye in Fyvie.

31. "I wadna for my braw new goon,
Nor a' your gifts sae many,
That it were known in Fyvie's lands
Sae cruel ye are to Annie.

32. "But if ye strike me, I'll cry out,
An' gentlemen will hear me;
Lord Fyvie he'll be riding by,
An' he'll come in an' see me."

33. At that same time the Lord came in,
Said, "What ails thee, my Annie?"—
"It's a' for love that I maun dee,
For bonnie Andrew Lammie."

34. "Pray, Mill o Tifty, gie consent,
An' let your daughter marry."—
"It will be wi some higher match
Than the trumpeter o Fyvie."

35. "If she'd been come o as high kin
As she's adorned wi beauty,
I wad hae teen her to mysel,
An' made her my ain lady."

36. "Fyvie's lands are far an' wide,
An' they're a' wondrous bonnie,
But I wadna gie my ain true love
For a' the lands o Fyvie."

37. Her father struck her wondrous sore,
As also did her mother,
Her sisters also did her scorn,
But woe be to her brother!

38. Her brother struck her wondrous sore
Wi cruel strokes an' many;
He broke her back at the ha' door
For liking Andrew Lammie.

39. "Alas, my father an' mother dear,
Why so cruel to your Annie?
My heart was broken first by love,
My brother broke my body.

40. "Ye neighbours hear, baith far an' near,
An' pity Tifty's Annie,
Who dies for loving one poor lad,
My bonnie Andrew Lammie.

41. "No kind o vice e'er stained my life,
Nor hurt my virgin honour;
My youthfu heart was won by love,
But death will me exoner.

42. "O mother dear, now make my bed,
An' lay my face to Fyvie;
Thus will I lie, an' thus will die
For my dear Andrew Lammie."

43. Her mother then she made her bed,
An' laid her face to Fyvie;
Her tender heart it soon did break,
An' she never saw Andrew Lammie.

44. Lord Fyvie he did wring his hands,
Said, "Alas for bonnie Annie!
The fairest flower cut down by love
That ever sprang in Fyvie.

45. "Woe be to Mill o Tifty's pride,
He micht have let them marry;
I wad hae gien them baith to live
Within the lands o Fyvie."

46. Her father sair now laments
The loss o his dear Annie,
An' wishes he had gien consent
To wed wi Andrew Lammie.

47. When Andrew hame from Edinburgh came
Wi muckle grief an' sorrow,
Said, "My love has died for me to-day,
I'll die for her to-morrow.

48. "Now I will rin to Tifty's den
Where the burn rins clear an' bonnie;
Wi tears I'll view the brig o Sleuch,
Where I parted wi my Annie.

49. "Then I will rin to the green churchyard,
To the green churchyard o Fyvie;
Wi tears I'll water my love's grave
Till I follow Tifty's Annie."

50. Ye parents who dear children have,
In crossing them be canny;
Or when too late ye may repent,
Remember Tifty's Annie.

Mr. Duncan's text, written from his mother's singing in Buchan, 1885, is inaccessible. According to Keith (*Last Leaves*, p. 272), it has these differences from Mrs. Gillespie's: omitted sts. 49-50; gave sts. 23-26 in the order 25, 26, 23, 24; put st. 42 between 39 and 40. "Otherwise the differences are verbal and slight at that." (Cf. note, *ante*, p. xii, on the Duncan MSS.)

12. "Tifty's Annie"

Greig-Duncan MS. 785 (Walker transcript), p. 149; from Duncan MS., No. 294. Sung by Mrs. Harper, Cluny, 1907; learned from her grandmother.

p π^2

At Mill o' Tifty there lived a man
I' the neighbourhood o' Fyvie
He had an only daughter fair
Was called bonny Annie.

GROUP AC

13. "Mill o' Tifty"

Greig MSS., III, p. 119. Also in Greig and Keith, 1925, p. 178(2a). Sung by Mrs. Thain, New Deer, June 1908; learned from her grandmother.

a I, ending on the octave

14. "Tifty's Annie"

Greig and Keith, 1925, p. 179(4). Sung by Mrs. Goodall, Alford; learned from her grandmother.

p I, ending on II

15. "Tiftie's Annie"

Greig MSS., I, p. 110. Also in Greig and Keith, 1925, p. 177(1a). Sung by Miss Annie Ritchie, Whitehill, February 1906.

p π^1

It's up & down in Tiftie's glen,
Where the burn rins clear & bonnie,

16. "Tiftie's Annie"

Greig MSS., IV, p. 5. Also in Greig and Keith, 1925, p. 179(3). Sung by Mrs. Coutts, Ellon.

p π^1

At Mill o' Tiftie lived a man,
In the neighbourhood o' Fyvie;
He had an only daughter fair,
Was callèd bonnie Annie.

The Earl of Aboyne

CHILD NO. 235

THREE types of melody appear to have been used for this ballad. The best established is our A group, found in the Blaikie and Harris MSS. of the early nineteenth century, and recorded by Christie in the form used by his maternal grandmother. The tune is major in tonality, of duple rhythm, and usually has a full authentic octave plus the plagal range. We may sub-divide the copies into three classes, of I/Ly, Major, and I/M, the last being plagal and of more recent vintage. As Keith points out, the type is affiliated with "The Mill, Mill O," printed many times in the eighteenth century and later, and used in various ballad-operas and by Burns ("When wild war's deadly blast").

The second type is represented by Mrs. Gillespie's copy, and she sang also another tune to the same ballad-text. As Keith notes, the present is the tune of the popular "Bonnie Lass of Fyvie"; it has easy connections with "Binorie" (Child No. 10), which was Mrs. Gillespie's other tune for "Aboyne." In its present form it is a plagal major. MacColl's variant is of the same kind.

The third type is illustrated by but one example for this ballad, although it, too, is very familiar in other connections, particularly "Binorie" and "Barbara Allan" (No. 84). It appears also with "The Rantin' Laddie" (No. 240), another ballad connected with Aboyne. Here it is plagal D/Æ.

Mrs. Harris's tune deserves a special word. It was incorrectly printed in Child's Appendix of Airs (V, p. 422), and in fact very inexpertly noted in the original MS. The barring is wrong from the mid-cadence on; eighths are written as quarter-notes. Also, I have no doubt that the fifth and sixth notes from the end (C♯ A) are a simple slip of the pen for A F♯, being written each a space higher when the transcriber returned after extending the lines of the staff to get a little more room to finish the tune. The penultimate note in the MS. is not G (as in Child) but A. In the MS. there is a bass that confirms these readings:

Motherwell transmitted to C. K. Sharpe, before October 8, 1825, a tune noted by Andrew Blaikie from a woman's singing of "Lord Aboyne" or "Peggy Irvine." (Cf. Child MSS., HCL 25241.56 F*.) Presumably, this was either variant 1 or 4 below. It is no longer among Sharpe's known MSS. There is said to be a tune for this ballad also in the Bunyan MS., 1877, p. 145 (cf. Gray-Muir MS., NL Scotland MS. 2254).

LIST OF VARIANTS

GROUP Aa

1. "Earl Aboyne." Blaikie MS., National Library of Scotland MS. 1578, No. 71, p. 23.
2. "The Earl of Aboyne." W. Christie, *Traditional Ballad Airs*, I, 1876, p. 22.
3. "The Earl of Aboyne." Harris MS., No. 16, and fol. 21 b, Harvard College Library. Also in Francis James Child, *The English and Scottish Popular Ballads*, 1882-1898, V, p. 422, and IV, p. 317.

GROUP Ab

4. "Earl Aboyne," or "Peggy Irvyne." Blaikie MS., National Library of Scotland MS. 1578, No. 68, p. 22.

GROUP AC

5. "The Laird o' Aboyne." Greig MSS., IV, p. 26, King's College Library, Aberdeen. Also in Gavin Greig and Alexander Keith, *Last Leaves of Traditional Ballads and Ballad Airs*, 1925, p. 182(1b). (Dunbar)
6. "The Earl o' Aboyne." Greig MSS., I, p. 92. Also in Greig and Keith, 1925, p. 181(1a). (Pyper)

GROUP B

7. "The Earl o' Aboyne." Greig and Keith, 1925, pp. 182(3) and 180. From Duncan MS., No. 16. (Gillespie)
8. "The Earl of Aboyne." Ewan MacColl, Riverside recording No. RLP 12-627(A3), *The English and Scottish Popular Ballads*, IV, ed. Kenneth S. Goldstein.

GROUP C

9. "The Laird o' Aboyne." Greig MSS., III, p. 120. Also in Greig and Keith, *Last Leaves*, 1925, p. 182(2). (Thain)

TUNES WITH TEXTS

GROUP Aa

1. "Earl Aboyne"

Blaikie MS., NL Scotland MS. 1578, No. 71, p. 23.

m I/Ly

2. "The Earl of Aboyne"

Christie, I, 1876, p. 22. From his maternal grandmother.

m I/Ly

The Earl o' Aboyne to Lunnon's gane,
And a' his nobles wi' him;
Sair was the heart his fair lady had,
Because she didna win wi' him.
As she was walking in her garden green,
Amang her gentlewomen,
Sad was the letter that came to her,—
That her lord was wed in Lunnon.
[*Etc.*]

Christie's text is a collation, based on the way he heard the ballad sung and on the version in Buchan's *Gleanings*, 1825, p. 71.

3. "The Earl of Aboyne"

Harris MS., No. 16; text, fol. 21 b. Also in Child, 1882-98, V, p. 422; text, IV, p. 317. From Mrs. Amelia Harris; learned from an old nurse during childhood in Perthshire, late eighteenth century. Noted by her daughter.

m I/Ly

1. "My maidens fair, yoursels prepare."

2. You may weel knaw by her hair, wi the diamonds sae rare,
That the Earl of Aboyne was comin.

3. "My minstrels all, be at my call,
Haud a' your rooms a ringin,
. . . .
For the Earl of Aboyne is comin."

4. "Tomorrow soud hae been my bonnie waddin-day,
If I had staid in London."

5. She turned her aboot wi an angry look,
An sic an angry woman!
"Gin tomorrow soud hae been your bonnie waddin-day,
Gae back to your miss in Lunnon."

6. For mony a day an year that lady lived in care,
An doctors wi her dealin,
Till just in a crack her very heart did brak,
An her letters went on to Lunnon.

7. There waur four-an-twenty o the noblest lords
That Lonnon could aford him,
A' clead in black frae the saidle to the hat,
To convey the corpse o Peggy Ewan.

8. "I'd rather hae lost a' the lands o Aboyne
Than lost my pretty Peggy Ewan."

The above text is that printed by Child (E). In the tune MS. there is a single stanza, as follows:

Ye minstrels all, be at my call,
Haud a' your rooms a ringin':
You may weel ken by her hair, wi' the diamonds sae rare,
That the Earl o' Aboyne is comin.

GROUP Ab

4. "Earl Aboyne," or "Peggy Irvyne"

Blaikie MS., NL Scotland MS. 1578, No. 68, p. 22.

a I

GROUP AC

5. "The Laird o' Aboyne"

Greig MSS., IV, p. 26. Also in Greig and Keith, 1925, p. 182(1b). Sung by Mrs. Dunbar, Longhill of Crimond, 1910.

p I/M

6. "The Earl o' Aboyne"

Greig MSS., I, p. 92. Also in Greig and Keith, 1925, p. 181(1a). Sung by Mrs. Pyper, Whitehill, December 1905.

p I/M

The Earl o Aboyne is to England gone,
And a' his nobles wi' him;
Sair was the heart that his lovey had
Because she wan na wi' him.

GROUP B

7. "The Earl o' Aboyne"

Greig and Keith, 1925, p. 182(3); text, p. 180. From Duncan MS., No. 16. Sung by Mrs. Gillespie.

p I

1. The Earl o Aboyne to London's gane,
   An' a' his nobles wi him [O],
   An' sair was the heart that his fair lady got
   Because she couldna win wi him [O].

2. As she was walkin on the green,
   Among her gentle women,
   Sad was the letter that this fair lady got,
   That her lord was wed in London.

3. "O is it true, my Jean," she said,
   "O Jean my gentlewoman?
   O is it true, my Jean," she said,
   "That my lord is wed in London?"

4. When she lookt ower her castle wa,
   She saw twa boys rinnin:
   "What news, what news, my bonnie little boys,
   What news hae ye fae London?"

5. "Good news, good news, my lady fair,
   For the lord o Aboyne he is comin;
   Ere he won within twa miles o the place,
   Ye'll hear his bridles ringin."

6. "O my grooms all, be well in call,
   An' hae your stable shinin;
   Wi corn an' hay spare none this day,
   For the lord o Aboyne he's comin.

7. "O my minstrels all, be well in call,
   An' hae your harps a-tunin;
   Wi the finest o springs spare not the strings,
   Sin the lord o Aboyne he's comin.

8. "My cooks all, be well in call,
   An' hae your spits a-rinnin;
   Wi the best o roast ye'll spare nae cost,
   For the lord o Aboyne he's comin.

9. "My housemaids all, be well in call,
   An' hae your floors a-shinin;
   Ye'll cover the stair wi the herbs sweet an' fair,
   An' the floors wi the finest o linen.

10. "An' dress my body in the finest array,
    My hood o the finest linen,
    My apron shall be o the good silk gauze,
    Sin the lord o Aboyne he's comin."

11. Sae stately's she stept down the stair,
    To see gin he was comin;
    Her gown was o the good green silk,
    Fasten't wi the red silk trimmin.

12. She called on Kate her waitin-maid,
    On Jean her gentlewoman:
    "Gae bring me a glass o the very best wine
    To drink his health that's comin."

13. She's gane out to the close, taen him fae his horse,
    Said, "Ye're welcome for your comin";
    She's gane to the close, taen him fae his horse,
    Says, "Ye're thrice welcome fae London."

14. "If I be half as welcome as ye say,
    Come kiss me for my comin,
    For to-morrow should hae been my weddin day
    Gin I'd stayed ony langer in London."

15. She turned about wi a disdainful look
    To Jean her gentlewoman:
    "If to-morrow should hae been your weddin day,
    Go kiss your miss in London."

16. "O my nobles all, now turn your steeds,
    I'm sorry for my comin;
    Tonight we'll alight at the bonnie Bog o Gight,
    An' to-morrow take horses for London."

17. "O Thomas, my man, rin after him,
    An' see gin I'll win wi him."—
    "O I hae been pleadin sair for you,
    But a mile an' ye'll no win wi him."

18. A year an' mair she lived in care,
    An' doctors wi her dealin,
    But in a crack her bonnie heart did brak,
    An' letters gaed to London.

19. When he saw the letters sealed in black,
    He fell in grievous weepin:
    "If she be deid whom I loe best,
    If I'd but her heart a-keepin."

20. Fifteen o the noblest lords
That London could afford him,
From their hose to their hat let them be in black,
To mourn for my bonnie Peggy Irvine.

21. The further he went the sairer he wept,
"If I'd but her heart a-keepin [O],
For I'd rather hae lost all the lands o Aboyne
Than lost my bonnie Peggy Irvine [O]."

8. "The Earl of Aboyne"

Sung by Ewan MacColl; learned from his father. Riverside rec. No. RLP 12-627(A3), ed. K. S. Goldstein.

p I

1. The Earl o' Aboyne is to London gane,
An' a' his servants are wi' him, O,
An' sair is the hairt that his fair lady got,
Because she couldna ride wi' him, O.

2. As she was a-walkin' on the green,
Wi' a' her gentle women, O,
The news that she got made the tears doon fa',
That her Lord was married in London, O.

3. She looked frae her window and there she saw,
Two bonnie boys a runnin', O,
"Whit news hae ye brocht, my bonny lads,
Whit news hae ye brocht frae London, O.

4. "Good news, my lady, good news we bring,
The Lord o' Aboyne he is comin', O,
And ere he wins tae a mile o' your bower,
Ye'll hear his bridles ringin', O.

5. "Ye'll dress my body in the finest array,
My smock o' the Holland linen, O,
My kerchie shall be the finest cramasie,
For the Lord o' Aboyne he is comin', O.

6. And she's looked oot ower her castle wa',
To see gin he was comin', O,
Her goon was o' the finest silk,
Fastened wi' the red silk trimmin's, O.

7. She's gane oot tae the close, to fetch him from his horse,
"Ye're welcome, Aboyne, for comin', O,
Ye're welcome, my lord, tae your abode,
Ye're welcome hame frae London, O."

8. "If it be true that I'm welcome to you,
Then kiss me for my comin', O,
For tomorrow should hae been my wedding day,
Gin I'd stayed any longer in London, O."

9. She's turned awa' and the tears did doon-fa',
And O, but her hairt it was heavy, O,
"Gin' tomorrow should hae been your weddin' day,
Gae kiss your miss in London, O."

10. "Turn ye aroond, my merry men a',
I'm sorry for my comin', O,
This night we will sleep at the bonnie bog o' Gight,
And tomorrow we'll tak' horse for London, O."

11. A year and mair she lived in care,
The doctors could gie her nae healin', O,
But in a crack her hairt did brak,
And a letter gaed to London, O.

12. When first he looked the letter on,
And O, but he was a-weepin', O,
"O, curse on the day I left my bonnie may,
When I had her hairt in keepin', O."

13. Fifty o' his noblemen,
Through London they went ridin', O,
From hose to hat they went a' in black,
To mourn for bonnie Peggy Irvine, O.

14. The further he went, the sairer he wept,
"If I'd but her hairt a keepin', O,
For I'd rather hae lost the lands o' Aboyne,
Than lost my bonnie Peggy Irvine, O."

GROUP C

9. "The Laird o' Aboyne"

Greig MSS., III, p. 120. Also in Greig and Keith, 1925, p. 182(2). Sung by Mrs. Thain, New Deer, June 1908.

p D/Æ

She callèd on Kate her chambermaid,
An' Jean her gentlewoman,
Go dress my body in some fine array,
For the Laird o Aboyne he's a-coming.

The Laird o Drum

CHILD NO. 236

The main melodic tradition of this favorite ballad-version of King Cophetua is a lively tune in duple time, authentic, and basically π^1 even where the gaps are supplied either as Ionian or as Mixolydian. Of this type Greig collected a dozen examples, and these are given added weight by Christie's fancy copy.

Another half-dozen tunes are impossible to group, and have been ordered on the hypothesis that they would have conformed to the type except for deflecting influences from other tunes. Thus B is π^1 but plagal and is of the type found with the "Earl of Errol" (No. 231) and "Lang Johnny More" (No. 251) and, as Keith notes, "Maybe I'll be married yet." Another late traditional copy may be a cousin, and is entered here. C is probably also π^1 plagal, with a falling close on IV below. It may be related to B, but has lost its obvious resemblances. It might be classified by its final as π^2. D departs from the strong duple rhythm, and is a plagal Mixolydian variant of the tune which the same singer had already sung as π^1 to "Tifty's Annie" (No. 233). E is something of a puzzle. As it stands it makes no musical sense and we may suppose something went wrong, not in transcribing but in the printing. We may, at least, confidently remove the B♭ as an error; and almost as confidently the G♯ as an editorial blunder. What then remains is a clearly recognizable Dorian form of the tune which we saw in an almost identical D/Æ form with "Geordie" (No. 209; Greig and Keith, *Last Leaves*, 1925, p. 133[1a]), and have met elsewhere in various guises (e.g., "Gypsy Laddy," "Athole's Nurse"). But it is at least equally probable that the third of the tune should be major, and the whole therefore Mixolydian.

It should be noted that Child's Fa, which goes back traditionally to the mid-eighteenth century at least, was sung to "Boyne Water," but in a form of that tune, judging by the triple repetition of the last line, to which I cannot recall a parallel.

There remain two tunes which are associated with secondary or even tertiary forms of the ballad. The first has a special interest on account of Burns's connection with it. Glen, who is very grudging of commendation here, says, "It appears to be a mongrel. The latter half of it is a palpable plagiarism of 'When the King cam' o'er the Water.' Stenhouse . . . says Burns altered the words of it, but it would have been better had he done it somewhat more. We are doubtful if the song was ever printed before the Museum" (*Early Scottish Melodies*, 1900, p. 184). I concur with Dick (ed., *The Songs of Robert Burns*, 1903, p. 492) in believing that the tune ends on the "relative minor," the tonic being B♭. As for plagiarism, blame an old song for that and which shall 'scape damnation? The song has been popular also in many parts of England. C. J. Sharp collected it in Somerset ("I'm seventeen come Sunday") and gives references (in *One Hundred English Folksongs*, 1916, p. xxxiv) to *JFSS*, I, No. 3 (1901), p. 92; II, No. 6 (1905), p. 9; II, No. 9 (1906), p. 269; Baring-Gould, Sheppard, and Bussell, *Songs of the West*, 1905, No. 73; and Ford, *Vagabond Songs and Ballads of Scotland*, 1904, p. 99 ("My rolling Eye"). A text appears on a Manchester broadside in the Baring-Gould collection (British Museum: L.R. 271. a. 2. vol. VII, fol. 73) and is known also in this country. Cf. Eddy, *Ballads and Songs from Ohio*, 1939, pp. 188ff., where other references are given. Cf. also Group B of the preceding ballad.

A tune which Barry got from a Scottish singer in New Brunswick might, by a bare possibility, be related to the preceding. It is a fine authentic Dorian tune, mated to obviously modern words which have the look of being made over from matter represented in Child's Appendix to this ballad.

The musical record, it might be observed, lends no corroboration to the assumption that the secondary forms of the ballad have grown traditionally from the earlier.

A tune is said to be in the Bunyan MS., 1877, p. 37 (cf. Gray-Muir MS., NL Scotland MS. 2254).

LIST OF VARIANTS

GROUP A

1. "The Laird of Drum." W. Christie, *Traditional Ballad Airs*, I, 1876, p. 24. Also in Robert Ford, *Vagabond Songs and Ballads of Scotland*, 1904, p. 4.
2. "The Laird of Drum." Miss M. Douglas Gordon (singer), Archive, School of Scottish Studies, University of Edinburgh.
3. "The Laird o' Drum." Greig MSS., III, p. 36, King's College Library, Aberdeen. (Greig)
4. "Laird o' Drum." Greig MSS., III, p. 6, and Bk. 722, XII, p. 69. Also in Greig-Duncan MS. 785 (transcription of W. Walker), p. 159, King's College Library, Aberdeen. (McAllan)
5. "Laird o' Drum." Greig-Duncan MS. 785 (Walker), p. 160; from Duncan MS., No. 3. Also in Greig MSS., II, p. 6; and Gavin Greig and Alexander Keith, *Last Leaves of Traditional Ballads and Ballad Airs*, 1925, pp. 185(1b) and 183. (Gillespie)
6. "The Laird o' Drum." John Strachan (singer), Archive, School of Scottish Studies.
7. "The Laird o Drum." Greig MSS., II, p. 7. Also in Greig and Keith, *Last Leaves*, 1925, p. 185(1a). (Milne)
8. "The Laird o Drum." Greig-Duncan MS. 785 (Walker); from Duncan MS., No. 291. Also in Greig and Keith, 1925, p. 185(1a). (Harper)
9. "The Gates o' Drum." Togo Crawford, Sound Archives of the British Broadcasting Corporation, London, recording No. 21865.
10. "The Laird o' Drum." Elsie Morrison (singer), Archive, School of Scottish Studies.
11. "The Laird o Drum." Greig MSS., IV, p. 136. (Corbet)
12. "The Laird o' Drum." Greig MSS., I, p. 164. (Spence)
13. "The Laird o' Drum." Greig and Keith, *Last Leaves*, 1925, p. 185(1c). From Duncan MS., No. 442. (Matheson)
14. "The Laird o' Drum." Greig MSS., I, p. 186. (Riddell)
15. "The Laird o' Drum." Greig MSS., III, p. 146, and Bk. 742, XXXII, p. 32. Also in Greig and Keith, *Last Leaves*, 1925, p. 185(1a). (Reid)
16. "The Laird o' Drum." Ewan MacColl, Riverside recording No. RLP 12-621(A3), *The English and Scottish Popular Ballads*, I, ed. Kenneth S. Goldstein.

17. "The Laird o Drum." Greig and Keith, *Last Leaves*, 1925, p. 185(1d). From Duncan MS., No. 466. (Troup)
18. "The Laird o Drum." Greig MSS., IV, p. 28. Also in Greig and Keith, 1925, p. 186(1f). (Dunbar)
19. "The Laird o Drum." Greig and Keith, 1925, p. 186(1e). From Duncan MS., No. 494. (Dalgarno)

GROUP B

20. "Laird o' Drum." Greig-Duncan MS. 785 (Walker), p. 159; from Duncan MS., No. 104. (Christie)
21. "The Laird o' Drum." Willie Mathieson (singer), Archive, School of Scottish Studies.

GROUP C

22. "The Laird o Drum." Greig MSS., II, p. 145. Also in Greig and Keith, *Last Leaves*, 1925, p. 186(2). (Fowlie)

GROUP D

23. "The Laird o Drum." Greig MSS., I, p. 150, and Bk. 716, VI, p. 1. Also in Greig and Keith, 1925, p. 186(3). (Ritchie)

GROUP E

24. "The Laird of Drum." George R. Kinloch, *Ancient Scottish Ballads*, 1827, App'x. to p. 199, and p. 200.

APPENDIX

25. "As I went out ae May morning." James Johnson, *The Scots Musical Museum*, IV [1792], No. 397, p. 410 (repr. 1853).
26. "The Laird and the Shepherd's Daughter." Phillips Barry, Fannie H. Eckstorm, and Mary W. Smyth, *British Ballads from Maine*, 1929, p. 300. (McGill)

TUNES WITH TEXTS

GROUP A

1. "The Laird of Drum"

Christie, I, 1876, p. 24. Also in Ford, 1904, p. 4. From Aberdeenshire and Banff tradition.

a M

1. The Laird o' Drum has a-hunting gane,
   All in the morning early;
And he has spied a weel-faur'd May
   A-shearing her father's barley.
"My bonnie May, my weel-faur'd May,
   It's will ye fancy me, O,
And gang and be the Leddy o' the Drum,
   And let your shearing a-be, O?"

2. "O, I mauna fancy you, kind sir,
   Nor lat my shearing a-be, O;
For I'm owre low to be Leddy o' the Drum,
   And your Miss I scorn to be, O.
"My father he is a shepherd mean,
   Keeps sheep on yonder hill, O;
And ye may gang and speir at him,
   I'm entirely at his will, O."

3. Now Drum has to her father gane,
   Keeping sheep on yon green hill, O:
"I'm come to marry your a'e dochter
   If ye'll gi'e your goodwill, O."
"My dochter can neither read nor write,
   She ne'er was bred at school, O;
But weel she can work, baith oot and in,
   For I learned the girlie mysel', O.

4. "She'll work in your barn and at your mill,
   She'll brew your malt or ale, O;
She'll saddle your steed in the time o' need,
   And she'll draw aff your boots hersel', O."
"I'll learn the lassie to read and write,
   And I'll put her to the school, O;
And she'll never need to saddle my steed,
   Nor draw aff my boots hersel', O.

5. "But wha will bake my bridal bread,
   Or wha will brew my ale, O;
And wha will welcome my lowly bride,
   Is mair than I can tell, O."
O, four-and-twenty gentle knights,
   Gaed in at the yett o' Drum, O;
But ne'er a ane has lifted his hat
   When the Leddy O' Drum cam' in, O.

6. But he has ta'en her by the hand,
   And led her but and ben, O;
Says, "You're welcome hame, my Leddy Drum,
   For this is a' your ain, O."
And he has ta'en her by the hand,
   And led her through the ha', O;
Says, "You're welcome hame, my Leddy Drum,
   To your bowers, ane and a', O."

7. Then up and spak' his brother John,
   "Ye've done us meikle wrang, O;
Ye've married a wife 'neath your degree,
   She's a mock to a' our kin, O.
It's Peggie Coutts is a bonnie bride,
   And Drum is big and gaucey;
But ye micht hae chosen a higher match
   Than just a shepherd's lassie."

8. Out then spak' the Laird o' Drum,
   Says, "I've dune ye nae wrang, O;
I've married a wife to work and win,
   Ye've married ane to spend, O.

The first time that I married a wife,
She was far owre my degree, O;
And I durstna gang in the room where she was
But my hat below my knee, O!

9\. "For the first wife, sirs, that I did wed,
She lookit doon on me, O;
She wadna walk to the yetts o' Drum
But the pearlins abune her bree, O.
And she was adored but for her gold,
As Peggie for her beautie, O;
And she might walk to the yetts o' Drum
In as gude companie, O."

10\. Yet four-and-twenty gentle knights
Stood at the yetts o' Drum, O,
And there wasna ane amang them a'
Would welcome Peggie in, O.
So he's taen her by the milk-white hand
And led her in himsel', O;
And through the ha's, and through the bowers,
And "Ye're welcome, Leddy Drum, O!"

11\. And twice he kissed her cherry cheek,
And thrice her cherry chin, O,
And twenty times her comely mou'—
And "Ye're welcome, Leddy Drum, O!"
When they had eaten and drunken weel,
And a' were bound for bed, O,
The Laird o' Drum and his Leddy fair
In a'e bed they were laid, O.

12\. "Gin ye had been o' high renown,
As ye're o' low degree, O,
We might hae baith gane down the street
Amang gude companie, O.
And o' a' yon four-and-twenty knights
That gaed in at the yett o' Drum, O,
There ne'er was ane but wad lifted his hat
When the Leddy o' Drum cam' in, O."

13\. "I tell'd ye weel ere we were wed
Ye was far abune my degree, O;
But now I'm married, in your bed laid,
I'm just as gude as ye, O.
And when I am dead and you are dead
And baith in a'e grave lain, O,
Ere seven years are at an end
They'll no ken your dust frae mine, O."

The text is given from Ford, who describes his copy as "the pure bothy version of the ballad—preferable in every way to Buchan's, Kinloch's [from which Christie's was epitomized], and Aytoun's copies of it" (Ford, p. 9).

2. "The Laird of Drum"

Archive, School of Scottish Studies. Sung by Miss M. Douglas Gordon, Kildrummie, 1953. Collected by Francis M. Collinson for the School of Scottish Studies; transcribed by the collector.

a M (–IV)

The Laird of Drum is a hunting gaen,
All in the morning early O
And there he spied a bonny May
A-shearin' her father's barley.

3. "The Laird o' Drum"

Greig MSS., III, p. 36. Sung by Alexander Greig, Oldwhat, New Deer, September 1907.

a π^1

The Laird o' Drum's a-wooin' gane,
All in a mornin' early;
And there he spied a weel-faur'd maid,
She was shearin' her father's barley.

4. "Laird o' Drum"

Greig MSS., III, p. 6; text, Bk. 722, XII, p. 69. Also in Greig-Duncan MS. 785 (Walker transcript), p. 159. Sung by John McAllan, Shevado, September 1907.

a π^1

1\. The Laird o' Drum's a hunting gone
All in a morning early
And he espied a weel-faured maid
She was shearin' her father's barley.

2\. Thou bonnie maid—thou weel-faurd maid
Oh will ye fancy me, oh
Oh will ye fancy the Laird o' Drum
And let your shearin' be o'

3\. I wouldna fancy the Laird o' Drum
He is far above my degree o'
For I'm not fitted his bride to be
And his miss I wad scorn to be o'.

4. You'll cast aff the goon o' gray
Put on the silk & scarlet
And you will be the Lady o' Drum
And neither miss nor harlot.

5. Your silken goons I canna wear
They wad rustle at my heels o'
But I will wear the colour o' my ewe,
For it suits my body weel o'

6. Your china cups I canna wash
Nor mak' a cup o' tea o'
But I can milk the cow or the ewe
Wi the cogie on my knee o'

7. My father is an auld shepherd
Keeps sheep on yonder hill o'
And ilka thing that he bids me do
I work aye at his will o'

8. He's taen her to the auld shepherd
Keeps sheep on yonder hill o'
Says, oh but you have a bonny daughter
And oh, but I like her weel oh.

9. She'll winnow yer corn, she'll sift yer meal
And drive to mill or kiln o'
And in time o' need, she'll saddle yer steed
And she'll draw yer boots hersel o'

10. But who will bake my bridal bread
And who will brew my ale o'
And who will welcome my love in
It's more than I can tell o'.

11. The baker will bake your bridal bread
The brewer will brew your ale o'
And fa' will welcome your love in,
You can welcome her in yersel' o'.

12. There was four & twenty lairds & lords
Stood at the gates o' Drum o'
But nane o' them a' put his hand to his hat
To welcome the shepherd's daughter in o'.

13. But he's taen her by the milk white hand
And he's led her gently in o'
And he's given her the keys into her hand
And he's styled her Lady o' Drum o'.

14. Out and spoke his brother John
An angry man was he o'
You've married a wife my brother dear,
She'll be an affront to all your kin o'.

15. The first wife that I married
She was far above my degree o'
I couldna enter the room where she was
Without my hat down by my knee o'.

16. Now I've married a wife to win my bread
But you've married one to spend o'
And as long as my head shall carry my hat
She'll aye be Lady o' Drum o'.

17. When a' was eaten & a' was drunken
And all were bound for bed o'
The Laird o' Drum & the Shepherd's daughter
They were baith in ae bed laid o'.

18. If ye had been as good as me
As good as the Laird o' Drum o'
We would have walked the streets last night
Among good company o'

19. I told ye afore ye marriet me
Ye were far above my degree o'
But noo that we're mairriet & in ae bed laid
Ye'll be forced to be deein wi me o'.

20. When Adam & Eve our first parents
Did eat the forbidden tree o'
O where were a' your gentry then
Am not I just as good as thee o'.

21. Gin ye were deid and I were deid
And baith in ae grave laid o'
And seven lang years had passed and gane
They wad scarce ken your dust by mine o'.

5. "Laird o' Drum"

Greig-Duncan MS. 785 (Walker transcript), p. 160; from Duncan MS., No. 3. Also in Greig MSS., II, p. 6; and Greig and Keith, 1925, p. 185(1b); text, p. 183. Sung in 1905 by Mrs. Gillespie, who learned it from Betty Milne, Fyvie, c. 1862.

a π^1

1. The laird o Drum's a-huntin gane
All in a mornin early,
An' there he spied a weel-faur'd maid
A-shearin her father's barley.

2. "O will ye fancy me, fair maid,
Or will ye marry me, O,
An' gang an' be the leddy o Drum
An' lat your shearin be, O?"

3. "O I maunna fancy you, kind sir,
Nor lat my shearin be, O,
For I'm ower low to be leddy o Drum,
An' your miss I would scorn to be, O.

4. "My father he's an auld shepherd man,
Keeps hoggs on yonder hill, O,
An' ilka thing he bids me do,
I'm always at his will, O."

5. "But ye'll pit aff the gowns o grey,
Pit on the silk an' scarlet,
An' come an' be the leddy o Drum,
An' ye'll neither be miss nor harlot."

6. "I canna wear your gowns o silk,
They wid harrel at my heel, O,
But weel can I wear the colour o the ewe,
It becomes my body weel O."

7. Now he has to her father gane
Keepin hoggs on yonder hill, O:
"I'm come to marry your ae dachter,
If ye'll gie your good will, O."

8. "My dachter can neither read nor write,
She was never taught at school, O,
But weel can she milk baith cows an' ewes,
For I learned the lassie mysel, O.

9. "She'll work in your barn, she'll winnie your corn,
She'll gang to mill or kill, O;
In time o need she'll saddle your steed,
An' draw your boots hersel, O."

10. "I'll learn the lassie to read an' write,
I'll pit her to the school, O,
An' she'll never need to saddle my steed,
Nor draw my boots hersel, O.

11. "But fa will bake my bridal breid,
Or fa will brew my ale, O,
An' fa will welcome the leddy o Drum,
Is mair than I can tell, O."

12. There was four an' twenty gentlemen
Stood at the gates o Drum, O,
But neer a een pit his han' till his hat
When the leddy o Drum cam in, O.

13. But he has taen her by the han',
An' led her but an' ben, O,
Says, "Ye're welcome hame, my Leddy Drum,
For this is a' your ain, O."

14. An' he has taen her by the han'
An' led her through the ha', O,
Says, "Ye're welcome hame, my Leddy Drum,
To your bowers een an' a', O."

15. Then up an' spak his ae brither,
"Ye've deen us muckle wrang, O;
Ye've marriet a wife neath your degree,
A disgrace to a' oor kin, O.

16. "It's Peggy Coutts is a bonnie bride,
An' Drum is big an' gaucey,
But he micht hae chosen a higher match
Than just a shepherd's lassie."

17. Out then spak the laird o Drum,
Says, "I've done ye nae wrang, O,
For I've marriet a wife to work an' win,
An' ye've marriet een to spen', O.

18. "The firstan wife that I did wed,
She was far abune my degree, O,
I durstna gang in the room she was in
But my hat low by my knee, O.

19. "For the first wife that I did wed,
She lookit doon on me, O;
She widna walk to the gates o Drum,
But the pearlins abune her bree O.

20. "An' she was adored but for her gold,
An' Peggy for her beauty, O,
An' she micht walk to the gates o Drum
In as good company, O."

21. Yet four an' twenty gentle knights
Stood at the gates o Drum, O,
An' there wasna een amang them a'
Wid welcome Peggy in, O.

22. But he has taen her by the han',
An' led her in himsel, O,
An' pit the keys into her lap,
An' styled her Leddy Drum, O.

23. An' twice he kissed her cherry cheek,
An' thrice her cherry chin, O,
An' twenty times her comely mou,
Said, "Ye're welcome, Leddy Drum, O."

24. When they had eaten an' drunken weel,
An' a' were bound for bed, O,
The laird o Drum an' the shepherd's dachter
In ae bed they were laid, O.

25. "Gin ye had been o as high kin
As ye're o low degree, O,
We might hae baith gane doon the street
Mang the best o company, O.

26. "An' o a' yon four an' twenty knights
That gaed in at the yett o Drum, O,
There neer was een but wid lifted his hat
When the leddy o Drum cam in, O."

27. "I tell't ye weel ere we were wed,
Ye was far abune my degree, O,
But noo I'm wed an' in your bed laid,
I'd scorn to carry your keys, O.

28. "I tell't ye weel ere we were wed,
Ye was far too high for me, O,
But noo I'm wed an' in your bed laid,
An' I'm just as good as ye, O.

29. "When I am deid an' you are deid,
An' baith in ae grave laid, O,
They wid need to look wi very clear een
To ken your mould by mine, O."

6. "The Laird o' Drum"

Archive, School of Scottish Studies. Sung by John Strachan. Collected by Hamish Henderson for the School of Scottish Studies; transcribed by Francis M. Collinson.

a I/Ly

The Laird o' Drum is a huntin' gane
All in a morning early
And there he spied a weel-faur'd maid
Shearin' her father's barley.

7. "The Laird o Drum"

Greig MSS., II, p. 7. Also in Greig and Keith, 1925, p. 185(1a). Sung by Mrs. Milne, Auchreddie, May 1906.

a I

The Laird o' Drum has a-wooin gone,
All in a mornin' early,
And there he spied a weel-faur'd maid,
She was shearin' her father's barley.

8. "The Laird o Drum"

Greig-Duncan MS. 785 (Walker transcript); from Duncan MS., No. 291. Also in Greig and Keith, 1925, p. 185(1a). Sung by Mrs. Harper, Cluny; learned from her grandmother.

a π^1

9. "The Gates o' Drum"

BBC Sound Archives, rec. No. 21865. Sung by Togo Crawford, Galloway. Tune transcribed by Francis M. Collinson. Text sent to Editor by Hamish Henderson.

a I/Ly

As I gaed oot for to look aboot
Ae Monday mornin early,
It was there that I spied a fair pretty maid,
She was shearin her faither's barley.

For the lassie she could neither read nor write;
She had ne'er been at the schuil O.
For ony ither thing she could dae richt weel,
For I learned the lassie mysel O.

Tak ye up tae yon shepherd man
That lives on yon high hill O.
Be an old shepherd man or a young shepherd man
Then he'll get ye a' tae himsel O.

10. "The Laird o' Drum"

Archive, School of Scottish Studies. Sung by Elsie Morrison. Collected by Hamish Henderson for the School of Scottish Studies; transcribed by Francis M. Collinson.

a I/Ly

The Laird O' Drum a-hunting went,
'Twas early in the morning,
And there he spied a pretty fair maid,
She was shearin' her fathers barley.

11. "The Laird o Drum"

Greig MSS., IV, p. 136. Sung by George Corbet, Weetingshill, New Deer.

a π^1

12. "The Laird o' Drum"

Greig MSS., I, p. 164. Sung by J. W. Spence, Rosecroft, Fyvie, April 1906.

a π^1

The Laird o' Drum has a huntin' gane
All in the mornin' early,
And 'twas then he spied a weel-faur'd maid;
She was shearin' her father's barley.

13. "The Laird o' Drum"

Greig and Keith, 1925, p. 185(1c); from Duncan MS., No. 442. Sung by Mrs. Matheson, Torphins.

a π^1

The laird o' Drum has a-wooin' gane
Oot in a mornin' early
An' there he spied a weel faur'd maid
She was shearin' her father's barley.

14. "The Laird o' Drum"

Greig MSS., I, p. 186. Collected by George Riddell, Rosehearty.

a I/M

The laird o' Drum was a-hunting gone,
All in a morning early,
And there he spied a weel faur'd maid
She wis shearin at her barley.

15. "The Laird o' Drum"

Greig MSS., III, p. 146; text, Bk. 742, XXXII, p. 32. Also in Greig and Keith, 1925, p. 185(1a). Sung by Miss Georgina Reid, Collieford, New Deer, December 1908.

a I/M

1. The Laird o' Drum has a huntin' gane,
'Twas in the mornin' early,
And there he spied a weel-faured maid,
She was shearin' her father's barley.

2. "Oh wad ye fancy me, fair maid,
Or lat your shearin' be O?
Or wad ye be the Lady o' Drum
An' gang alang wi' me O?"

3. I wadna fancy you, kind sir,
Nor lat my shearin' be O,
I wadna be the Lady o' Drum,
Nor gang alang wi' you O,

4. My father he is an auld shepherd carle,
Herdin' sheep on yon high hill O,
An' ye can gang an' get his consent,
I dae a' thing by his will O,

5. He's gane up to her father dear,
Herdin' sheep on yon high hill O,
Says, "I've fa'en in love wi' your ae daughter,
An' oh but I like her weel O,"

6. "She canna wear your silken goons,
That reestle at her heels O,
But weel can she wear the colour o' the ewes,
For it sets her body weel O,

7. "She canna wash your cheeny cups,
Nor cook ye a cup o' tea O,
But weel can she milk your cows & your ewes
Wi' the cogie on her knee O,

8. "She will gang to your barn & she'll winnie your corn,
She will gang to the mill & the kiln O,
In the time o' need she will saddle your steed,
And she'll clean your boots hersel' O.

9. "She can neither read nor write,
She was never brought up at schule O,
But a' ither kinds o' work she can dae,
For I learned the lassie mysel' O."

10. "Oh wha will bake my bridal bread?
Or wha will brew my ale O?
Or wha will welcome my bonnie lady in,
It's mair than I can tell O,"

11. "The baker will bake your bridal bread,
And the brewer will brew your ale O,
And wha wad welcome your bonnie lady in,
If ye didna dae't yersel' O?"

12. Four & twenty lairds & lords
Stood a' at the gates o' Drum O,
But nane o' them put their hand to their hat,
To welcome the bonnie Lady in O.

13. "If ye had been come o' as high kin
As ye are o' low degree O,
Ye micht hae ridden in your carriage & steed,
But ye canna gang wi' me O."

14. "Yestreen I was the shepherd's daughter,
Herdin' sheep on yon high hill O,
But the nicht I am the Lady o' Drum,
And I'd scorn for to carry your keys O.

15. "An ye were dead an' I were dead
And seven lang years in the grun' O,
I think it wad tak' ane wi' fey clear e'en
To ken your dust by mine O.

16. "When Adam & Eve in the Garden o' Eden
Were eating the forbidden tree O,
Whare was a' your gentry then?
I am jist as good as ye O[.]"

16. "The Laird o' Drum"

Sung by Ewan MacColl, Riverside rec. No. RLP 12-621(A3), ed. K. S. Goldstein. Learned from his father.

a π^1

The text was learned in fragmentary form and collated with Greig's variants.

17. "The Laird o Drum"

Greig and Keith, 1925, p. 185(1d); from Duncan MS., No. 466. Sung by Isaac Troup, Ythanwells, who learned it 40 years before (c. 1860?).

a π^1

The laird o Drum went oot to woo
Twas in a mornin' early
And there he spied a weel faur'd maid
She was shearin' at the barley.

18. "The Laird o Drum"

Greig MSS., IV, p. 28. Also in Greig and Keith, 1925, p. 186(1f). Sung by Mrs. Dunbar, Longhill, Crimond.

a π^1

19. "The Laird o Drum"

Greig and Keith, 1925, p. 186(1e); from Duncan MS., No. 494. Sung by Miss M. A. Dalgarno, Laurencekirk.

m I

The Laird o Drum is a huntin' gane
A-hunting one morning early
When who did he spy but a bonny fair maid
She was shearin her father's barley.

GROUP B

20. "Laird o' Drum"

Greig-Duncan MS. 785 (Walker transcript), p. 159; from Duncan MS., No. 104. Sung by Frank Christie, Cluny.

p π^1

21. "The Laird o' Drum"

Archive, School of Scottish Studies. Sung by Willie Mathieson, Banffshire. Collected by Hamish Henderson for the School of Scottish Studies; transcribed by Francis M. Collinson.

p π^1

1. The Laird o' Drum's a-hunting gane
   All in the morning early;
   Wha did he spy but a weel faured maid
   Shearin her father's barley.

2. 'Ts my bonny maid, my weel faured maid,
   Oh will ye fancy me O,
   And will ye come an' be Lady o' Drum
   And lat your shearin' be O.

3. I winna fancy you kind sir
   Nor lat my shearin' be O,
   Nor will I come and be Lady o' Drum
   And your miss I'd scorn to be O.

4. It's o ye'll cast off that gown o grey
   Put on the silk and scarlet,
   And ye shall come and be Lady o' Drum
   And be neither miss nor harlot.

5. 'Ts ye're silken gowns I canna wear,
   They would rustle at my heels O,
   I would rather the colour o' my yowe
   —It sets my body weel O.

6. Your china cups I canna wash,
   Nor mask a cup o' tea O,
   But I can milk my daddy's yowes
   Wi my cogie on my knee O.

7. 'Ts yonder stands my old father
   Keeps sheep on yonder hill O.
   What he says, or bids me do,
   I work aye at his will O.

8. He's taen her to the auld shepherd
   Keeps sheep on yonder hill O;
   I'm come to marry your ae dochter,
   If you'll gie me your guidwill O.

9. My dochter can neither read nor write
   She was ne'er brought up at school O,
   But ony other thing she can do it very weel—
   I learned the girl mysel O.

10. She'll thrash in your barn and winnow your corn
    And gang to the mill and kiln O;
    In time o' need she will saddle your white steed
    She'll draw aff your beets hersel O.

11. I'll learn the lassie to read and write,
    And put her to the school O;
    But she'll never need to saddle my steed—
    I'll draw aff my boots mysel O.

12. But wha will bake my bridal bread
    Or brew my bridal ale O,
    Or wha will welcome my lady in
    Is mair nor I can tell O.

13. The baker will bake your bridal bread,
    The brewer will brew your ale O,
    And for to welcome your lady hame
    I think you're fittest yersel O.

14. There was four and twenty Lords and Lairds
    Stood at the gates o' Drum O,
    But neen o' them a' pit their hands to their hats
    To welcome the Lady in O.

15. But he's taen her by the milk white hand
    And he's led her through the hall O,
    And he's gien her the keys of ilka room,
    And he's made her the Lady o' Drum O.

16. Out then spake his brither John,
    Says ye've dane us muckle wrang O,
    Ye've married a wife below your degree—
    It's a mock to all our kin O.

17. Then oot spake the Laird o' Drum
    Says, I've deen ye nae great wrang O.
    I've married a wife to win my bread,
    Ye've married een to spend O.

18. The first time that I married a wife
    She was far abune my degree O,
    I couldna enter the room where she was
    But with my hat below my knee O.

19. When they had eaten and weel drunken
    And a' were bound for bed O
    The Laird o' Drum and the lady fair
    In ae bed they were laid O.

20. Gin ye had been o' high renown
    As ye are o' low degree O
    We micht hae baith gane doon the street
    Amang guid company O.

21. I taul ye weel ere we were wed
    Ye were far abune my degree O
    But noo we are married and in ae bed laid
    I'm jist as guid as ye O.

22. When Adam and Eve our first parents
    Did eat the forbidden tree O
    Oh where were all your gentry then?
    I'm jist as guid as ye O.

23. Gin I were dead and you were dead
    And baith laid in one grave O
    When seven lang years hae gane an' come
    They'll nae ken your dust by mine O.

GROUP C

22. "The Laird o Drum"

Greig MSS., II, p. 145. Also in Greig and Keith, 1925, p. 186(2). Sung by Mrs. Fowlie, Bonnykelly, New Deer, September 1907.

a π^2

I canna wash your china cups,
Nor I canna mak your tea, O,
But weel can I milk my daddie's coo,
Wi' the cogie on my knee, O.

GROUP D

23. "The Laird o Drum"

Greig MSS., I, p. 150; text, Bk. 716, VI, p. 1. Also in Greig and Keith, 1925, p. 186(3). Sung by Miss Annie Ritchie, Whitehill, March 1906.

p M

1. The Laird o' Drum is a huntin' gone
A' in a mornin' early
There he spied a weel faured maid
She was shearin' her father's barley.

2. Will ye gang wi' me he said
And let your sheerin' be o'
Or will ye gang and be Lady o' Drum
Or will ye fancy one o'.

3. I canna gang wi' you she said
Nor lat my shearin' be o'
For I'm owre low to be Lady o' Drum
And you'r miss I'd scorn to be o'

4. I canna wash your cheena cups
Nor mak a cup o' tea o'
But weel can I milk oor ewe
Wi' the cogie on my knee o'

5. I'll shak your barn, I'll winnow your corn
I'll gang to mull or kiln o'
In the oor o' need, I'll paddle your steed
And I'll dry your boots mysel o'.

6. I canna wear your silken dress
It scarce come to my knee o'
But weel can I the colour o' the ewe
For It sets my body weel o'.

7. But fa will bake my bridal bread
And brew my bridal ale o'
Fa'll welcome my bonnie bridie hame
It's mair nor I can tell o'.

8. O I can bake your bridal bread
And brew your bridal ale o'
And fa' can welcome your bonnie bridie hame
I think ye're fittest yoursel' o'.

9. There were four & twenty lairds & lords
Stood at the gates o' Drum o'
And in the ha' amo' them a'
He styled her the Lady o' Drum o'.

10. When a' had eaten and a' had drunk
And all were bound for bed o'
The Laird o' Drum and the shepherd's daughter
Both in one bed were laid o'.

11. And ye had been as guid as me
As guid as me said he o'
We might have been in the high parlour
Among good company o'.

12. I told you long ere you wedded me
I was far below your degree o'
But now since we're in one beddie laid
Ye'll be forced to be daen wi' me o'.

13. Wasn't Adam & Eve, our first parents
When they eat the forbidden tree o'
Waur was a' oor gentry then
Am not I as good as they

14. Gin you & I were seven years deid
And both dug up again o'.
I think they wid see wi' a very clear e'e
That wid ken your mould by mine o'.

GROUP E

24. "The Laird of Drum"

Kinloch, 1827, App'x. to p. 199; text, p. 200.

a D (?); or (assuming F♯) a M

See the headnote above for this variant (E).

236. THE LAIRD O DRUM

1. The Laird o' Drum is a-wooing gane,
It was on a morning early,
And he has fawn in wi' a bonnie may
A-shearing at her barley.

2. "My bonnie may, my weel-faur'd may,
O will ye fancy me, O;
And gae and be the Lady o' Drum,
And lat your shearing abee, O."

3. "It's I canna fancy thee, kind sir,
I winna fancy thee, O,
I winna gae and be Lady o' Drum,
And lat my shearing abee, O.

4. "But set your love on anither, kind sir,
Set it not on me, O,
For I am not fit to be your bride,
And your hure I'll never be, O.

5. "My father he is a shepherd mean,
Keeps sheep on yonder hill, O,
And ye may gae and speir at him,
For I am at his will, O."

6. Drum is to her father gane,
Keeping his sheep on yon hill, O;
And he has gotten his consent
That the may was at his will, O.—

7. "But my dochter can neither read nor write,
She was ne'er brought up at scheel, O;
But weel can she milk cow and ewe,
And mak a kebbuck weel, O.

8. "She'll win in your barn at bear-seed time,
Cast out your muck at Yule, O,
She'll saddle your steed in time o' need,
And draw aff your boots hersell, O."

9. "Have not I no clergymen?
Pay I no clergy fee, O?
I'll scheel her as I think fit,
And as I think weel to be, O.

10. "I'll learn your lassie to read and write,
And I'll put her to the scheel, O;
She'll neither need to saddle my steed,
Nor draw aff my boots hersell, O.

11. "But wha will bake my bridal bread,
Or brew my bridal ale, O;
And wha will welcome my bonnie bride,
Is mair than I can tell, O."

12. Drum is to the hielands gane,
For to mak a' ready,
And a' the gentry round about,
Cried, "Yonder's Drum and his lady!

13. "Peggy Coutts is a very bonnie bride,
And Drum is a wealthy laddie,
But he micht hae chosen a hier match,
Than onie shepherd's lassie."

14. Then up bespak his brither John,
Says, "Ye've deen us meikle wrang, O,
Ye've married een below our degree,
A lake to a' our kin, O."

15. "Hold your tongue, my brither John,
I have deen you na wrang, O,
For I've married een to wirk and win,
And ye've married een to spend O.

16. "The first time that I had a wife,
She was far abeen my degree, O;
I durst na come in her presence,
But wi' my hat upo' my knee, O.

17. "The first wife that I did wed,
She was far abeen my degree, O,
She wadna hae walk'd to the yetts o' Drum
But the pearls abeen her bree, O.

18. "But an she was ador'd for as much gold,
As Peggy's for beautie, O,
She micht walk to the yetts o' Drum
Amang gueed companie, O."

19. There war four and twenty gentlemen
Stood at the yetts o' Drum, O,
There was na ane amang them a'
That welcom'd his lady in, O.

20. He has tane her by the milk-white hand,
And led her in himsel, O,
And in thro' ha's, and in thro' bouers,—
"And ye're welcome, Lady o' Drum, O."

21. Thrice he kissed her cherry cheek,
And thrice her cherry chin, O;
And twenty times her comely mou',—
"And ye're welcome, Lady o' Drum, O.

22. "Ye sall be cook in my kitchen,
Butler in my ha', O;
Ye sall be lady in my command,
Whan I ride far awa, O."—

23. "But I told ye afore we war wed,
I was owre low for thee, O;
But now we are wed, and in ae bed laid,
And ye maun be content wi' me, O:

24. "For an I war dead, and ye war dead,
And baith in ae grave laid, O,
And ye and I war tane up again,
Wha could distan your mouls frae mine, O?"

APPENDIX

25. "As I went out ae May morning"

Johnson, IV [1792], No. 397, p. 410 (repr. 1853). From Robert Burns.

p I, ending on *VI* (inflected IV)

1. As I went out, ae May morning,
 A May morning it chanc'd to be;
 There I was aware of a weelfar'd maid
 Cam linkin o'er the lea to me.

2. O but she was a weelfar'd maid,
 The boniest lass that's under the sun;
 I spier'd gin she could fancy me,
 But her answer was, I am too young.

3. To be your bride I am too young,
 To be your loun wad shame my kin,
 So therefore pray young man begone,
 For you never, never shall my favour win.

4. But amang yon birks and hawthorns green,
 Where roses blaw and woodbines hing,
 O there I learn'd my bonie lass,
 That she was not a single hour too young.

5. The lassie blushed, the lassie sigh'd,
 And the tear stood twinklin in her e'e;
 O kind Sir, since ye hae done me this wrang,
 It's pray when will ye marry me.

6. It's of that day tak ye nae heed,
 For that's a day ye ne'er shall see;
 For ought that pass'd between us twa,
 Ye had your share as weel as me.

7. She wrang her hands, she tore her hair,
 She cried out most bitterlie,
 O what will I say to my mammie
 When I gae hame wi' my big bellie!

8. O as ye maut, so maun ye brew,
 And as ye brew, so maun ye tun;
 But come to my arms, my ae bonnie lass,
 For ye never shall rue what ye now hae done!

26. "The Laird and the Shepherd's Daughter"

Barry, Eckstorm and Smyth, 1929, p. 300. Sung by Mrs. James McGill, Chamcook, N.B., 1928; learned in Scotland. Noted by George Herzog.

a D

1. It's up yon wild an' lonely glen,
 Beside, there's many a lofty mountain,
 'Twas there I spied a bonnie lass
 Ae day as I rode oot a huntin'.

2. Her face was fair, her heart was true,
 Her features they were comely, slender,
 Her dooncast looks an' sparklin' ee
 Has cast my heart nae mair tae wander.

3. Says I, "Fair lass, whaur is thy hame?
 In maire or dell, pray tell me whither?"
 "Kind sir, I tent my fleecy flocks
 That feed amang the bonny heather."

4. "It's wull ye wed the laird o Drum
 And sleep wi' him on a bed o' feathers?
 Ye'll wear fine silks an' satins braw,
 An' be the flower amang the heather."

5. "O it's deed, kin' sir, your offer's fair,
 I really think wi' me ye're jokin',
 For ye are sure some rich man's heir,
 An' I a lowly shepherd's daughter."

6. "It's true, I am my faither's heir,
 But he can ne'er control my fancy;
 For it's herdin' sheep on yon hill side
 I'll gang wi' you, my lovely Nancy."

The Duke of Gordon's Daughter

CHILD NO. 237

FORMALLY, this ballad is somewhat anomalous, possibly unique. Other ballads which have a feminine ending on lines one and three are clearly dactylic or anapaestic, and generally (I believe) go to triple-time tunes of twelve bars instead of the usual sixteen. The evidence of the tune-variants seems to prove that basically the present ballad is metrically of the same kind, and should be read as six-stress couplets (or three-stress quatrains). But the melodic tradition is clearly one, and none of the variants is in triple time: all are duple, either 2/4 or 4/4. The verbal rhythm is thus treated as containing a good many consecutive unstressed syllables, as may be seen if some of the lines are read with only three stresses:

Till Lady Jéan fell in lóve with Captain Ógilvie,
And awáy with hím she would gáe.

In one variant in 2/4 (Greig's 1d; variant 6 below), the singer evidently found it necessary to insert an extra bar in the third phrase in order to accommodate so long a line. The result was a tune of thirteen bars instead of the regular twelve. Of the variants in common time, three are eight-bar tunes, a half-bar being added to each phrase-ending. The secondary accents are thus brought into prominence, and the usual CM or ballad-metre is the result. But in a fourth case (variant 9), there are but seven bars. This situation appears to have arisen from the singer's having swung uncertainly between two possibilities, the first-phrase cadence being held for the extra half-bar, the second and third not.

All the tunes collected belong to the same family, but may be sub-divided into three groups for present purposes. The first is plagal, the second authentic by means of lessening the characteristic octave plunge of the earlier forms. These variants all properly belong to the D/Æ or Æolian field, but the oldest copies are given the leading-note instead of a flattened seventh. Greig's hypermetrical copy, 1d, is also singular in deserting the usual pattern for its mid-cadence and final cadence; and one is tempted to see it as an authentic Dorian (really M/D) variant ending on the fifth.

The third sub-group is composed of two authentic tunes, one major, the other I/M. These also have lost the octave drop, and the latter variant ends on the upper octave.

Burns left a note in his interleaved copy of Johnson's *Museum* to the effect that the present ballad was sung to the tune of "Ewe-buchts Marion" (reprinted here as appendix for comparison; for other early references, cf. Dick, ed., *The Songs of Robert Burns*, 1903, p. 371). Stenhouse has a comment on Burns's assertion: "The words of the ballad are no doubt sometimes sung to the air of *Ewe-bughts Marion*, in the south of Scotland; but it is owing to their ignorance of the original air to which the ballad is uniformly sung in the North. Mr. Clarke took down the air as it was chanted by a lady of his acquaintance, and thus restored the ballad to its original tune. The words and music first appeared together in print in the Museum" (*Museum*, 1853, IV [Stenhouse, *Illustrations*], No. 419, p. 378). Although most extant copies of "Ewe-buchts" are not easily confused with the ballad-tune, there are resemblances which might facilitate an exchange between the later form of "Ewe-buchts" (e.g., *Museum*, No. 85) and the ballad-tune, particularly the octave-skips and the metrical kinship. As pointed out earlier, the "Ewe-buchts" tune has also something of "Lizie Lindsay" in it (cf. Child No. 226).

Glen thinks little of the present tune, at least in its *Museum* form, which he calls "a silly chant" (*Early Scottish Melodies*, 1900, p. 192). He suggests that possibly a tune in Wm. McGibbon's second *Collection of Scots Tunes*, 1746, entitled "Gordon Castle," may have been the original melody for the ballad. This is a pure wishful guess.

There is, according to the Gray-Muir MS. (NL Scotland MS. 2254), a tune in Bunyan MS., 1877, p. 83.

LIST OF VARIANTS

GROUP Aa

1. "The Duke of Gordon has three daughters." James Johnson, *The Scots Musical Museum*, V [1796], No. 419, p. 431 (repr. 1853).
2. "The Duke o' Gordon's Daughter." Lady John Scott's MS., National Library of Scotland MS. 840.
3. "The Duke of Gordon has three Daughters." Robert Archibald Smith, *The Scotish Minstrel* [1820-24], IV, p. 98. Also in Joseph Ritson, *Scotish Songs*, ed. of 1869, II, p. 507.
4. "The Duke of Gordon's Daughters." Greig MSS., II, p. 9, and Bk. 715, V, p. 62, King's College Library, Aberdeen. Also in Gavin Greig and Alexander Keith, *Last Leaves of Traditional Ballads and Ballad Airs*, 1925, p. 189(1b). (Milne)
5. "The Duke of Gordon's three Daughters." W. Christie, *Traditional Ballad Airs*, I, 1876, p. 4.
6. "The Duke of Gordon's Daughters." Greig and Keith, *Last Leaves*, 1925, p. 189(1d). From Duncan MS., No. 338. (Harper)

GROUP Ab

7. "The Duke of Gordon's Daughters." Greig and Keith, 1925, pp. 189(1a) and 187. From Duncan MS., No. 14. (Gillespie and Duncan)
8. "The Duke of Gordon's Daughters." Greig and Keith, 1925, p. 189(2). From Duncan MS., No. 391. (Lyall)
9. "The Duke o' Gordon's Daughter." Greig MSS., IV, p. 23. Also in Greig and Keith, 1925, p. 189(1c). (Johnstone)
10. (Untitled.) Greig MSS., I, p. 6. (J.S.S.)
11. "The Duke of Gordon's Daughters." Miss M. Douglas Gordon (singer), Archive, School of Scottish Studies, University of Edinburgh.

GROUP AC

12. "The Lord of Gordon's three Daughters." Christie, *Traditional Ballad Airs*, I, 1876, p. 2.

13. "The Duke of Gordon's Daughters." Greig and Keith, *Last Leaves*, 1925, p. 190(3). From Duncan MS., No. 418. (Troup)

APPENDIX

14. "Duke of Gordon's Daughters." W. Thomson, *Orpheus Caledonius*, 1733, II, opp. p. 32.

TUNES WITH TEXTS

GROUP Aa

1. "The Duke of Gordon has three daughters"

Johnson, V [1796], No. 419, p. 431 (repr. 1853).

p Minor (–VI)

1. The Duke of Gordon has three daughters
 Elizabeth, Margaret, and Jean;
They would na' stay in bonny Castle Gordon,
 But they would go to bonny Aberdeen.

2. They had not been in Aberdeen
 A twelvemonth and a day,
Till lady Jean fell in love with cap[t]. Ogilvie,
 And away with him she would gae.

3. Word came to the duke of Gordon,
 In the chamber where he lay,
Lady Jean has fell in love with cap[t]. Ogilvie,
 And away with him she would gae.

4. "Go saddle me the black horse,
 And you'll ride on the grey;
And I will ride to bonny Aberdeen,
 Where I have been many a day."

5. They were not a mile from Aberdeen,
 A mile but only three,
Till he met with his two daughters walking,
 But away was lady Jean.

6. "Where is your sister, maidens?
 Where is your sister, now?
Where is your sister, maidens,
 That she is not walking with you?"

7. "O pardon us, honoured father,
 O pardon us, they did say;
Lady Jean is with captain Ogilvie,
 And away with him she will gae."

8. And when he came to Aberdeen,
 And down upon the green,
There did he see captain Ogilvie,
 Training up his men.

9. "O wo to you, captain Ogilvie,
 And an ill death thou shalt die;
For taking to my daughter,
 Hanged thou shalt be."

10. Duke Gordon has wrote a broad letter,
 And sent it to the king,
To cause hang captain Ogilvie,
 If ever he hanged a man.

11. "I will not hang captain Ogilvie,
 For no lord that I see;
But I'll cause him to put off the lace & scarlet,
 And put on the single livery."

12. Word came to captain Ogilvie,
 In the chamber where he lay,
To cast off the gold lace and scarlet,
 And put on the single livery.

13. "If this be for bonny Jeany Gordon,
 This pennance I'll take wi';
If this be for bonny Jeany Gordon,
 All this I will dree."

14. Lady Jean had not been married,
 Not a year but three,
Till she had a babe in every arm,
 Another upon her knee.

15. "O but I'm weary of wandering!
 O but my fortune is bad!
It sets not the duke of Gordon's daughter
 To follow a soldier lad. &c. &c. &c.

The *Museum* text, as Child notes, is taken from Joseph Ritson's *Scotish Songs*, 1794, II, pp. 169ff. It ends at stanza 15, but the other, printed from garland or broadside, and without music, continued as follows:

16. "O but I'm weary of wandering!
 O but I think lang!
It sets not the duke of Gordon's daughter
 To follow a single man."

17. When they came to the Highland hills,
 Cold was the frost and snow;
Lady Jean's shoes they were all torn,
 No farther could she go.

18. "O! wo to the hills and the mountains!
 Wo to the wind and the rain!
My feet is sore with going barefoot,
 No further am I able to gang.

19. "Wo to the hills and the mountains!
 Wo to the frost and the snow!
My feet is sore with going barefoot,
 No farther am I able for to go."

20. "O! if I were at the glens of Foudlen,
 Where hunting I have been,
I would find the way to bonny Castle-Gordon,
 Without either stockings or shoon."

21. When she came to Castle-Gordon,
 And down upon the green,
The porter gave out a loud shout,
 O yonder comes lady Jean.

22. "O you are welcome, bonny Jeany Gordon,
 You are dear welcome to me;
You are welcome, dear Jeany Gordon,
 But away with your captain Ogilvie."

23. Now over seas went the captain,
 As a soldier under command;
A message soon followed after,
 To come and heir his brother's land.

24. "Come home, you pretty captain Ogilvie,
 And heir your brother's land;
Come home, ye pretty captain Ogilvie,
 Be earl of Northumberland."

25. O! what does this mean? says the captain,
 Where's my brother's children three?
"They are dead and buried,
 And the lands they are ready for thee."

26. "Then hoist up your sails, brave captain,
 Let's be jovial and free;
I'll to Northumberland, and heir my estate,
 Then my dear Jeany I'll see."

27. He soon came to Castle-Gordon,
 And down upon the green;
The porter gave out with a loud shout,
 Here comes captain Ogilvie.

28. "You're welcome, pretty captain Ogilvie,
 Your fortune's advanced I hear;
No stranger can come unto my gates,
 That I do love so dear."

29. "Sir, the last time I was at your gates,
 You would not let me in;
I'm come for my wife and children,
 No friendship else I claim."

30. "Come in, pretty captain Ogilvie,
 And drink of the beer and the wine;
And thou shalt have gold and silver,
 To count till the clock strike nine."

31. "I'll have none of your gold and silver,
 Nor none of your white money;
But I'll have bonny Jeany Gordon,
 And she shall go now with me."

32. Then she came tripping down the stair,
 With the tear into her eye;
One babe was at her foot,
 Another upon her knee.

33. "You're welcome, bonny Jeany Gordon,
 With my young family;
Mount and go to Northumberland,
 There a countess thou shall be."

2. "The Duke o' Gordon's Daughter"

Lady John Scott's MS., NL Scotland MS. 840.

p Minor

1. The Duke o' Gordon has three Daughters
Elizabeth Margaret & Jean
They wadna bide in bonnie Castle Gordon
But they wad awa to Aberdeen

2. They hadna been in bonnie Aberdeen
But a twelve month & a day
The lady Jean, fell in love wi Capt Ogilvie
An awa wi him she wad gae

3. Word has come to the Duke o' Gordon
In the chamber where he lay
Lady Jean fa'en in love wi Capt Ogilvy
An' awa wi him she maun gae

4. The Duke rade awa frae bonnie Aberdeen
Within a mile but ane
Till he met his twa daughters walking
But awa was Lady Jean.

5. Whar is yr sister maidens tell me
Whaur is your sister now
Whar is your sister maidens tell me
That she is na walking wi you

6. Oh pardon us my honoured father
Oh pardon us they did say
Lady Jean is married to Capt Ogilvie
An awa wi' him she wad gae

7. Duke Gordon has written an angry letter
An sent it to the King
To cause him to hang up Capt Ogilvie
If ever he hanged a man.

8. I will not hang up Capt Ogilvie
For nae Lord that I see
But Ill cause him to put off the gowd lace & scarlet
An' put on the single livery

9. Word has come to Capt Ogilvie
In the chamber where he lay
To cast off the gowd lace & scarlet
An' put on single Livery

10. If this be for bonnie Jeannie Gordon
All this & muir I will dree
If this be for bonnie Jeannie Gordon
This penance Ill tak wi'.

11. Lady Jean she had na been married
Not a year, but only three
Till she had a bairn in every arm
& a third rinning at her knee.

12. Oh but I'm weary o' wandering
Oh but my fortune it is bad
It little sits the Duke O' Gordons daughter
To follow a soger lad

The text appears to derive, through imperfect memory, from the *Museum* copy preceding.

3. "The Duke of Gordon has three Daughters"

Smith [1820-24], IV, p. 98. Also in Ritson, ed. of 1869, II, p. 507.

p Minor

The duke of Gordon has three daughters,
Elizabeth, Margaret, and Jean;
They would na stay in bonnie castle Gordon,
But they would go to bonnie Aberdeen.

They had not been in Aberdeen
A twelvemonth and a day,
Till lady Jean fell in love with Capt. Ogilvie,
And away with him she would gae.

Etc., as in the *Museum*, without significant alteration.

4. "The Duke of Gordon's Daughters"

Greig MSS., II, p. 9; text, Bk. 715, V, p. 62. Also in Greig and Keith, 1925, p. 189(1b). Sung by Mrs. Milne, New Deer, May 1906.

m D/Æ

The Duke o' Gordon had three pretty daughters
Lizbeth, Marget, & Jean,
They wadna stay at Castle Gordon
They boud be in Bonnie Aiberdeen.

They hadna been in bonnie Aiberdeen
A Twelvemonth & a day
Till Jeannie Gordon fell in love wi' Captain Noble
And awa' wi' him she gae.

Oh but I'm weary wanderin',
Oh but my fortune's been bad
It sets not the Duke o' Gordon's daughter
To follow a sodger lad.

If I were at the bonnie hills o' Foudlan,
Where mony merry nichts I have been
I wad get the road tae Castle Gordon
Without either stockins or sheen.

5. "The Duke of Gordon's three Daughters"

Christie, I, 1876, p. 4. From Buchan and Banffshire tradition.

m D/Æ (Dorian VI in 2nd strain)

The Duke of Gordon has three daughters,
Elizabeth, Margaret, and Jean;
They would not stay in bonny Castle Gordon,
But they would go to bonny Aberdeen.
They had not been in Aberdeen,
A twelvemonth and a day,
Till Jean fell in love with Captain Ogilvie,
And away with him she would gae.
[*Etc.*]

Christie took his text from Ritson's *Scotish Songs*, omitting seven stanzas.

6. "The Duke of Gordon's Daughters"

Greig and Keith, 1925, p. 189(1d); from Duncan MS., No. 338. Sung by Mrs. Harper, Cluny; learned from her mother.

p D/Æ

GROUP Ab

7. "The Duke of Gordon's Daughters"

Greig and Keith, 1925, p. 189(1a); text, p. 187. From Duncan MS., No. 14. Sung by Mrs. Gillespie and George F. Duncan; learned from their parents, c. 1885.

a D/Æ

1. The Duke o Gordon had three bonnie daughters,
   Eliza, Marget, an' Jean,
An' they widna stay at Castle Gordon,
   But went to bonnie Aberdeen.

2. They hadna been in bonnie Aberdeen
   A year but an' a day,
Lady Jean's fa'en in love wi Captain Ogilvie,
   An' from him she winna stay.

3. Word cam to the Duke o Gordon,
   In the chamber where he lay,
That Lady Jean's fa'en in love wi Captain Ogilvie,
   An' from him she winna stay.

4. "Go saddle to me the black horse,
   Yoursel ride on the grey,
An' we'll reach bonnie Aberdeen
   By the dawnin o the day."

5. They were not a mile from bonnie Aberdeen,
   A mile but barely three,
When the Duke met his twa daughters
   To bear him company.

6. "Where is your sister, maidens?"
   He unto them did say;—
"Lady Jean's fa'en in love wi Captain Ogilvie,
   An' from him she winna stay.

7. "O pardon, O pardon us, father,
   O pardon us," they did say;
"Lady Jean's fa'en in love wi Captain Ogilvie,
   An' awa wi him she did gae."

8. When he cam to bonnie Aberdeen,
   An' stood upon the green,
An' there he saw Captain Ogilvie
   A-trainin o his men.

9. "O woe be to you, Captain Ogilvie,
   An ill death may ye dee,
For takin to you my daughter
   High hangit ye shall be."

10. The Duke he wrote a broad letter,
   An' sent it to the King,
Said, "Ye'll cause hang Captain Ogilvie
   If ever ye hanged a man."

11. "I will not hang Captain Ogilvie
   For nae lord that I see;
I'll cause him put off the lace an' scarlet,
   An' put on single livery."

12. Word cam to bonnie Captain Ogilvie
   In his chamber where he lay,
To put off the lace an' scarlet,
   An' don the single livery.

13. "If this be for bonnie Jeanie Gordon,
   A' this an' mair wid I dree;
If this be for bonnie Jeanie Gordon,
   It's thrice welcome to me."

14. Lady Jean had not been married
   Years but only three,
When she had twa babies at her fit
   An' anither on her knee.

15. "O but I'm weary wanderin,
   O but I think lang:
It ill sets the Duke o Gordon's daughter
   To follow a single man.

16. "Woe to the hills an' the mountains,
   Woe to the frost an' snow,
My shoes an' stockins are a' torn,
   Nae farther can I go.

17. "But O, gin I were at the bonnie hills o Foudland,
   Faur mony merry days I hae been,
I wid get the road to Castle Gordon
   Without either stockins or sheen."

18. When she cam to bonnie Castle Gordon,
   An' stood upon the green,
The porter let oot a loud huzza,
   "Here comes our Lady Jean."

19. "O ye're welcome hame, Jeanie Gordon,
   You an' your bairnies three;
Ye're welcome here, Jeanie Gordon,
   But awa wi your Ogilvie."

20. Now over the seas went the Captain,
   As a soldier under command;
A message soon followed after
   To come an' heir his brother's land.

21. "Come hame, come hame, Captain Ogilvie,
   An' heir your brother's land,
Come hame, ye pretty Captain Ogilvie,
   An' be Earl o Northumberland."

22. "O what does this mean, Captain,
   Where are my brother's children three?"—
"They are a' deid an' buried,
   Northumberland is waitin for thee."

23. "Then hoist up your sails," said the Captain,
   "An' let us be joyful an' free,
For I'll to Northumberland an' heir my estates,
   An' then my dear Jeanie I will see."

24. When he cam to bonnie Castle Gordon,
   An' stood upon the green,
He was the prettiest young man
   That ever they had seen.

25. "Ye're welcome here, Captain Ogilvie,
Ye're thrice welcome to me,
Ye're welcome here, Captain Ogilvie,
To your wife an' bairnies three."

26. "The last time I was at your gates
Ye widna let me in;
I am come for my wife an' my children,
Nae ither friendship I claim."

27. "Come in, my pretty Captain Ogilvie,
Drink the red beer an' the wine,
An' we'll count ye oot gold an' silver
Until that the clock strikes nine."

28. "I winna come in," said the Captain,
"I'll drink neither your red beer nor wine,
I want neither your gold nor your silver,
I've enough in Northumberland."

29. Down the stairs cam bonnie Jeanie Gordon,
The tears were blindin her ee,
Down cam bonnie Jeanie Gordon
Wi her bairnies three.

30. "Ye're welcome, my bonnie Jeanie Gordon,
You an' my young family;
We'll haste an' go to Northumberland,
An' a countess ye shall be."

8. "The Duke of Gordon's Daughters"

Greig and Keith, 1925, p. 189(2); from Duncan MS., No. 391. Sung by Mrs. Lyall, Skene.

a D/Æ

Ah haud yer tongue Jeannie Gordon
Oh haud yer tongue my doo
I've but ae half-croon in this wardle
I'll buy shoes and stockins [for you?]

9. "The Duke o' Gordon's Daughter"

Greig MSS., IV, p. 23. Also in Greig and Keith, 1925, p. 189(1c). Sung by John Johnstone, New Deer.

a D

Gin I were at the bonnie hills o' Foudlan'
Where aft times I hae been,
I wad gang to bonnie Castle Gordon,
Tho' I'd neither stockings nor sheen.

10. [Untitled]

Greig MSS., I, p. 6. From J.S.S., 1905.

m M/D

11. "The Duke of Gordon's Daughters"

Archive, School of Scottish Studies. Sung by Miss M. Douglas Gordon, 1953. Collected by Francis M. Collinson for the School of Scottish Studies; transcribed by the collector.

m I

The Duke of Gordon had three daughters
Elizabeth Margaret and Jane.
They wouldna stay in bonny . . . garden
But they would stay in Bonny Aberdeen.

They hadna been in bonny Aberdeen—
A twelve months and a day
Before Lady Jane fell in love with Captain Ogilvie,
And awa with him she would gae.

GROUP AC

12. [The Lord of Gordon's three Daughters]

Christie, I, 1876, p. 2. Tune sung by "a crazy man, 'Johnny Toll,'" the Enzie, Banffshire.

a I

The Lord of Gordon had three daughters,
Elizabeth, Marg'ret, and Jean;
They wou'dna stay at bonnie Castle Gordon,
But they'd on to bonnie Aberdeen.
They hadna been in bonnie Aberdeen
A twelvemonth and a day;
Till Jean fell in love wi' Captain Ogilvie,
And away wi' him she would gae.
[*Etc.*]

Christie's text is "from three traditional copies." It differs materially from Ritson's, however, only in the following lines, which constitute his eighth stanza, as sung, he says, in Banff and Moray:

"Oh, hold your tongue, bonnie Jeanie Gordon,
Oh, hold your tongue, my dow!
I hae but ae siller crown,
And I'll buy hose and shoon to you."
"Oh, coarse, coarse would be the stockings,
And coarser would be the shoon;
Oh, coarse, coarse would they baith be,
You would buy for ae siller crown.["]

13. "The Duke of Gordon's Daughters"

Greig and Keith, 1925, p. 190(3); from Duncan MS., No. 418. Sung by Isaac Troup, Ythanwells; learned from his grandfather (c. 1860?).

a I/M, ending on the octave

Gin I were at the bonnie Tents o Foudlan,
Where mony merry day I hae been,
I wid skip to bonnie Castle Gordon
Without any stockins an' sheen.

APPENDIX

14. [Duke of Gordon's Daughters]

Thomson, 1733, II, opp. p. 32 ("Ew-Bughts Marion").

a M, ending on the octave; or m I, ending on V

Glenlogie, or, Jean o Bethelnie

CHILD NO. 238

THE melodic tradition of this ballad is remarkably consistent. All the variants are of one tribe, all are in triple time, most are π^1, or all but pentatonic. Of two branches, the first is the steadiest. The first accent is always the tonic; the first cadence-point (really the middle of the tune) almost always on the second; the second half, or long phrase, invariably swings down from the tonic to the lower octave and back, like a hammock. An apparent exception is Christie's first tune (variant 18), which he causes to end on the fifth and gives a Mixolydian seventh for a grace; but these are surely editorial features. The second branch is D/Æ. R. A. Smith's copy (variant 20), which has been often reprinted, though not the most characteristic form, is written 6/8 but would be better in 3/4. It has suggestions, not only of other Scottish tunes, but of English also—e.g., "Spanish Ladies," "I will give my love an apple" (in its Æolian form)—and American might be added, e.g., "The Wagoner's Lad." Cf. also the ballad following this (No. 239).

Mrs. Harris's text (Child's D) was sung, according to a note in the Harris MS., to "Auld Rob Morris." That well-known tune has certainly something of this one in its veins, but the contour is nothing like a close variant of the established pattern here.

The question might arise, whether the D/Æ (R. A. Smith) variant arose by a simple relative minor translation of the π^1 tradition. This, it appears to me, it can hardly have done: a good deal more in the way of change seems to have gone into its modal transformation. But I am more doubtful about a recent copy (variant 21), of which the tonic is open to debate. It appears to me that this might be an artificial derivative of the Smith tune, and not the result of simple tradition.

LIST OF VARIANTS

GROUP A

1. "Bonnie Jean o' Bethelnie." W. Christie, *Traditional Ballad Airs*, I, 1876, p. 282.
2. "Bethelnie." Greig MSS., I, p. 109, King's College Library, Aberdeen. (Ritchie)
3. "Bethelnie." Greig MSS., I, pp. 27 and 50. (Knowles)
4. "Bethelnie." Greig MSS., III, p. 20. Also in Gavin Greig, *Rymour Club Miscellanea*, I (1910), p. 199. (Rae)
5. "Glenlogie." Greig MSS., III, p. 6, and Bk. 722, XII, p. 75. (McAllan)
6. "Glenlogie." Greig MSS., III, p. 107. (Milne)
7. "Glenlogie." Greig MSS., III, p. 177. (Mrs. Corbet)
8. "Bethelnie." Greig MSS., I, p. 109. (Morrison)
9. "Bethelnie." Greig MSS., IV, p. 137. Also in Gavin Greig and Alexander Keith, *Last Leaves of Traditional Ballads and Ballad Airs*, 1925, p. 192(a). (G. Corbet)
10. "Glenlogie." John Adams (singer), Archive, School of Scottish Studies, University of Edinburgh.
11. "Bethelnie." Greig MSS., III, p. 22. Also in Greig and Keith, *Last Leaves*, 1925, p. 192(b). (Angus)
12. "Glenlogie." John Strachan, Caedmon recording No. TC 1146(B1).
13. "Bethelnie." Greig MSS., I, p. 150. (Duncan)
14. "Glenlogie." Greig MSS., I, p. 50, and Bk. 719, IX, p. 46. Also in Greig-Duncan MS. 785 (transcription of W. Walker), King's College Library, Aberdeen. (Spence)
15. "Bethelnie." Greig MSS., IV, p. 23. (Johnstone)
16. "Bethelnie." Greig MSS., III, p. 122. (Thain)
17. "Glenlogie." Greig MSS., III, p. 62, and Bk. 716, VI, pp. 50 and [51a]. Also in Greig-Duncan MS. 785 (Walker). (Robb)
18. "Bonnie Jean o' Bethelnie." Christie, *Traditional Ballad Airs*, I, 1876, p. 54.
19. "Bethelnie." Greig MSS., II, p. 49. Also in Greig and Keith, *Last Leaves*, 1925, p. 192(c). (Stuart)

GROUP Ba

20. "Glenogie." Robert Archibald Smith, *The Scottish Minstrel* [1820-24], IV, p. 78. Also in Robert Maver, *Genuine Scottish Melodies*, 1866, No. 328, p. 164; Alfred Moffat, *The Minstrelsy of Scotland*, 2nd ed. [1896], p. 239; and George Eyre-Todd, *Ancient Scots Ballads* [1894], p. 112.

GROUP Bb

21. "Glenlogie." Miss M. Douglas Gordon (singer), Archive, School of Scottish Studies.

TUNES WITH TEXTS

GROUP A

1. "Bonnie Jean o' Bethelnie"

Christie, I, 1876, p. 282. Sung by a native of Monquhitter, 1836.

a π^1, ending on the octave

2. "Bethelnie"

Greig MSS., I, p. 109. Sung by Miss Annie Ritchie, Whitehill, February 1906.

a π^1, ending on the octave

Six hundred brave nobles,
Rode up the King's ha',
And bonnie Glenlogie
Was the flower o' them a'
And bonnie Glenlogie
Was the flower o' them a'.

3. "Bethelnie"

Greig MSS., I, pp. 27 and 50. Sung by J. D. Knowles, Buckie, 1904.

a π^1, ending on the octave

4. "Bethelnie"

Greig MSS., III, p. 20. Also in Greig, *Rymour Club Miscellanea*, I (1910), p. 199. Sung by Mrs. Rae, Burngrains, Banffshire, September 1907.

a π^1, ending on the octave

There were six and six ladies,
Sat in the Queen's ha';
Bonnie Jean o' Bethelnie
Was the floo'er o' them a'.

5. "Glenlogie"

Greig MSS., III, p. 6; text, Bk. 722, XII, p. 75. Sung by John McAllan, Shevado, New Deer.

a π^1, ending on the octave

1. There were six and six nobles
 Rode round Banchory fair
 But bonny Glenlogie
 Was flower that was there

2. There were nine & nine nobles
 Sat in the king's hall
 But bonny Glenlogie
 Was flower o'er them a'

3. Down came Jeanie Gordon
 She came tripping downstairs
 And she has faun sick wi' Glenlogie
 Above all that was there

4. She called on his footman
 As he passed by her side
 Says oh what's he that young man
 And where does he bide

5. His title is Glenlogie
 When he is from home
 But he of the grand Gordons
 And his name is Lord John

6. Glenlogie, Glenlogie
 You'll be constant and kind
 I've laid my love on you
 And I'll tell you my mind

7. He turned him round quickly
 As the Gordons do a'
 Says I thank you Jeanie Gordon
 But your tocher's owre sma.

8. She called on her maiden
 To make her a bed
 Wi' ribbons and napkins
 To tie up her head

9. And down came her father
 He came tripping down stairs
 Says oh what ails you Jeannie
 That you're lying there.

10. He's a nice little fellow
 With a dark rolling eye
 If I get not Glenlogie
 For him I will die

11. O hold your tongue Jeanie
 And give up your folly
 I'll lead you to Drumwhindle
 He has more gold than he

12. Oh hold your tongue father
 And let Jeannie be
 If I get not Glenlogie
 For him I will dee.

13. Her father had a chaplain
 A man o' great skill
He wrote a broad letter
 And he penned it weel

14. When Glenlogie got the letter
 He was among men
He gave a loud laugh
 Says oh what does she mean.

15. But ere Glenlogie read the letter
 The tears came down large
 What a pity a leal virgin
 Should die for my cause

16. You'll go saddle the black steed
 Go saddle the brown
For bonny Jeanie Gordon
 She'll be deid or I win.

17. Or they got them saddled
 And down by yon green
 Bonny Glenlogie
He was three miles him leen

18. When they came to Bethelnie
 There was nobody there
But ae bonny lassie
 She was combing her hair

19. He said "Bonny lassie
 You'll take me by the hand
And lead me to the chamber
 Jeannie Gordon lies in.[")]

20. Oh pale and wan was she
 When Glenlogie came in
But red and rosy grew she
 Or Glenlogie got ben

21. Oh where's your pain Jeannie,
 Does it lie in your head
The pain that ye be under
 Does it lie in your side

22. Oh no no Glenlogie
 You're far from the part
The pain that I lie under
 It lies in my heart.

23. You'll turn you round Jeanie
 Turn to your right side
And I'll be the bridegroom
 And you'll be the bride

24. Now Jeannie she's got married
And her tocher down told
 Bonny Jean o' Bethelnie
Scarcely sixteen years old

25. Oh Bethelnie, oh Bethelnie,
 It shines where it stands
And the heather bells round it
 Shines o'er Fyvie's land.

6. "Glenlogie"

Greig MSS., III, p. 107. Sung by Mrs. Milne, Auchreddie, New Deer.

a π^1, ending on the octave

There were six and six nobles
 Rode round Banchory fair:
But bonnie Glenlogie
 Was flower that was there.
But bonnie Glenlogie
 Was flower that was there.

7. "Glenlogie"

Greig MSS., III, p. 177. Sung by Mrs. Corbet, New Deer.

a π^1, ending on the octave

Come saddle the black steed,
 And bring to the green,
Till I ride to Bethelnie,
 And see bonnie Jean,
Till I ride to Bethelnie,
 And see bonnie Jean.

8. "Bethelnie"

Greig MSS., I, p. 109. Sung by G. Morrison, March 1906.

a I/M, ending on the octave

Her father being a chaplain,
And a man of great skill,
He wrote a braid letter
Glenlogie to tell,
He wrote a braid letter
Glenlogie to tell.

9. "Bethelnie"

Greig MSS., IV, p. 137. Also in Greig and Keith, 1925, p. 192(a). Sung by George Corbet, Weetingshill, New Deer; from his mother.

a I/M, ending on the octave

10. "Glenlogie"

Archive, School of Scottish Studies. Sung by John Adams. Collected by Hamish Henderson for the School of Scottish Studies; transcribed by Francis M. Collinson.

a I, ending on the octave

1. There was nine and nine horsemen
   Rode through Banchory Fair,
An' bonnie Glenlogie
   Was the floo'er o' a' there
An' bonnie Glenlogie
   Was the floo'er o' a' there.

2. There was nine and nine ladies
   Sat in the Queen's dine,
An' bonnie Jeannie o' Bethelnie
   Was the floo'er o' twice nine
An' bonnie Jeannie o' Bethelnie
   Was the floo'er o' twice nine.

3. She has callèd his footboy
   That walked by his side,
Saying, Who is your master
   And where does he bide?
Saying, Who is your master
   And where does he bide?

4. He is stylèd Glenlogie
   When he is at home,
But he's of the noble Gordons
   And his name is Lord John.

5. Glenlogie, Glenlogie,
   If ye will prove kind,
A maiden's love laid on you,
   Must she die in her prime
A maiden's love laid on you,
   Must she die in her prime.

6. He's turned aboot lichtly,
   As Gordons dee a',
My thanks, Lady Jean,
   My love's promised awa'.
My thanks, Lady Jean,
   My love's promised awa'.

7. She has called her father's chaplain,
   A man of great skill,
And he has wrote a letter
   And indited it well
And he has wrote a letter
   And indited it well.

8. When Glenlogie got the letter
   A licht lauch gied he;
But ere he read it over
   A tear dimmed his e'e.
But ere he read it over
   A tear dimmed his e'e.

9. Go saddle my black horse,
   And bring it to the green;
But ere they had it ready
   He was twa mile him leen*
But ere they had it ready
   He was twa mile him leen.

10. Pale and wan was she
   When Glenlogie gaed in,
But red and rosy grew she
   When she kent it was him,
But red and rosy grew she
   When she kent it was him.

* him leen = alone

11. "Bethelnie"

Greig MSS., III, p. 22. Also in Greig and Keith, 1925, p. 192(b). Sung by William Angus, Cuminestown, September 1907.

p I/Ly (?)

Bethelnie, O Bethelnie,
Ye shine where ye stand
May the heather bells around you
Shine o'er Fyvie's land.

12. "Glenlogie"

Sung by John Strachan, Fyvie, Aberdeenshire. Caedmon rec. No. TC 1146(B1); recorded by Alan Lomax and Hamish Henderson; collected and edited by Peter Kennedy and Alan Lomax.

p I/Ly

1. There were four and twenty nobles stood at the king's ha',
   And bonny Glenlogie was flo'or o' them a'.

2. There were nine and nine nobles rode roon' Bankley Fair
   And bonny Glenlogie was flo'or o' them there.

3. Doon come Jeannie Gordon, she come trippin' doonstairs,
   And she's fa'en in love with Glenlogie over a' that was there.

4. She called on his footboy that stood by his side,
   "Now who is that young man and far does he bide?"

5. "His name is Glenlogie when he is at hame,
   And he's o' the Gay Gordons, and his name is Lord John."

6. "Glenlogie, Glenlogie, you'll be constant and kind,
   I've laid my love on you and you're aye in my mind."

7. He turned him roon' quickly as the Gordons do a',
   Says, "I thank you, Jeannie Gordon, but your tocher's ower sma'."

8. Her father was a chaplain and a man o' great skill,
   And he penned a brave letter and he penned it richt weel.

9. When he looked on the letter a light laugh laughed he,
   But when he read the letter the tear blind his e'e.

10. "Go saeddle the black horse and saeddle the broon,
    Bonny Jean O' Bethalnie'll be dead ere I win."

11. An' pale and wan was she when Glenlogie come in,
    But reid and rosy grew she when she kent it was him.

12. O Bethalnie, O Bethalnie, it shines where it stands;
    And the heather bells o'er it shines o'er Fyvie's land.

13. "Bethelnie"

Greig MSS., I, p. 150. From the Rev. James B. Duncan, Lynturk, 1905.

a I/M, ending on the octave

There were six & six ladies
Sat in the Queen's ha',
Bonnie Jean o' Bethelnie
Was the flooer o' them a',
Bonnie Jean o' Bethelnie
Was the flooer o' them a'.

14. "Glenlogie"

Greig MSS., I, p. 50; text, Bk. 719, IX, p. 46. Also in Greig-Duncan MS. 785 (Walker transcript). Sung by J. W. Spence, Rosecroft, Fyvie, August 1905.

a π^1, ending on the octave

1. There was sax & sax nobles
   Rode around Banchory Fair
   And bonnie Glenlogie
   Was the flower that was there.

2. There was nine & nine of them
   Sat at the King's dine,
   And bonnie Glenlogie
   Was the flower o' twice nine.

3. There was nine and nine maidens
   Sat in the King's ha',
   And Bonnie Jeannie Gordon
   Was the flower o' them a'.

4. Doon cam' Jeannie Gordon,
   She cam' trippin' doon stairs,
   And she fancied Glenlogie
   Above all that was there.

5. She called on his footboy
   That walked by his side,
   Says, "What call you that young man
   Or where does he bide?"

6. He's styled Glenlogie,
   When he is at home,
   But he's o' the gay Gordons,
   And his name is Lord John.

7. Glenlogie, Glenlogie,
    Ye'll be constant & kind,
For I lay my love upon you,
    And I'll tell you my mind.

8. He's turned round smartly,
    As the Gordons do all,
I'm obliged to you, love Jeannie,
    But I'm promised awa'.

9. She called to her maiden
    To make her a bed,
She'd some fine sheets & blankets
    They were quickly down spread.

10. Down came her father
    He came tripping downstairs
Says, ["]Oh what ails ye Jeannie
    That ye are lyin' there."

11. He's a nice little fellow,
    With a dark rolling eye,
If I get na Glenlogie
    For him I will die.

12. Her father had a chaplain,
    A man of great fame,
He wrote a braid letter
    And pennèd it well.

13. Glenlogie, Glenlogie,
    Be constant & kind
And let not this virgin
    Now die in her prime.

14. When Glenlogie got the letter
    He was among men,
It's out spake Glenlogie
    What does young Lemon mean?
        (women)

15. Ye'll saddle the black horse,
    Go saddle the brown,
Bonnie Jeannie o' Bethelnie
    Will be dead ere I win.

16. Lang or the black horse was saddled
    And o'er to the Green,
Bonnie Glenlogie
    Was three miles him lane.

17. When he came to Bethelnie,
    There was nobody there,
But ae bonnie lassie
    Sat combing her hair.

18. If ye be the maiden
    Tak' me by the han'
And ye'll lead me to the chamber
    Jeannie Gordon lies in.

19. O pale and weary was she
    When he gaed in,
But red and rosy grew she
    When she saw it was him.

20. O where does your pain lie,
    Does it lie in your side?
O where does your pain lie,
    Does it lie in your head?

21. Glenlogie, O Glenlogie,
    Ye are far frae the place,
For the pain that I lie under
    Lies below my left breast.

22. Come turn to your side, Jeannie,
    Come turn to your side,
For the morn I'll be the bridegroom,
    And ye'll be the bride.

23. Now Jeannie's got married,
    And her tocher doon told,
Bonnie Jeannie o' Bethelnie
    Was scarce sixteen years old.

24. Bethelnie, O Bethelnie,
    Ye shine where ye stand,
May the heather bells around you
    Shine o'er Fyvie's land.

15. "Bethelnie"

Greig MSS., IV, p. 23. Sung by John Johnstone, New Deer.

a π^1, ending on the octave

Pale an' wan was she
    When Glenlogie gaed in;
But red an' rosy grew she
    When she knew it was him;
But red an' rosy grew she
    When she knew it was him.

16. "Bethelnie"

Greig MSS., III, p. 122. Sung by Mrs. Thain, New Deer, June 1908.

a I/M, ending on the octave

There were six & six ladies
    Walked round the Queen's ha',
And bonnie Jeannie Gordon
    Was the floo'er o' them a';
And bonnie Jeannie Gordon
    Was the floo'er o' them a'.

17. "Glenlogie"

Greig MSS., III, p. 62; text, Bk. 716, VI, pp. 50 and [51a]. Also in Greig-Duncan MS. 785. Sung by Alexander Robb, New Deer.

a π^1, ending on the octave

1. There was six and six nobles
Rode through Banchory fair
And Logie Glen Logie
Was the fairest that was there.

2. There were six and six ladies
Sat in the queen's ha'
And bonnie Jeanie Gordon
Was the fairest o' them a'.

3. There was nine & nine lords
A' sat doon to dine
And bonnie Glen Logie's
The flooer o' thrice nine.

4. There were nine & nine ladies
A-combin' their hair
And bonnie Jeanie Gordon
Was the fairest that was there.

5. . . . .
Be constant & true
I'll lay my love on you
And tell you my mind.

6. And syne fin Glen Logie read the letter
He being among men
I wonder says Glen Logie
What does young women mean.

7. Go saddle the black horse
And also the brown
Or else Jeanie Gordon
Will be dead or I won.

8. The black horse wasna saddled
Nor brought to the green
When Logie, Glen Logie
Was three miles him lane.

9. When he gaed to Bethelnie
There was naebody there
But one pretty fair maid
She was combin her hair.

10. He says to this fair maid
You'll take me by the hand
And lead me to the chamber
Jeanie Gordon lies in.

11. O pale & wan was she
When Glen Logie went in
But red & ruddy grew she
When she kent it was him.

12. O turn Jeanie Gordon
O turn to your side
And I'll be the bridegroom
And ye'll be the bride.

13. When her age it was counted
And her tocher doon told
Bonnie Jeanie Gordon
Was scarce sixteen years auld.

He said—"My pretty maiden,
Ye'll tak' me by the han',
Lead me to the bedroom
Jeannie Gordon lies in."

She led him thro' one room,
She led him thro' nine,
And the next was the bedroom
Jeannie Gordon lay in.

The attribution to Robb of this text is not confidently made, but the two additional stanzas at the end (the first a variant of stanza 10, the second without counterpart) are so credited on an unnumbered page of the MS. following the 13-stanza text. In *Last Leaves*, 1925, p. 243, Keith lists Robb's version as Greig's D, with 14 stanzas; unless it is the present text, it has not been found.

18. "Bonnie Jean o' Bethelnie"

Christie, I, 1876, p. 54. From Aberdeenshire tradition back to 1775.

a π^1, ending on V

There were four-and-twenty ladies
Din'd in the Queen's ha';
Bonnie Jean o' Bethelnie
Was flower o' them a'. Bonnie Jean, &c.
[*Etc.*]

Christie "epitomized" the text from Buchan, *Ancient Ballads and Songs of the North of Scotland*, 1828, I, p. 188, making some changes according to the way he had heard it sung.

19. "Bethelnie"

Greig MSS., II, p. 49. Also in Greig and Keith, 1925, p. 192(c). Sung by Mrs. Stuart, Mitchellhill, Auchmaliddie, New Deer, July 1906.

a I/Ly, ending on VI

When I gaed to Bethelnie,
There was naebody there
But one pretty fair maid
Was combin' her hair.

GROUP Ba

20. "Glenogie"

Smith [1820-24], IV, p. 78. Also in Maver, 1866, No. 328, p. 164; Moffat, 2nd ed. [1896], p. 239; and Eyre-Todd, [1894], p. 112.

p D/Æ

1. Threescore o' Nobles rade up the King's ha',
But bonny Glenogie's the flow'r o' them a';
Wi' his milk-white steed, and his bonny black ee,
Glenogie, dear Mither, Glenogie for me.

2. O had your tongue, dochter, ye'll get better than he;
O say nae sae, mither, for that canna be,
Tho' Drumlie is richer, and greater than he,
Yet if I maun tak him, I'll certainly dee.

3. Where will I get a bonny boy, to win hose and shoon,
Will gae to Glenogie, and cum shune again?
O here am I, a bonny boy, to win hose and shoon,
Will gae to Glenogie, and cum shune again.

4. When he gaed to Glenogie, 'twas wash and go dine;
'Twas wash ye, my pretty boy, wash and go dine;
O 'twas ne'er my Faither's fashion, and it ne'er shall be mine,
To gar a Lady's hasty errand wait till I dine:

5. But there is, Glenogie, a letter to thee;
The first line that he read, a low smile gae he;
The next line that he read, the tear blindit his ee;
But the last line that he read, he gart the table flee.

6. Gar saddle the black horse, gae saddle the brown;
Gar saddle the swiftest steed e'er rade frae a town;
But lang ere the horse was drawn, and brought to the green,
O bonny Glenogie was twa mile his lane.

7. When he cam to Glenfeldy's door, little mirth was there,
Bonny Jean's Mother was tearing her hair;
Ye're welcome, Glenogie, ye're welcome! said she;
Ye're welcome, Glenogie, your Jeanie to see.

8. Pale and wan was she, when Glenogie gaed ben;
But red and rosy grew she whene'er he sat down;
She turned awa her head, but the smile was in her ee;
O binna feared, Mither, I'll may be no dee.

GROUP Bb

21. "Glenlogie"

Archive, School of Scottish Studies. Sung by Miss M. Douglas Gordon, Aberdeenshire, 1953. Collected by Francis M. Collinson for the School of Scottish Studies; transcribed by the collector.

a D, ending on IV?

There were four and twenty nobles
Sat in the king's hall,
And bonnie Glenlogie
Was the pride of them all;

In came Lady Jane
Curtsying on the floor,
She had chosen Glenlogie
From among them all.

Lord Saltoun and Auchanachie

CHILD NO. 239

Christie is alone in recording a tune for this ballad. It came, he says, from "aged relatives," through whom he can trace the ballad back almost to the mid-eighteenth century. The tune is a plagal D/Æ variant of the minor form which we have just met in No. 238, and has the same affiliations.

We need not take Christie too literally when he says that he "can trace the accompanying ballad" through a relative and her forebears almost back to the event which it purports to commemorate. Comparison of Christie's text with that of the Murison MS.—the latter being Child's Ba and Christie's, Child Bb—will make it clear that to accommodate his second strain Christie has doubled his stanzas, largely inventing the second half of each double stanza. Thus Murison's stanzas correspond to the first halves of Christie's, until the ballad grows too direct and plain-spoken for drawing-room use.

There seems no just reason for connecting the modern very widespread ballad of "Johnny Doyle" with this ballad, except a general similarity of theme. (So Phillips Barry would do. Cf. Flanders, *et al.*, *New Green Mountain Songster*, 1939, p. 250.) The latter ballad has been collected in Scotland, Ireland, England, and the U.S.A. References will be found in Sharp and Karpeles, *Appalachians*, 1932, II, p. 27, in *JFSS*, V, No. 19 (1915), pp. 142-46, etc. There is no discernible relation in the tune tradition.

LIST OF VARIANTS

"Lord Saltoun and Annachie." W. Christie, *Traditional Ballad Airs*, I, 1876, p. 10.

TUNE WITH TEXT

"Lord Saltoun and Annachie"

Christie, I, 1876, p. 10. Sung by relatives of Christie; from family tradition back to c. 1756.

p D/Æ

Oh, Buchan is bonnie, and there lives my love;
My heart's fixèd on him, it will not remove;
It will not remove for a' that I can dee:
Oh, never will I forget my love Annachie!
For Annachie Gordon is bonnie and braw,
He'd entice any woman that ever him saw;
He'd entice any woman, and sae he has done me,
And I'll die if I getna my love Annachie.

[*Etc.*]

The Rantin Laddie

CHILD NO. 240

So FAR as a musical tradition exists for this ballad, it belongs to the familiar "Binorie" type. Copies are preserved in two favorite patterns, both known in other connections. One was sent by Burns to the *Scots Musical Museum*, and later repeated in R. A. Smith. The other was collected by Greig at the beginning of our own century. All are D/Æ plagal, and in common time. Keith cites also *Museum*, No. 320 ("The Cruel Mother") as a relative.

Christie's tune, from Buchan tradition, is too unlike these to be grouped with them. It is a six-phrase tune, plagal, and I/M. There are vague echoes of other tunes in it, especially, perhaps, of "The False Lover Won Back" (No. 218).

A further tune, quite unlike the rest, was collected by Barry in 1928 in New Brunswick, ostensibly from Scottish tradition (Kirkcudbright). It is a nearly π^3 tune (oddly, however, Æolian lacking III), irregular in timing, and with a very un-balladlike burden which must have been idiosyncratically added, probably by the singer.

Very lately, Ewan MacColl has given us a fine Mixolydian tune, distinct from all others, as from his own family tradition.

LIST OF VARIANTS

GROUP Aa

1. "The Rantin Laddie." James Johnson, *The Scots Musical Museum*, V, [1796], No. 462, p. 474 (repr. 1853). Also in Robert Archibald Smith, *The Scotish Minstrel* [1820-24], IV, p. 6.

GROUP Ab

2. "The Rantin Laddie." Gavin Greig and Alexander Keith, *Last Leaves of Traditional Ballads and Ballad Airs*, 1925, p. 194(a). From Duncan MS., No. 15. (Gillespie)
3. "The Rantin Laddie." Greig MSS., II, p. 5, and Bk. 717, VII, p. 99, King's College Library, Aberdeen. Also in Greig and Keith, 1925, p. 194(b). (Findlay, Calder)

GROUP B

4. "Lord Aboyne." W. Christie, *Traditional Ballad Airs*, I, 1876, p. 210.

GROUP C

5. "The Rantin Laddie." Ewan MacColl, Riverside recording No. RLP 12-622(B4), *The English and Scottish Popular Ballads*, I, ed. Kenneth S. Goldstein.

GROUP D

6. "The Rantin' Laddie." Phillips Barry, Fannie H. Eckstorm, and Mary W. Smyth, *British Ballads from Maine*, 1929, p. 303. (McGill)

TUNES WITH TEXTS

GROUP Aa

1. "The Rantin Laddie"

Johnson, V [1796], No. 462, p. 474 (repr. 1853). Also in Smith [1820-24], IV, p. 6 (with a parallel text). From Robert Burns.

p D/Æ

Aften hae I play'd at the cards and the dice,
  For the love of a bonie rantin laddie;
But now I maun sit in my fathers kitchen neuk
  And Be-low a bastard babie.
For my father he will not me own,
  And my mother she neglects me,
And a' my friends hae lightlyed me,
  And their servants they do slight me.
But had I a servant at my command,
  As aft times I've had many,
That wad rin wi' a letter to bonie Glenswood,
  Wi' a letter to my rantin laddie.
Oh, is he either a laird, or a lord,
  Or is he but a cadie,
That ye do him ca' sae aften by name,
  Your bonie, bonie rantin laddie.
Indeed he is baith a laird and a lord,
  And he never was a cadie;
But he is the Earl o' bonie Aboyne,
  And he is my rantin laddie.
O ye'se get a servant at your command,
  As aft times ye've had many,
That sall rin wi' a letter to bonie Glenswood,
  A letter to your rantin laddie.
When lord Aboyne did the letter get,
  O but he blinket bonie;
But or he had read three lines of it,
  I think his heart was sorry.
O wha is daur be sae bauld,
  Sae cruelly to use my lassie?

. . . .
. . . .

For her father he will not her know,
  And her mother she does slight her;
And a' her friends hae lightlied her,
  And their servants they neglect her.
Go raise to me my five hundred men,
  Make haste and make them ready;

With a milkwhite steed under every ane,
For to bring hame my lady.
As they cam in thro' Buchan-shire,
They were a company bonie,
With a gude claymor in every hand,
And O, but they shin'd bonie.

GROUP Ab

2. "The Rantin Laddie"

Greig and Keith, 1925, p. 194(a); from Duncan MS., No. 15. Sung by Mrs. Gillespie.

p D/Æ

Mrs. Gillespie also sang this ballad with a repeat of the first half of the tune.

I will raise five hundred men,
An' that will mak a company bonnie,
An' I'll mount them a' on milk white steeds,
To bring home my bonnie rantin lassie.

3. "The Rantin Laddie"

Greig MSS., II, p. 5; text, Bk. 717, VII, p. 99. Also in Greig and Keith, 1925, p. 194(b). Tune from Andrew Findlay, New Deer, June 1906; text from Rev. J. C[alder].

p D/Æ

The Reverend J. Calder's text is referred to Findlay's tune in the MS.

1. My father feed me far far awa
I was far awa as Kircaldy
He's feed me hame to an auld widow wife
And wi' her lives a bonnie rantin' laddie.

2. On this side the burn & on yon side the burn
And it's oh but the burn rins bonnie
And yon man promised to marry me
If ever he married any.

3. If I had been wise I'd taen my love's advice
I'd da'en as my bonnie love bade me
I micht have been married at Martinmas
And awa wi' the bonnie rantin laddie.

4. But I wasna wise nor yet took advice
Nor did as my bonnie lovie bade me
So I now maun sit in my father's kitchie nook
Singin' ba to my bonnie bastard bairnie

5. My father has come trippin' doon the stair
Wi' shy shy looks and angry
Says Is't to a laird or is't to a lord
Or is it to a caddie.

6. My father is a very proud man
My mother she's gone & left me
My friens & relations they a' do me forget
And my father's servant men they hate me.

7. It's nae to a laird nor yet to a lord
Nor is it to a caddie
But it is to the young Earl of Aboyne
Tho' they ca' him the bonnie rantin' laddie.

8. And where will I get a bonnie wee boy
That will carry a letter cannie
That will run on to the Castle o' Aboyne
Wi' a letter to the bonnie rantin' laddie.

9. As ye gang up by bonnie Deeside
The banks they are a' bloomin' bonnie
Oh then ye will spy the castle o' Aboyne
Doon among the bushes sae bonnie.

10. As he gaed up by bonnie Deeside
The banks they were bloomin' bonnie
And there he spied the Earl o' Aboyne
Doon among the bushes sae bonnie

11. Oh where are you going my bonnie wee boy
Where are ye going my caddie
I'm gaen on to the Castle o' Aboyne
Wi' a letter to the bonnie rantin' laddie.

12. Ye needna gang farther my bonnie wee boy
Ye needna gang farther my caddie
For I am the Earl o' Aboyne
Tho they ca' me the bonnie rantin' laddie.

13. He took the letter & he read the letter
And oh but it was bonnie
But lang ere he had the letter far read
The tears fell thick and many

14. Oh where will I get twenty-four gentlemen
And as many of young ladies
That will mount on milk-white steeds
To welcome home my Peggy.

15. Oh here I'll get twenty four young gentlemen
And as mony ladies
That will mount on to milk-white steeds
And welcome home your Peggy.

16. As we cam' thro' by bonnie Aiberdeen
The folks they were a' makin' ready
But said I to them ye needna buckle braw
To welcome home my Peggy.

17. I shall na bide lang at Aiberdeen,
Nor yet into this low country
But I shall run into the Castle o' Aboyne
To be Aboyne's young lady.

GROUP B

4. "Lord Aboyne"

Christie, I, 1876, p. 210. From Buchan tradition.

p I/M

Aft ha'e I play'd at the ring and the ba',
And lang was a rantin' lassie;
But now my father does me forsake,
And all my friends neglect me.
But now my, &c.
[*Etc.*]

Christie "adapted" his text from Buchan, *Ancient Ballads and Songs of the North of Scotland,* 1828, II, p. 66.

GROUP C

5. "The Rantin Laddie"

Sung by Ewan MacColl, Riverside rec. No. RLP 12-622 (B4), ed. K. S. Goldstein. Learned from his father.

a M

1. "Oft hae I played at the cards and dice
Wi' my ain dear rantin laddie,
But noo I maun sit in my faither's ha'
And sing ba to my bastard baby.

2. "If I'd been wise as I've been nice,
And done what my bonnie lad tauld me,
I'd ha' been married a year or mair,
And been wi' my rantin laddie.

3. "My faither dear he knows me not,
An' my mither she ignores me,
My friends and relations a' slight me,
And the servants they quite hate me.

4. "Gin I had ane horse at my command,
As oft times I've had mony,
I would ride it on to the gates o' Aboyne
Wi' a letter to my rantin laddie."

5. "Is your love a laird or is he a lord,
Or is he but a caddie,
That ye sae aft ca' on his name,
Your ain dear rantin laddie?"

6. Then oot and spak' a kitchie boy,
Says "Though I'm but a caddie,
It's I will run to the gates o' Aboyne,
Wi' a letter for your rantin laddie."

7. When he was near tae the banks o' Dee,
The birds they sang sae bonny,
And there he spied the Earl o' Aboyne,
That they ca' the rantin laddie.

8. And when he looked the letter on,
But O, and he was sorry,
"They've been cruel and fell unkind,
Tae my ain dear rantin lassie."

9. "My faither dear, he knows me not,
My mither she ignores me,
My frien's and relations a' slight me,
And the servants they quite hate me."

10. "Gae get to me five hundred men,
And they'll ride oot sae bonnie,
And we'll bring the bonnie lassie back to Aboyne,
My ain dear rantin lassie."

11. When she was up ahint his back,
Wrapped in a hielan' plaidie,
The birds in the trees sang not sae sweet,
As the bonnie, bonnie rantin lassie.

12. And they rode on through Buchanshire,
And Buchan it shone bonnie,
"Rejoice, rejoice, ye bonnie mays
And see that ye be na' sorry."

13. Gin ye lay your love on a lowland lad,
Be sure that he'll betray ye,
But lay your love on a hielan' lad,
He'll do a' he can to raise ye.

GROUP D

6. "The Rantin' Laddie"

Barry, Eckstorm, and Smyth, 1929, p. 303. Sent by Mrs. James McGill, Chamcook, New Brunswick, November 8, 1928; learned in Kirkcudbrightshire, Scotland, before 1911.

a Æ (–III)

240. THE RANTIN LADDIE

Aft hae I played at the cards an' dice
For the love o' a rantin' laddie, O,
But noo I maun sit in the ingle neuk,
An' by-lo a bastard babbie O.

Refrain:

Sing hush-a-by, an' hush-a-by,
An' hush-a-by-lo babbie, O,
O hush-a-by, an' hush-a-by,
An' hush-a-by, wee babbie O.

Sing hush-a-by, an' hush-a-by,
An' hush-a-by-lo babbie, O,
O had your tongue, ma ain wee wean,
An A gae a sook o' the pappie, O.

The Baron o Leys

CHILD NO. 241

Perhaps the most striking feature in this surprisingly light-hearted song of plenary indulgence is the instant forgiveness by the Lady of Leys for her husband's escapade. All Child's copies except Kinloch's (B) display this tolerance; a fact which prompts the suggestion that Kinloch's punctuation at the crucial point mistakes the intention of the ballad. Instead of:

> But word's gane down to the Lady o' Leys
> That the Baron had got a babie:
> 'The waurst o news!' my lady she said,
> 'I wish I had hame my laddie,'
> (B,8)

we should read:

> The waurst o news my lady she said,
> 'I wish I had hame my laddie,' &c.—

meaning the lady did not scold. Compare the Skene copy (Child's A):

> The warst word she said to that was,
> 'I wish I had it in my arms';

the Buchan (Child C):

> She clapped her hands, and this did say,
> 'I wish he were in my arms';

the Greig copy:

> The very first word that the lady she spoke,
> Was, 'I wish I had hame my laddie.'

This ballad, incidentally, better deserves the title of "The Rantin Laddie" than does its predecessor. Adding to the obvious parallels of Child Nos. 110 and 217, mention may be made of Baring-Gould's "The Witty Shepherd," for which he cites a printing by Catnach and Birt (Brit. Mus. 11621. K. 4). Cf. Baring-Gould and Sheppard, *A Garland of Country Song*, 1895, p. 65.

In the general spate of pathetic melodies of the "Binorie" type which accompany these ballads with feminine endings on lines two and four, it is an agreeable relief to find one of which the tradition is clearly a merry one, in keeping with the mood of the text. It seems clear that although the tunes recorded or mentioned for this ballad have few close resemblances, all the singers had in mind a brisk 6/8 measure with a characteristic cadence of an octave drop. The tune Burns sent to the *Scots Musical Museum* (No. 237) has in its first strain, as Stenhouse rightly notes, much of "Jenny come down to Jock" (for which cf., e.g., Ritson, *Scotish Songs*, ed. of 1869, I, p. 264; R. Chambers, *The Songs of Scotland Prior to Burns*, 1880, pp. 109ff.). Nor is it difficult to see resemblances in the second strain, as he also points out, to "Saw ye Johnny comin'" (cf. *Museum*, No. 9). The latter suggestion is not incompatible with Glen's counter-suggestion that Sheridan's "Here's to the maiden of bashful fifteen" is the related tune (*Early Scottish Melodies*, 1900, p. 139). The second strain of Sheridan's tune has, indeed, a good deal of the folk idiom. For earlier parallels, cf. "Jamaica" in Playford, *English Dancing Master*, 4th ed., whence also "The Jolly Trades-Men" in D'Urfey's *Pills*, 1719-20, VI, p. 91, and doubtless "Country Gardens."

The tune, as Burns gave it, is apparently a D/Æ one, the first strain being a true pentatonic of the fourth class (– II, VI). To me it appears that Greig's tune is probably a worn-down variant of this or a similar tune. We have seen more than once already a tendency in tradition to shorten the range of old airs with a wide gamut; and the drop here of a fifth on the cadence seems a palpable substitute for the earlier octave drop. Likewise the tune's upper reach is shortened by one degree. From another singer, Greig collected this ballad to the tune of "Wha'll be King but Charlie," which has the same characteristic octave drop, the same rhythm of 6/8 and is also Æolian. (Cf. Graham, *The Songs of Scotland*, 1848-49, I, p. 138.)

LIST OF VARIANTS

1. "The Linkin Laddie." James Johnson, *The Scots Musical Museum*, III [1790], No. 237, p. 246 (repr. 1853). Also in Herd MSS., I, p. 233, British Museum Library, Add. MSS. 22311-12.
2. "The Baron o' Leys." Gavin Greig and Alexander Keith, *Last Leaves of Traditional Ballads and Ballad Airs*, 1925, p. 195. From Duncan MS., No. 204. (Petrie)

TUNES WITH TEXTS

1. "The Linkin Laddie"

Johnson, III [1790], No. 237, p. 246 (repr. 1853). Also in Herd MSS., I, p. 233. From Robert Burns.

a D/Æ (π^4 in the first strain); or possibly a I/Ly, ending on *VI*

> Waes me that e'er I made your bed,
> Waes me that e'er I saw ye,
> For now I've lost my maiden head,
> And I ken na how they ca' ye!

My name's weel kend in my ain countrie,
They ca' me the linkin laddie:
An ye had na been as willing as I,
Shame fa' them wad e'er hae bade ye.

2. "The Baron o' Leys"

Greig and Keith, 1925, p. 195; from Duncan MS., No. 204. Sung by Mrs. Petrie, Alford.

a M/D

The Baron o Leys has to London gane,
An' shown his folly fairly,
He shod his horse wi siller sheen,
An' turned a rantin laddie.

The Dæmon Lover (The House Carpenter)

CHILD NO. 243

The earliest copies of this ballad are English broadsides of the Restoration period. They are directed to be sung to three alternative tunes, of which the first was probably that most closely associated with the ballad—though not originally, since the wife in question here was from Plymouth, not Bristol. The Pepys broadside, IV, f. 101, given as Child's A (another is Pepys, I, f. 502), is "To a West-country tune called 'The Fair Maid of Bristol,' 'Bateman,' or 'John True.'" Copies in Brit. Mus. c.22 f.6, fol.24, and Bodleian Douce Ballads, II, fol.249^v, omit "Bateman." Child cites others, which do not, I believe, add information on tunes. I have not discovered any of the three tunes mentioned and have no confidence that any of them was that printed in Chappell, *Popular Music* [1855-59], I, p. 198, as "Peascod Time." The tune should at any rate have been a CM tune, unlike that for Child's text B (mid-eighteenth century), which is LM. (Keith cites an earlier edition of B from a collection of 1737. Cf. Greig and Keith, *Last Leaves*, 1925, p. 196.) The outlines of B, but not the metre, are closest to the text which has been most popular in recent tradition in this country. But the very beautiful variant collected by Hammond, from Dorset, and later set by Vaughan Williams, is a perhaps solitary offspring of the LM variety.

To judge by the few airs, either Scots or English, which have been recovered in Britain (Ireland yielding none to my inquiries), the ballad was sung there to tunes mainly in a major tonality. Motherwell's was such (cf. Group Ae below); also Christie's (Group B), which relates to "Auld Rob Morris," and to Nos. 238, 239, *ante*; also Greig's (Group Af); the Dorset variant (Group Ab) mentioned above is Dorian. On the other hand, Laidlaw wrote Scott that the tune he had heard was "very solemn and melancholy" (Jan. 3, 1803; quoted Child, 1882-98, IV, p. 369). There is a fair number of other, American, variants in a major tonality; but I believe they derive from the typically D/M pattern which comprises the central tradition for this ballad in this country. Of it a very large number of examples have been recorded, for this is still one of the best loved of the Child ballads, whatever its original credentials. The tune-variants are nearly always attractive, often remarkably so: indeed, probably none of the ballads, unless we except No. 79, gives a richer impression of the American melodic tradition.

The majority of these tunes are of extended range (plagal plus authentic), and conform with surprising consistency to a contour of which the mid-cadence is ♭VII-V, the first phrase ends on I, and the two first accents are on V and ♭VII. When the pattern becomes heptatonic, the result is generally Dorian. Variants also occur on either side of this norm: D/Æ, π^4, Æ; and M and I/M—even to I/Ly. But the farther from the norm, the more the tune inclines to lose its characteristic outlines, to forget its tonic and end on another final (*V*, V, or II), to pick up accidentals, and to become aware of other tunes from which it may borrow hints. These cases, which show the tradition deteriorating, are difficult to analyze and classify, and frequently unsatisfying musically. But they are valuable for study, as showing how tunes become loosened from their moorings. The tune may vary the cadence-point of its first phrase from I to II, or IV to V, without losing its identity so long as it keeps a mid-cadence on V. But with the loss of that anchorage, the outlines begin to grow unrecognizable; and it may be that another reader would prefer to dissociate the sub-groups after Ab, or Ac, to Ah from the family of Aa altogether. I have not done so, out of a feeling that they still dimly aim at approximating a common archetypal musical image. But one of the melancholy possibilities of a study like the present is that the *idée fixe* may reside nowhere but in the editor's own head.

Ag and Ah show an impression, respectively, of the "Lord Lovel" pattern (No. 75) and the "Lady Gay" (No. 79); and other intrusions, like "Gypsy Laddie" (No. 200) and "Geordie" (No. 209), appear from time to time.

The ballad of the "Cruel Ship's Carpenter," which also has traditional currency (e.g., Sharp's MSS., 1334/, 1576/, 1613/; and Grainger MS., NYPL MS. *MO + [English]) has no relation to our ballad in either text or tune.

A tune is said to be in the Bunyan MS., 1877, p. 14 (*penes* Gray-Muir MS., NL Scotland MS. 2254).

LIST OF VARIANTS

GROUP Aa

1. "The Daemon Lover." Sharp MSS., 3853/, Clare College Library, Cambridge. (Patrick)
2. "The Daemon Lover." Sharp MSS., 3189/2335. Also in Cecil J. Sharp and Maud Karpeles, *English Folk Songs from the Southern Appalachians*, 1932, I, p. 244(A). (Sands)
3. "The Daemon Lover." Sharp MSS., 4318/. (Bowyer)
4. "The Daemon Lover." Sharp MSS., 4466/. (Richards)
5. "The House Carpenter." Vance Randolph, *Ozark Folk-songs*, I, 1946, p. 173(M).
6. "The Daemon Lover." Sharp MSS., 3992/. Also in Sharp and Karpeles, *Appalachians*, 1932, I, p. 256(O). (Carter)
7. "The Daemon Lover." Sharp MSS., 3422/2513. Also in Sharp and Karpeles, 1932, I, p. 251(H). (Gentry)
8. "The House Carpenter." E. C. and M. N. Kirkland, *Southern Folklore Quarterly*, II (1938), p. 75(A).
9. "The Daemon Lover." Sharp MSS., 4594/3213. Also in Sharp and Karpeles, *Appalachians*, 1932, I, p. 254(M). (Bennett)
10. "The Daemon Lover." Sharp MSS., 3488/2572. Also in Sharp and Karpeles, 1932, I, p. 245(B). (Buckner)
11. "The Daemon Lover." Sharp MSS., 4196/. (Birch)
12. "The Daemon Lover." Sharp MSS., 3869/. (Hensley)
13. "The Ship Carpenter." Clay Walters, LC Archive of American Folk Song, recording No. 1580(B2).
14. "The Daemon Lover." Sharp MSS., 3326/2430. Also in Sharp and Karpeles, *Appalachians*, 1932, I, p. 252(J). (Chandler)

15. "House Carpenter." Mrs. Allie Long Parker, LC Archive of American Folk Song, recording No. 11,903(B14).
16. "House Carpenter." Celia Kelter, LC Archive of American Folk Song, recording No. 10,505(B30).
17. "The Daemon Lover." Sharp MSS., 3647/. (Poff)
18. "House Carpenter." Warde H. Ford, LC Archive of American Folk Song, recording No. 11,337(B3).
19. "The House Carpenter." Elizabeth Walker Ford, LC Archive of American Folk Song, recording No. 11,-336(A1).
20. "House Carpenter." Drucilla Hall, LC Archive of American Folk Song, recording No. 11,691(B27).
21. "The Daemon Lover." Sharp MSS., 4088/. Also in Sharp and Karpeles, *Appalachians*, 1932, I, p. 257(Q). (Pratt)
22. "The Daemon Lover." Sharp MSS., 4428/. (Jones)
23. "The Daemon Lover." Sharp MSS., 3412/. Also in Sharp and Karpeles, *Appalachians*, 1932, I, p. 250(G). (Mrs. T. Shelton)
24. "The House Carpenter." Pete Steele, Folkways LP recording No. FS 3828(B8).
25. "The House Carpenter." Dorothy Scarborough, *A Song Catcher in Southern Mountains*, 1937, pp. 401(C) and 153.
26. "The Daemon Lover." Winston Wilkinson MSS., 1936-37, p. 26(C), University of Virginia.
27. "The Daemon Lover." Wilkinson MSS., 1936-37, p. 29(E).
a. "Sweet Wildee." Arthur Kyle Davis, *More Traditional Ballads of Virginia*, 1960, p. 283(FF).
b. "On the Banks of the Sweet Willie." Davis, 1960, p. 284(GG).
28. "Housecarpenter," or "Well Met." Mrs. Bertha Basham Wright, LC Archive of American Folk Song, recording No. 11,453(A14).
c. "The Salt Sea." Davis, *More Traditional Ballads of Virginia*, 1960, p. 279(DD).
29. "The Daemon Lover." Sharp MSS., 3473/. Also in Sharp and Karpeles, *Appalachians*, 1932, I, p. 251(I). (House)
d. "Salt Water Sea." Davis, *More Traditional Ballads of Virginia*, 1960, p. 287(II).
30. "The Daemon Lover." Sharp MSS., 4325/. (Grey)
31. "House Carpenter." Viola Cole, LC Archive of American Folk Song, recording No. 12,006(B3).
32. "The House Carpenter." John Harrington Cox, *Traditional Ballads Mainly from West Virginia*, 1939, p. 38; and 1964 (ed. George Boswell), p. 48.
33. "The Daemon Lover." Wilkinson MSS., 1936-37, p. 24(A).
34. "The Daemon Lover." Wilkinson MSS., 1936-37, p. 28(D).
35. "The Daemon Lover." Wilkinson MSS., 1936-37, p. 26(B).
36. "The Daemon Lover." Sharp MSS., 4330/. Also in Sharp and Karpeles, *Appalachians*, 1932, I, p. 256(P). (Donald)
37. "The Daemon Lover." Sharp MSS., 4309/. (Dooley)
38. "Daemon Lover," or "House Carpenter." Mrs. Oscar Allen, LC Archive of American Folk Song, recording No. 10,004(A16).
39. "The Daemon Lover." Sharp MSS., 4393/. (Gross)
40. "The Daemon Lover." Sharp MSS., 4673/. (Webb)
e. "The House Carpenter." Davis, *More Traditional Ballads of Virginia*, 1960, p. 281(EE).
41. "House Carpenter." Myrtle Downing, LC Archive of American Folk Song, recording No. 11,715(B29).
42. "The House Carpenter." Arthur Kyle Davis, Jr., *Traditional Ballads of Virginia*, 1929, pp. 592(D) and 445.
43. "House Carpenter's Wife." Frank C. Brown MSS., 16 a 4 c, Library of Congress, photostat.
f. "The House Carpenter." Brown MSS., 16 a 4 c. Also in *The Frank C. Brown Collection of North Carolina Folklore*, IV (*The Music of the Ballads*, ed. Jan P. Schinhan), 1957, p. 98(C).
44. "The House Carpenter." Jean Ritchie, Folkways LP recording No. FA 2301(A5), ed. Kenneth S. Goldstein.
45. "The Daemon Lover." Wilkinson MSS., 1935-36, p. 89(C).
46. "House Carpenter." Brown MSS., 16 a 4 c. Also in Schinhan, *Music, Brown Collection*, IV, 1957, p. 101(J).
g. "The House Carpenter." Schinhan, *Music, Brown Collection*, IV, 1957, p. 97(A2).
47. "The House Carpenter." Mrs. Texas Gladden, LC Archive of American Folk Song, Album 1, record No. 1(A).
48. "The Daemon Lover." Sharp MSS., 4269/. Also in Sharp and Karpeles, *Appalachians*, p. 257(R). (Roberts)
49. "House Carpenter." H. L. Maxey, LC Archive of American Folk Song, recording No. 2742(B2).
50. "The Daemon Lover." Sharp MSS., 3608/2670. Also in Sharp and Karpeles, *Appalachians*, 1932, I, p. 242(L). (Ray)
51. "The House Carpenter." Jean Thomas, *Devil's Ditties*, 1931, p. 172.
h. "The House Carpenter." Davis, *More Traditional Ballads of Virginia*, 1960, p. 276(BB).
i. "The House Carpenter." Davis, 1960, p. 285(HH).
52. "The House Carpenter." Davis, *Traditional Ballads of Virginia*, 1929, pp. 594(V) and 469. Also in C. Alphonso Smith, *The Musical Quarterly*, II (1916), p. 127(B).
53. "The House Carpenter." Phillips Barry, Fannie H. Eckstorm, and Mary W. Smyth, *British Ballads from Maine*, 1929, p. 306(B). (Young)
54. "The Old Salt Sea." Sharp MSS., 3110/?. Also in Sharp and Karpeles, *Appalachians*, 1932, I, p. 246(C). (Bishop)
55. "The House Carpenter." Mary O. Eddy, *Ballads and Songs from Ohio*, 1939, p. 74(C).
56. "House Carpenter." Mrs. Mary Bird McAllister, LC Archive of American Folk Song, recording No. 11,-868(A5).
57. "House Carpenter." Robert Shiflett, LC Archive of American Folk Song, recording No. 12,004(A3).
58. "A House Carpenter." Scarborough, *A Song Catcher in Southern Mountains*, 1937, pp. 401(B) and 152.
j. "The House Carpenter." Davis, *More Traditional Ballads of Virginia*, 1960, p. 289(JJ).
59. "House Carpenter." Florence Shiflett, LC Archive of American Folk Song, recording No. 12,004(B10).
60. "The Daemon Lover." Wilkinson MSS., 1935-36, p. 87(A).
61. "The Daemon Lover." Wilkinson MSS., 1935-36, p. 88(B).
62. "The House Carpenter." Davis, *Traditional Ballads of Virginia*, 1929, pp. 593(H) and 451.
k. "The House Carpenter." Davis, *More Traditional Ballads of Virginia*, 1960, p. 274(AA*).

63. "The House Carpenter" (A). Smith Harmon; from a MS. in possession of Edward Cray, Los Angeles, Calif.
l. "The House Carpenter." Davis, *More Traditional Ballads of Virginia*, 1960, p. 278(CC).
64. "The House Carpenter." Scarborough, *A Song Catcher in Southern Mountains*, 1937, pp. 400(A) and 151.
65. "The Daemon Lover." Sharp MSS., 4745/. Also in Sharp and Karpeles, *Appalachians*, 1932, I, p. 256(N). (Chrisom)
66. "The House Carpenter." Emelyn Elizabeth Gardner and Geraldine Jencks Chickering, *Ballads and Songs of Southern Michigan*, 1939, p. 56(B).
67. "The House Carpenter." Alton C. Morris, *Folksongs of Florida*, 1950, p. 313.
68. "The Daemon Lover." Sharp MSS., 4543/. (Godfrey)
m. "The Housecarpenter." Schinhan, *Music, Brown Collection*, IV, 1957, p. 95(A).
n. "The House Carpenter." Schinhan, *Music, Brown Collection*, IV, 1957, p. 99(E).
69. "The House-Carpenter." Phillips Barry, *JAF*, XXV (1912), p. 274.
70. "The House Carpenter." Clarence Ashley, Columbia recording 15654 D [1930]. Also on Folkways LP recording FP 251(A3), ed. Harry Smith.
71. "The House Carpenter." Almeda Riddle, Prestige-International LP recording No. INT-DS 25003(A3).
72. "The House Carpenter." Anonymous singer; from a MS. in possession of Edward Cray, Los Angeles, Calif.
73. "House Carpenter." Mellinger Edward Henry, *JAF*, XLV (1932), p. 23(B). Also in Henry, *Folk-Songs from the Southern Highlands* [1938], p. 115(B).

GROUP Ab

o. "The House Carpenter." Schinhan, *Music, Brown Collection*, IV, 1957, p. 96(A1).
74. "Daemon Lover." Sharp MSS., 3744/. Also in Sharp and Karpeles, *Appalachians*, 1932, I, p. 258(T). (Kinnard)
75. "If you will leave your house carpenter." "Tunes of Old Ballads and Folksongs," unpublished collection from the singing of Mrs. John Williams, edited by Charles A. Williams and Mabel Williams Kemmerer, 1963.
76. "The House Carpenter." Mabel Evangeline Neal, "Brown County Songs and Ballads" (Indiana University, M.A. thesis), 1926, p. 69.
77. "The Daemon Lover." Sharp MSS., 3341/2446. Also in Sharp and Karpeles, *Appalachians*, 1932, I, p. 248(D). (W. R. Shelton)
78. "The Ship Carpenter." Clay Walters, LC Archive of American Folk Song, recording No. 1580(A, B1). Also in LC/AAFS, recording No. L58(A5).
79. "The House Carpenter." Ruth A. Musick, *JAF*, LXX (1957), pp. 352 and 340.
80. "Daemon Lover." Sharp MSS., 3696/. Also in Sharp and Karpeles, *Appalachians*, 1932, I, p. 257(S). (Berea College students)
81. "The Daemon Lover." Sharp MSS., 4063/?. Also in Sharp and Karpeles, 1932, I, p. 258(U). (Hindman School girls)
82. "Well Met, Well Met, My Own True Love." H. E. D. Hammond, *JFSS*, III, No. 11 (1907), p. 84.
83. "The House Carpenter." Cox, *Traditional Ballads Mainly from West Virginia*, 1939, p. 41; and 1964 (ed. Boswell), p. 51.
84. "The Daemon Lover." Wilkinson MSS., 1935-36, p. 91(D).
85. "The House Carpenter." Captain Pearl R. Nye, LC Archive of American Folk Song, recording No. 1001(A1).
86. "The House Carpenter." Davis, *Traditional Ballads of Virginia*, 1929, pp. 593(G) and 449. Also in Smith, *The Musical Quarterly*, II (1916), p. 126(A).
87. "The House Carpenter." George Vinton Graham, LC Archive of American Folk Song, recording No. 3377(A1, A2).
p. "The House Carpenter." Schinhan, *Music, Brown Collection*, IV, 1957, p. 97(B).
88. "Well Met, Well Met, My Old True Love." Asher E. Treat, *JAF*, LII (1939), p. 46.
q. "The House Carpenter." Schinhan, *Music, Brown Collection*, IV, 1957, p. 101(L).
89. "The House Carpenter." Davis, *Traditional Ballads of Virginia*, 1929, pp. 594(X) and 470.
90. "The House Carpenter." Randolph, *Ozark Folksongs*, I, 1946, p. 171(J).
91. "The House Carpenter." George Lyman Kittredge, *JAF*, XXX (1917), p. 327. Also in Loraine Wyman and Howard Brockway, *Twenty Kentucky Mountain Songs* [1920], p. 54.
92. "The House Carpenter." Helen Hartness Flanders, Elizabeth Flanders Ballard, George Brown, and Phillips Barry, *The New Green Mountain Songster*, 1939, p. 95. Also in Helen Hartness Flanders, *Ancient Ballads Traditionally Sung in New England*, III, 1963, p. 289.
r. "The House Carpenter." Schinhan, *Music, Brown Collection*, IV, 1957, p. 100(H).
93. "The House Carpenter." Paul G. Brewster, *Ballads and Songs of Indiana*, 1940, p. 138. Also in Brewster, *JAF*, XLVIII (1935), p. 296.
94. "The Demon Lover." Louis W. Chappell, *Folk-Songs of Roanoke and the Albemarle*, 1939, p. 38.

GROUP AC

95. "The House Carpenter." Eddy, *Ballads and Songs from Ohio*, 1939, p. 77(E). Also in Albert H. Tolman and Mary O. Eddy, *JAF*, XXXV (1922), p. 347(B).
96. "The Ship's Carpenter." Lester A. Hubbard, *Ballads and Songs from Utah*, 1961, p. 28(A).
97. "The House Carpenter." Randolph, *Ozark Folksongs*, I, 1946, p. 176(P).
98. "The House Carpenter's Wife," or "The Daemon Lover." Fred High, LC Archive of American Folk Song, recording No. 10,818(B10).
99. "The House Carpenter." David Rice, LC Archive of American Folk Song, recording No. 3204(A). Also in Randolph, *Ozark Folksongs*, I, 1946, p. 169(E).
100. "The House Carpenter." Mrs. Hallie Griffin, LC Archive of American Folk Song, recording No. 11,891(A20).
101. "The House Carpenter." Mrs. May Kennedy McCord, LC Archive of American Folk Song, recording No. 5301(B1). Also in Randolph, *Ozark Folksongs*, I, 1946, p. 174(N).
102. "The House Carpenter." William A. Owens, *Texas Folk Songs*, 1950, p. 57.
103. "Well Met, My Old True Love." Mrs. Pearl Jacobs Borusky, LC Archive of American Folk Song, recording No. 4175(B)–4176(A). Also in LC/AAFS, recording No. L58(A4).
104. "The House Carpenter." Morris, *Folksongs of Florida*, 1950, p. 311.

105. "The Sea-Faring Man." W. W. Parsley, LC Archive of American Folk Song, recording No. 10,814(B1).
106. "The House Carpenter." H. M. Belden, *Ballads and Songs,* 1940, p. 82(D). Also in Phillips Barry MSS., IV, No. 205, Harvard College Library.
107. "The House Carpenter." Ben Gray Lumpkin, *Colorado Folksong Bulletin,* III (1964), p. 3.
108. "House Carpenter." Mrs. Roxie Phillips, LC Archive of American Folk Song, recording No. 11,905(A3).
109a. "The Daemon Lover." Sharp MSS., 3355/. Also in Sharp and Karpeles, *Appalachians,* 1932, I, p. 252(K). (Crane)
109b. "Daemon Lover," or "House Carpenter." Mrs. Kiah (Attie) Crane, LC Archive of American Folk Song, recording No. 10,010(A1).
110. "The House Carpenter." Editor, from Fletcher Collins, Berkeley, Calif., 1939.
111. "House Carpenter." Dan Tate, LC Archive of American Folk Song, recording No. 12,006(A26).
112. "House Carpenter." Rebecca Jane Collins, LC Archive of American Folk Song, recording No. 12,006(A30).
113. "The Daemon Lover." Sharp MSS., 3363/2462. Also in Sharp and Karpeles, *Appalachians,* 1932, I, p. 249(E). (Ramsey)
114. "The House Carpenter." Randolph, *Ozark Folksongs,* I, 1946, p. 168(B).

GROUP Ad

115. "The House-Carpenter." Mabel Major, *Publications of the Texas Folk-Lore Society,* X (1932), p. 159.
116. "The House Carpenter." Wayland D. Hand, *Western Folklore,* XVIII (1959), p. 42.
117. "The House Carpenter." Randolph, *Ozark Folksongs,* I, 1946, p. 166(A). Also in Randolph, *Ozark Mountain Folks,* 1932, p. 201.
118. "The House Carpenter." Carl Sandburg, *The American Songbag,* 1927, p. 66.
119. "The House Carpenter." Lumpkin, *Colorado Folksong Bulletin,* III (1964), p. 34.
120. "The House Carpenter." John Harrington Cox, *Folk-Songs of the South,* 1925, p. 524.
121. "The House Carpenter." Eddy, *Ballads and Songs from Ohio,* 1939, p. 70(A). Also in Tolman and Eddy, *JAF,* XXXV (1922), p. 347(A).
122. "The House Carpenter." Randolph, *Ozark Folksongs,* I, 1946, p. 176(O).

GROUP Ae

123. "The Demon Lover." William Motherwell, *Minstrelsy: Ancient and Modern,* 1827, App'x., No. 1 and p. xv.
124. "The House Carpenter." Kittredge, *JAF,* XXX (1917), p. 327. Also in Belden, *Ballads and Songs,* 1940, p. 84(G).
125. "The House Carpenter." Eddy, *Ballads and Songs from Ohio,* 1939, p. 72(B). Also in Tolman and Eddy, *JAF,* XXXV (1922), p. 348.
126. "The Daemon Lover." Sharp MSS., 3618/2681. (Pope)
127. "The House Carpenter." Brewster, *Ballads and Songs of Indiana,* 1940, p. 144.
128. "The House Carpenter." Gardner and Chickering, *Ballads and Songs of Southern Michigan,* 1939, p. 58(C).
129. "The Daemon Lover," or "Well Met." Mr. Dol Small, LC Archive of American Folk Song, recording No. 10,004 (A2).
130. "The House Carpenter's Wife." Cox, *Traditional Ballads Mainly from West Virginia,* 1939, p. 43; and 1964 (ed. Boswell), p. 53.
131. "The House Carpenter." Gardner and Chickering, *Ballads and Songs of Southern Michigan,* 1939, p. 54(A).
132. "House Carpenter." Dan Tate, LC Archive of American Folk Song, recording No. 12,005(A3).

GROUP Af

133. "The Daemon Lover." Sharp MSS., 3816/. (Connor)
134. "James Harris." Greig MSS., II, p. 139, and Bk. 769, LIX, p. 8, King's College Library, Aberdeen. Also in Gavin Greig and Alexander Keith, *Last Leaves of Traditional Ballads and Ballad Airs,* 1925, p. 197. (Robb)
135. "The House Carpenter," or "The Salt Water Sea." Sharp MSS., 3183/2325. Also in Sharp and Karpeles, *Appalachians,* 1932, I, p. 250(F). (F. B. Shelton)
136. "The Daemon Lover." Sharp MSS., 4752/. Also in Sharp and Karpeles, 1932, I, p. 258(V). (Boone)

GROUP Ag

137. "The House Carpenter." Davis, *Traditional Ballads of Virginia,* 1929, pp. 593(Q) and 462.
138. "The House Carpenter." David Seneff McIntosh, "Some Representative Illinois Folk-Songs" (Iowa State University, M.A. thesis in music), 1935, p. 34.
139. "The House Carpenter." Davis, *Traditional Ballads of Virginia,* 1929, pp. 592(C) and 444.

GROUP Ah

140. "The House Carpenter." Henry, *Folk-Songs from the Southern Highlands* [1938], p. 116(C).

APPENDIX A

141. "The Banks of Claudy." Phillips Barry, *BFSSNE,* No. 7 (1934), p. 11. Text, Barry, *BFSSNE,* No. 6 (1933), p. 8. Also in Flanders, *Ancient Ballads,* III, 1963, p. 317.

GROUP B

142. "The Banks of Italy," or "James Herries." W. Christie, *Traditional Ballad Airs,* I, 1876, p. 138.
143. "The Carpenter's Wife." Sabine Baring-Gould MSS., CXLIV and (A), Plymouth Public Library.
144. "The House Carpenter." Elsie Surber, LC Archive of American Folk Song, recording No. 9915(B2).
145. "House Carpenter." Allen Johnson, LC Archive of American Folk Song, recording No. 10,366(A6).

243. THE DÆMON LOVER (THE HOUSE CARPENTER)

TUNES WITH TEXTS

GROUP Aa

1. [The Daemon Lover]

Sharp MSS., 3853/. Sung by Mrs. Polly Patrick, Hart's Creek, Manchester, Ky., August 14, 1917.

m D

She dressed herself in the finest of silk
Put on a bonnet of green
And every town that she passed through
They taken her to be some queen.

2. [The Daemon Lover]

Sharp MSS., 3189/2335. Also in Sharp and Karpeles, 1932, I, p. 244(A). Sung by Mrs. Mary Sands, Allanstand, N.C., August 1, 1916.

m D

1. If you could have married the King's daughter dear,
You'd have better[1] married her,
For I've lately got married to a house-carpenter
And I'm sure he's a fine young man.

2. If you will forsaken your house-carpenter
And go along with me,
I will take you away where the grass grows green
On the banks of sweet Da Tee.[2]

3. She picked up her tender little babe
And give it kisses three.
Stay here, stay here, my tender little babe,
And keep your papa company.

4. She dressed herself as in a yellow rose,
Most glorious to behold,
And she walked the streets all round and about,
And shined like glittering gold.

5. They had not been on the sea more than two weeks,
I'm sure it was not three,
Till she begin to weep and mourn
And wept most bitterly.

6. Are you weeping for your gold?
Or are you for your store?
Or are you weeping for your house-carpenter
That you never shall see more?[3]

7. I'm neither weeping for my gold,
Nor neither for my store;
I'm weeping about my tender little babe
I left a-sitting on the floor.

8. And if I had it's all the gold
That ever crossed the sea,
So free would I give it to see land again
And my tender little babe with me.

9. If you had all the gold
You should give it all to me,
For you shall never see land any more,
But stay here for ever with me.

10. Don't you see yon light cloud arising
As light as any snow?
That's the place called heaven, she says,
Where all righteous people go.

11. Don't you see yon dark cloud arising
As dark as any crow?
That's the place called hell, she says,
Where I and you must go.

12. They had not been on the sea more than three weeks,
I'm sure it was not four,
Till the ship sprung a leak, to the bottom it went,
And it went to rise no more.

[1] 1932: better have
[2] 1932: Lee
[3] 1932: see no more

3. [The Daemon Lover]

Sharp MSS., 4318/. Sung by Mrs. Molly E. Bowyer, Villamont, Va., June 4, 1918.

m M/D

Well met, well met, my old true love,
Well met, well met, said he
For I've just returned from the salt, salt sea,
And it's all for the sake of thee.

4. [The Daemon Lover]

Sharp MSS., 4466/. Sung by Mrs. Francis Richards, St. Peter's School, Callaway, Va., August 17, 1918.

m M/D

Here we have met, said that house carpenter,
And it's here we have met, said he,
And it's here we have met, said that house carpenter,
And a nice young man was he.

5. "The House Carpenter"

Randolph, I, 1946, p. 173(M). Sung by Miss Louise Copeland, Aldrich, Mo., March 19, 1941. Noted by Mrs. May Kennedy McCord, Springfield, Mo.

m M/D

Well met, well met my own true love,
Well met, well met said he,
For I have returned from the salt salt sea,
And it's all for the love of thee.

6. [The Daemon Lover]

Sharp MSS., 3992/. Also in Sharp and Karpeles, 1932, I, p. 256(O). Sung by Mrs. Francis Carter, Proctor, Ky., September 7, 1917.

m M/D

Well met, well met, my own true love,
Well met, well met, said he,
For I've just returned from the old salt sea
And it's all for the sake of thee.

7. [The Daemon Lover]

Sharp MSS., 3422/2513. Also in Sharp and Karpeles, 1932, I, p. 251(H). Sung by Mrs. Jane Gentry, Hot Springs, N.C., September 12, 1916.

m M/D

N.B. that the passage between asterisks occurred only with the first stanza.

1. O come you home, my own true love,
   O come you home from sea?
   It's are you married? he said,
   Yes, I am married to a house carpenter
   And I think he is a nice young man.

2. It's I could have married the king's daughter fair,
   And she would have married me,
   But I refused a thousand weight of gold,
   And 'twas all for the love of thee.

3. If you could have married the king's daughter fair,
   I'm sure you are to blame,
   For I am married to a house carpenter
   And I think he's a nice young man.

4. It's won't you forsake your house carpenter
   And go along with me?
   I will take you to where the grass grows green
   On the banks of sweet Willie.

5. She pick-ed up her sweet little babe
   And kisses give it three,
   Saying: Stay at home, mother's sweet little babe,
   And keep your papee company.

6. She hadn't been on sea three days,
Not more than a week, I'm sure,
Till she fainted away in her true love's arms,
And she fainted for to rise no more.

7. It's are you weeping for my gold, he says,
Or are you weeping for my store,
Or are you weeping for your house carpenter,
That you never shall see any more?

8. It's I'm not a-weeping for your gold, she says,
And I'm not a-weeping for your store,
But I am a-weeping for my sweet little babe
That I never shall see any more.

9. She hadn't been dead but about three days,
Not more I will ensure,
Till there come a leak in her true love's ship
And it sunk for to rise no more.

8. "The House Carpenter"

E. C. and M. N. Kirkland, *SFQ*, II (1938), p. 75(A). Sung by Dr. Claudius M. Capps, Knoxville, Tenn., July 25, 1937; probably learned from his mother.

m M/D

I have married a king's daughter,
Most rich in gold and lands.
You have married a house carpenter;
I'm sure he's a fine young man.

9. [The Daemon Lover]

Sharp MSS., 4594/3213. Also in Sharp and Karpeles, 1932, I, p. 254(M). Sung by Mrs. Virginia Bennett, Burnsville, N.C., September 13, 1918.

m M/D

1. Well met, well met, my own true love,
Well met, well met, said he.
I've just returned from the salt, salt sea,
And it's all for the sake of thee,
And it's all for the sake of thee.
I've just returned from the salt, salt sea,
And it's all for the sake of thee.

2. I could have married a king's daughter fair,
I'm sure she would have married me,
But I refused those golden crowns,
And it's all for the sake of thee.

3. If you could have married a king's daughter fair,
I'm sure you are to blame,
For I am married to a house-carpenter,
And I think he's a nice young man.

4. I pray you leave your house-carpenter
And go away with me;
I'll take you down where the grass grows green
On the banks of the Aloe Dee.

5. Have you anything to support me on
To keep me from slavery?
Have you anything to supply my wants
To keep me from slavery?

6. I have three ships on the ocean wide,
Sailing towards dry land;
Three hundred and sixty sailor men
Shall be at your command.

7. She took her babe up in her arms,
And kisses gave it three,
Saying: Stay at home with your papa dear
And keep him company.

8. She dressed herself in silk so fine,
Most beautiful to behold.
As she marched down by the brine water side,
Bright shined those glittering golds.

9. She had not been on the sea two weeks,
I'm sure it was not three,
Till she lay on deck of her true lover's boat
And wept most bitterly.

10. Are you weeping for your silver and gold,
Or is it for your store,
Or is it for your house-carpenter
You never shall see any more?

11. I'm not weeping for my silver and gold,
Neither for my store;
'Tis all for the love of my darling little babe
I never shall see any more.

12. She had not been on sea but three weeks,
I'm sure it was not four,
Till a leak sprung in her true lover's boat,
And sank it to rise no more.

13. Accursed, accursed be all sea-men,
Accursed for ever more.
They've robbed me of my darling little babe,
I never shall see any more.

"Mrs. Bennett is Sam Bennett's second wife. She is a Kentucky woman raised on Sandy River on the edge of the blue grass country—a very sad-looking dour woman, very unlike the ordinary mountain-type of woman. Nearly all her songs she learned from her mother. She sings very beautifully in a very free way, but has a great dislike to tragedies and 'bluggy' songs, e.g. Young Hunting. For this reason she refused to sing The Cruel Mother which was one of her mother's songs." [*Sharp's MS. note.*]

10. [The Daemon Lover]

Sharp MSS., 3488/2572. Also in Sharp and Karpeles, 1932, I, p. 245(B). Sung by Mrs. Sarah Buckner, Black Mountain, N.C., September 18, 1916.

m M/D

1. Well met, well met, my old true love,
Well met, well met, says he,
I've just returned from the salt water sea
And it's all for the sake of thee.

2. We've met, we've met, my old true love,
We've met, we've met, says she,
I have just married a house carpenter,
A nice young man is he.

3. If you'll forsake your house carpenter
And go along with me,
I'll take you where the grass grows green
On the banks of sweet Tennessee.

4. She pick-ed up her tender little babe
And kisses gave it three.
Stay here, stay here, my tender little babe,
And keep your pa company.

5. They hadn't been a-sailing but about two weeks,
I'm sure it was not three,
Till this fair damsel began for to weep,
She wept most bitterly.

6. O what are you weeping for, my love?
Is it for my gold or store?
Or is it for your house carpenter,
Whose face you'll see no more?

7. I'm neither weeping for your gold,
Nor neither for your store,
But I'm weeping for my tender little babe
Whose face I'll see no more.

8. What banks, what banks before us now
As white as any snow?
It's the banks of Heaven, my love, she replied,
Where all good people go.

9. What banks, what banks before us now
As black as any crow?
It's the banks of hell, my love, he replied,
Where I and you must go.

10. They hadn't been sailing but about three weeks,
I'm sure it was not four,
Till that fair ship begin for to sink,
She sank and riz' no more.

11. [The Daemon Lover]

Sharp MSS., 4196/. Sung by Mrs. Nanny Birch, Buena Vista, Va., April 30, 1918.

m M/D

Well met, well met, my own true love,
Well met, well met, says he,
I've just returned from the salt sea side
And it's all for the sake of thee.

12. [The Daemon Lover]

Sharp MSS., 3869/. Sung by Mrs. Sophie Annie Hensley, Oneida, Ky., August 17, 1917.

m M/D

Well met, well met, my own true love,
Well met, well met, cried he;
Its I've just returned from the salt, salt sea
And it's all for the sake of thee.

13. "The Ship Carpenter"

Sung by Clay Walters, Salyersville, Ky., 1937. LC/AAFS, rec. No. 1580(B2). Collected by Allan and Elizabeth Lomax.

m M/D

Mr. Walters knew a different version of this ballad. See variant 78 below.

1. Well met, well met my old true love,
   Long I have been searching for thee,
 I have lately crossed the salt rolling sea
   And it's all for the sake of thee.

2. O I could have married the king's daughter fair,
   I'm sure that she would have had me
 But I refused that rich crown of gold
   And it's all for the sake of thee.

3. If you could have married the king's daughter fair
   I'm sure that you are to blame
 For I am married to the ship's carpenter
   And I think he's a nice young man.

4. O what have you to maintain me on?
   Is it houses, land or fee?
 I have seven loaded ships a-sailing on the sea,
   Besides one that brought me to land.

5. She pick'd up her babe all in her arms
   And kisses she give it three
 And laid it down on a soft bed of down
   To keep its pappy company.

6. (?)Now as they(?) sailed all on the sea
   The music it seemed so sweet
 She thought of her babe she left behind
   And sat herself down to weep.

14. [The Daemon Lover]

Sharp MSS., 3326/2430. Also in Sharp and Karpeles, 1932, I, p. 252(J). Sung by Mrs. Anelize Chandler (51), Alleghany, N.C., August 28, 1916.

m M/D

1. We've met, we've met, my own true love,
 We've met, we've met once more.
 I've lately crossed the salt water sea
 And it's all for the sake of you.

2. It's I could have married the king's daughter dear,
 I'm sure she'd a' married me,
 But I forsaked her crowns all in gold
 And it's all for the sake of you.

3. It's if you could have married the king's daughter dear,
 I'm sure that you ought to,
 For I am married to the house carpenter,
 I'm sure he's a fine young man.

4. It's if you forsake your house carpenter
 And go along with me,
 I'll take you where the grass grows green
 On the banks of sweet Lilee.

5. Pray tell me what wealth you have on board
 To keep me from slavery?
 I have three ships a-sailing from Spain
 Besides three hundred soldier boys,
 You can have all at your command.

6. She picked up her tender little babe,
 She kissed it two or three.
 It's you a-stay with your papee,
 I'm sure he'll be good to thee.

7. It's are you weeping for your house and land,
 Or are you weeping for your stores,
 Or are you weeping for your house carpenter
 Whom you never shall see no more?

8. I'm neither weeping for my house carpenter,
 Nor neither for my stores,
 I'm a-weeping for my tender little babe
 Whom I never shall see no more.

9. They'd been on sea about three weeks,
 I'm sure it was not four,
 Till this old ship sprang with a leak
 To sink, to rise no more.

15. "House Carpenter"

Sung by Mrs. Allie Long Parker, Arkansas, September 2, 1958. LC/AAFS, rec. No. 11,903(B14). Collected by Max Hunter.

m D

1. We've met, we've met, my own true love,
   We've met, we've met, cried he.
 I've just returned from the salt salt sea
   And it's all for the love of thee.

2. I could have married a king's daughter,
   I'm sure she'd have married me,
But strings of gold I did refuse
   And it's all for the love of thee.

3. If you could have married a king's daughter,
   I'm sure you are to blame,
For I'm married to a house carpenter
   And I'm sure he's a nice young man.

4. Won't you forsake your house carpenter
   And go along with me?
I'll take you to where the grass grows green
   On the banks of the sweet lily.

5. If I forsake my house carpenter
   And go along with you,
What have you there to maintain me upon,
   And to keep me from slavery?

6. O don't you see them seven ships
   A-sailing for dry land?
There's a hundred and ten of the finest waiting men
   And they'll all be at your command.

7. She pickèd up her precious little babe
   And kisses gave it three,
Say'ng, Stay here, stay here, my precious little babe,
   Keep your papa company.

8. They had not been at sea two weeks,
   I'm sure it was not three,
Till this fair damsel began for to weep,
   And she wept most bitterly.

9. What are you weeping for my gold
   Or is it for my store,
Or is it for your house carpenter
   That you left on old England's shore?

10. I'm neither weeping for your gold
   Nor is it for your store;
I'm weeping for my precious little babe
   That I never shall see any more.

11. They had not been on sea three weeks,
   I'm sure it was not four,
Till under the deck there sprang a leak,
   And she sank to rise no more.

12. O curse, o curse all seamen, cried she,
   O curse them unto me,
They have robbed me of my house carpenter
   And now they are drownding me.

13. O don't you see that turtle-dove
   A-flying from vine to vine?
He's mourning for his own true love
   Just like I mourn for mine.

16. "House Carpenter"

Sung by Celia Kelter, New York City (?), October 7, 1950 (?). LC/AAFS, rec. No. 10,505(B30). Collected by Sam Eskin.

a I (inflected IV?)

If you'll [*sic*] forsake your house carpenter
   And go along with me, [*sic*]
What have you got to support me on
   And to keep me from slavery?

Don't you see those yonder ships,
   As bright as bright can be?
I will make you the mistress of them all,
   If you will follow me.

17. [The Daemon Lover]

Sharp MSS., 3647/. Sung by Mrs. Poff, Barbourville, Ky., May 7, 1917.

m M/D

Come along my pretty little miss,
And come and go with me,
I'll take you where the grass grows green
On the banks of Sweet Galilee.

18. "House Carpenter"

Sung by Warde H. Ford, Crandon, Wisc., August 1954. LC/AAFS, rec. No. 11,337(B3). Collected by Sidney Robertson Cowell.

m D

1. I'm going away from you, Mary Anne,
   I'm going away for awhile.
   I'm going away but I'll come back again
   If I go ten thousand miles.
   I'm going away but I'll come back again
   If I go ten thousand miles.

2. Now, if I prove false to you, Mary Anne,
   If I should not return,
   May the sun turn to blood and the moon shade the earth,
   And the raging billows burn,
   May the sun turn to blood and the moon shade the earth,
   And the raging billows burn.

3. And to you I'll swear by the stars above,
   And the rolling waves of the sea,
   By the lily of the valley and the fowls of the air
   That I'll ever prove constant to thee,
   By the lily of the valley and the fowls of the air
   That I'll ever prove constant to thee.

4. Well met, well met, my own Mary Anne,
   Well met I say to thee,
   For I have just returned home from sea
   And it's all for the love of thee,
   For I have just returned home from sea
   And it's all for the love of thee.

5. Now I could have married the Queen's daughter fair,
   She fain would have married me,
   But I rejected all power and wealth,
   And it's all for the love of thee.
   Yes, I rejected all power and wealth,
   And it's all for the love of thee.

6. If you could have married the Queen's daughter fair,
   I'm sure you are undone,
   For I have married the house carpenter
   And he is a nice young man,
   For I have married the house carpenter
   And he is a nice young man.

7. O remember you swore by the stars above,
   The rolling waves of the sea,
   By the lily of the valley and the fowls of the air
   That you'd ever prove constant to me,
   By the lily of the valley and the fowls of the air
   That you'd ever prove constant to me.

8. But will you leave your house carpenter
   And go along with me?
   I'll take you to where the grass grows green
   On the banks of a sweet valley.
   I'll take you to where the grass grows green
   On the banks of a sweet valley.

9. If I should leave my house carpenter
   And go along with thee,
   What have you got to maintain me with
   And to keep me from poverty?
   What have you got to maintain me with
   And to keep me from poverty?

10. I have three ships upon the sea,
    And one upon the land,
    And they're all manned with brave gallant men
    And they're all at your command.
    Yes, they're all manned with gallant brave men
    And they're all at your command.

11. She laid her baby upon the bed,
    And kisses gave it three,
    Saying, Stay at home, my sweet little babe,
    Keep your father sweet company.
    Saying, Stay at home, my sweet little babe,
    Keep your father sweet company.

12. Now they had not sailed a league past two,
    I'm sure it was not three,
    When this fair lady was seen for to weep
    And to weep most bitterly,
    When this fair lady was seen for to weep
    And to weep most bitterly.

13. Now do you weep for the want of gold
    Or do you weep for fear?
    Or do you weep for that house carpenter
    Whom once you called your dear?
    O do you weep for that house carpenter
    Whom once you called your dear?

14. No, I do not weep for the want of gold
    Nor do I weep for fear.
    But I do weep for my sweet little babe,
    Likewise my husband dear.
    Yes, I do weep for my sweet little babe,
    Likewise my husband dear.

15. O cursed be you salt sailor men,
    And cursed be your lives,
    When you come to the homes of the house carpenters
    And steal away their wives,
    When you come to the homes of the house carpenters
    And steal away their wives.

16. Then three times round went this gallant ship
    And three times round went she.
    Yes, three times round went this gallant ship
    And she sank to the bottom of the sea.
    [*No repeat*]

19. "The House Carpenter"

Sung by Elizabeth Walker Ford, of Crandon, Wisc., in Central Valley, Calif., September 1952. LC/AAFS, rec. No. 11,336(A1). Collected by Sidney Robertson Cowell.

m D

a b c d

Mrs. Ford's text is the same as the preceding one, with slight differences. In singing, she did not repeat the last two lines of stanzas 5 and 10 (but did of the final stanza), and omitted stanza 8. In stanza 9, she sings "misery" in place of "poverty"; in 10, for "they're all" she sings "shall be"; in 12, for "to weep," "she wept"; in 15, "salt sea" for "salt sailor" men. In repeating lines, she never varies them as her son sometimes does with his trick of initial "yes."

20. "House Carpenter"

Sung by Miss Drucilla Hall, Milford, Ala., July 23, 1952. LC/AAFS, rec. No. 11,691(B27). Collected by Ray Browne.

m M/D

1. I'm just returned from sailing over sea
   And it's all for the love of thee.
   I could have married the king's daughter fair
   But refused for the love of thee.

2. . . . .
   . . . .
   Now I am married to the house carpenter
   And I think we can agree.

3. If you will come and go with me
   I'll carry you far far away,
   I'll carry you where the grass grows green
   On the banks of the sea, salt sea.

4. They had not sailed more than two weeks,
   I'm sure they hadn't sailed three,
   Till this fair damsel began for to weep,
   And she wept most bitterly.

5. Are you a-weeping for your gold
   Or is it for your store?
   Are you weeping for the house carpenter
   Which you never can see any more?

6. I'm neither weeping for my gold
   Nor is it for my store,
   But I'm weeping for my tender little babe
   Which I never can see any more.

7. What banks, what banks are those I see?
   They're just as white as a snow.
   'Tis the banks of heaven, she cried unto me,
   Where all good people go.

8. What banks, what banks are those I see?
   They're just as black as a crow.
   'Tis the banks of hell, she cried unto me,
   Where you and I shall go.

9. I hope no good will come to you,
   For stealing the house carpenter's wife.
   There sprang a leak into their ship,
   And it sank to arise no more.

21. [The Daemon Lover]

Sharp MSS., 4088/. Also in Sharp and Karpeles, 1932, I, p. 257(Q). Sung by Mrs. Doc Pratt, Hindman, Ky., September 22, 1917.

m D

Well met, well met, my old true love,
Well met, well met, said he,
For I've returned from the salt, salt sea,
And it's all for the sake of thee.

22. [The Daemon Lover]

Sharp MSS., 4428/. Sung by Mrs. Fulton Jones, St. Peter's School, Callaway, Va., August 14, 1918.

m M/D

If you forsake your house carpenter
And come along with me,
I'll carry you where the sugar cane grows
On the banks of Sweet Norlee.

23. [The Daemon Lover]

Sharp MSS., 3412/. Also in Sharp and Karpeles, 1932, I, p. 250(G). Sung by Mrs. Tempa Shelton (48), Spillcorn, N.C., September 6, 1916.

m M/D (III in variant)

We've met, we've met, my own true love
We've met we've met once more
I have lately crossed the salt water sea
And it's all for the sake of thee.

24. "The House Carpenter"

Sung by Pete Steele, Hamilton, Ohio, August 1957; learned from his sister Elizabeth Steele Jones. Folkways LP rec. No. FS 3828(B8). Collected by Ed Kahn.

m D

1. We have met, we have met, said my old true love,
We have met, we have met, said he,
For I've just come from a salt salt sea,
And it's all for the sake of thee.

2. I have refused a king's daughter fair,
I'm sure she'd have married me,
I have refused a crown of gold,
And it's all for the sake of thee.

3. If you have refused a king's daughter fair,
I'm sure you are to blame,
For I have married to a house carpenter,
And I'm sure he's a very fine man.

4. If I was to leave my house carpenter
And go along with you,
I'll take you where the sugar cane grows
On the bank of the deep blue sea.

5. She went unto her little babe,
Of kisses she gave three,
Lie there, lie there, my sweet little babe
And keep your father's company.

6. She went unto her golden store,
She dressed herself in green,
And as she walked the streets all around,
She looked like a lovely queen.

7. I'm not weeping for my house carpenter,
I'm not weeping for my store,
I am weeping for my sweet little babe
That I never shall see no more.

8. They had not gone but a week or two,
I'm sure not more than four,
Till her gallant ship by night did leak
And it sunk for to rise no more.

9. May cursed be to all sea men,
May cursed be their life,
For they have been the ruin of a house carpenter
In persuading away his wife.

10. Don't never believe what a young man says,
Let his hair be dark or brown,
Unless he's on some high gallis drop
And say he would like to come down.

11. Don't never believe what a young girl says,
Let her hair be dark or brown,
For she'll tell you more lies than the stars in the skies
Or the grass that grows on the ground.

25. "The House Carpenter"

Scarborough, 1937, p. 401(C); text, p. 153. Sung by Leonard Stevens, Council, Va., c. 1932.

m D

1. Well met, well met, my old true love,
Well met, well met, cried he.
I've just returned from the salt, salty sea
And it's all for the sake of thee.

2. Why I could have married the king's daughter Jane,
I'm sure she'd have married me,
But I've forsaken the crown of gold
All for the sake of thee.

3. If you could have married the king's daughter Jane,
I'm sure you are to blame,
For I have married to a house carpenter,
And I'm sure he's a nice young man.

4. Leave off, leave off your house carpenter
And go along with me,
I'll take you to where the green grass grows
On the banks of the sweet Andee.

5. Then she picked up her tender little babe
And kissed it one, two, three;
Says, You stay here till your pappy comes home
And keep him company.

6. Then she dressed herself all neat and clean,
And she dressed herself in green;
She glittered and she shined as she walked the streets
And they took her to be some queen.

7. They sailed along for two long weeks,
I'm sure it was not three,
Till this young lady began to weep
And she wept most bitterly.

8. Do you weep for gold, said he?
Or do you weep for store?
Or do you weep for the house carpenter
That you left on the distant shore?

9. I do not weep for gold, said she,
I do not weep for store.
But how I, how I weep for my tender little babe
That I never shall see any more.

10. They sailed along for three long weeks,
    I'm sure it was not four,
  Till the ship struck a leak and it sunk in the deep
    And it sunk to rise no more.

26. [The Daemon Lover]

Wilkinson MSS., 1936-37, p. 26(C). Sung by Mrs. Fred Hite, Thaxton, Va., October 13, 1936.

m D

Query if the original key signature was not intended for three flats? A Mixolydian variant here would be surprising, and I have assumed the Dorian on the strength of the powerful tradition. But observe Sharp's note to variant 30 following, and variant 31.

1. If you will forsaken your house carpenter,
   And go along with me,
   I will take you where the grass grows green,
   On the banks of sweet Willie.

2. She picked up her sweet little babe,
   And kisses gave it three;
   Saying, stay at home, my sweet little babe,
   And keep your father's company.

3. They had not been on sea two weeks,
   I am sure it was not three,
   Until she began to weep,
   And wept most bitterly.

4. Are you weeping for your house carpenter?
   Or are you weeping for your store?
   Or are you weeping for your sweet little babe,
   Whose face you shall see no more?

5. I am not weeping for my house carpenter,
   Nor neither for your store;
   But I am weeping for my sweet little babe,
   Whose face I shall see no more.

27. [The Daemon Lover]

Wilkinson MSS., 1936-37, p. 29(E). Sung by Mrs. Nellie M. Lawhorne, Waynesboro, Va., May 5, 1937.

m D

Cf. the note to the preceding variant.

1. Well met, well met, my old true love,
   Well met, well met, said he.
   I've just returned from the salt, salt sea,
   And it's all for the sake of thee.

2. I once could have married the king's daughter dear,
   And she would have married me.
   But I refused a crown of gold,
   And it's all for the sake of thee.

3. Well if you could have married the king's daughter dear,
   I'm sure you are to blame;
   For I have married a house carpenter,
   And I'm sure he's a nice young man.

4. Won't you forsake your house carpenter,
   And come and go with me?
   I'll take you where the grass grows green,
   On the banks of sweet Willie.

5. She gathered up her sweet little babe,
   And the kisses gave it three.
   Saying, Stay at home, my sweet little babe;
   Keep your father's company.

6. She dressed herself in silk array,
   Most beauty to behold;
   And as she walked along the street
   She shone like glittering gold.

7. They hadn't been on the sea quite two weeks,
   I'm sure it was not three,
   Before the lady began to weep,
   And she wept most bitterly.

8. Curse be to all the seafaring men,
   And woe be unto light;
   You've stolen me away from my house carpenter,
   And have robbed me of my life.

9. They hadn't been on the sea quite three weeks,
   I'm sure it was not four,
   Before the ship it sprang a leak,
   And sank to rise no more.

28. "Housecarpenter," or "Well Met"

Sung by Mrs. Bertha Basham Wright, of Franklin County, Ohio. LC/AAFS, rec. No. 11,453(A14). Collected by Anne Grimes.

m D

1. Well met, well met, my old true love,
   Well met, well met, cried he,
   I'm just returning from the salt salt sea
   And it's all for the sake of thee.

2. I once could have married a king's daughter dear,
   And she would have married me,
   But I've forsaken her crowns of gold
   And it's all for the sake of thee.

3. If you could have married a king's daughter dear,
   I'm sure you are to blame,
   For I am married to a house carpenter
   And I think he's a fine young man.

4. If you'll forsake your house carpenter
   And go along with me,
   I'll take you to where the grass grows green
   On the banks of sweet Willie.

5. If I forsake my house carpenter
   And go along with you,
   What have you got to maintain a wife upon
   Or keep her from slavery?

6. O I have thirteen ships on the sea,
   Three out on dry land,
   Three hundred and forty-five jolly sailor boys,
   And they're all at your command.

7. She pickèd up her sweet little babe
   Give it kisses one two three,
   Saying, Stay here, stay here, my sweet little babe
   And keep your papa's company.

8. She had not been on sea but two weeks,
   And I'm sure that it was not three,
   Till this young lady begin for to weep
   And wept most bitterly.

9. Are you weeping about my silver and gold,
   Are you weeping about my store,
   Are you weeping about your house carpenter
   That you'll never get to see any more?

10. I'm neither weeping for your gold,
    And neither for your store,
    But I'm weeping about my sweet little babe
    I'll never get to see any more.

11. They had not been on sea but three weeks,
    And I'm sure that it was not four,
    Till this young lady's ship sprang a leak
    And sank for to rise no more.

12. It's woe unto the seafaring man,
    It's woe unto his wife,
    For robbing of the house carpenter
    And taking away my life.

29. [The Daemon Lover]

Sharp MSS., 3473/. Also in Sharp and Karpeles, 1932, I, p. 251(I). Sung by Mrs. Hester House, Hot Springs, N.C., September 15, 1916.

m I—M (inflected VII)

Well met well met my own true love
Well met well met says he
I've just returned from the salt water sea
And its all for the sake of thee

30. [The Daemon Lover]

Sharp MSS., 4325/. Sung by Mrs. Lawrence Grey, Montvale, Va., June 4, 1918.

m D—M (inflected III)

"The [B♮] was always sung in penultimate bar but only occasionally in the 5th bar.

"Mrs. Smelts sang the song with her mother, and she evidently preferred the [B♭] in bar 5." [*Sharp's MS. notes.*]

You once could have married the king's daughter dear,
I'm sure you are to blame.
For I am married to a house-carpenter,
And I think he is a nice young man.

31. "House Carpenter"

Sung by Viola Cole, Fancy Gap, Va., July 10, 1962. LC/AAFS, rec. No. 12,006(B3). Collected by George Foss.

m M (VII sometimes sharp)

1. Well met, well met, my own true love,
 Well met, well met, cried he.
 I've just returned from the deep blue sea
 And it's all for the sake of thee.

2. I could have married a king's daughter fair,
 I'm sure she'd have married me.
 But I refused her crown of gold
 And it's all for the sake of thee.

3. If you could have married a king's daughter fair,
 I'm sure you are to blame,
 For now I am a house carpenter's wife,
 And I think he's a nice young man.

4. If you'll forsake your house carpenter
 And go and live with me,
 I'll take you where the grass grows green
 On the banks of the deep blue sea.

5. If I forsake my house carpenter
 And go and live with thee,
 What have you there to support me on
 To keep me from slavery?

6. I have six ships sailing on the ocean,
 I have a wealthy store,
 I have one hundred and sixty sailor men,
 Who will sail up to your door.

7. Then picking up her sweet little babe
 And kisses she gave it three,
 Saying, Stay at home with your papa dear
 To keep him company.

8. We hadn't been on ship more than two weeks,
 I'm sure it was not three,
 Till that young lady began to weep,
 And she wept most bitterly.

9. O is it for my gold you weep,
 Or is it for my store?
 Or is it for the house carpenter
 His (whose?) face you'll see no more?

10. It is not for your gold I weep,
 It is not for your store.
 It's all for the sake of the sweet little babe
 Which I left on the other shore.

11. We hadn't been on ship more than three weeks,
 I'm sure it was not four,
 Till there came a break in the bottom of the boat,
 And it sank to rise no more.

12. I wish to the Lord I'd never been born,
 Or died when I was young,
 I'd never seen your red rosy cheeks,
 Or heard your lying tongue.

32. "The House Carpenter"

Cox, 1939, p. 38; and 1964 (ed. Boswell), p. 48. Contributed by Aubrey F. Goff, Lenore Mingo County, W.Va., October 18, 1927. Obtained from Lawrence Johnson, who had it from Troy Newsome, Dingess, Mingo County, c. 1910.

m D

1. "Well met, well met, my old true love,
 Well met, well met," said he,
 "For I've just returned from the salt, salt sea,
 And it's all for the sake of thee."

2. "I once could have married a king's daughter fair,
 I'm sure she'd have married me,
 But I forsaken that king's daughter fair,
 And it's all for the sake of thee."

3. "If you could have married a king's daughter fair,
 Much better 'twould have been for thee;
 For I am married to a house-carpenter,
 And a fine young man is he."

4. "If you'll forsaken your house-carpenter,
 Come, go along with me,
 I'll take you where the grass is ever green,
 On the banks of the old Tennessee."

5. "What have you got to support me upon,
 And save me from slavery?"
 "Six ships and an ark on the salt-water sea,
 And it's all for the sake of thee."

6. She picked up her tender little babes,
 And kissed them, one, two, three:
 "Stay at home, stay at home with your papa, little ones,
 And keep him company."

7. She walked all up and down the deck,
 All dressed in purple and green,
 And every station that they sailed by,
 They thought she was a queen.

8. They hadn't been sailing more than two weeks,
   I'm sure that it wasn't three,
When this young lady began to weep,
   And she wept most bitterly.

9. "Are you weeping for gold, my love,
   Or are you a-weeping for store?
Or are you a-weeping for your house-carpenter,
   Which you never expect to see any more?"

10. "I'm not a-weeping for gold," she said,
   "And I'm not a-weeping for store,
But I'm a-weeping for my tender little babes,
   Which I never expect to see any more."

11. "What hills, what hills are those my love,
   That look so bright and green?"
"Those are the hills of heaven, my love,
   Which you and I will never see."

12. "What hills, what hills are those, my love,
   That look so rough and steep?"
"Those are the hills of hell, my love,
   Where you and I must meet."

13. They hadn't been sailing more than three weeks,
   I'm sure it was not four,
When there sprang a leak in the bottom of the ship,
   And she sank to rise no more.

33. [The Daemon Lover]

Wilkinson MSS., 1936-37, p. 24(A). Sung by T. M. Snead, Montebello, Va., September 24, 1936.

m D (III sometimes neutral)

1. Well met, well met, my old true love,
Well met, well met, says he;
I've lately returned from the salt sea,
And it's all for the love of you.
I've lately returned, &c.

2. If you will forsaken your house carpenter,
And go along with me,
I'll take you where the grass grows green,
On the banks of sweet Italy.
I'll take you, &c.

3. She took her babe from her breast,
And kisses gave it three,
Says, stay at home, my sweet little babe,
Bear your father's company.
Says, stay at home, &c.

4. I could have married a king's daughter,
And faith she would have married me;
But I refused the crown of gold,
And it's all for the sake of thee.
But I refused, &c.

5. If you could have married the king's daughter,
I'm sure you are to blame;
For I am married to a house carpenter,
And they say he's a nice young man.
For I am married, &c.

6. She dressed herself in glittering gold,
Her waist was trimmed in green;
As she went marching down the street
She was taken to be some queen.
As she went, &c.

7. They had not been on sea two weeks,
I'm sure it was not three,
Till she began to mourn and to weep,
And she wept most bitterly.
Till she began, &c.

8. What are you weeping for, my dear,
My silver or my gold?
Or is it for your house carpenter
You never will see anymore?
Or is it, &c.

9. They had not been on sea three weeks,
I'm sure it was not four,
Before the ship sprang a leak in the bottom,
And it sank for to rise no more.
Before the ship, &c.

34. [The Daemon Lover]

Wilkinson MSS., 1936-37, p. 28(D). Sung by J. W. Allen, Thaxton, Va., October 13, 1936.

m D

1. Well met, well met, my own true love,
Well met, well met, says he;
I've just returned from the Salt Lake sea,
And 'twas all for the sake of thee.

2. Once I could have married a king's daughter,
   I'm sure she'd have married me;
   But I forsaken that crown of gold,
   And 'twas all for the sake of thee.

3. If you could have married a king's daughter,
   I'm sure you were for to blame;
   For I am married to a house carpenter,
   And I'm sure he's a nice young man.

4. If you will forsake your house carpenter,
   And go along with me,
   I'll take you where the grass grows green,
   On the banks of our sweet Willie.

5. She dressed herself in the finest of silk,
   Most glorious to behold;
   And as she walked along the street,
   She shined like glittering gold.

35. [The Daemon Lover]

Wilkinson MSS., 1936-37, p. 26(B). Sung by J. Y. Anderson, Montebello, Va., October 11, 1936.

m D/Æ

If you will forsaken your house carpenter
And go along with me,
I will take you away where the grass grows green,
On the banks of sweet Willie.

36. [The Daemon Lover]

Sharp MSS., 4330/. Also in Sharp and Karpeles, 1932, I, p. 256(P). Sung by Mrs. Laura V. Donald (68), Dewey, Va., June 6, 1918.

m D (inflected III)

We've met, we've met, my old true love,
We've met, we've met, cried he,
I'm just returned from the salt water sea
And it's all for the love of thee.

37. [The Daemon Lover]

Sharp MSS., 4309/. Sung by Hiram L. Dooley, Blue Ridge Springs, Va., June 2, 1918.

m D

Well met, well met, my old true love,
Well met, well met, cries he,
I have just returned from the salt water sea
And it's all for the sake of thee.

38. "Daemon Lover," or "House Carpenter"

Sung by Mrs. Oscar Allen (62), Lynchburg, Va., September 15, 1950. LC/AAFS, rec. No. 10,004(A16). Collected by Maud Karpeles and Sidney Robertson Cowell.

m D (III once sharp)

1. Well met, well met, my own true love,
      Well met, well met, said he.
   I've just returned from the salt water sea,
      And 'twas all for the sake of thee.

2. I once could have married a king's daughter dear,
      And she would have married me.
   But I refused the crown of gold,
      And 'twas all for the sake of thee.

3. If you could have married a king's daughter dear,
      Vow married at your command [*sic*],
   For I have married a house carpenter,
      And I think he's a nice young man,
      And I think he's a nice young man.

4. If you forsake your house carpenter,
      And come and go with me,

I'll take you where the grass grows green
On the banks of sweet Willie.

5. She picked her little baby up,
And kisses gave it three,
Saying, Stay at home, my darling little babe,
And keep your Dad's company,
Saying, Stay at home, my darling little babe,
And keep your Dad's company.

6. They had not been on sea two weeks,
I'm sure it was not three,
Before the lady she began to weep,
And she wept most bitterly.

7. Are you weeping for your house carpenter,
Are you weeping for your gold?
Or are you weeping for your house carpenter
Whose face you'll see no more?

8. I am not weeping for my house carpenter,
Or neither for my gold.
I'm weeping for my darling little babe,
Whose face I'll see no more.
I'm weeping for my darling little babe,
Whose face I'll see no more.

9. They had not been on sea three weeks,
I'm sure it was not four,
Before the ship it sprang a leak,
And it sank to rise no more.

39. [The Daemon Lover]

Sharp MSS., 4393/. Sung by William Gross, Peaks of Otter, Bedford County, Va., July 26, 1918.

m D

If you could have married a King's daughter dear,
I'm sure you are to blame,
For now I'm married to a house carpenter,
And I think he's a nice young man.

40. [The Daemon Lover]

Sharp MSS., 4673/. Sung by David Webb, Burnsville, N.C., September 22, 1918.

m M/D

41. "House Carpenter"

Sung by Myrtle Downing, Somerton, Ariz., December 10, 1948. LC/AAFS, rec. No. 11,715(B29). Collected by Sam Eskin.

m M/D

The intonation was very uncertain.

Will you forsake your house carpenter
And come along with me?
I'll take you where the grass grows green
On the banks of some rolling sea.

How can I forsake my house carpenter
And go along with thee?
What have you got to support me on
To keep me from slavery?

She caught up her sweet little babe,
She kissed him one two or three,
Saying, Stay at home with your papa dear,
And keep him company.

42. "The House Carpenter"

Davis, 1929, p. 592(D); text, p. 445. Contributed by Juliet Fauntleroy, February 19 and August 1, 1914, from the singing of Mrs. Jessie Maxie, Altavista, Va.

m M/D

1. "I've come, I've come, my own true love,
I've come, I've come," said he.
"I've crossed the salty waters deep, } *Repeat*
And it's all for the love of thee."

2. "I could have married a king's daughter fair,
She would have married me,
But 't was all for refuses of her silver and her gold,[1]
And all for the love of thee."

3. "If you could have married a king's daughter fair,
I'm sure you are to blame;
For I have married a house carpenter,
I'm sure he's a nice young man."

4. "If you will leave your house carpenter
And go along with me,
I'll carry you where the grass grows green,
On the banks of sweet Italy."

5. "If I should leave my house carpenter
And go along with thee,
What have you there to maintain me upon
And keep me from a slav'ry?"

6. "I have a hundred ships on sail,
All sailing for dry land,
Five hundred and ten brave, jolly sailor men[2]
Shall be at your command."

7. She called to her side her sweet little babe,
Her kisses was one, two, three,
Saying, "Stay at home, my sweet little babe,
And keep your papa company."

8. She hadn't been on water two weeks,
I'm sure it was not three,
'Fore this fair lady she began to weep,
And she wept most bitterly.

9. "Are you weeping for your money, my love?
Are you weeping for your store?
Are you weeping for your house carpenter
That you left so far on shore?"

10. "No, I'm not weeping for my money, my love,
Nor neither for my store;
I'm weeping for my sweet little babe
That I never shall see any more."

11. She hadn't been on water three weeks,
I'm sure it was not four,
'Fore this fair lady she began to weep,[3]
And sank for to rise no more.

12. Come all of you now, nice young girls,
Take warning now from me
And never leave your house carpenter
To go with a man on sea.

[1] Variant reading: "But 't was all for the *refusal* of her *riches* and her gold."
[2] Variant reading: *One* hundred and ten, etc."
[3] Variant reading: "*Before* this fair lady she *sprang a leap*."

43. "House Carpenter's Wife"

Brown MSS., 16 a 4 c. From Mrs. Maude M. Sutton.

m M/D

We have met we have met my own true love
We have met we have met said he
I am just returning from the salt salt sea
And it's all for the love of thee.

44. "The House Carpenter"

Sung by Jean Ritchie. Folkways LP rec. No. FA 2301(A5), ed. K. S. Goldstein.

m D

1. Well met, well met, my own true love,
Well met, well met, said he,
I've come from far across the sea
And it's all for the sake of thee.

2. I could have married the King's daughter fair,
And she would've married me,
But I have forsaken the crowns of gold
And it's all for the sake of thee.

3. If you could've married a king's daughter fair,
I'm sure I'm not to blame,
For I have married me a house carpenter
And I'm sure he's a fine young man.

4. Oh will you leave your house carpenter
And sail away with me
I'll take you where the grass grows green
Down in sweet Italy.

5. Oh if I leave my house carpenter,
And sail away with ye,
What will ye have to maintain me upon
When we are far away.

6. Oh I have seven ships upon the sea
Seven ships upon the land
Four hundred and fifty bold sailor men
To be at your command.

7. She turned herself three times around
She kissed her babies three,
Farewell, farewell you sweet little babes
Keep your father sweet company.

8. They hadn't been sailin' but about two weeks,
I'm sure it was not three
When this fair lady begin for to weep
And she wept most bitterly.

9. Are you weepin' for your house carpenter
Are you weepin' for your store
Or are you weepin' for your sweet little babes,
That you never shall see any more.

10. Not a-weepin' for my house carpenter
Not a-weepin' for my store
Yes, I'm weepin' for my sweet little babes
That I never will see any more.

11. They hadn't been sailin' but about three weeks,
I'm sure it was not four,
When the ship spring a leak and down she sank
And she sank to rise no more.

12. What hills, what hills so fair and so bright,
What hills so white and fair?
Oh those be the hills of heaven, my dear,
But you won't never go there.

13. What hills, what hills down in yonder sea,
What hills so black as coal?
Oh those be the hills of hell, my dear,
Where we must surely go.

45. [The Daemon Lover]

Wilkinson MSS., 1935-36, p. 89(C). Sung by R. H. Mace, Grottoes, Va., October 30, 1935.

m D (inflected III once)

"Mr. Mace invariably sang [B♭] after he had got into the song." [*Wilkinson's MS. note.*]

1. Well met, well met, my own true-love,
Well met, well met, says he.
I've lately returned from the salt water sea,
And it's all for the sake of thee.
I've lately returned from the salt water sea,
And it's all for the sake of thee.

2. I once could have married a King's daughter dear,
And he would have agree.
And I refused that crown of gold,
And it's all for the love of thee.

3. If you could have married a king's daughter dear,
I'm sure you are to blame.
I've lately been married to a house carpenter,
And I think he's a nice young man.

4. Won't you forsaken your house carpenter
And go along with me?
I'll take you where the grass grows green
On the banks of the salt water sea.

5. She picked all up her sweet little babe,
And kisses she gave it three.
Stay at home, stay at home, with your papa dear
And keep him company.

6. Oh they hadn't been sailing but about three weeks,
Not more than four I know.
Until this lady she began to weep,
And she wept most bitterly.

7. Are you weeping for the gold I have?
Are you weeping for my store?
Are you weeping for your house carpenter,
That you'll never get to see no more?

8. Oh I'm not weeping for the gold you have,
Neither weeping for your store.
But I am weeping for my sweet little babe
That I'll never get to see no more.

9. O they hadn't been sailing but about three weeks,
Not more than four I know.
Until there sprang a leak in the bottom of the ship,
And she sank for to rise no more.

46. "House Carpenter"

Brown MSS., 16 a 4 c. Also in Schinhan, *Music, Brown Collection*, IV, 1957, p. 101(J). Sung by Mrs. James Thomas; collected by Jessie Hauser.

a M/D

47. "The House Carpenter"

Sung by Mrs. Texas Gladden, Salem, Va., 1941. LC/AAFS, Album 1, rec. No. 1(A). Collected by Alan and Elizabeth Lomax.

m D

1. "Well met, well met, you old true-love!
Well met, well met!" said she [*i.e.*, he]
"I've just returned from the seashore sea,
From the land where the grass grows green.

2. "Well, I could have married a king's daughter there,
And she would have married me;
But I refused the golden crown
All for the sake of thee.

3. "If you'll forsake your house carpenter,
And come and go with me,
I'll take you where the grass grows green,
To the lands on the banks of the sea."

4. She went 'n' picked up her sweet little babe
And kissed it one, two, three,
Saying, "Stay at home with your papa dear,
And keep him good company."

5. She went and dressed in her very best,
As everyone could see.
She glistened and glittered and proudly she walked
The streets on the banks of the sea.

6. They hadn't been sailing but about three weeks—
I'm sure it was not four—
Till this young lady began to weep,
And her weeping never ceased any more.

7. "Are you mourning for your house carpenter?
Are you mourning for your store?"
"No, I'm mourning for my sweet little babe
That I never will see any more."

8. They hadn't been sailing but about four weeks—
I'm sure it was not more—
Till the ship sprang a leak from the bottom of the sea,
And it sank to rise no more.

"Copyright by Texas Gladden."

48. [The Daemon Lover]

Sharp MSS., 4269/. Also in Sharp and Karpeles, 1932, I, p. 257(R). Sung by Mrs. Willie Roberts, Nellysford, Va., May 22, 1918.

m Æ; or m M, ending on II

Well met, well met, my old true love,
Well met, well met, said he,
I've just returned from the salt, salt, sea,
And it's all for the sake of thee.

49. "House Carpenter"

Sung by H. L. Maxey, Ferrum, Va., 1939. LC/AAFS, rec. No. 2742(B2). Collected by Herbert Halpert.

m D (usually D/Æ)

1. Cursèd be the salt sea man
Cursèd be his life
For the robbing of the house carpenter
And taking away his wife.

2. Come in, come in, my old true love,
And set right here by me.
Oh, it's been three quarters of a year or more
Since I've spoke one word to thee.

3. If you will forsake your house carpenter
And go ā-long with me,
I'll carry you to where the grass grows green,
On the banks of the sweet Bewlea.

4. If I should forsake my house carpenter,
And go ā-long with you,
What have you there to support me on
And keep me from slavery?

5. Six ships was out on the ocean, dear,
And they all lined with gold:
Before you should suffer, my darling little girl,
I would have them all anchored and sold.

6. She hadn't a' been there but a week or two
I'm sure that it couldn't been three,
Before that ship she sprang a leak
And she wept most bitterly.

50. [The Daemon Lover]

Sharp MSS., 3608/2670. Also in Sharp and Karpeles, 1932, I, p. 252(L). Sung by Miss May Ray, of Lee County, Va., at Lincoln Memorial University, Harrogate, Tenn., April 29, 1917.

m Æ

1. O, I have married a queen's daughter,
I'm sure you are to blame,
And you have married a house-carpenter,
But I think he's a nice young man.

2. If you will leave your house-carpenter
And come and go with me,
I'll take you where the grass grows green
On old sweet Cavalry.

3. If I should leave my house-carpenter,
Go strolling along with thee,
What have you to keep and clothe me with
And to keep me from slavery?

4. I have a ship on the ocean a-sailing,
A-sailing for dry land,
Over one hundred and ten jolly men
Are here at your command.

5. She went picked up her sweet little babe,
And kisses she gave it three.
Stay at home, stay at home with your papa, little love,
And give him company.

6. She dressed herself in scarlet red,
Her belt was in green,
And every station that she came through
Her glittering gold was seen.

7. They hadn't been on sail but about two weeks,
I'm sure it was not three,
Till she began to weep and she began to mourn,
She wept most bitterly.

8. O are you weeping for gold, my love,
Or are you weeping for fee,
Or are you weeping for your house-carpenter
That you love much better than me?

9. I neither weep for gold, my love,
I neither weep for fee,
But I weep to return back again,
My sweet little baby to see.

10. You need not weep for gold, my love,
You need not weep for store,
You need not weep for your sweet little babe,
You'll see it never no more.

11. They hadn't been on sail but about three weeks,
I'm sure it was not four,
Till the ship sprang a leak and to bottom began to sink,
I'm sinking to rise no more.

12. Farewell, farewell to my sweet little babe,
Farewell to my friends on the shore,
Farewell, farewell to the man that parted me,
I'm sinking to rise no more.

13. What banks, what banks is that, my love,
As black as any crow?
The banks, the banks of hell, my love,
Where you and I shall go.

14. What banks, what banks is that, my love,
As white as any snow?
The banks, the banks of heaven, my love,
Where all tender little babes shall go.

51. "The House Carpenter"

Thomas, 1931, p. 172.

a Æ

1. "I have just returned from the salt, salt sea.
Just returned from the salt, salt sea,
And I had the offer of a King's daughter fair,
And she would have married me."

2. "If you had the offer of a king's daughter fair,
I am sure you are greatly to blame,
For I am married to a house carpenter
And I am sure he is a nice young man."

3. "Won't you leave your house carpenter
And go along with me?
For I am going where the grass grows green
On the banks of Italy."

4. "If I were to leave my house carpenter
And go along with you
You have nothing to support me upon.
Oh, then, what shall I do?"

5. "I have seven ships on sea,
And seven more at hand,
I have gold and silver, too,
It would all be at your command."

6. Then she picked up her darling little babe
And gave it kisses three,
Saying, "Stay at home with your pappy
And keep him company."

7. They had not been sailing above two weeks,
I am sure it was not three,
Until this fair girl began to weep
And she wept most bitterly.

8. "Are you mourning about your house carpenter?
Or are you mourning about your fees?
Or are you mourning about your darling little babe
For fear you never her will see?"

9. "I am not mourning about my house carpenter
Nor neither am I mourning about my fee,
But I am a-mourning about my darling little babe
For fear I never her shall see."

10. They had not been sailing above three weeks,
I am sure it was not four
Until under the deck, lo! she sprung a leak
And she sank for to rise no more.

By permission of the author, Jean Thomas, The Traipsin' Woman, from *Devil's Ditties* (published in Chicago by W. Wilbur Hatfield in 1931).

52. "The House Carpenter"

Davis, 1929, p. 594(V); text, p. 469. Also in Smith, *MQ*, II (1916), p. 127(B). Contributed by Juliet Fauntleroy, February 1914, from the singing of Alonzo and Miss Callie Hogan, Lynch Station, Va.

a D/Æ, or m M/D (with fallen close on *V*)

"Come in, come in, my own true love,
Come in, come in," said she.
"I haven't spoken a word to my own true love
In five or seven years."

"I can't come in, I can't stay here,
For I have not a moment of time;
For I heard you were married to a house carpenter,
And your heart is no more mine.

"If you will leave your house carpenter,
And go along with me,
I'll carry you where the grass grows green,
On the banks of sweet Willee."

She picked her babe up in her arms,
And kissed it one, two, three,
Saying, "Stay at home, my sweet little babe,
And keep your father company."

"O, do you weep for the gold that you left,
Or the dangers of the sea?
Or is it for fear of that house-carpenter
That you left when you came with me?"

"I do not weep for the gold that I left,
Or the dangers of the sea;
But it's all for the love of that little baby
That I left when I came with thee."

53. "The House Carpenter"

Barry, Eckstorm, and Smyth, 1929, p. 306(B). Sung by Mrs. Susie Carr Young, Brewer, Me.; traditional in her family. Tune recorded by George Herzog, 1928.

p π^5; or a π^4, ending on V

She took her baby [on her knee]
And she gave it kisses three,
Saying, "Stay at home, you sweet pretty babe,
Keep your father company."

They had not been out more than two weeks,
I'm sure it was not three,
Before this lady began to weep,
And she wept most bitterly.

54. "The Old Salt Sea"

Sharp MSS., 3110/?. Also in Sharp and Karpeles, 1932, I, p. 246(C). Sung by Mrs. Bishop, Clay County, Ky., July 16, 1909.

a M/D

1. Well met, well met, my own true love
Well met, well met, says he;
O I am from a foreign land,
All alone for the sake of thee.

2. I could have been married to the Queen's daughter
And she would a-married me,
But I've forsaken her and her gold
All alone for the sake of thee.

3. If you could have married the Queen's daughter
And she would a-married you,
I'm sure you must be for to blame,
For I am married to a little house-carpenter,
And I think him a neat young man.

4. O will you forsake that house-carpenter
And go, O go along with me?
And I will take you where the grass grows green
On the banks of old Willie.

5. What have you got to maintain me?
And what have you got? says she;
O what have you got to maintain me on
While sailing on the sea?

6. Seven vessels all on shore,
Seven more on sea;
And I have got one hundred and ten neat young men
All alone for to wait on thee.

7. She dressed herself in finest silk,
Her baby she kissed, 'twas one, two, three.
O stay, O stay, O stay at home
And bear your father company.

8. She hadn't sailed but a day or two,
I'm sure it was not three,
Till she began to weep
And wept most bitterly.

9. Are you a-weeping for my gold and my silver?
Or are you a-weeping for my store?
Or are you a-weeping for that house-carpenter
That you will never see no more?

10. I'm neither weeping for your gold nor your silver,
I'm neither weeping for your store;
I'm a-weeping for my poor little baby
That I will never see no more.

11. Cheer up, cheer up, my pretty, fair maid,
Cheer up, cheer up, cried he,
For I will take you where the grass grows green
On the banks of the sweet Willie.

12. They did not sail but a day or two,
I'm sure it was not four
Till the vessel sprung a leak and began to sink,
And sank for to rise no more.

Text from the 1932 printing. Mrs. Campbell's texts are not in the numbered Sharp MSS.

55. "The House Carpenter"

Eddy, 1939, p. 74(C). Sung by Mrs. Galen W. Summer, Canton, Ohio.

m M/D (Dorian III in grace-note)

1. "We have met, we have met, my pretty fair maid,
We have met, my love," said he;
"For I've just returned from the salty, salty sea,
And it's all for the love of thee."

2. "You could have married a rich king's daughter,
And a handsome one was she;
But I am married to a house carpenter,
And a handsome man is he."

3. "If you will forsake your house carpenter,
And go along with me,
I'll take you where the grass grows green
On the banks of sweet liberty."

4. "If I forsake my house carpenter,
And go along with thee,
What have you got to maintain me upon,
Or to keep me from poverty?"

5. "Oh, don't you see those seven, seven ships,
All sailing for dry land?
Five hundred and ten brave and jolly men
Shall be at your command."

6. She called aloud to her sweet and pretty babe,
She gave it kisses three,
Saying, "Stay at home, my sweet and pretty babe,
Keep your father's company."

7. He dressed her up in rich array,
Most beautiful to behold,
And as she walked the city streets,
She shone bright as the glittering gold.

8. They had not been aboard two weeks,
'Twas neither two nor three,
Until this fair lady began to weep,
And she wept most bitterly.

9. "Oh, is it for my gold you weep,
Or is it for my fee,
Or is it for the house carpenter
That you left across the sea?"

10. "It's neither for your gold I weep,
Nor is it for your fee,
But alas, it is for that sweet and pretty babe
I left to mourn for me."

11. They had not been aboard two weeks,
It was neither two nor four,
Until under deck there sprang a leak,
And her mourning was heard no more.

56. "House Carpenter"

Sung by Mrs. Mary Bird McAllister, Brown's Cove, Va., October 31, 1959. LC/AAFS, rec. No. 11,868(A5). Collected by Paul C. Worthington.

m M/D

1. O I am married to a house carpenter
And he is a fine young man.

2. O will you forsaken your house carpenter
And go along with me?
I'll take you where the grass grows green
On the banks of sweet Kiddie.

3. She taken her little babe on her knee,
Gave't kisses one two three:
Stay at home, stay at home, my tender little friend,
And keep your pap's company.
Stay at home, stay at home, my tender little friend,
And keep your pap's company.

4. She hadn't been a-trav'lin' but the last two weeks,
I'm sure it was not three,
Before this vessel sprung out a leak,
And she wept most bitterly.
Before this vessel sprung out a leak,
And she wept most bitterly.

5. Or are you a-weeping for your gold,
Are you weeping for your store?
Are you weeping for your house carpenter
'At you never will see no more?

6. I'm neither weeping for my store
Nor neither for my gold.
I'm a-weeping for my tender little friend
That I never will see no more.
I'm a-weeping for my tender little friend
That I never will see no more.

7. She hadn't been sailing but the last three weeks,
I'm sure it was not four,
Before this vessel sprung out a leak,
And it sunk to rise no more,
Before this vessel sprung out a leak,
And it sunk to rise no more.

6. I have six ships upon the sea
All sailing for this land,
And a hundred and ten brave jolly bold men
Shall be at your command.

7. She picked up her three little babes
And gave them kisses three,
Saying, Stay here with your papa, my dear(s)
To keep him company.

57. "House Carpenter"

Sung by Robert Shiflett, Brown's Cove, Va., July 15, 1961. LC/AAFS, rec. No. 12,004(A3). Collected by George Foss.

m π^3

1. Well met, well met, my old true love
Well met, well met, cried he,
I have just returned from the great salt sea
To take thee away with me.

2. I once could have married a king's daughter fair,
She wanted to marry me,
But a crown of gold have I refused
Because of my love for thee.

3. If you could have married a king's daughter fair
I'm sure you are to blame,
For I am married to a house carpenter
And he is a nice young man.

4. Will you forsake your house carpenter
To sail away with me?
I will take you where the grass grows green
On the bank of the Low Country.

5. How can I leave my house carpenter,
O how could I leave I say?
How could I leave my sweet little babes
To sail so far away?

8. She arrayed herself in rich attire
Most glorious to behold,
And every hamlet they rode through
She shone and glittered like gold.

9. They had been on the sea about two weeks,
I'm sure it was not three,
When there sprang a leak in the bottom of the ship
And she sank to the bottom of the sea.

10. What is it that looms so dark,
As black as the feathers of a crow?
That is the smoke from the fires of hell
Where you and I must go.

11. What is it that looks so bright,
As white as the driven snow?
That is the gates of heaven itself
Where we may never go.

[*In talk following, he remembers there was a stanza on her weeping, and also*]

[Are you weeping for your gold]
Or is it for the store,
Or are you grieving for your house carpenter
That you'll never see any more?

It is not for the gold that I weep
And neither for the store,
But I am grieving for my three little babes
I'll never see any more.

"And then the last stanzas where she cursed herself and accused him of taking away her life." [*Singer's statement.*]

8. Oh, I don't weep for my gold, said she,
Nor I don't weep for my stow,
But I do weep for my tender little babe
that I never can see no more.

9. They hadn't been saling on the sea
Three weeks, I am sure it was not four,
Before the vessel sprung a leak
And it sank to rise no more.

10. Oh coursed be the sailor's life,
or any other strife
For he has robed me of my house carpenter
and he's taken away my life.

Miss Scarborough's text follows a MS. copy of Miss Morris's.

58. "A House Carpenter"

Scarborough, 1937, p. 401(B); text, p. 152. Sung by Miss Polly Morris, Yellow Branch, Pirkey, Va., c. 1932.

m M/D

1. Well met, well met, my own true love,
Well met, well met, said he.
I have lately returned from the salt water sea
And it's all for the sake of thee.

2. Oh, I could have married a king's daughter,
So free as she would me,
But all the rich crowns of gold I refused,
And it's all for the sake of thee.

3. If you could have married a king's daughter,
I am sure you air to blame,
For I have married to a house carpenter,
and he is a fine young man.

4. Oh do forsaken your house carpenter
And go along with me.
I will take you where the grass grows green
On the banks of the sweet Willie.

5. She picked up her tender little babe
And kisses gave it three,
Saying, stay here my tender little babe
keep your papa company.

6. They hadn't been sailing on the sea
Two weeks, I am sure it was not three,
Before this Damsel began for to weep
And she wept most bitterly.

7. Oh do you weep for your gold, said he,
Or do you weep for your stow?
Or do you weep for your house carpenter
that you never will see no more?

59. "House Carpenter"

Sung by Florence Shiflett (84), Wyatt's Mountain, near Dyke, Va., June 5, 1962. LC/AAFS, rec. No. 12,004(B10). Collected by George Foss.

m M/D

The repeat is not invariable.

1. We've met, we've met, my own true love,
We've met, we've met, says he,
I have lately returned from the salt water sea
And it was for the sake of you,
I have lately returned from the salt water sea,
And it was for the sake of you.

2. I once could have married to a king('s) daughter dear,
And she would have married me,
But offer 'f the crowns of gold I refused
And it was for the sake of you,
It was all for the sake of you.

3. If you could have married to the king('s) daughter dear,
I'm sure you wears the blame,
For I am married to a house carpenter
And they says he's a fine young man.

4. Will you forsaken your house carpenter
And go along with me?
I will carry you where the grass grow(s) green
On the banks of sweet Willie.

5. What have you to maintain me, my love,
   To keep me from starvation? says she.
I have a hundred of ships a-sailing on the sea,
   And they're sailing for dry land;
And a hundred and ten the finest waiting-men
   Will be at your command.

6. She picked up her tender little baby,
   The kisses they was three.
Stay at home, stay at home, my tender little one
   And keep your papa company.
Stay at home, stay at home, my tender little one
   And keep your papa company.

7. She wasn't sailing on the sea two weeks,
   I'm sure it was not three,
Before this fair damsel began for to weep,
   And she wept most bitterly.

8. Are you a-weeping for your husband, said he,
   Or are you weeping for your gold?
Or are you a-weeping for your house carpenter
   That you never will see no more?

9. I'm not a-weeping for my house carpenter
   Nor neither for my gold.
I am weeping for my tender little baby
   That I never will see no more.

10. She wasn't sailing on the sea three weeks,
   I'm sure it was not four,
Before this vessel sprung a leak and sunk,
   And it sunk for to rise no more.

60. [The Daemon Lover]

Wilkinson MSS., 1935-36, p. 87(A). Sung by Mrs. Jane Morris, Harriston, Va., October 9, 1935.

m M/D

Will you forsaken your house carpenter
And go along with me?
I will take you where the grass grows green
On the banks of the Sweet Marie.

61. [The Daemon Lover]

Wilkinson MSS., 1935-36, p. 88(B). Sung by Mrs. Mary McAllister, Grottoes, Va., October 30, 1935.

m M/D

She taken her little babe on her knee,
The kisses, one, two, three.
Stay at home, stay at home, my tender little friend,
And keep your papa's company.

She hadn't been a-sailing but the last two weeks,
I'm sure it was not three.
Before this vessel sprung out a leak,
And she wept most bitterly.

She hadn't been a-sailing but the last three weeks,
I'm sure it was not four.
Before this vessel sprung out a leak,
And it sunk to rise no more.

62. "The House Carpenter"

Davis, 1929, p. 593(H); text, p. 451. Contributed by John Stone, November 3, 1920, from the singing of Mrs. J. A. Mitchell, Miss Mary Mitchell, and Mrs. Holland Hoffman, Criglersville, Va.

m M/D

1. "Well met, well met, my old true love,
   Well met, well met," says he,
"I have just returned from the salt-water sea,
   And it's all for the sake of thee.

2. "I could have married a king's daughter dear,
   How vain she would have married me;
I refused her gold and her silver too,
   And it was all for the sake of you."

3. "If you could have married a king's daughter dear,
   I'm sure you are to blame;
For I have married a house carpenter
   And I think him a nice young man."

4. "Leave off, leave off your house carpenter,
   And go along with me.
I will carry you where the grass grows green
   On the banks of sweet relief."[1]

5. "What have you to keep me from slavery
   Or any other disagree?"

"I have a hundred and ten of the nicest waiting-men,
And they shall all be at your command.

6. "There are seven ships all sailing on the sea,
All sailing for dry land,
And a hundred and ten of the nicest waiting-men,
And they shall all be at your command."

7. She picked up her sweet little babe
And gave it kisses three,
Saying, "Along, along with your pappy go,
And keep his company."

8. She was sailing on the ship about two weeks,
I'm sure it was not three,
Before the damsel began to weep,
And she wept most bitterly.

9. "What are you a-weeping for? my gold?
Or are you for my store?
Or are you for that house carpenter
Whose face you will see no more?"

10. "I am neither a-weeping for your gold,
And neither for your store,
But a-weeping for my sweet little babe
Whose face I'll see no more."

11. She was sailing on the ship about three weeks,
I'm sure it was not four,
Before the vessel sprang a leak
And sank to rise no more.

12. "Cursed be, cursed be to a sailor's life
Or any other such a strife,
Who has robbed me off my house carpenter
And has taken away my life."

[1] "One sang the line, 'On the banks of the Sweet Moree.'" [*Davis's note.*]

63. "The House Carpenter"

Sung by Smith Harmon, Beech Creek, N.C., c. 1939. Collected by Hilda Kasting and Mrs. Carl Wiseman. Sent to Editor by Edward Cray, Los Angeles, Calif.

a M

1. "Well met, well met, my own true love.
Well met, well met are we.
I've just returned from the old salt sea,
And 'twas all for the sake of thee.

2. "I once could have married the king's daughter dear,
And she would have married me.
But I refused a crown of gold,
And it was all for the love of thee."

3. "And you could have married the king's daughter dear,
I am sure you are not to blame;
For I am married to a house-carpenter,
And I think he is a nice young man."

4. "If you will forsake your house-carpenter,
And go along with me,
I'll take you where the grass grows so green,
On the banks of sweet Relee."

5. She took up her sweet little innocent babe
And gave it kisses three.
Saying, "Stay at home, my sweet little babe,
And keep your papa company."

6. She dressed herself in silk so fine,
Most glorious to behold.
And as she walked down to the sea
She outshone the glittering gold.

7. She had not been on sea two weeks,
I'm sure it was not three,
Till she burst out a-weeping.
And she wept most bitterly.

8. "Are you weeping for my silver or my gold?
Are you weeping for my store?
Or are you a-weeping for that sweet little babe,
Which you shall never see anymore?"

9. "I'm not a weeping for your silver nor gold,
Neither for your store,
But I am a-weeping for that sweet little babe,
Which I shall never see anymore."

10. She had not been on the sea three weeks, I think;
I am sure it was not four,
Till there came a leak in her true lover's ship,
And it sank to rise no more.

11. Once around went our gallant ship,
Twice around went she,
Three times around went our gallant ship,
And she sank to the bottom of the sea.

12. Oh, cursed be the sea-going train,
And all the sailors' lives,
For the robbing of the house-carpenter
And the taking away of his wife.

64. "The House Carpenter"

Scarborough, 1937, p. 400(A); text, p. 151. Sung by Mrs. Evelyn Collier, Pirkey, Va., c. 1932; learned from her father.

m Æ

1. Well met, well met, my old true love,
   Well met, well met, said he.
   I've come from the land where the grass grows green
   On the banks of the Sweet Willie.

2. I could have married a king's daughter,
   So freely she would to me,
   But it's all for the sake of thee,
   But it's all for the sake of thee.

3. If you could have married a king's daughter,
   I'm sure you were to blame,
   For I have married a house carpenter
   And he is a fine young man.

4. Can't you forsake your house carpenter
   And go along with me?
   I'll take you to the land where the grass grows green
   On the banks of the Sweet Willie.

5. She picked up her tender little babe,
   The kisses she gave it was three,
   Saying, Stay at home, my tender little babe,
   Keep your papa company.

6. They hadn't been sailing on the sea two weeks,
   And I'm sure it was not three,
   Before the damsel began to weep,
   And she wept most bitterly.

7. What are you weeping for,—my gold,
   Or is it for my store?
   Or is it for the house carpenter
   That you shall never see any more?

8. I'm not a-weeping for your gold,
   And it is neither for your store,
   I'm weeping for my tender little babe
   That I shall never see any more.

9. They hadn't been sailing on the sea three weeks,
   And I'm sure it was not four,
   Before the vessel began to sink,
   And it sank to rise no more.

65. [The Daemon Lover]

Sharp MSS., 4745/. Also in Sharp and Karpeles, 1932, I, p. 256(N). Sung by Mrs. Ef Chrisom, Cane Branch, Burnsville, N.C., October 3, 1918.

m M/D

Well met, well met, my own true love,
Well met, well met, said he
I've just returned from the salt water sea
And it's all for the sake of thee.

66. "The House Carpenter"

Gardner and Chickering, 1939, p. 56(B). Sung by Otis Evilsizer, Alger, Mich., 1935.

m M/D

1. "Well met, well met, my pretty fair maid,
   Well met, well met," cried he,
   "For I have crossed the salty, salty sea,
   And 'twas all for the love of thee.
   For I have crossed the salty, salty sea,
   And 'twas all for the love of thee.

2. "O I could have married a king's daughter,
   And she would have married me;
   But I have returned to old Amerikie,
   And 'twas all for the love of thee."

3. "If you could have married the king's daughter,
   I'm sure you're much to blame,
   For I have married the house carpenter,
   And I think he's a fine young man."

4. "If you will forsake your house carpenter
   And go along with me,
   I will take you to where the grass grows green
   On the banks of Italy."

5. "If I should forsake my house carpenter
   And go along with thee,
   O what have you got to maintain me on
   Or to keep me from slavery?"

6. "O I have ten ships that's now in port
   And ten more out at sea,
   A hundred and ten brave sailor men,
   And they're all for to wait upon thee."

7. She dressed herself in scarlet red
   Most beautiful to behold,
   And then she went up and down the street,
   And she shone like glittering gold.

8. Then she picked up her lily-white babe
   And kisses she gave it three,
   Saying, "Stay at home for your papa's company
   While I am going on sea."

9. O they had not been on board two weeks,
   I'm sure it was not three,
   When this fair maid was known for to weep,
   And she wept most bitterly.

10. "O do you weep for more riches,
    Or could you ask for more,
    Or do you weep for that house carpenter
    That you left on the other shore?"

11. "O I do not weep for more riches,
Nor could I ask for more,
But I do weep for that pretty little babe
That I left on the other shore."

12. O they had not been on board three weeks,
I know it was not four,
When under deck there sprung a leak,
And their voices were heard no more.

67. "The House Carpenter"

Morris, 1950, p. 313. Sung by Mrs. C. S. McClellan, High Springs, Fla.; learned from her mother.

a M/D

1. "I have just come from the salt, salt sea,
And it was on account of thee,
For I've had an offer of a king's daughter fair,
And she fain would marry me."

2. "If you've had an offer of a king's daughter fair,
I think you're much to blame,
For I've lately been married to a house carpenter,
And I think he's a nice young man."

3. "If you'll forsake your house carpenter
And come, and come along with me,
I'll take you where the grass grows green,
On the banks of the deep blue sea."

4. "If I'd forsake my house carpenter
And go along with you,
And you'd have nothing to support me upon,
And then what would I do?"

5. She dressed herself in rich array
All from her golden store,
And as she walked the streets all-around,
She shone like a glittering star.

6. She called her baby unto her,
And gave it kisses three,
Saying, "Stay at home my pretty little babe,
And be your father's company."

7. We had not sailed more than two weeks;
I'm sure it was not over three,
Till this fair maid began to weep,
And she wept most bitterly.

8. "Are you weeping for your house carpenter,
Or for your golden store,
Or weeping for that sweet little babe
You never shall see any more?"

9. "I do not weep for my house carpenter,
Nor for my golden store,
I'm weeping for my sweet little babe,
That I never shall see any more."

10. Accursed be the sea-going train
And all the sailors' lives
For the robbing of the house carpenter
And the taking away of his wife!

11. They hadn't been on board but a week,
Or two or three, I am sure,
Before the vessel sprung a leak,
And it sank to rise no more.

12. "I'm neither weeping for your silver nor your gold,
And I'm neither weeping for my store,
And I'm just a-weeping for my sweet little babe,
Whom I'll not see any more.

13. "Adieu, adieu, to all seamen,
Adieu to sailors, too;
You have robbed me of my house carpenter
And my babe I'll not see no more."

68. [The Daemon Lover]

Sharp MSS., 4543/. Sung by Mrs. William L. Godfrey, Marion, N.C., September 3, 1918.

a M/D

It's neither for your gold nor your silver,
It's neither for your store.
But I am weeping for my sweet little babe
That I never shall see any more.

69. "The House-Carpenter"

Barry, *JAF*, XXV (1912), p. 274. Sung by O. F. A. C[onner], Harrisburg, Pa., January 19, 1908.

a D

The notation of the original leaves the timing largely a matter of guess-work.

1. "Well-met, well-met, my own true love,
 Well-met, well-met," says he,
"I've just returned from the salt water sea,
 And it's all for the love of thee!"

2. "I might have married a king's daughter fair,
 In vain she'd have married me,
But I refused the crown of gold,
 And it's all for the love of thee!"

3. "If you could have married a king's daughter fair,
 I think you are much to blame,
For I have married a house-carpenter,
 And I think he's a nice young man."

4. "If you will forsake your house-carpenter,
 And will run away with me,
I'll take you where the grass grows green,
 On the banks of Italy!"

5. "If I forsake my house-carpenter,
 And will run away with thee,
What have you for to maintain me upon,
 And keep me from slavery?"

6. "I have four and twenty ships at sea,
 All making for dry land,
I've a hundred and forty jolly sailor boys,
 They shall all come at your command."

7. She pressed her babe up to her lips,
 And gave it kisses three,
Saying, "Stay here, stay, my sweet little babe,
 And keep your papa's company!"

8. She dressed herself in rich array,
 Most glorious to behold,
And as she walked the streets along,
 She shone like glittering gold.

9. They had not sailed but about two weeks,
 I'm sure it was not three,
Until this lady began to weep,
 And she wept most bitterly.

10. "Are you weeping for my gold?" said he,
 Or is it for my store?
Or are you weeping for that house-carpenter
 Which you never shall see any more?"

11. I'm not weeping for your gold," said she,
 "Nor is it for your store,
But I'm weeping for my sweet little babe,
 Which I never shall see any more."

12. They had not sailed but about three weeks,
 I'm sure it was not four,
Until this good old ship sprang a leak,
 And she sunk for to rise no more.

13. "Adieu, adieu, my jolly sailor boys!
 Adieu, adieu!" he cried,
"For I have robbed a house-carpenter,
 By the stealing away of his bride."

70. "The House Carpenter"

Sung by Clarence Ashley, 1930. Columbia rec. No. 15654 D; also on Folkways LP rec. No. FP 251(A3), ed. Harry Smith.

a D/Æ (Dorian VI in variants)

1. Well met, well met, said an old true love,
 Well met, well met, said he.
I'm just returning from the salt, salt sea
 And it's all for the love of thee.

2. Come in, come in, my old true love,
 And have a seat with me.
It's been three fourths of a long, long year
 Since together we have been.

3. Well I can't come in or I can't sit down
 For I haven't but a moment's time.
They say you're married to a house-carpenter
 And your heart will never be mine.

4. Now it's I could have married a king's daughter dear,
 I'm sure she'd have married me
But I've forsaken her crowns of gold
 And it's all for the love of thee.

5. Now will you forsaken your house-carpenter
 And go along with me?
I'll take you where the grass grows green
 On the banks of the deep blue sea.

6. She picked up her little babe
 And kisses gave it three,
Says, Stay right here, my darling little babe,
 And keep your Papa company.

7. Well they hadn't been on ship but about two weeks,
 I'm sure it was not three,
When his true love began to weep and mourn
 And (she) weeped most bitterly.

8. Says, Are you weeping for my silver or my gold?
 Says, Are you weeping for my store?
Are you weeping for that house-carpenter
 Whose face you'll never see any more?

9. No it's I'm not a-weeping for your silver or your gold
 Or neither for your store.
I am weeping for my darling little babe
 Whose face I'll never see any more.

10. Well they hadn't been on ship but about three weeks,
    I'm sure it was not four,
Till they sprung a leak in the bottom of the ship
    And it sunk for to rise no more.

71. "The House Carpenter"

Sung by Almeda Riddle, of the Ozark foothills, 1959-60. Prestige International LP rec. No. INT-DS 25003(A3). Collected by Alan Lomax.

a M/D

1. "Well met, well met, my own true love,
Well met, well met," quoth he.
"Now I could have been married to a King's daughter fair,
And would have but for love of thee—
I would have, but remembered thee."

2. "Now if you could have married a King's daughter fair,
I'm sure you're much to blame,
For I am now married to a house carpenter,
And I think he's a fine young man—
And I proudly wear his name."

3. "Now if you leave your house carpenter
And will come and go with me,
I'll take you where the grass grows green
On the banks of the sweet Willie—
And pleasure we will see."

4. "And if I leave my house carpenter
And go along with thee,
What have you to maintain me on
To keep me from poverty—
To keep me from poverty?"

5. "Well, seven ships on the ocean sail,
And the eighth one brought me in,
A hundred and ten big nigger men
Will come at your command—
They'll come at your command."

6. Now, she picked up her sweet little baby
And kisses gave it three,
Said, "Stay at home with your father, my darling,
And keep him company—
And try to remember me."

7. Then she dressed herself in a scarlet dress,
Most beautiful to be seen,
And she wrapped herself in a purple cloak,
And she looked like a gypsy queen—
O she looked like a gypsy queen.

8. Now they hadn't been sailing but about two weeks,
I'm sure it was not three,
When this little lady began to weep
And she wept most bitterly—
O she wept most piteously.

9. "Now, why do you weep, my own true love?
Is it for more gold or store?
Or is it for that house carpenter
We left on England's shore—
That you'll never see anymore?"

10. "Cursed be your gold and silver;
Thrice cursed be your store,
I'm weeping for my own little baby,
I left on England's shore—
Will I see it anymore?"

11. "Cheer up, cheer up, my own true love,
Cheer up, cheer up," said he,
"For as I live, you will not return,
I will keep you here with me—
And land you'll never see."

12. Now they sailed on about three weeks,
I'm sure it was not four,
When the bottom of the ship sprung a leak
And the ocean in did pour—
And the flames began to roar.

13. "O cursed be a sailor's life,
Thrice cursed all men of the sea,
One has taken me from my house carpenter,
And now he's drownding me—
Or else he is burning me."

14. "What are those hills, my love," she said,
"They look as white as snow."
"Those are the hills of heaven, my love,
Where your little baby will go—
But you and I will not know,
Heaven we'll never know."

15. "And what are those other hills," she said,
"They look as black as night."
"Those are the hills of Hell," he said,
"Where you and I'll unite—
Where you and I'll unite."

72. "The House Carpenter"

Singer anonymous; probably a member of the Harmon family. Collected by Hilda Kasting and Mrs. Carl Wiseman, c. 1939. Sent to Editor by Edward Cray, Los Angeles, Calif.

a M/D

73. "House Carpenter"

Henry, *JAF*, XLV (1932), p. 23(B). Also in Henry [1938], p. 115(B). Sung by Cleophas L. Franklin, Crossnore, Avery County, N.C., July 14, 1929; learned from his great-grandmother.

m I (inflected IV)

The original is written straight through in 4/4 bars.

1. I once could have married a king's daughter,
And she would have married me;
But I forsaken the crown of gold—
Was all for the love of thee.

2. If you could have married the king's daughter,
I'm sure that you are to blame;
For I have married a house carpenter
And I think he's a nice young man.

3. If you'll forsake your house carpenter
And go along with me,
I'll take you to where the grass grows green
And the banks of sweet relief.

4. If I forsake my house carpenter
And go along with thee,
What have you to maintain me on
Or keep me from slavery?

5. I have five ships on the ocean wide
A sailing for dry land;
Five hundred and twenty bold seamen
Will be at your command.

6. She picked up her sweet little babe
And kisses gave it three,
Saying, "Go, stay with your papa, my sweet little babe,
And keep him company."

7. She dressed herself in silk so fine—
Most glorious to be seen.
As she walked along the shore—
Outshined the glittering sun.

8. But she had not been on the ship two weeks,
I'm sure it were not three,
Till she li-mented in her true-lover's ship
And wept most bitterly.

9. "Is it for my gold you weep?
Or is it for my store?
Or is it for your house carpenter
That you never shall see any more?"

10. "It is not for your gold I weep;
Nor it is not for your store.
I was just weeping for my sweet little babe,
That I never shall see any more."

11. She had not been on the ship three weeks,
I'm sure it were not four,
Till there sprang a leak in the true-lover's ship
And she sank to rise no more.

12. "A curse, a curse to all seamen,
A curse forever more!
They robbed me of my house carpenter
That I never shall see any more."

GROUP Ab

74. [Daemon Lover]

Sharp MSS., 3744/. Also in Sharp and Karpeles, 1932, I, p. 258(T). Sung by H. D. Kinnard, Berea, Ky., May 27, 1917.

m I—M (inflected VII)

It's I could have married a Queen's daughter
And she would have married me
But I refused a crown of gold
And all for the sake of thee.

75. "If you will leave your house carpenter"

Sung by Mrs. John Williams (née Violet Selena Hankins), Iowa City, Iowa. Learned in 1865-70, in Penn Township, Johnson County, Iowa, probably from Mrs. Tim Tierney. Text noted by her son Charles Williams, September 16, 1921; tune recorded by Mrs. Flora Brennan, February 5, 1922.

a M

"If you will leave your house carpenter
And go away with me,
I'll take you where the sweet winds blow
On the banks of sweet Italy."

This gallant lady had cause for to weep,
And she wept most bitterly

. . . .
. . . .

"It is not for your gold I weep,
It is not for your store,
But O it is for the darling sweet babe
That I left on yonder shore."

76. "The House Carpenter"

Neal, 1926, p. 69. From Miss Neal's mother(?).

a π^4; a π^1, ending on *VI*; or m π^3, ending on *V*

1. "Well met, well met, my own true love
    Well met, well met," says he.
  I've just returned from the salt, salt sea,
    And it's all for the sake of thee."

2. "I could have married a king's daughter fair,
    And she fain would have married me,
  But I refused her crown of gold,
    And it's all for the sake of thee."

3. "If you could have married a king's daughter fair,
    I think 'twould have been your plan,
  For I have married a house carpenter,
    And I think him a nice young man."

4. "If you'll forsake your house carpenter
    And go along with me,
  I'll take you where the grass grows green
    On the banks of Italy."

5. She called her babe unto her knee,
    And kisses gave it three,
  Saying, "Stay at home, you pretty little babe,
    Keep your father company."

6. She dressed herself in scarlet red,
    Most glorious to behold,
  And as they sailed the ports around,
    She shone like the glittering gold.

7. They had not been aboard the ship two weeks,
    I'm sure it was not three,
  When the fair lady began for to weep,
    And she wept most bitterly.

8. "O, is it for my gold that you weep,
    Or is it for my store,
  Or is it for your house carpenter,
    Whom you ne'er shall see no more?"

9. "It is not for your gold that I weep,
    Nor neither for your store,
  But I do mourn for the pretty little babe
    That I left on the other shore."

10. They had not been on board three weeks,
    I'm sure it was not four,
  When the gallant ship she sprang a leak,
    And she sank for to rise no more.

11. A curse, a curse on that young man,
    And a curse on the seaman's life,
  A-robbing of the house carpenter,
    And a-stealing away his wife.

77. [The Daemon Lover]

Sharp MSS., 3341/2446. Also in Sharp and Karpeles, 1932, I, p. 248(D). Sung by William Riley Shelton, Alleghany, N.C., August 29, 1916.

m M/D

1. We've met, we've met, my own true love,
  We've met, we've met once more,
  For I've lately crossed this salt water sea
  And it's all for the sake of thee.

2. It's I could have married the King's daughter dear,
  I'm sure she'd have married me;
  But I've forsaken them crowns of gold,
  And it's all for the sake of thee.

3. If you could have married the King's daughter dear,
  I'm sure [she][1] ought to have married thee,
  For I am married to the house carpenter,
  I'm sure he's a fine young man.

4. If you'll forsake your house carpenter
  And go along with me,
  I'll take you where the grass grows green
  All on the banks of sweet Lilee.

5. If I forsake my house carpenter
  And goes along with [thee],[2]
  Pray tell me the wealth you have on board
  To keep me from slavery.

6. I have three ships all sailing on the sea,
  All making for dry land,
  And besides three hundred jolly sailor boys,
  You can have them at your command.

7. She catched her tender little babes in her arms,
  Kisses give them, one, two, three,
  Saying: Stay at home with your papee,
  I'm sure he'll be good to thee.

8. They hadn't been sailing but a day or two,
  Not more than two or three,
  Till she began to weep and mourn
  And she weep most bitterly.

9. Are you weeping about my gold, said he,
  Are you weeping about my stores,
  Or are you weeping about your house carpenter
  That you never shall see no more?

10. I'm neither weeping for your gold,
  For neither for your store,
  But I am weeping about my tender little babes
  That I never shall see any more.

[1] MS. has "you."
[2] MS. has "me."

78. "The Ship Carpenter"

Sung by Clay Walters, Salyersville, Ky., 1937. LC/AAFS, rec. No. 1580(A, B1); also LC/AAFS, rec. No. L58(A5). Collected by Alan and Elizabeth Lomax.

a D

Cf. the same singer's other version, *ante*, variant 13.

1. Well met, well met, my own true love
Long I've been searching for thee
I've been all across the salt roaring sea
And it's all for the sake of thee.

2. Oh, I could have married the king's daughter fair
She all the same would have had me
But I refused that rich crown of gold
And it's all for the sake of thee.

3. If you could have married the king's daughter dear
I'm sure that you are to blame
For I wouldn't have my husband to hear tell of thee
For ten thousand pounds of gold.

4. Oh, I am married to a ship carpenter
And a ship carpenter I obey
And by him I have a little son
Or I would go along with thee.

5. What have you to maintain me on?
Is it houses, land, gold, and fee?
I've seven loaded ships a-sailing on the sea
Besides the one that brought me to land.

6. She picked up her baby all in her arms
And kissed it sweetlie embraced
And laid it down on a soft bed of down
And bid it to go to sleep.

7. As they walked down by the seashore
The water is set running so bold
The sides was lined with silver so bright
And the top was the purest of gold.

8. As they sailed all on the sea
The music did seem so sweet
She thought of her babe she had left behind
And set herself down to weep.

9. Are you weeping for my gold, said he?
Are you weeping for fee?
Or are you weeping for some other man
That you love far better than me?

10. I'm not a-weeping for your gold
Neither am I a-weeping for fee
But I'm weeping to return to dry land again
My poor little babe to see.

11. If you had ten thousand pounds of gold
And would give it all unto me
You never should return to dry land again
Your babe you never will see.

12. What hills, what hills, my own true love,
That look so white like snow?
It's the hills of Heaven, my own true love
Where all righteous people go.

13. What hills, what hills, my own true love,
That look so dark and low?
It's the hills of Hell, my own true love,
Where you and I must go.

14. Straight news, straight news to the ship carpenter
Straight news come back to the land
The ship that his own dear wife sailed in
Went sinking to the sand.

15. Sailors may be the worst of men
That lead poor women astray
The sailor has ruined the ship carpenter
By deluding his poor wife away.

79. "The House Carpenter"

Musick, *JAF*, LXX (1957), p. 352; text, p. 340. Contributed by George R. Jefferson, Benton's Ferry, W. Va.; learned from his uncle.

a M/D

1. "Well met, well met, my old true love,
Well met, well met," cried he.
For it's I have crossed the old salt sea
And all for the love of thee—ee—ee
And it's all for the love of thee."

2. "Oh, I could have married a king's daughter dear,
And fain would she had me;
But I have deserted both silver and gold,
And it's all for the love of thee—ee—ee,
And it's all for the love of thee."

3. "If you could have married a king's daughter dear,
I am sure I'm not to blame,
For I have married a house carpenter,
And I'm sure he's a fine young man—man—man,
And I'm sure he's a fine young man."

4. "If you'll desert your house carpenter
And go along with me,
I will take you to where the grass grows green
On the banks of the sweet Willie—ee—ee,
On the banks of the sweet Willie."

5. "If I desert my house carpenter
And go along with thee,
What have you got to maintain me on
And keep me from slavery—ee—ee,
And keep me from slavery?"

6. "If you'll desert your house carpenter,
And go along with me,
I've five hundred and ten brave, bold seamen,
And they all shall wait on thee—ee—ee,
And they all shall wait on thee!"

7. She pick-ed up her wee little babe
And she gave it kisses three,
Saying, "You must stay with your papa dear,
And keep him company—ee—ee,
And keep him company."

8. They had not been at sea two weeks,
I'm sure it was not three,
Until this fair maiden began to weep,
And she wept most bitterly—ee—ee,
And she wept most bitterly.

9. "Oh, is it for my gold that you weep,
Or is it for my store?
Or is it for that house carpenter
That you'll never see any more—more—more,
That you'll never see any more?"

10. "It is not for your gold that I weep,
Nor is it for your store,
But it is for that sweet, little babe
That I'll never see any more—more—more,
That I'll never see any more!"

11. They had not been at sea three weeks,
I am sure it was not four,
Till the old salt ship, she sprang a leak,
And she sank to rise no more—more—more,
And she sank to rise no more.

12. Well, cur'sed be a sailor's lot,
Well, cur'sed be his wife,
For he has deprived me of my house carpenter,
And deprived me of my life—life—life,
And deprived me of my life.

80. [Daemon Lover]

Sharp MSS., 3696/. Also in Sharp and Karpeles, 1932, I, p. 257(S). Sung by students at Berea College, Madison County, Ky., May 20, 1917.

m π^4

The next-to-last note was "occasionally neutral," "never sharp," "sometimes definitely natural," according to the MS.

Well met, well met, says an old true love
Well met, well met, says he,
I've come from far across the sea,
And its all for the sake of thee.

81. [The Daemon Lover]

Sharp MSS., 4063/?. Also in Sharp and Karpeles, 1932, I, p. 258(U). Sung by girls at Hindman School, Knott County, Ky., September 20, 1917.

m D/Æ

The next-to-last note was sung "sometimes rather sharp."

Well met, well met, my own true love,
Well met, well met, says he.[1]
I've just returned from the old salt sea,
And its all for the sake of thee,[2]
And it's all for the sake of thee.[2]

[1] 1932 reading. MS. has *she*.
[2] 1932 reading. MS. has *me*.

82. "Well Met, Well Met, My Own True Love"

Hammond, *JFSS*, III, No. 11 (1907), p. 84. Sung by Mrs. Russell, Upwey, Dorset, January 1907.

a D

This variant was superbly set for mixed voices by Vaughan Williams in 1915.

Well met, well met, my own true love,
Long time have I been absent from thee.
I am lately come from the salt sea,
And 'tis all for the sake, my love, of thee.

I have three ships all on the salt sea,
And (by) one of them has brought me safe to land.
I've four and twenty mariners on board;
You shall have music at your command.

The ship, my love, that you shall sail in,
It shall be of the fine beaten gold.
I've four and twenty mariners on board;
It is a beauty for to behold.

83. "The House Carpenter"

Cox, 1939, p. 41; and 1964 (ed. Boswell), p. 51. Communicated by John A. Moore, Wheeling, W. Va., January 1927, from the singing of Mrs. Flora A. Williams, who had it from her mother, of Columbia County, Pa.

a D (inflected III)

1. "Well met, well met, my pretty fair maid,
 Well met, well met," said he,
"I've just come over the sea, salt sea,
 And it's all for the love of thee."

2. "I can not go away with thee,
 I can not go," said she,
"For I am married to a house carpenter,
 And a handsome man is he."

3. "If you will leave your house carpenter,
 And come along with me,
I'll take you to where the grass grows green
 On the banks of the Sweet Libertie."

4. She took her babe upon her knee,
 And gave it kisses three,
Saying, "Stay at home, my sweet and pretty babe,
 Keep your father's company."

5. She dressed herself in purple and green,
 Most beautiful to behold,
And as she walked along the street,
 She shone like glittering gold.

6. They had not sailed for about two weeks,
 I'm sure it was not three,
When she began for to weep, for to weep,
 And she wept most bitterly.

7. "Oh, is it for your house carpenter,
 Or is it for your fee,
That you've began for to weep, for to weep,
 And weep so bitterly?"

8. "It is not for my house carpenter,
 Nor is it for my fee,
But it is all for the sweet and pretty babe,
 That I left when I followed thee."

9. They had not sailed for about three months,
 I'm sure it was not four,
When under the deck the ship sprung a leak,
 And her weeping was heard no more.

10. Now here's a curse to all sailor men,
 As long as they have life,
For the robbing of the house carpenter,
 And the coaxing away of his wife.

84. [The Daemon Lover]

Wilkinson MSS., 1935-36, p. 91(D). Sung by Miss Tyrah Lam, Elkton, Va., November 6, 1935.

a π^2

1. Well met, well met, says an old true love,
Well met, well met, says he.
I've come from far across the sea,
And it's all for the sake of thee, of thee,
And it's all for the sake of thee.

2. O hold your tongue of your former vows,
For they'll bring bitter strifes.
O hold your tongue of your former vows,
For I have become a wife, wife, wife,
For I have become a wife.

3. O I could have married a King's daughter dear,
And she would have married me.
But I have forsaken those crowns of gold,
And it's all for the sake of thee, thee, thee,
And it's all for the sake of thee.

4. If you could have married a King's daughter dear,
I'm sure you are to blame.
For I have married a house carpenter,
And I think he's a nice young man, man, man,
And I think he's a nice young man.

5. If you will leave your house carpenter,
And go along with me.
I'll take you where the grass grows green,
On the banks of sweet Italy-ly-ly,
On the banks of sweet Italy.

6. If I was to leave my house carpenter,
And go along with thee.
What have you got to maintain me on?
And keep me from slavery-ry-ry?
And keep me from slavery.

7. I've seven ships upon the sea,
Seven more upon dry land.
A hundred and twenty bold seamen,
You may have at your command, mand, mand,
You may have at your command.

8. She turned herself three times around,
And looked at her babies three.
Good bye, my sweet little babies,
Keep your father company, ny-ny,
Keep your father company.

9. They'd just been a-sailing about two weeks,
I'm sure it was not three.
Till this fair lady began to weep,
She wept most bitterly,-ly-ly,
She wept most bitterly.

10. Now is it for your lands you weep?
Or is it for your store?
Or is it for your house carpenter,
That you will see no more, more, more,
That you will see no more.

11. It's neither for my lands I weep,
Nor is it for my store.
It's all for the love of my sweet little babes,
That I will see no more, more, more,
That I will see no more.

12. They sailed, they sailed, two weeks or three,
I'm sure it was not four.
Till the ship sprung a leak, and sank in the sea,
And sank to rise no more, more, more,
And sank to rise no more.

13. What hills, what hills, my false true love,
What hills so black and blue?
The hills you see are the hills of Hell,
Awaiting both me and you, you, you,
Awaiting both me and you.

14. What hills, what hills, my false true love,
What hills so white as snow?
The hills you see are the hills of Heaven,
Where you and I can't go, go, go,
Where you and I can't go.

85. "The House Carpenter"

Sung by Captain Pearl R. Nye, Akron, Ohio, 1937. LC/AAFS, rec. No. 1001(A1). Collected by John A. Lomax.

a π^2

1. Well met, well met, my own true love,
Well met, well met, says he
I've just returned from the salt-water sea
And it's all for the love of thee-ee-ee,
And it's all for the love of thee.

2. I might have married a king's daughter fair,
If she would have married me
But I have forsaken all her crowns of gold
And it's all for the love of thee-ee-ee,
And it's all for the love of thee.

3. If you could have married a king's daughter fair,
I'm sure you are much for to blame
For I have married a house carpenter
And I think he's a nice young ma-a-an,
And I think he's a nice young man.

4. If you will leave your house carpenter,
And go along with me
I'll take you where the grass grows green
On the shores of Italy-y-y,
On the shores of Italy.

5. I have seven ships a-lying in port,
And seven more out on sea
One hundred and forty brave sailor-men
And all for the love of thee-ee-ee,
And all for the love of thee.

6. Oh then she called her little babe,
And kisses gave it three,
Saying, Stay at home, my little dear,
Keep your father's company-y-y,
Keep your father's company.

7. Then she prepared for the trip,
She dressed in the richest attire,
And as she walked the streets along,
Everyone did her admi-i-ire,
Everyone did her admire.

8. She had not been at sea three weeks,
I'm sure it was not four,
Until she began to weep, alas,
And wept most bitter so-o-ore,
And wept most bitter sore.

9. Is it for my gold you weep,
Or is it for my [*sic*] friends?
Or is it for your house carpenter
You'll never see any mo-o-ore,
You'll never see any more?

10. It's neither for your gold I weep,
Or neither for my friends
It is for my dear little babe
That I never can see any more.

11. The gallant ship she sprang a leak,
As she sailed those surging sea
And sank beneath the stormy waves
And never more to be-e-e,
And never more to be.

12. No matter how high a bird may fly,
 It must come down for to drink,
The deeds we sow into harvest grow,
 Lord help us to stop and thi-i-ink,
 Lord help us to stop and think.

86. "The House Carpenter"

Davis, 1929, p. 593(G); text, p. 449. Also in Smith, *MQ*, II (1916), p. 126(A). Contributed by Martha M. Davis, August 14, 1914, from the singing of an old nurse in Fairfax County, Va., who had learned it 40-50 years before.

p Æ

1. "Well met, well met, my own true love,
 Well met, well met," says he;
"I've just returned from the salt, salt sea,
 And it's all for love of thee.

2. "I could have married the king's daughter fair."
 "You might as well," said she,
"For now I'm married to a house carpenter,
 And a nice young man is he."

3. "If you will forsake your house carpenter
 And go along with me,
I'll carry you away where the grass grows green
 On the isle of sweet Willee."

4. "If I forsake my house carpenter
 And go away with thee,
What have you to maintain me on
 Or keep me from slavery?"

5. "I have ten ships on the sea sailing wide,
 A-making on for land;
One hundred of my bold sailor men
 Will be at your command."

6. She took her babe up in her arms
 And kisses gave it three.
"Now stay at home, my sweet little babe,
 For your father's company."

7. She dressed herself in her richest to wear,
 And the weather being cold,
She walked, she walked the streets around,
 She glittered like beaten gold.

8. She hadn't been sailing more than two weeks,
 I'm sure it was not three,
Before this damsel began for to weep,
 And she wept most bitterly.

9. "What are you weeping for, silver or gold?
 Are you weeping for my store?
Are you weeping for your house carpenter
 You never shall see any more?"

10. "I neither weep for your silver nor gold,
 Nor do I weep for your store;
I'm weeping for my sweet little babe
 I never shall see any more."

11. She hadn't been sailing more than three weeks,
 I'm sure it was not four,
Before this ship had sprung a leak
 And sunk to rise no more.

12. A curse, a curse to this young man
 That sails the ocean wide;
He has robbed the poor house carpenter
 And taken away his bride.

87. "The House Carpenter"

Sung by George Vinton Graham, San Jose, Calif., August 16, 1939. LC/AAFS, rec. No. 3377(A1, A2). Collected by Sidney Robertson Cowell.

p D (inflected III)

88. "Well Met, Well Met, My Old True Love"

Treat, *JAF*, LII (1939), p. 46. Sung by Mrs. M. G. Jacobs, Bryant, Wisc., September 1933 and September 6, 1938; learned from her mother.

p D

1. "Well met, well met, my old true love.
 Well met, well met," said he.
 "I have just returned from the salt, salt sea;
 And 'twas all for the sake of thee,
 And 'twas all for the sake of thee."

2. "I once could have married a king's daughter fair,
 And she would have married me.
 But I refused that rich crown of gold,
 And it's all for the sake of thee."

3. "If you could have married a king's daughter fair
I'm sure you're much to blame,
For I am married to a house carpenter,
And I think he's a fine young man."

4. "If you'll forsake your house carpenter
And go along with me,
I will take you where the grass grows green,
{On the banks of the Sweet Willee}
{On the banks of the Sweet Liberty}."

5. "If I forsake my house carpenter
And go along with thee,
What have you got for my support,
And to keep me from slavery?"

6. "I have six ships sailing on the sea,
The seventh one at land,
And if you'll come and go with me
They shall be at your command."

7. She took her babe into her arms
And gave it kisses three,
Saying, "Stay at home, my pretty little babe
For to keep your father company."

8. She dressed herself in rich array
To exceed all others in the town,
And as she walked the streets around
She shone like a glittering crown.

9. They had not been on board more than two weeks,
I'm sure it was not three,
Until she began to weep
And she wept most bitterly.

10. "Are you weeping for your houses and your land,
Or are you weeping for your store,
Or are you weeping for your house carpenter
You never shall see any more?"

11. "I'm not weeping for my houses nor my land,
Nor I'm not weeping for my store,
But I'm weeping for my pretty little babe
I never shall see any more."

12. They had not been on board more than three weeks,
It was not four I'm sure,
Until at length the ship sprung a leak,
And she sank to arise no more.

13. "A curse, a curse to all sea men!
A curse to a sailor's life!
For they have robbed me of my house carpenter
And taken away my life."

89. "The House Carpenter"

Davis, 1929, p. 594(X); text, p. 470. Contributed by Dr. Launcelot M. Harris, September 11, 1923, from the singing of Mrs. Marshall, near Charlottesville, Va.

a P/Æ; or p D/Æ, ending on *V*

1. "Well met, well met, my own true love;
Well met, well met," said he.
"I have lately returned from the salt water sea,
And it's all for the love of thee.

2. "I could have married a king's daughter dear,
And she would have married me;
But all for crowns of gold I refused,
And it's all for the love of thee."

3. "If you could have married a king's daughter dear,
I am sure I am not to blame;
For I am married to a house carpenter,
And a nice young man is he."

4. "Won't you forsaken your house carpenter,
And go along with me?
I will take you to the banks of the river,
And to the banks of sweet Willie."

5. O, she picked it up, her little babe,
And kissed it one, two, three,
Saying, "Stay at home, my tender little babe,
And keep poor papa company."

6. O, she had not been sailing but two weeks,
I am sure it was not three,
Before she began for to weep,
And wept most bitterly.

7. "What are you weeping for, my miss?
Are you weeping for my gold?
Or are you weeping for your house carpenter?
His face you will see no more."

8. "I am neither weeping for my house carpenter,
I am neither weeping for your gold.
I am weeping for my tender little babe;
Its face I will see no more."

9. O, she had not been sailing but three weeks,
I am sure it was not four,
Before the vessel sprung for to leak,
For to sink to rise no more.

10. ". . . . .
. . . .
He made me believe by the false of his tongue
That the sun rose in the west."

90. "The House Carpenter"

Randolph, I, 1946, p. 171(J). Sung by Miss Rose O'Neill, Day, Mo., June 14, 1940; learned in 1904 from Mrs. Nannie A. Setters, Branson, Mo.

a Æ

1. Well met, well met, my own true love,
Well met, well met said he,
I've just returned from the salt briny seas,
An' it's all for the love of thee.

2. I could have married a king's daughter,
I' faith she'd have married me,
But I refused, carin' not for her gold
An' it's all for the love of thee.

3. If you could have married a king's daughter
I count you much to blame,
For I have married a house carpenter
An' I think he's a fine young man.

4. If you will leave your house carpenter
An' go along with me,
I'll take you to where the grass grows so green
On the banks of Italy.

5. For I have gold and ships, said he,
All sailing for dry land,
An' two hundred and ten Bojollisy men
All waiting for your command.

6. He dressed her all in rich array,
Most beautiful to behold,
And as she walked the streets around
She gleamed like the glittering gold.

7. Oh she's took up her sweet little babe
An' gave it kisses three,
Saying stay at home, my sweet little babe
While I go and sail on the sea.

8. They had not been on the sea two weeks,
I'm sure it was not three,
When this damsel began for to weep
And she wept most bitterly.

9. Oh do you weep for my gold, said he,
Or do you weep for my store?
Or do you weep for your house carpenter
That you never will see no more?

10. I do not weep for your gold, said she,
Neither do I weep for your store,
But I do weep for the sweet little babe,
That I left on the English shore.

11. They had not been on the sea three weeks,
I'm sure it was not four,
When down under decks she sprang a leak
An' she sank for to rise no more.

91. "The House Carpenter"

Kittredge, *JAF*, XXX (1917), p. 327. Also in Wyman and Brockway [1920], p. 54. Collected by Loraine Wyman in Kentucky.

a π^4

"Well met, well met, my own true love,
Well met, well met," said he;
"I've just returned from the old salt sea,
And it's all for the sake of thee."

92. "The House Carpenter"

Flanders, *et al.*, 1939, p. 95. Also in Flanders, III, 1963, p. 289. Sung by Orlon Merrill, Charlestown, N.H., who learned it from a woodsman. Recorded and transcribed by Helen Hartness Flanders. From *The New Green Mountain Songster*, edited by Helen Hartness Flanders, Elizabeth Flanders Ballard, George Brown, and Phillips Barry; copyright 1939 by Helen Hartness Flanders.

m M/D

1. "I might have married a king's daughter fair,
And she would have married me,
But I have come across the sal [*sic*], salt sea,
And it's all on account of thee."

2. "If you could have married a king's daughter fair,
I am sure that you're to blame
Because I am married to a house carpenter
And I'm sure that he's a nice young man."

3. "But if you forsake your house carpenter
And go along with me
I will take you to the place where the grass grows green
On the banks of the sweet Will-lea.

4. "I have three ships sailing on the sea,
All sailing for dry land
And one hundred and ten jolly good seamen
And they're at your command."

5. She took her baby on her knee
And she gave it kisses three,
Saying, "Stay at home, my darling little baby,
To keep your father company."

6. Then she dressed herself in a stylish dress.
Methinks she looks so gay!
As she walked through those streets of gold,
She shone like a lily gay.

7. They had not been on sea two hours
And I'm sure it was not three
Before this maid she was found to weep
And she wept most bitterly.

8. "Is it for my gold you weep
Or is it for my store
Or is it for your house carpenter
That you never shall see any more?"

9. "No, it's neither for your gold I weep
Nor it's neither for your store
But it's all for the sake of my darling little baby
That I never shall see any more."

10. They had not been on the sea three months
And I'm sure it was not four
Before the ship it sprang a leak
And it sank for to rise no more.

11. "A curse, a curse to all the seamen
And a curse on me this life
For robbing of a house carpenter
And a-stealing away his wife!"

93. "The House Carpenter"

Brewster, 1940, p. 138. Also in Brewster, *JAF*, XLVIII (1935), p. 296. Sung by Mrs. A. J. Hopkins, Boonville, Ind., May 21, 1935. Noted by Mrs. I. L. Johnson.

m I/Ly

The variant (a) is from the *JAF* printing.

1. "O I've just returned from the salt-water sea,
And it's all for the sake of thee;
For I could have married the king's daughter dear,
And she fain would have married me."

2. "If you could have married the king's daughter dear,
I'm sure you are not free;
And I am married to a house carpenter,
And a fine young man is he."

3. "If you'll forsake your house carpenter
And go along with me,
I'll take you where the grass grows green
On the banks of the Sweet Malea."

4. "If I'll forsake my house carpenter
And go along with thee,
What have you to maintain me on
To keep me from slavery?"

5. "I have seven ships upon the sea,
All sailing for dry land;
One hundred and fifty sailor-men
Shall be at your command."

6. "O yes, I'll leave my house carpenter
And go along with thee;
I'll go to where the grass grows green
On the banks of the Sweet Malea."

7. She then picked up her little babe
And kisses gave it three,
Saying, "Stay at home, my little babe,
And bear papa company."

8. They had not been on sea two weeks,
I'm sure it was not three,
Until this lady began to weep,
And she wept most bitterly.

9. "O is it for my gold you weep,
Or is it for my store,
Or is it for your house carpenter
You left on a distant shore?"

10. "It is not for your gold I weep,
Nor is it for your store,
But it is for my little babe
I ne'er shall see no more."

11. They had not been on sea three weeks,
I'm sure it was not four,
Until the vessel it sprung a leak
And sank to rise no more.

94. [The Demon Lover]

Chappell, 1939, p. 38. Sung by Henry Cooper, Chapanoke, N.C. Words noted in 1924; tune, 1935.

a I

1. Well met, well met, cried my own true love,
Well met, well met, cried he;
I'm just from the old salt sea,
And it's all for the sake of thee.

2. Says, I could have married the king's daughter dear,
And she would have married me;
But I refused the crowns of gold,
And it's all for the sake of thee.

3. If you could have married the king's daughter dear,
And she would have married you;
I do think you are so very much to blame
To refuse the crowns of gold,
For I've just married a house-carpenter
And I think he's a nice young man.

4. Go away, go away and leave your house-carpenter
And come and go with me;
I will carry you where the grass grows green
On the banks of old Tennessee.

5. If I forsake my house-carpenter
And go along with thee,
It's what have you got to support me upon,
To keep me from cruel slavery?

6. Don't you see them seven, seven ships,
A-sailing for yonders harbor?
A hundred and ten bold sailormen
Will all be at your command.

7. She dressed herself in robes of silk,
And the robes they did shine like gold;
She called unto her darling tender babe,
And gave it a kiss or two.

8. Says, Stay right here, stay right here,
O my darling tender babe,
And keep your poor papa company,
And keep your poor papa company.

9. She marched all around and around the town,
And on the deck she did go.

10. She sailed onward two weeks,
I'm sure it was not three;
Before she began to weep,
And she wept most bitterly.

11. Says, What are you weeping for, my dear,
What are you weeping for?
Are you weeping for my gold or silver,
Or is you weeping for my store?
Or is you weeping for the house-carpenter
That you left on yonder shore?

12. Neither weeping for your gold nor your silver,
Neither weeping for your store;
Neither weeping for the house-carpenter,
The one's on yonder shore.

13. She sailed onward three weeks,
I'm sure it was not four;
Before she began to weep
And she wept and wept still more.

14. What are you weeping for, my love,
What are you weeping for?
Are you weeping for my gold or my silver,
Are you weeping for my store?

15. Neither weeping for your gold nor your silver,
Neither weeping for your store;
Neither weeping for the house-carpenter,
But the one on yonder shore;
I'm weeping for my darling tender babe,
The one I'll never see no more.

16. Dry up your tears I say, my love,
Dry up your tears I say;
You will soon reach your happy, happy home
On the banks of old Tennessee.

17. She sailed onward four weeks,
I'm sure it was not five.

18. Cursed be to the seafaring men,
And cursed be to their lives;
Robbing of the house-carpenter
And coaxing away their wives.

GROUP AC

95. "The House Carpenter"

Eddy, 1939, p. 77(E). Also in Tolman and Eddy, *JAF*, XXXV (1922), p. 347(B). Sung by Mrs. Melissa Moores, Perrysville, Ohio.

p I

"Well met, well met, my own true love,
Well met, well met," said he;
"I've just returned from the salt, salt sea,
And it's all for the love of thee."

The text is practically identical with that of Mrs. Ross in variant 121 below, q.v.

96. "The Ship's Carpenter"

Hubbard, 1961, p. 28(A). Sung by Mrs. Rosina Staley Reber, Santa Clara, Utah, August 10, 1947; learned in childhood.

p I

1. "I've just returned from the salt, salt sea,
My own true love for to see,
But she was married to a house carpenter,
And a nice young man was he.

2. "If you'll forsake your house carpenter
And go along with me,
I'll take you to the place where the grass grows green
On the banks of the sweet Treelee."

3. "If I'll forsake my house carpenter
And go along with thee,
What have you to maintain me upon
And to keep me from slavery?"

4. "I've seven ships just sailed to shore
And seven more at sea,
Three hundred and ten brave, jolly, brave men,
And they all shall wait on thee."

5. She called her babe unto her knees
And gave it kisses three,
Saying, "Stay at home, my sweet little babe,
Keep your father's company."

6. She dressed herself in rich array
Most beauteous to behold,
And as she walked the streets along,
She shone like the glittering gold.

7. They had no more than sailed two weeks,
It cannot be 'twas three,
Before the lady began for to weep,
And she wept most bitterly.

8. "What do you weep for gold?" he cried,
"Or do you weep for fear,
Or do you weep for the house carpenter
That you left when you sailed out here?"

9. "I do not weep for gold," she cried,
"Nor do I weep for fear,
But I do weep for the sweet little babe
That I left when we sailed out here."

10. Three times around went the gallant ship,
Three times around went she,
Three time[s] around went the brave-hearted men,
And they sank to the bottom of the sea.

11. There is a curse to the seafaring men,
And to this lady's life,
For the robbing of the house carpenter
And the coaxing away his wife.

97. "The House Carpenter"

Randolph, I, 1946, p. 176(P). Sung by Mrs. H. L. McDonald, Farmington, Ark., February 10, 1942. Learned from her mother c. 1910.

p M

Oh is it for my gold you weep,
Or is it for my store?
Or is it for the house carpenter
You left on the other shore,
You left on the other shore?

No, it's not for your gold I weep,
Nor is it for your store,
But it is for my sweet little babe
That I never shall see any more,
That I never shall see any more.

98. "The House Carpenter's Wife," or "The Daemon Lover"

Sung by Fred High, High, Ark., March 20, 1951. LC/AAFS, rec. No. 10,818(B10). Collected by Mrs. Irene Carlisle.

p M

1. Well met, well met, my own true love,
Well met, well met, says he;
I'm just returning from the salty water sea
And it's all for the sake of you—
And it's all for the sake of thee.

2. I once could have married a king's daughter O,
And she would have married me.
But I've just received [*for refused?*] the rich crown of gold,
And it's all for the sake of you—
And it's all for the sake of thee.

3. Well, if you could have married a king's daughter O,
I'm sure you are to blame,
For I have married a house carpenter
And I think he's a nice young man—
And I think he's a nice young man.

4. Will you leave your own true love
And go along with me?
I'll take you where the grass grows green
On the banks of sweet Willie—
On the banks of sweet Willie.

5. What have you got to maintain me on,
   Or keep me from slavery?

6. I have seventeen fine ships on board,
   Seventeen boatsmens or more,
   Seventeen that's a-sailing for sea,
   That shall be at your command—
   That shall be at your command.

7. She called her babe all to her knee,
   And kisses she give him three.
   Says, Stay at home, my sweet little babe,
   Keep your poppy good company—
   Keep your poppy good company.

8. She dressed herself all neat and clean,
   All ?fested o'er with green.
   Every town that she passed through
   They would take her to be some queen—
   They would take her to be some queen.

9. They hadn't been on sea two weeks,
   I'm sure it was not three,
   Till this young lady begin to weep,
   And she wept most bitterly—
   And she wept most bitterly.

10. Are you weeping for silver or for gold,
   [Or] Are you weeping for fear?
   Or are you weeping for the house carpenter
   That you left when you come with me here—
   That you left when you come with me here?

11. I'm am not weeping for silver or for gold,
   Or I am not a-weeping for fear,
   But I am weeping for the sweet little babe
   That I left when I come with you here—
   That I never shall see any more.

12. They hadn't been (gone) on sea three weeks,
   I'm sure it was not four,
   Till this young lady she sprang from the ship,
   And she sank for to rise no more—
   And she sank for to rise no more.

13. A curse, a curse to all sea-men,
   A curse, a curse, cried she.
   You've robbed me of my sweet little babe
   And stolèd my life away—
   And stolèd my life away.

99. "The House Carpenter"

Sung by David Rice, Springfield, Mo., December 14, 1936. LC/AAFS, rec. No. 3204(A). Also in Randolph, I, 1946, p. 169(E). Collected by Sidney Robertson Cowell.

p M

1. We've met again, my love, he said,
   We've met again, said he,
   I'm just across from the salt, salt sea,
   And it's all for the love of thee-ee-ee
   And it's all for the love of thee.

2. I once could have married a king's daughter fair,
   I'm sure she'd have married me,
   But I have forsaken those crowns of gold
   And it's all for the love of thee-ee-ee
   And it's all for the love of thee.

3. O if you could have married a king's daughter fair
   I'm sure you were (?) to blame,
   For I have married a house carpenter
   And I think he's a nice young ma-a-an
   And I think he's a nice young man.

4. If you will leave your house carpenter
   And go along with me,
   I will take you to where the grass grows green
   On the banks of the sweet Willie-ie-ie
   On the banks of the sweet Willie.

5. O if I should leave my house carpenter
   And go along with thee,
   What have you got to maintain me on
   Or to keep me from slavery-y-y
   Or to keep me from slavery.

6. I have three ships all on the sea
   A-sailing for dry land,
   These have twenty oarsmen (?) on each ship
   That shall lie at your comma-a-and,
   That shall lie at your command.

7. She pickèd up her sweet little babe
   And kisses gave it three,
   Saying, Stay at home, you sweet little babe,
   And keep your Papa company-y-y
   And keep your Papa company.

8. She dressed herself in scarlet red
   And trimmed it off with green,
   And every station they went through
   They took her to be some que-e-een
   They took her to be some queen.

9. They hadn't been a-sailing more than two weeks,
   I'm sure it was not three,
   Till this fair lady began to weep
   And she wept most bitterly-y-y
   And she wept most bitterly.

10. Is it for my silver and gold that you weep,
   Or is it for my store?
   Are you weeping for your house carpenter
   That you left on the other sho-o-ore
   That you left on the other shore?

11. It is not for your silver and gold that I weep,
   Neither is it for your store,
   But I am weeping for my sweet little babe
   That I never shall see any mo-o-ore
   That I never shall see any more.

12. They hadn't been a-sailing more than three weeks,
   I'm sure it was not four,
   Till they struck a leak in the bottom of the ship

And it sank to rise no mo-o-ore
And it sank to rise no more.

13. A curse a curse to all mankind,
A curse a curse said she,
You've forsaken me of my house carpenter
And now you're drownding me
And now you're drownding me.

100. "The House Carpenter"

Sung by Mrs. Hallie Griffin, Conway, Ark., December 12, 1953. LC/AAFS, rec. No. 11,891(A20). Collected by Mary Celestia Parler.

p I

1. Well met, well met, my own true love,
It is all for the sake of thee.
I have returned from the salt salt sea,
And it's all for the sake of thee,
And it's all for the sake of thee.

2. I had the offer of a king's daughter fair,
She offered marriage to me,
But I refused a handful of gold,
And it's all for the sake of thee,
And it's all for the sake of thee.

3. If you've had the offer of a king's daughter fair,
I'm sure have done wrong,
For I have married a house carpenter
And I think he's a nice young man,
And I think he's a nice young man.

4. But won't you leave your house carpenter,
And go along with me?
I will carry you where the grass grows green
On the banks of the sweet Willie,
On the banks of the sweet Willie.

5. If I were to leave my house carpenter
And go along with thee,
What have you got to sustain me upon
Or keep me from slavery,
Or keep me from slavery?

6. I have seven ships sailing on the sea,
They shall sail at your command,
One hundred twenty-five sailor boys
To keep you from slavery,
To keep you from slavery.

7. She caught her babes unto her arms
And gave them kisses three,
Saying, Stay at home, my sweet little babes
And keep your father company,
And keep him company.

8. She dressed herself in silk so fine
Most beautiful to behold,
And as she walked the streets around
She shone like the glittering gold,
She shone like the glittering gold.

9. They had not been on the sea more than weeks one or two,
I'm sure it was not three,
Till this fair damsel began to weep,
And she wept most bitterly,
(And) she wept most bitterly.

10. What are you weeping for? said the seafaring man,
Are you weeping for our gold?
Or is it for your house carpenter
That you'll never see any more,
That you'll never see any more?

11. I am not weeping for your gold
And neither for your store.
But I do weep for my sweet little babes
That I'll never see any more,
That I'll never see any more.

12. They had not been on the sea more than weeks [two or three],
I'm sure it wasn't four,
Till this fair vessel sprung a leak
And sank to rise no more,
And sank to rise no more.

13. What a curse it will be to the seafaring men,
Likewise a sailor's life,
Robbing of the house carpenter
And stealing away his wife,
And stealing away his wife.

101. "The House Carpenter"

Sung by Mrs. May Kennedy McCord, Springfield, Mo., 1941. LC/AAFS, rec. No. 5301(B1). Also in Randolph, I, 1946, p. 174(N). Collected by Vance Randolph.

p M

1. I've just returned from the salt, salt sea,
Returned from the salt, salt sea
And I could have married a king's daughter fair,
She would have married me—
She would have married me.

2. If you have the offer of a king's daughter,
   I'm sure you are to blame
For I am married to a house carpenter
   And he is a nice young man—
   And he is a nice young man.

3. O won't you leave your house carpenter
   And go along with me
For I am going where the grass grows green
   On the banks of the sweet Dundee—
   On the banks of the sweet Dundee.

4. If I was to leave my house carpenter
   And go along with you,
You have nothing to support me on
   And then what should I do—
   O then what should I do?

5. O I have seven ships on the sea,
   And seven ships on the land,
And I have gold and silver too
   Which shall be at your command—
   Which shall be at your command.

6. She then picked up her darling little babe
   And gave it kisses three,
Saying, Stay at home with your father dear
   And keep him company—
   And keep him company.

7. They had not been sailing above two weeks,
   I'm sure it was not three,
Until this fair lady began to weep
   And she wept most bitterly—
   And she wept most bitterly.

8. O are you mourning for your house carpenter
   Or mourning about your fee,
O are you mourning for your sweet little babe
   That you never more will see—
   That you never more will see?

9. O I am not mourning for my house carpenter
   Or mourning about my fee
But I am mourning for my darling little babe
   That I never more will see—
   That I never more will see.

10. They had been sailing above three weeks,
   I'm sure it was not four,
Till under the deck the ship sprung a leak
   And she sank to rise no more—
   And she sank to rise no more.

102. "The House Carpenter"

Owens, 1950, p. 57; learned from Owens's mother.

p I

1. "We've met, we've met," said the seafaring man,
"We've met most joyfully,
For I have come across the salt water sea,
And it's all for the sake of thee.

2. "I could have married a king's daughter there,
She offered marriage to me,

But I have come across the salt water sea,
And it's all for the sake of thee."

3. "If you could have married a king's daughter there,
I'm sure you are to blame,
For I have married a house carpenter,
And I think he's a nice young man."

4. "Oh, won't you forsake your house carpenter
And go along with me?
I'll take you where the grass grows green
On the banks of the sweet Willie."

5. She took herself into a room,
And dressed in silk most gay,
And spread a veil all over her face
And outshone the glittering day.

6. She had not been sailing more'n two weeks,
I'm sure it was not three,
When this fair lady set herself to weeping,
And she wept most bitterly.

7. "Are you a-weeping for the house carpenter,
Are you a-weeping for fear,
Are you a-weeping for the three little babes
That you left when you come with me here?"

8. "I'm neither a-weeping for the house carpenter,
I'm neither a-weeping for fear,
I'm only a-weeping for three little babes
That I left when I come with you here."

9. She had not been sailing more'n three weeks,
I'm sure it was not four,
Till this fair lady threw herself overboard,
And her mourning was heard no more.

10. He threw himself around three times,
With a dark and dreary eye,
Saying, "The nearest, dearest on earth must part,
And so must you and I."

103. "Well Met, My Old True Love"

Sung by Mrs. Pearl Jacobs Borusky, Antigo, Wisc., 1940. LC/AAFS, rec. No. 4175(B)-4176(A). Also in LC/AAFS, rec. No. L58(A4). Collected by Robert F. Draves.

p D

1. Well met, well met, my old true love
Well met, well met, said he
I have just returned from the salt, salt sea
And it's all for the sake of thee.
And it's all for the sake of thee.

2. I once could have married a king's daughter fair
And she would have married me
But I refused that rich crown of gold
And it's all for the sake of thee.
And it's all for the sake of thee.

3. If you could have married a king's daughter fair
I'm sure you are much to blame
For I am married to a house carpenter
And I think he's a fine young man.
And I think he's a fine young man.

4. If you'll forsake your house carpenter
And go along with me
I will take you where the grass grows green
On the banks of the sweet Willie.
On the banks of the sweet Willie.

5. If I forsake my house carpenter
And go along with thee
What have you got for my support
And to keep me from slavery?
And to keep me from slavery?

6. I have six ships upon the sea
And the seventh one at land
And if you come and go with me
They shall be at your command.
They shall be at your command.

7. She took her babe into her arms
And gave it kisses three
Saying, stay at home my pretty little babe
To keep your father company.
To keep your father company.

8. She dressed herself in rich array
To exceed all others in the town
And as she walked the streets around
She shone like a glittering crown.
She shone like a glittering crown.

9. They had not been on board more than two weeks
I'm sure it was not three
Until one day she began to weep
And she wept most bitterly.
And she wept most bitterly.

10. O are you weeping for your houses or your land?
Or are you weeping for your store?
Or are you weeping for your house carpenter
You never shall see any more?
That you never shall see any more.

11. I'm not weeping for my houses or my land
Nor I'm not weeping for my store
But I am weeping for my pretty little babe
I never shall see any more.
I never shall see any more.

12. They had not been on board more than three weeks
It was not four, I am sure
Until at length the ship sprung a leak
And she sunk to arise no more.
And she sunk to arise no more.

13. A curse, a curse to all seamen
And a curse to a sailor's wife
For they have robbed me of my house carpenter
And have taken away my life.
And have taken away my life.

104. "The House Carpenter"

Morris, 1950, p. 311. Sung by Mrs. G. A. Griffin, Newberry, Fla.; learned from her father.

p D

1. "Once I could have married a rich man's daughter,
And she would have married me.
But I've just returned from the salt water sea,
All for the love of thee,
All for the love of thee.

2. "If you will forsake of the house carpenter,
And come go along with me,
Where the grass grows green
On the banks of the Sweet Malee,
On the banks of the Sweet Malee."

3. She dressed her babes so neat and clean,
And laid them down on a feather bed.
"Lie there, lie there, my darling babes,
To bear your father's company,
To bear your father's company."

4. She hadn't been on board but about three weeks,
I'm sure hit wasn't four,
When she weeped, she weeped and she weeped,
Till she weeped most bitterly,
Till she weeped most bitterly.

5. "Are you weeping for my gold?
Or are you weeping for my store,
Or are you weeping for your little house carpenter
Which you'll never see no more,
Which you'll never see no more?"

6. "I'm not weeping for my house carpenter;
I'm not weeping for your store;
I'm weeping for my poor little babes,
Which I'll not see any more,
Which I'll not see any more."

7. She hadn't been gone but about six weeks;
I'm sure it wasn't nine,
Till the boat sprung a leak and it sunk for the deep,
And it sunk to rise no more,
And it sunk to rise no more.

8. "It's cursed, cursed, to all mankind,
It's cursed to all mankind,
For I'm taken away from my darling babe,
Which I'll never see no more,
Which I'll never see no more.

9. "What banks, what banks, what banks?" says she.
"What banks as white as snow?"
"It's banks of Heaven, a Heaven on high,
Where all good people go,
Where all good people go."

105. "The Sea-Faring Man"

Sung by W. W. Parsley, Springdale, Ark., February 7, 1951. LC/AAFS, rec. No. 10,814(B1). Collected by Irene Carlisle.

p M

What a life, what a life, says the seafaring man,
What a life, what a life, says he.
I've just returned from the salt salt sea,
And it's all for the sake of thee,
And it's all for the sake of thee.

If you will forsake your house carpenter
And come and go with me,
I'll take you where the grass grows green
On the banks of sweet Val Varie,
On the banks of sweet Val Varie.

She (We?) hadn't been on board not more than three weeks,
I'm sure it hadn't been four,
Till, alas! th' fair lady jumped overboard
And her weeping was heard no more,
And her weeping was heard no more.

106. "The House Carpenter"

Belden, 1940, p. 82(D). Also in Barry MSS., IV, No. 205. Sung by T. B. Chandler, Farmington, Mo., 1912; learned from his mother, of Tennessee, about the time of the Civil War. Noted by Miss Colquitt Newell.

p M (inflected IV, VII)

1. 'We have met, we have met, we have met, my dear,
We have met, we have met,' said he;
'For I've just returned from the salt, salt sea,
And 'twas all for the love of thee.

2. 'I once could have married the king's daughter,
And she would have married me;
But I refused her crowns of gold,
And 'twas all for the love of thee.'

3. 'If you could have married the king's daughter
I'm sure you were to blame.
For I have married a house-carpenter,
And I think he's a nice young man.'

4. 'If you will forsake your house-carpenter
And go along with me
I'll take you to where the grass grows green
On the banks of the sweet Dundee.'

5. 'If I should forsake my house-carpenter
And go along with you,
What would you have to support me on
And keep me from slavery?'

6. 'Seven hundred ships on yonder sea
All sailing for dry land,
Ten thousand and fifty jolly sea-boys—
They shall be at your command.'

7. Then she dressed her babe so neat and clean
And gave it kisses three,
Saying, 'Lie still, lie still, my sweet little babe,
And keep your father company.'

8. Then she dressed herself so neat and clean (*or* in the finest silk)
And along with me did go,
And as she walked along the street
She looked like the glittering gold.

9. She hadn't been gone more than two weeks,
I'm sure it was not three,
Until she sat herself down to weep
And she wept most bitterly.

10. 'What are you weeping for? My gold?
Or is it for my store?
Or is it for your house-carpenter
That you never expect to see any more?'

11. 'I am not weeping for your gold
Nor neither for your store;
I am weeping for my sweet little babe
That I never expect to see any more.'

12. She hadn't been gone more than three weeks,
I'm sure it was not four,
Until the ship she was on sprung a leak
And she sunk, for to rise no more.

13. 'A curse, a curse, a curse,' said she,
'A curse to all sea-men,
For they robbed me of my sweet little babe
That I never can see again.'

107. "The House Carpenter"

Lumpkin, *CFB*, III (1964), p. 3. Sung by Mrs. Martha Martin, Granada, Colo., June 19, 1963.

p I (or a I, ending on the octave)

* This bar was written in notes double the length of the rest.

1. "Well met, well met, well met," said she,
"Well met, well met," said she.
"I could have married a rich young man,
And he would have married me;
And he would have married me."

2. "If you did not marry the rich young man,
I'm sure I'm not to blame.
So I'll give you leave to go away,
And you can go with him;
And you can go with him."

3. She dressed her babe all neat and clean,
And laid him on the bed,
Saying, "Stay here, stay here, my sweet young babie,
And keep your father companie;
Keep your father companie."

4. Then she dressed herself in the richest of colors.
I think her dress was green,
And every street that she passed through,
They took her to be some queen;
They took her to be some queen.

5. They hadn't been on board but a very short time—
Two weeks—I'm sure it wasn't three—
Till she began to weep; she began to mourn,
And she wept most bitterly;
And she wept most bitterly.

6. "What are you weeping for, my dear?
Are you weeping for my store?
Are you weeping for that little house carpenter
That you never shall see any more;
You never shall see any more?"

7. "I am not weeping for the little house carpenter,
Nor neither for your store.
I'm weeping for my sweet little babe
That I never shall see any more;
I never shall see any more."

8. They hadn't been on board but a very short time—
Three weeks—I'm sure it was not four—
Till the little ship, it sprang a leak,
And it sank to rise no more;
And it sank to rise no more.

108. "House Carpenter"

Sung by Mrs. Roxie Phillips, Berryville, Ark., November 4, 1958. LC/AAFS, rec. No. 11,905(A3). Collected by Max Hunter.

p I

1. Well met, well met, my own true love,
Well met, well met, cried he,
I've just returned from the salt water sea
And it's all for the sake of thee,
And it's all for the sake of thee.

2. I could have married a king's daughter fair,
She offered marriage to me,
But I refused all the crown(s) of gold
And it's all for the sake of thee,
And it's all for the sake of thee.

3. If you could have married a king's daughter fair
I'm sure you are to blame,
But I am married to a house carpenter
And I think he's a fine young man,
And I think he's a fine young man.

4. O won't you forsake your house carpenter
And go along with me?
I'll take you where the lilies grow green
On the banks of the sweet Willie,
On the banks of the sweet Willie.

5. Then she went into another room
And dressed herself most gay,
And a veil she threw all over her face
Outshined the glittering day,
Outshined the glittering day.

6. Then she called her babes around her knees
And gave them kisses three,
Saying, Stay at home with your papa dear
And keep him company,
And keep him company.

7. We hadn't been on sea but about two weeks,
   I'm sure o' not quite three,
When the fair young lady began to weep,
   And she wept most bitterly,
   And she wept most bitterly.

8. O do you weep for gold ?alone
   Or do you weep for fear?
Or do you weep for the house carpenter
   That you never shall see any more,
   That you never shall see any more?

9. I do not weep for gold alone,
   I do not weep for fear,
But I do weep for the three little babes
   That I left when I came with you here,
   That I left when I came with you here.

10. We hadn't been on sea but about three weeks,
   I'm sure not quite four,
When the fair young lady threw herself overboard
   And her weeping was heard no more,
   And her weeping was heard no more.

109a. [The Daemon Lover]

Sharp MSS., 3355/. Also in Sharp and Karpeles, 1932, I, p. 252(K). Sung by Mrs. Addy Crane (21), Flag Pond, Tenn., August 31, 1916.

p I

O are you weeping for my gold
Or is it for my store
Or is it for your House Carpenter
Whose face you shall see no more

109b. "Daemon Lover," or "House Carpenter"

Sung by Mrs. Kiah (Attie) Crane (56), ?Flag Pond, Tenn., October 3, 1950. LC/AAFS, rec. No. 10,010(A1). Collected by Maud Karpeles and Sidney Robertson Cowell.

p M (?inflected VII)

1. Well met, well met, my old true love,
   Well met, well met, says she,
I have just married a house carpenter,
   A nice young man is he.

2. If you'll forsake your house carpenter
   And go along with me,
I'll take you where the grass grows green,
   On the banks of Tennessee.

3. She picked up her tender little babe
   And gave it kisses three.
Stay here, stay here, my tender little babe,
   While I go sail the sea.

4. They hadn't been gone but about two weeks,
   I'm sure it was not three,
Till this fair lady began to weep,
   She wept most bitterly.

5. Are you weeping for my gold
   Or is it for my store?
Or is it for your house carpenter,
   Whose face you'll see no more?

6. I'm neither weeping for your gold,
   Nor either for your store.
I'm only weeping for my tender little babe,
   Whose face I'll see no more.

7. What banks, what banks before us now,
   As white as any snow?
It's the banks of Heaven, my love, she [*sic*] replied,
   Where all good people go.

8. What banks, what banks before us now,
   As black as any crow?
It's the banks of Hell, my love, she replied,
   Where you and I must go.

9. They hadn't been gone but about three weeks,
   I'm sure it was not four,
Till that fair ship began to sink,
   It sank to rise no more.

110. "The House Carpenter"

Editor, from Fletcher Collins, Berkeley, Calif., July 24, 1939; learned from Mrs. Hooper in Yanceyville, N.C.

m D

She picked up her poor little babe
Her kisses was one two three
Saying stay here with my house carpenter
And keep your pappy company.

111. "House Carpenter"

Sung by Dan Tate (66), with banjo, Fancy Gap, Va., July 10, 1962. LC/AAFS, rec. No. 12,006(A26). Collected by George Foss.

m M (inflected VII)

See 132 below for another version sung by the same singer.

Well met, well met, my old true love,
Well met, well met, said she.
For seven long years I've been sailing on the ocean
And it's all for the love of thee.

For I could have married a king's daughter dear,
Being she would have married me.
But I refused her crown of gold,
It was all for the love of thee.

112. "House Carpenter"

Sung by Rebecca Jane Collins, Mount Airy, N.C., July 10, 1962. LC/AAFS, rec. No. 12,006(A30). Collected by George Foss.

m M (inflected VII)

If you will leave your house carpenter,
And go along with me,
I will take you where the grass grows green
On the banks of the sweet Murree.

113. [The Daemon Lover]

Sharp MSS., 3363/2462. Also in Sharp and Karpeles, 1932, I, p. 249(E). Sung by Mrs. Sylvaney Ramsey, Flag Pond, Tenn., September 1, 1916.

p M

Well met, well met, my own true love,
It's well met, said he.
I've just returned from the State of Tennessee,
And it's all for the sake of thee.

. . . .

O who will clothe my little babe,
And who will shoe its feet,
And who will sleep in its lily white arms
While we're sailing for dry land?

Its papa will kiss its little cheek,
And also shoe its feet
And also sleep in its lily white arms
While we're sailing for dry land.

She picked up her little babe,
And kissed it on the cheek,
She laid it down on a soft bed of down
And bid it go to sleep.

114. "The House Carpenter"

Randolph, I, 1946, p. 168(B). Sung by Mrs. Tom Bradley, McDonald County, Mo., November 4, 1928.

p I/M

1. Oh won't you leave your house carpenter
An' go along with me?
I'll take you to where th' grass grows green,
On th' banks of th' sweet Willie.

2. If I was to leave my house carpenter
An' go along with you,
What have you there to support me on,
An' keep me from slavery?

3. I have seven ships that are landed here,
An' seven more on sea,
An' a hundred an' ten jolly soldiers there
All ready for to wait upon me.

4. She called her children to her knee,
An' kisses she give them three,
Sayin' stay at home with your father dear,
An' keep him company.

5. An' then she went into the house,
An' she dressed herself out gay,
She spread a veil all over her face
An' shined on the glitterin' day.

6. She had not been on board two weeks,
I'm sure it was not three,
Till this beautiful lady was heard for to weep,
An' she wept most bitterly.

7. She had not been on sea three weeks,
I'm sure it was not four,
Till this beautiful lady throwed herself overboard,
An' her weepin' was heard no more.

8. If she had of stayed with her house carpenter,
Who always treated her kind,
But now she's sunk to the bottom of the sea,
An' her soul has gone farewell.

GROUP Ad

115. "The House-Carpenter"

Major, *PTFLS*, X (1932), p. 159. Sung by Mrs. J. C. Marshall, Quanah, Tex.

p I/Ly

1. "We've met, we've met, my own true love,
We've met, we've met," said he;
"I've just returned from the salt, salt sea,
And it's all for the love of thee."

Chorus: "And it's all for the love of thee."

2. "Once I could have married a king's daughter fair,
I'm sure she'd have married me;
But I've forsaken the richest crowns of gold,
And it's all for the love of thee."

3. "If you could have married a king's daughter fair,
I'm sure you're much to blame,
For I have married a house-carpenter,
And I think he's a fine young man."

4. "If you'll forsake your house-carpenter,
And go along with me,
I'll carry you down where the grass grows green,
On the banks of the sweet Wil-lee."

5. "If I forsake my house-carpenter,
And go along with thee,
What have you there to maintain me on,
And keep me from slavery?"

6. "Seven fine ships are sailing on the sea,
A-sailing for dry land,
Five hundred and ten brave jolly seamen,
And they're all at your command."

7. She dressed her babe both neat and nice,
And gave it kisses three;
"Lie there, lie there, you sweet little babe,
And keep your pa's company."

8. She dressed herself in ladies' array,
To go with the sailor bold;
And as she walked along the streets,
She shone like glittering gold.

9. They had not been on board more than three weeks,
I'm sure it was not three,
Till this fair lady sat down to weep,
And she wept most bitterly.

10. "What are you weeping for, my love,
Are you weeping for my store?
Are you weeping for your house carpenter,
That you never shall see any more?"

11. "I'm not weeping for my house-carpenter;
I'm not weeping for your store,
I am weeping for my sweet little babe,
That I never shall see any more."

12. They had not been on board more than four weeks,
I'm sure it was not four;
When this fair lady threw herself overboard,
And she sank to rise no more.

13. "A curse, a curse, to all seamen,
A curse, a curse," said she.
"You've robbed me of my sweet little babe,
You've stole my life away."

116. "The House Carpenter"

Hand, *WF*, XVIII (1959), p. 42. Sung by Mrs. Rosalie Sorrels, Salt Lake City, Utah, July 20, 1957. Tune learned from her uncle, perhaps of Virginia; text learned c. 1947 from her grandmother's ballad notebook, since lost.

p I

1. "Well met, well met, my own true love,
Well met, well met," said he;
"I've lately come from the salt, salty sea,
And it's all on account of thee.
I've lately come from the salt, salty sea,
And it's all on account of thee.

2. "I've lately come from the salt, salty sea,
And it's all on account of thee.
I've had an offer of a king's daughter fair,
And she fain would have married me.
Oh, I've had an offer of the king's daughter fair,
And she fain would have married me."

3. "If you've had an offer from a king's daughter fair,
I think you're much to blame,
For I've lately married a house carpenter,
And I think he's a nice young man.
Oh, I've lately married a house carpenter,
And I think he's a nice young man."

4. "Oh, will you leave your house carpenter,
And follee (follow?) along with me?
I'll give you jewels and fine silken gowns,
And I'll live but for thee.
Oh, I'll give you jewels and fine silken gowns,
And I'll live but for thee."

5. "Oh keep your jewels and fine silken gowns,
And keep your fine silken hose.
Rest assured, I'm not so poor,
As to have to marry for clothes.
Rest assured, I'm not so poor,
As to have to marry for clothes."

6. They hadn't been sailing about three weeks,
I'm sure it was not four;
Before the gallant ship turned 'round three times,
And sank to rise no more.
Before the gallant ship turned 'round three times,
And sank to rise no more.

7. "Oh, cursed be the sailor's life,
And all the other strife.
For the robbing of the house carpenter,
And the taking away of my life.
For the robbing of the house carpenter,
And the taking away of my life."

117. "The House Carpenter"

Randolph, I, 1946, p. 166(A). Also in Randolph, 1932, p. 201. Sung by Mrs. Carrie Baber, Pineville, Mo., September 3, 1921. Learned from her parents, c. 1889.

p I/M

1. Well met, well met, my own true love,
Well met, well met, says he,
I just come home from th' salt salt sea,
An' it's all for th' love of thee.

2. I could of married the king's daughter,
She wanted to marry me,
But I forsook her crown of gold,
An' all for the love of thee.

3. You should of married the queen, she says,
An' thought no more of me,
For I have wed with a house carpenter
An' a fine young man is he.

4. Oh won't you forsake your house carpenter
An' sail along with me,
I'll take you down where the grass grows green
On the shores of the sweet Mawrie.

5. Should I forsake my house carpenter
An' sail along with thee,
What have you-all to support me on,
An' keep me from poverty?

6. Oh I got seventy ships at sea,
An' seventy more on land,
An' a hunderd an' ten of your countrymen
Shall be at your command.

7. They had not been on the sea two weeks,
I'm sure it was not three,
Until this woman began for to weep,
An' she wept most bitterly.

8. Oh do you weep for my gold, says he,
Or do you weep with fear,
Or do you weep for the house carpenter
That you left when you come with me here?

9. I do not weep for gold, says she,
Neither do I weep with fear,
But I do weep for them three little babes
That I left when I come with you here.

10. They had not been on the sea three weeks,
I'm sure it was not four,
Till the ship it busted ag'in a rock
An' she sunk to rise no more.

118. "The House Carpenter"

Sandburg, 1927, p. 66.

p I/M

1. "I have just come from the salt, salt sea,
      And 'twas all on account of thee;
   For I've had an offer of a king's daughter fair,
      And she fain would have married me."

Repeat the last two lines in each verse

2. "If you've had an offer of a king's daughter fair,
      I think you're much to blame;
   For I've lately been married to a house carpenter,
      And I think he's a nice young man."

3. "If you'll forsake your house carpenter,
      And come along with me,
   I will take you to where the grass grows green,
      On the banks of Italy."

4. "If I'd forsake my house carpenter,
      And go along with you,
   And you'd have nothing to support me upon,
      Oh, then what would I do?"

5. "I have three ships upon the main,
      All sailing for dry land,
   And twenty-five jolly sailor lads
      That you can have at your command."

6. She dressed herself in rich array,
      All from her golden store,
   And as she walked the streets all 'round,
      She shone like a glittering star.

7. She called her baby unto her,
      And gave it kisses three,
   Saying, "Stay at home, my pretty little babe,
      And be your father's company."

8. We had not sailed more than two weeks,
      I'm sure it was not three,
   Till this fair maid began to weep,
      And she wept most bitterly.

9. "Oh, why do you weep, my pretty maid?
      Do you weep for your golden store,
   Or do you weep for your house carpenter
      Which you never shall see any more?"

10. "I do not weep for my house carpenter,
      Or for my golden store,
   But I do weep for my pretty little babe
      Which I never shall see any more."

11. We had not sailed more than three weeks,
      I'm sure it was not four,
   Till our gallant ship she sprang a leak,
      And she sank to rise no more.

12. Once around went our gallant ship,
      Twice around went she,
   Three times around went our gallant ship,
      And she sank to the bottom of the sea.

13. Oh, cursed be the sea-going train,
      And all the sailors' lives,
   For the robbing of the house carpenter,
      And the taking away of his wife.

119. "The House Carpenter"

Lumpkin, *CFB*, III (1964), p. 34. Sung by Mrs. Beulah Greer, of Boulder, Colo., November 1963; text supplied in MS. December 26, 1963.

p I

1. "Well met, well met, my own true love.
   Well met, well met," said he.
   "For seven long years I have been away,
   And all for the sake of thee;
   And all for the sake of thee.

2. "I could have married a king's daughter fair,
   And she would have fain married me.
   But I forsook her crowns of gold—
   And all for the sake of thee,
   And all for the sake of thee."

3. "Well, if you could have married a king's daughter fair,
   I'm sure you are to blame;
   For I am married to a house carpenter,
   And I think he's a nice young man,
   And I think he's a nice young man."

4. "If you will leave your house carpenter,
   And go along with me,
   I'll take you where the grass grows green
   On the banks of sweet Italee.
   On the banks of sweet Italee."

5. "If I should leave my house carpenter,
   And go along with thee,
   What have you got to maintain me on,
   And to keep me from slaveree,
   And to keep me from slaveree?"

6. "O, I have gold and silver in store,
   And I have a house and lands,
   And I have sixteen jolly seamen,
   You can have at your command,
   You can have at your command."

7. So then she picked up her sweet little babe,
And kisses gave it three,
Saying, "Stay at home with your father dear,
And keep him companee,
And keep him companee."

8. They had been at sea about two weeks;
I am sure it was not three,
When this fair lady began to weep,
And she wept most bitterlee,
And she wept most bitterlee.

9. "O, is it for my gold you weep,
Or for what I have in store;
Or is it for your house carpenter
You shall never see any more,
You shall never see any more?"

10. "I weep not for my house carpenter
Nor for what you have in store;
But I weep for the sight of my sweet little babe
I shall never see any more,
I shall never see any more."

11. They had been at sea about three weeks;
I am sure it was not four,
When this same vessel sprang a leak,
And sank to rise no more.
And sank to rise no more.

12. "O woe betide this seafaring man,
And curse him o'er and o'er;
For he has robbed me of my house carpenter,
And I'll see him no more,
And I'll see him no more."

120. "The House Carpenter"

Cox, 1925, p. 524. From Professor A. J. Hare, Morgantown, W. Va. Learned from his mother.

a M; or p I, ending on *V*

"Well met, well met, my pretty fair maid,
Well met, well met," said he;
"I have just returned from the salt, salt sea,
And 'tis all for the love of thee."

121. "The House Carpenter"

Eddy, 1939, p. 70(A). Also in Tolman and Eddy, *JAF*, XXXV (1922), p. 347(A). Sung by Mrs. Daniel Ross, Shreve, Ohio.

p I/M

1. "Well met, well met, my own true love,
Well met, well met," said he,
"I've just returned from the salt, salt sea,
And it's all for the love of thee;
I've just returned from the salt, salt sea,
And it's all for the love of thee."

2. "I might have married a king's daughter,
And she would have married me,
But I refused the crown of gold,
And it's all for the love of thee."

Repeat the last two lines

3. "If you could have married the king's daughter,
And she would have married thee,
I say, young man, you've come too late,
For I'm married to the house carpenter."

4. "If you will leave your house carpenter,
And go along with me,
I'll take you to where the grass grows green
On the banks of the sweet Dundee."

5. "If I should leave my house carpenter,
And go along with thee,
What have you got to maintain me upon,
Or to keep me from slavery?"

6. "Oh, I have seven ships at port,
And seven more at sea,
With a hundred and fifty jolly sailors bold,
All for to wait on thee."

7. Then she called her two pretty babes,
And kisses gave them three,
Saying, "Stay at home, my pretty babes,
And keep your father company."

8. Then she left her house carpenter,
And went with the sailor bold,
And every port that she sailed through
She shone like the glittering gold.

9. She had not sailed two months at sea,
I'm sure she had not sailed three,
Till she was seen sitting in the ship's cabin door,
And weeping most bitterly.

10. "Oh, do you weep for the love of gold,
Or do you weep for fear,
Or do you weep for the house carpenter
You left when you came on here?"

11. "I do not weep for the love of gold,
Nor do I weep for fear,
But I do weep for my two pretty babes
I left when I came on here."

12. She had not sailed three months at sea,
    I'm sure she had not sailed four,
  Till from the deck in the deep she did spring,
    Her weeping was heard no more.

13. Let this be a curse to all sea-faring men,
    And a curse to the sailor's life,
  For the robbing of the house carpenter,
    And taking away his wife.

122. "The House Carpenter"

Randolph, I, 1946, p. 176(O). Sung by Charles Ingenthron, Walnut Shade, Mo., September 4, 1941.

a I

Oh what are you weeping about, says he,
Are you weeping for my store?
Or is it for that house carpenter
You ne'er shall see any more?

I'm not weeping for that house carpenter,
I'm neither weeping for your store,
But I'm weeping for that dear little babe
I ne'er shall see any more.

GROUP Ae

123. "The Demon Lover"

Motherwell, 1827, App'x., No. 1; text, App'x., p. xv. From A. Blaikie, Paisley.

a I/Ly

O where have ye been my long lost love,
    This long seven years and more?
O I'm come to seek my former vows
    Ye granted me before.

124. "The House Carpenter"

Kittredge, *JAF*, XXX (1917), p. 327. Also in Belden, 1940, p. 84(G). Tune sent by Mrs. Eva Warner Case, Harrison County, Mo., 1916; learned in childhood.

a I/Ly

1. "Well met, well met, my own true love,
    Well met, well met," said he;
  "I've just returned from the salt briny sea
    And it's all for the love of thee."

2. "If you have returned from the salt briny sea
    I'm sure you are to blame;
  For I have married a house carpenter,
    And I'm sure he's a nice young man."

3. "Would you leave your house carpenter
    And go along with me?
  I'll take you down yonder where the grass grows green
    On the banks of the sweet Wilee."

4. "If I was to leave my house carpenter
    And go along with thee,
  What have you got to maintain me upon
    Or to keep me from slavery?"

5. "I've seven fine ships all on the sea
    And seven on dry land,
  And a hundred and ten of the finest young men,
    And they are to wait on thee."

6. She dressed her babe so neat and clean
    And gave it kisses three,
  Saying, "Lie you there, you sweet little babe,
    And keep your father's company."

7. She dressed herself in scarlet red,
    Her waiting maid in green;
  And every city that they passed through
    They took her to be some queen.

8. She had not been on board the ship
    For weeks not more than three
  Till this young damsel began to weep,
    And she wept most bitterly.

9. "What are you weeping about, my love?
    Are you weeping about my fee?
  Or are you weeping about your house carpenter
    That you left when you came upon the sea?"

10. "It's I'm not weeping about your love
    Nor yet about my fee,
  But it's all for the love of my sweet little babe
    That I left when I came upon the sea!"

11. This lady hadn't been on board more than three weeks,
    I'm sure it was not four,
  Till in the bottom of the boat there sprang a leak
    And her weeping was heard no more.

12. "A curse, a curse to all sea boatmen,
A curse, a curse," said she;
"You have taken me away from my sweet babe
And stole my life away."

Kittredge prints only the first stanza (with "deep" for "sea" in line 3); Mrs. Case's full text is given here from Belden, 1940.

125. "The House Carpenter"

Eddy, 1939, p. 72(B). Also in Tolman and Eddy, *JAF*, XXXV (1922), p. 348. Tune from Miss Lily Bell Sefton, Granville, Ohio; text from her cousin, Mrs. Charles Bryan, Tarentum, Pa. Learned as young girls from a hired man.

a I/Ly

1. "I have just come from the salt, salt sea,
And 'twas all on account of thee;
For I've just had an offer of a king's daughter fair,
And she fain would have married me."

2. "Well, if you've had an offer of a king's daughter fair,
I think you're much to blame;
For I've lately been married to a house carpenter,
And I think he's a nice young man."

3. "If you'll forsake your house carpenter,
And come along with me,
I will take you to where the grass grows green
On the banks of Italy."

4. "If I'd forsake my house carpenter
And go along with you,
And you'd have nothing to support me upon,
Oh, then what would I do?"

5. "I have three ships upon the main,
All sailing for dry land,
And twenty-five jolly sailor lads
That you can have at your command."

6. She dresses herself in rich array,
All from her golden store,
And as she walked the streets all 'round,
She shone like a glittering star.

7. She called her baby unto her,
And gave it kisses three,
Saying: "Stay at home, my pretty little babe,
And be your father's company."

8. We had not sailed more than two weeks,
I'm sure it was not three,
Till this fair maid began to weep,
And she wept most bitterly.

9. "Oh, why do you weep, my pretty maid?
Do you weep for your golden store,
Or do you weep for your house carpenter
Which you never shall see any more?"

10. "I do not weep for my house carpenter,
Or for my golden store,
But I do weep for my pretty little babe
Which I never shall see any more."

11. We had not sailed more than three weeks,
I'm sure it was not four,
Till our gallant ship she sprang a leak,
And she sank to rise no more.

12. Once around went our gallant ship,
Twice around went she,
Three times around went our gallant ship,
And she sank to the bottom of the sea.

13. Oh, cursed be the sea-going train,
And all the sailors' lives
For robbing of the house carpenter,
And the taking away of his wife.

126. [The Daemon Lover]

Sharp MSS., 3618/2681. Sung by Mrs. Minnie Pope, Clear Creek, Wasioto, Ky., May 1, 1917.

m I/Ly

I could have married a king's daughter,
I am sure you were to blame.
But now you've married a house carpenter.
He is a nice young man.

(Last stanza)
Farewell all on ship,
Farewell all on shore,
Farewell to the first man married me,
I am sinking to rise no more.

127. "The House Carpenter"

Brewster, 1940, p. 144. Sung by Mrs. Will McCullough, Oakland City, Ind., June 11, 1935. Noted by Mrs. I. L. Johnson.

m I

1. "Well met, well met, my own truelove,
   Well met, well met," says he;
   "I've just returned from the saltwater sea,
   And it's all for the love of thee."

2. . . . .
   . . . .
   "Lie there, lie there, you sweet little babe,
   And keep your pa company."

3. They hadn't been sailing scarce two weeks,
   I'm sure it was not three,
   When the young wife began to weep and to cry,
   And she wept most bitterly.

4. "O is it for my money that you weep,
   Or is it for my store,
   Or is it for that house carpenter
   You know you'll see no more?"

5. "It's neither for your money that I weep,
   Nor is it for your store,
   But it is for that sweet little babe
   That I know I'll see no more."

6. They hadn't been sailing scarce three weeks,
   I'm sure it was not four,
   When the young man's ship it sprung a leak,
   And sank to rise no more.

128. "The House Carpenter"

Gardner and Chickering, 1939, p. 58(C). Sung by Mrs. Charles Muchler, Kalkaska, Mich., 1935.

m I (inflected IV)

1. "Well met, well met, my pretty little maid,
   Well met, well met for me.
   I have just come across the salt, salt sea,
   All for the sake of thee.
   I have just come across the salt, salt sea,
   All for the sake of thee."

. . . .

7. She dressed herself in rich array
   And with the sailor went;
   But as she stepped upon the deck,
   Her heart with grief was rent.

The rest of this singer's text differed little from variant 131 below.

129. "The Daemon Lover," or "Well Met"

Sung by Mr. Dol Small, Nellysford, Va., September 13, 1950. LC/AAFS, rec. No. 10,004(A2). Collected by Maud Karpeles and Sidney Robertson Cowell.

m I/Ly

1. Well met, well met my old true love,
   Well met, well met says she.
   I'm just returning from the salt salt sea,
   And it's all for the sake of thee.
   I'm just returning from the salt salt sea,
   And it's all for the sake of thee.

2. I could have married a king's daughter,
   And she would have married me.
   But I did slight the crowns of gold
   And it's all for the sake of thee.
   But I did slight the crowns of gold
   And it's all for the sake of thee.

3. If you could have married a king's daughter,
   I'm sure you are to blame,
   For I have married a house carpenter
   And they say he's a nice young man.
   For I have married a house carpenter
   And they say he's a nice young man.

4. Won't you forsake your house carpenter,
   And go along with me?
   I'll take you where the grass grows green,
   On the banks of sweet Willie.
   I'll take you where the grass grows green,
   On the banks of sweet Willie.

5. The ship had not been gone yet quite two weeks,
   I'm sure it was not three,
   Before this lady she began to weep,
   And she wept most bitterly,
   Before this lady she began to weep,
   And she wept most bitterly.

6. Are you weeping for your house carpenter,
   Or are you weeping for your store?
   Or are you weeping for your sweet little babes
   Whose face you'll see no more?
   Or are you weeping for your sweet little babes
   Whose face you'll see no more?

7. I'm not a-weeping for my house carpenter,
Neither am I weeping for my store.
But I am a-weeping for my sweet little babes
Whose face I'll see no more.
But I am a-weeping for my sweet little babes
Whose face I'll see no more.

8. Now this is a warning to all young men
Who try to get themself a wife.
They'll take you from your house carpenter,
And they'll cause you to lose your life.
They'll take you from your house carpenter
And they'll cause you to lose your life.

130. "The House Carpenter's Wife"

Cox, 1939, p. 43; and 1964 (ed. Boswell), p. 53. From Frances Sanders, Morgantown, W. Va., June 1924, as sung by Misses Emma and Effie Hewitt, who learned it from their mother.

a I/M

1. She took her babe upon her knee,
And gave it kisses three,
Saying, "Stay at home, you sweet little babe,
For your father's company."

2. She dressed herself in rich attire,
Most beautiful to behold,
And as she walked the streets along,
She shone like the glittering gold.

3. She had not been on board two days,
I'm sure it was not three,
Till this fair lady was seen to weep,
And she wept most bitterly.

4. "Oh is it for my gold that you weep,
Or is it for my store?
Or is it for the house carpenter,
That you left on the other shore?"

5. "It's neither for your gold that I weep,
Nor is it for your store,
But it's all for my darling sweet little babe,
That I left on the other shore."

6. They had not been on board three weeks,
I'm sure it was not four,
Till under the deck there sprung a leak
And it sank for to rise no more.

131. "The House Carpenter"

Gardner and Chickering, 1939, p. 54(A). Sung by Mrs. Allan McClellan, Bad Axe, Mich., 1935.

p I/M

1. "We have met, we have met once more, my love,
We have met once more," said he.
"I have just returned from the salt, salt sea,
And it's all for the sake of thee.

2. "All for your sake I've refused golden store,
And houses of high degree.
O the king's only daughter dear
With me she did comply."

3. "If you could have married the king's daughter,
Young man, I think you are to blame,
For I'm married to the house carpenter,
And I think him a fine young man."

4. "O can't you leave your house carpenter
And come along with me?
I'll take you where the grass grows green
On the banks of the sweet Lacolee."

5. "Have you got gold, or have you got store,
Or have you ships at sea?
Or what have you got to maintain me upon
And keep me from slavery?"

6. "Yes, I have gold and I have store,
And I have ships at sea
With a hundred and twenty gallant sailor boys,
And they will wait on me."

7. She went unto her darling little babes
And kissed them one, two, and three,
Saying, "Stay you on with your papa dear
And keep him company."

8. She dressed herself in silks and satins,
And velvet of the best;
And as she walked down the street,
She shone like glittering gold.

9. She had not been on the sea two weeks,
I am sure it was not three,
Before she began to weep and to sigh,
Weeping most bitterly.

10. "O is it for my gold you weep,
Or is it for my store?
Or is it for your two pretty babes
You never shall see any more?"

11. "It is not for your gold I weep,
Nor is it for your store.
It's all for my two pretty babes
I never shall see any more."

12. She had not been on the sea three weeks,
I am sure it was not four;
Before the *Albion* began for to sink,
And she sank to rise no more.

13. Her sisters cursed the seafaring men,
And cursed be the seaman's life,
For the robbing of the house carpenter,
And the taking away of his wife.

132. "House Carpenter"

Sung by Dan Tate (66), with banjo, Fancy Gap, Va., June 1, 1962. LC/AAFS, rec. No. 12,005(A3). Collected by George Foss.

m M (-VI)

Cf. *ante*, variant 111, for Mr. Tate's other tune.

1. Well met, well met, my old true love,
Well met, well met, says she.
For seven long years I've been sailing on the ocean
And it's all for the love of thee.

2. For I could have married the king's daughter dear,
Being she would have married me.
But I refused her crown of gold,
It was all for the love of thee.

3. If you could have married the king's daughter dear,
I am sure you're all to blame,
For now I am married to a house carpenter,
I believe he's a fine young man.

4. Forsake, forsake your house carpenter
And come along with me.
I'll take you away where the grass grows green
On the banks of sweet Otee.

5. O what shall I do with my house carpenter,
Likewise my tender babe?
Go lay it down in a soft bed of down,
And bid it go to sleep.

6. She took her babe all in her arm,
And kisses gave it three.
Lie there, lie there, my sweet little babe,
Keep your papa company.

7. O they hadn't been on board but about two weeks,
I'm sure that it was not three,
Till she began to weep and to mourn,
And she wept most bitterly.

8. Say, are you weeping for my sake,
Or either for my store?
Or are you a-weeping for your house carpenter
That you left on the other shore?

9. No, I'm not weeping for your sake
Or either for your store.
I'm weeping for my sweet little babe
Whose face I shall see no more.

10. What banks, what banks, my old true love?
They're as white as any snow.
'Tis the banks of Heaven, my old true love,
Where all Christian people go.

11. What banks, what banks, my old true love?
They're as black as any crow.
'Tis the banks of Hell, my old true love,
Where both you and I must go.

12. O they hadn't been on board but about three weeks,
I'm sure that it was not four,
Till there sprang a leak in the bottom of the ship
And it sank to rise no more.

GROUP Af

133. [The Daemon Lover]

Sharp MSS., 3816/. Sung by Mrs. Harriet Connor, Balsam, N.C., July 30, 1917.

a I/Ly, ending on the octave; or p I/Ly

She dressed herself in scarlet red
Around the waist was green
And every station she came through
They taken her to be some queen
They taken her to be some queen.

134. "James Harris"

Greig MSS., II, p. 139; text, Bk. 769, LIX, p. 8. Also in Greig and Keith, 1925, p. 197. Sung by Alexander Robb, New Deer, with text learned from his niece, Miss Annie Robb of Strichen.

a M (-IV)

. . . .

1. She's ta'en her young son in her arms,
And gi'en him kisses three,
And she bade adieu to auld Scotland,
And awa wi' you I'll gae.

2. She hadna sailed a week, a week,
A week but barely three,
When she began to mind on her man,
And her bonnie young son tee.

3. Oh, haud your tongue, my dear, he said,
Oh, haud your tongue, said he,
And I'll lat ye see the bonnie lilies grow
On the banks o' Italy.

4. They hadna sailed a week, a week,
A week but barely three,
Till dark and rainy grew the day,
And raging grew the sea.

. . . .

5. And I'll lat ye see the white fish swim
On, the banks o' Littertie.

6. He turnèd roon his bonnie ship
Wi' her topmast to the win';
And all her seven sails did sink,
And was never seen again.

4. If you'll forsake your house carpenter
And go along with me,
I'll take you where the grass grows green
On the banks of the sweet Lillee.

5. She took her babe all on her knee,
She kissed him two by three,
Saying: You go home to your Poppee,
I'm sure he'll be good to thee.

6. They hadn't been on sea but about two weeks,
I'm sure it was not three,
When this fair lady began to weep,
She wept most bitterly.

7. Are you weeping for my gold, my love,
Are you weeping for my store,
Are you weeping for your house carpenter
You never shall see no more?

8. I'm neither weeping for your gold, my love,
Neither for your store;
I'm weeping for my tender little babe
I never shall see no more.

9. They hadn't been on sea but about three weeks,
I'm sure it was not four,
Till this old ship she spring a leak
And sunk to rise no more.

135. "The House Carpenter," or "The Salt Water Sea"

Sharp MSS., 3183/2325. Also in Sharp and Karpeles, 1932, I, p. 250(F). Sung by Frankland B. Shelton, Allanstand, N.C., July 31, 1916.

a M (inflected VII), ending on V; or p D

1. We've met, we've met, my own true love
We've met, we've met once more.
I've lately crossed the salt water sea
And it's all for the love of thee.

2. For I could have married a king's daughter dear,
I'm sure she'd have married me;
But I've forsaken her crowns all in gold,
And it's all for the love of thee.

3. If you could have married a king's daughter dear,
I'm sure you'd have married her,
For I am married to a house carpenter,
And I'm sure he's a fine young man.

136. [The Daemon Lover]

Sharp MSS., 4752/. Also in Sharp and Karpeles, 1932, I, p. 258(V). Sung by Mrs. Julie Boone, Micaville, N.C., October 3, 1918.

a π^1, ending on II

She picked up her sweet little babe,
And gave it kisses three;
Set it down and told it to stay
And keep its Papa company.

GROUP Ag

137. "The House Carpenter"

Davis, 1929, p. 593(Q); text, p. 462. Contributed by John Stone, November 3, 1920, from the singing of C. F. Carpenter, Bolar, Va., who learned it from his mother.

a I/M

1. "Well met, well met, my dearest dear,
Well met, well met," cried he.
"I've just returned from the salt, salt sea,
'Twas all for the sake of thee,
'Twas all for the sake of thee.

2. "If you'll forsake your house carpenter
And go along with me,
I'll take you to where the grass grows green
On the banks of Sweet Liberty."

3. So she picked up her pretty little babe
And gave it kisses three,
Saying, "Stay at home, my pretty little babe,
And keep your father company."

4. She hadn't been on sea two weeks,
I'm sure it wasn't three,
Before Fair Ellen began for to weep,
And she wept most bitterly.

5. "O do you weep for my gold?" he said,
"Or do you weep for my store?
Or do you weep for your house carpenter
That you never will see no more?"

6. "I do not weep for your gold," she said,
"Nor do I weep for your store;
But I do weep for my pretty little babe
That I never shall see no more."

7. She had not been on sea three weeks,
I'm sure it was not four,
Before the ship she sprung a leak,
And she sunk to rise no more.

8. "Woe be unto a wayfaring man,
Woe be unto a sailor's life,
For robbing me of my house carpenter
And taking away my life."

138. "The House Carpenter"

McIntosh, 1935, p. 34. Sung by Frances Barbour, Carbondale, Ill., 1933.

m I/M

1. "I once could have married a king's daughter,
And she would have married me,
But I have crossed the deep briny ocean
All for the love of thee."

2. "If you could have married a king's daughter,
And she would have married thee,
You need not have crossed the deep briny ocean
All for the love of me.

3. "For I am married to a house carpenter,
And I think he's a fine young man."
. . . .
. . . .

4. "If you will leave your house carpenter
And come along with me,
I'll take you where the grass grows green
On the banks of liberty."

5. She picked up her dear little babe,
And gave it kisses three
Saying, "Stay at home, my dear little babe;
Keep father company."

6. She went into her dressing room
And dressed all up so gay
Just for to leave her house carpenter
And sail on the raging sea.

7. "And what have you got to maintain me upon
And keep me from slavery?"
. . . .
. . . .

8. "I've seven ships in harbor and on sea
And seven more on land
And three hundred of bright boatsmen
To rise at your command."

9. She picked up her dear little babe
And gave it kisses four
Saying, "Stay at home, my dear little babe,
Whose face I shall see no more."

10. This lady had not been a-sailing on deck
For more than two weeks or three
When she was down at the bottom of the boat
Weeping most bitterly.

11. "Oh, do you weep for your silver or your gold,
Or do you weep for your store,
Or do you weep for your house carpenter
You left on the other shore?"

12. "I neither weep for my silver nor my gold;
I neither weep for my store,
But I do weep for my poor little babe,
Whose face I shall see no more."

13. This lady had not been a-sailing on deck
No more than three weeks or four
When there sprang a leak at the bottom of the boat—
Her weeping was heard no more.

139. "The House Carpenter"

Davis, 1929, p. 592(C); text, p. 444. Contributed by Alfreda M. Peel, September 11, 1922, from the singing of Miss Rushia Richardson of Vinton, Va., and Sis Sears of Salem, Va.

a I/M

1. "Well met, well met, my own fair lady,
Well met, well met," cried [he],
"I've just returned from my castle,
All for the sake of thee."

2. "Too late, too late, my own fair knight,
Too late, too late," cried she,
"I've just been wed to a house carpenter,
And I think he's a nice young man."

3. "If you will leave your house carpenter
And come along with me,
I'll take you where the grass grows green
On the banks of the salt, salt sea.

4. "If you will leave your house-carpenter
And come along with me,
I'll take you where the grass grows green
Beside my castles three.

5. "I have three ships on the salt, salt sea,
They are sailing for my lands;
One hundred and ten so jolly knights
You can have at your command."

6. She picked up her sweet little babe,
And kisses gave it three,
Crying, "Stay at home, my little babe,
And keep him company."

7. She was not on the sea three weeks,
I'm sure it was not three,
Before this lady began to weep
And wept most bitterly.

8. "Oh, is it for my gold you weep?
Or is it for my store?"
"I'm weeping for my sweet little babe
That I shall see no more.

9. "If I live till another fall
And God will give me grace,
I'll buy a bottle of Jenico wine
To wash your deceitful face.

10. "I wish to the Lord I had never been born
And died when I was young;
I never would wet my rosy cheeks
With no man's lying tongue."

11. She was not on the sea three weeks,
I'm sure it was not four,
Before the ship began to sink,
And sank to rise no more.

GROUP Ah

140. "The House Carpenter"

Henry, 1938, p. 116(C). Sung by Mrs. Hiram Proctor, Cade's Cove, Tenn., August 1928.

a π^4

The rhythm here is very free, irregular but *quasi* 4/4.

1. "Well met, well met, my own true love;
Well met, well met," said he.
"I'm just returning from the old salt sea,
Returning for to marry thee.

2. "Have you wedded any other man?
I'm sure I've wedded no other woman."
"Yes, I'm wedded to a house carpenter,
And I think he's a very nice man."

3. "You better leave your house carpenter,
And come along with me.
We'll go till we come to the old salt sea
And married we will be."

4. She dressed her babies all in red
And laid them on the bed.
"Lay there, lay there, my sweet little babes,
To keep your papa company."

5. She dressed her pavage all in blue;
Herself she dressed in green;
And every town they rode through
They tuk her to be a queen.

6. They had not been on the sea two weeks,
I'm sure it was not three,
Till his true love began to weep;
She wept most bitterly.

7. "What are you weeping for, my love?
Are you weeping for my gold?
Are you weeping for some other man,
That you love more dear than me?"

8. "I'm not weeping for your gold,
Nor neither for your store;
I'm just weeping for my sweet little babes
That I never will see no more.

9. "If I had a thousand pounds of gold,
I'd give it all to thee,
If you'd take me to the land once more,
My poor little babies for to see."

10. "If you had a thousand pounds of gold
And would give it all to me,
I'd never take thee to the land no more,
Your poor little babies to see."

11. They had not been on the sea two months,
I'm sure it was not four,
Till they sprang a leak in her true love's ship
And it sank to rise no more.

12. "What hills, what hills, my own true love,
That look so bright above?"
"That's hills of heaven, my own true love,
Where all God's people doth go."

13. "What hills, what hills, my own true love,
That look so dark below?"
"That is hills of hell, my own true love,
Where you and I have started to go."

14. "A curse, a curse to all seaman,
A curse, a curse," she said,
"You've robbed me of my sweet little babes,
And stole my life away."

APPENDIX A

141. "The Banks of Claudy"

Barry, *BFSSNE*, No. 7 (1934), p. 11; text, No. 6 (1933), p. 8. Also in Flanders, III, 1963, p. 317. Sung by Mrs. E. M. Sullivan, Springfield, Vt., July 7, 1933.

p I/M

1. 'Twas on the banks of Claudy,
. . . .
. . . .
. . . .

A girl promises to marry a man who goes away, dies and as a ghost returns and says:

2. "Come with me to the banks of Claudy,—"
. . . .
. . . .
. . . .

3. "O begone, begone, young George Allis,
For I am a married wife;
O begone, begone, young George," she said,
"For fear there may be strife."

4. "This is the promise you gave to me,
To come in seven years and a day;
So come now on to the salty seas,
And perform your promises to me."

5. When she came to the banks of Claudy,
O sorry sore was she;
For the ships were made of the yellow
beaten gold,
And the sails were of silk so fine.

6. When she came to the banks of Claudy,
O sorry sore was she,
There were seven ships sailing to the brim,
They were sunk to the bottom and was
never seen no more.

In her later singing (from which our tune is taken) Mrs. Sullivan sang "floating" for "sailing" in st. 6, line 3, and recalled this additional line: "They sailed so far, and they sailed so fast."

GROUP B

142. "The Banks of Italy," or "James Herries"

Christie, I, 1876, p. 138. From an aged relative of Christie.

m π^1

He's given her a pair of shoes
To hold her frae the cold;
The one side of them was Velvaret,
And the other beaten gold.

. . . . . .

Up has she ta'en her little wee son,
And given him kisses three,—
Says, "Fare-ye-weel my little wee son,
I'm gaun to sail the sea."

Christie's text is "epitomized" from Buchan; these two stanzas, however, given in his note to the tune, are from the singer.

143. "The Carpenter's Wife"

Baring-Gould MSS., CXLIV; text (A). Sung by James Paddon, Holcombe Burnell, December 21, 1889.

a D/Æ (inflected VII)

1. Well met, well met, my own true love
Long time am I a seeking of thee.
I'm lately come from the salt, salt sea
And all for the sake sweet love of thee.

2. I might have had a King's daughter,
She fain would have a married me.
But I naught did hold for her crown of gold[1]
And all for the sake, sweet love of thee.

3. "If you might have had a King's daughter.
I think you were much to blame,
I would not 'twer found for a hundred pound[2]
That my husband should know the same.

4. "For my husband he is a Carpenter
A Carpenter good is he.
By him I have gotten a little son,
Or else I would go sweet love with thee.

5. "But if I should leave my husband dear,
My fair sweet boy also
O what have you got far, far away
That along with thee, I should go?"

6. "I have Seven ships that sail on the seas
It was one brought me to land.
I have mariners many to wait on thee
To be, sweet love, at thy command.

7. "A pair of slippers, thou shalt have
They are made of beaten gold,
They're lined within with coney's skin,
To keep thy feet from the cold.

8. "A gilded boat, thou also shalt have,
The oars be gilded also.
And the mariners shall pipe & sing
As thro' the salt waves we go."

9. They had not rowéd a bowshot off,
A bowshot on the main,
But o'er her shoulder she looked back,
"I would I were home again!"

10. They had not rowéd a bowshot off
A bowshot from the land,
But o'er her shoulder she looked and said,
"Set me back on the yellow sand!"

11. "For I have a child in my little chamber
And I think I hear him cry
I would not, I would not, my babe should wake
And his mother not standing by."

12. The Captain he smiled & stroked his arms
And said, "This may not be
Behind is the shore & the sea is before
And thou must go sweet love with me."

13. She had not been long upon the sea
Not long upon the deep,
Before that she was wringing her hands,
And loudly did wail & weep.

14. "O why do you wail, & where fore weep?
And wring your hands?" said he.
"Do you weep for the gold that lies in the hold
Or do you weep for my fee?"

15. "I do not weep for your gold," she said;
"Nor do I weep for your fee.
But by the mast-head is my baby dead,
And I weep for my dead baby."

16. She had not abeen upon the seas,
The days they were three or four.
And never a word she spoke, nor stirred
And she lookéd towards the shore.

17. She had not abeen upon the seas,
But six days of the week,
Before that she lay as cold as the clay
And never a word could speak.

18. They had not a sailed upon the seas,
Of weeks but three and four.
But down to the bottom the ship did swim,
And never was heard of more.

19. And when the news to England came,
The Carpenter's wife was drowned
The Carpenter rent his hair & wept,
And then as dead he swownd.

20. A curse be on all sea-captains
That lead such a godless life.
They will ruin a good ship-carpenter
His little one & his wife.

[1] MS. has marginal note: "J. Paddon 'naught did care for her crown of gold.' "
[2] MS. has marginal note: "J.P. 'I would not it were for a hundred pound.' "

144. "The House Carpenter"

Sung by Elsie Surber, Panama City, Fla. LC/AAFS, rec. No. 9915(B2). Collected by Alton C. Morris.

p π[1]

1. Well done, well done, my own true love,
   Well done, well done, said he,
   For I have returned from the old salt sea
   And it's all for the sake of thee.

2. Begone, begone, you brash young man,
   Begone, begone, said she,
   For I have married the house carpenter
   And I think he's a nice young man.

3. Cheer up, cheer up, my fair young maid,
   Cheer up, cheer up, said he,
   And I will carry you where the grass grows green,
   On the banks of sweet Willie.

4. O they sailed two weeks and I'm sure it's not three
   [*Forgotten line*]
   Until that fair maid began for to weep,
   And she wept most bitterly.

5. Are you weeping for my ship?
   Are you weeping for my stores?
   Or are you weeping for that house carpenter
   That you ne'er shall see any more?

6. I'm not a-weeping for your ship
   And I'm not a-weeping for your store,
   But I'm a-weeping for that precious little babe
   That I ne'er shall see any more.

7. O they sailed three weeks and I'm sure it's not four
   [*Forgotten line*]
   Until that gallant ship began for to sink,
   And she sank for to rise no more.

145. "House Carpenter"

Sung by Allen Johnson, Portland (?), Ore.; learned in Calais, Me. LC/AAFS, rec. No. 10,366(A6). Collected by William L. Alderson.

p I/M

1. Well met, well met, my fair pretty maid.
   No so very well met, said she,
   For I am married to a house carpenter,
   And a very fine man is he,
   For I am married to a house carpenter,
   And a very fine man is he.

2. If you'll forsake your house carpenter
   And come along with me,
   I'll take you there where the grass grows green,
   On the banks of the sweet Vallie,
   I'll take you there where the grass grows green,
   On the banks of the sweet Vallie.

3. O if I forsake my house carpenter
   And come along with thee,
   What have you there to entertain me with
   And keep me company?
   What have you there to entertain me with
   And keep me company?

4. I've a thousand ships all on the bay,
   And many more on land,
   A hundred and ten of as fine young men,
   And they're all at your command,
   A hundred and ten of as fine young men,
   And they're all at your command.

5. She went upstairs herself to dress,
   Very beautiful she was to behold,
   For when she walked along the streets
   She shone as though she were gold,
   For when she walked along the streets
   She shone as though she were gold.

6. She took her babe all in her arms
   And kissed him three times three.
   Stay at home, stay at home, stay at home, my lad,
   Your father's good company.
   Stay at home, stay at home, stay at home, my lad,
   Your father's good company.

7. They had not been sailing for more than six weeks,
   O no, not more than three,
   When this fair lady began to mourn
   And mourned most bitterly,
   When this fair lady began to mourn
   And mourned most bitterly.

8. O is it gold for which you mourn,
   Or do you mourn for me?
   Or do you mourn your house carpenter
   Who you left to follow me?
   Or do you mourn your house carpenter
   Who you left to follow me?

9. O it is not gold for which I mourn,
   Nor do I mourn for thee.
   But I do mourn my house carpenter
   Who I left to follow thee.
   But I do mourn my house carpenter
   And likewise my fair baby.

10. They had not sailed for more than eight weeks,
   O no, not more than four,
   When a hole in the ship it sprang a leak,
   And the mourner was heard no more,
   When a hole in the ship it sprang a leak,
   And the mourner was heard no more.